PROJECT PHYSICS

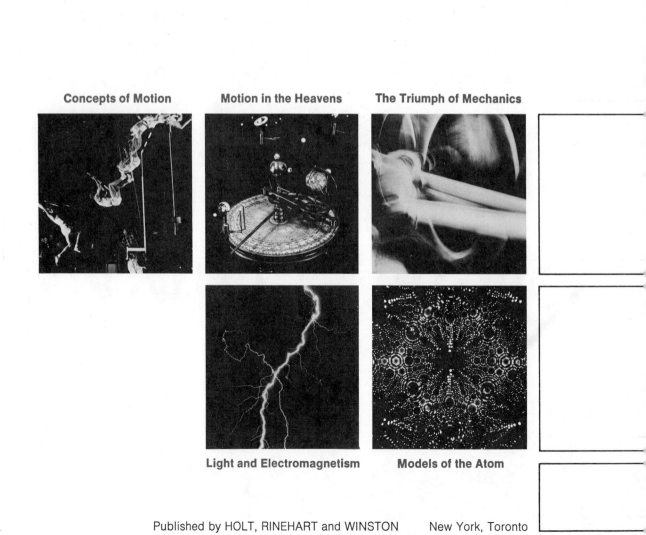

Concepts of Motion

Motion in the Heavens

The Triumph of Mechanics

Light and Electromagnetism

Models of the Atom

Published by HOLT, RINEHART and WINSTON   New York, Toronto

PROJECT PHYSICS

Text

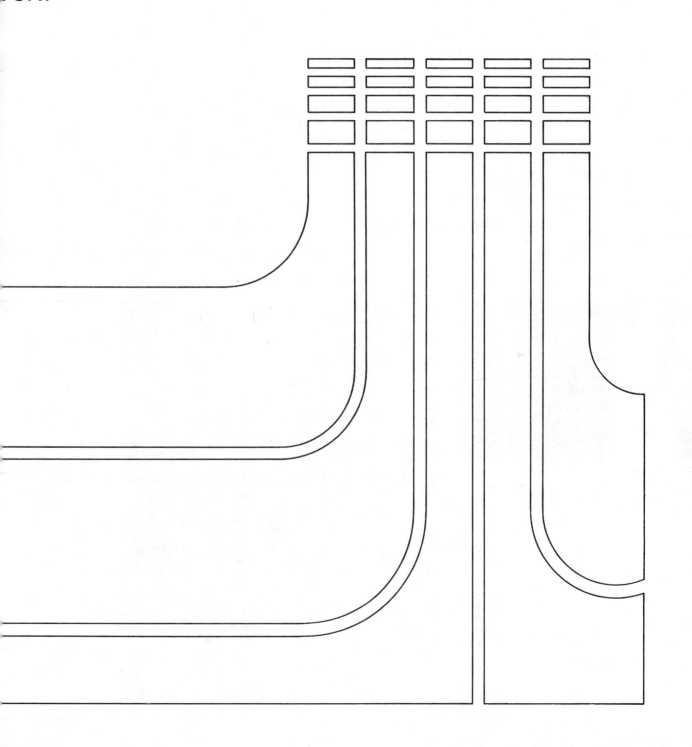

Directors of Harvard Project Physics

Gerald Holton, Department of Physics, Harvard University
F. James Rutherford, Chairman of the Department of
 Science Education, New York University
Fletcher G. Watson, Harvard Graduate School of Education

Special Consultant
to Project Physics

Andrew Ahlgren, University of Minnesota

A partial list of staff and consultants to Harvard Project
Physics appears in the Text on page A21 of the Appendix.

**This Text is one of the many instructional materials
developed for the Project Physics Course. These materials
include Text, Handbook, Resource Book, Readers,
Programmed Instruction Booklets, Supplemental Units,
Film Loops, Transparencies, 16mm films, and laboratory
equipment.**

Acknowledgments

The authors and publisher have made every effort to trace
the ownership of all selections found in this book and to
make full acknowledgement for their use. Many of the
selections are in the public domain.

Grateful acknowledgment is hereby made to the following
authors, publishers, agents, and individuals for use of their
copyrighted material.

Unit 1

Pp. 1-4 Fermi, Laura, *Atoms in the Family,* pp. 83-100 not
inclusive, copyright 1954 by University of Chicago Press.
Pp. 44-45, 47-49, 53,56, 59-60 Galilei, Galileo, *Two New
Sciences,* trans. Crew and DeSalvio, pp. 62-243 not inclusive,
copyright 1914 by Dover Publications, Inc.
P. 61 Aristotle, *De Caelo,* trans. J. L. Stokes, Book I, Chapter
6, Oxford University Press, p. 273b.
P. 79 Newton, Sir Isaac, *The Principia,* Vol. I, Motte's
translation revised by Florian Cajori, pp. 13-14, copyright ©
1961 by University of California Press.
P. 86 Ibid., pp. XIII-XV.
P. 113 Childe, V. Gordon, "Rotary Motion," *A History of
Technology,* Vol. I, Oxford University Press, p. 187.
P. 118 Whitehead, A. N., *Science and the Modern World,* a
Mentor Book published by The New American Library, pp.
46-47.
(Acknowledgments continued on Appendix page A14.)

Picture Credits

Unit 1

Cover Photograph, p. 118 Dr. Harold E. Edgerton, M.I.T.
Facing page 1 University of Chicago
P. 4 U.S. Atomic Energy Commission.
P. 6 (left) Mt. Wilson and Palomar Observatories; (right)
Professor Erwin W. Mueller, The Pennsylvania State
University.
P. 7 (left) Museum of Comparative Zoology, Harvard
University; (right) Brookhaven National Laboratory.
P. 8, 119 (top margin) Yale University Art Gallery, Collection
Société Anonyme.
P. 10 National Aeronautics and Space Administration.
P. 22 W. O. Roberts, Director, High Altitude Observatory,
Climax, Colorado; (glacier) from the film strip "Investigating
a Glacier"© 1966, Encyclopaedia Britannica Educational
Corporation, Chicago; (plants) Dr. Leland Earnest, Dept. of
Biology, Eastern Nazarene College.
P. 26 (1) Bayerisches Nationalmuseum, Munich; (2) (4)
George Eastman House, Rochester, N.Y.; (3) Bill Eppridge,
LIFE MAGAZINE, © Time Inc.
(Picture credits continued on Appendix page A16.)

Science is an adventure of the whole human race to learn to live in and perhaps to love the universe in which they are. To be a part of it is to understand, to understand oneself, to begin to feel that there is a capacity within man far beyond what he felt he had, of an infinite extension of human possibilities . . . . .

I propose that science be taught at whatever level, from the lowest to the highest, in the humanistic way. It should be taught with a certain historical understanding, with a certain philosophical understanding, with a social understanding and a human understanding in the sense of the biography, the nature of the people who made this construction, the triumphs, the trials, the tribulations.

I. I. RABI
Nobel Laureate in Physics

Preface

Background   The Project Physics Course is based on the ideas and research of a national curriculum development project that worked in three phases. First, the three authors collaborated to lay out the main goals and topics of a new introductory physics course. They worked together from 1962 to 1964 with financial support from the Carnegie Corporation of New York, and the first version of the text was tried out with encouraging results.

These preliminary results led to the second phase of the Project when a series of major grants were obtained from the U.S. Office of Education and the National Science Foundation, starting in 1964. Invaluable additional financial support was also provided by the Ford Foundation, the Alfred P. Sloan Foundation, the Carnegie Corporation, and Harvard University. A large number of collaborators were brought together from all parts of the nation, and the group worked together for over four years under the title *Harvard Project Physics*. At the Project's center, located at Harvard University, Cambridge, Massachusetts, the staff and consultants included physicists, astronomers, chemists, historians and philosophers of science, college and high school physics instructors, science educators, psychologists, evaluation specialists, engineers, film makers, artists and graphic designers. The instructors serving as field consultants and the students in the trial classes were also of vital importance to the success of Harvard Project Physics. As each successive experimental version of the course was developed it was tried out throughout the United States and Canada. The instructors and students reported their criticisms and suggestions to the staff in Cambridge. These reports became the basis for the next year's revision. The number of participating instructors during this period grew to over 100. Five thousand students participated in the last year of tryout in a large-scale formal research program to evaluate the results achieved with the course materials.

With the culmination of course development and data gathering activities, the final phase of Harvard Project Physics got under way. During the last two years the work of the Project concentrated on developing and conducting special training programs, disseminating information about the course, analyzing the large pool of final evaluation data and writing a complete report on the results, and trying to find out how the course might be reshaped to fit special audiences.

We wish it were possible to list in detail the contributions of each person who participated in some part of Harvard Project Physics. Unhappily it is not feasible, since most staff members worked on a variety of materials and had multiple responsibilities. Furthermore, every text chapter, experiment, piece of apparatus, film or other item in the experimental program benefitted from the contributions of a great many people. Elsewhere in this book is a partial list of contributors to Harvard Project Physics. There were, in fact, many other contributors too numerous to mention. These include administrators in participating colleges and schools, directors and staff members of training institutes, instructors who tried the course after the evaluation year, and most of all the thousands of students who not only agreed to take the experimental version of the course, but who were also willing to appraise it critically and contribute their opinions and suggestions.

Aims.* From the beginning Harvard Project Physics had three major goals in mind. These were to design a humanistically oriented physics course, to attract more students to the study of introductory physics, and to find out more about the factors that influence the learning of science. The last of these involved extensive educational research, and has now been reported to the teaching profession in books and journals.

About ten years ago it became clear that a new physics course, having far wider appeal than the existing ones, was needed. The challenge facing Harvard Project Physics was to design a humanistic course that would be useful and interesting to students with widely differing skills, backgrounds, and career plans. In practice, this meant designing a course that would have the following effect:

1. To help students increase their knowledge of the physical world by concentrating on ideas that characterize physics as a science at its best, rather than concentrating on isolated bits of information.

2. To help students see physics as the wonderfully many-sided human activity that it really is. This meant presenting the subject in historical and cultural perspective, and showing that the ideas of physics have a tradition as well as ways of evolutionary adaptation and change.

3. To increase the opportunity for each student to have immediately rewarding experiences in science even while gaining the knowledge and skill that will be useful in the long run.

4. To make it possible for instructors to adapt the course to the wide range of interests and abilities of their students.

5. To take into account the importance of the instructor in the educational process, and the vast spectrum of teaching situations that prevail.

How well did Harvard Project Physics meet the challenge? In a sense each student who takes this course must answer that question personally. It is a pleasure to report, however, that the large-scale study of student achievement and student opinion in the participating colleges and schools throughout the United States and Canada showed gratifying results—ranging from the excellent scores on the achievement test in physics to the personal satisfaction of individual students. It is clear that the diverse array of individual students in the experimental groups responded well to the physics content, the humanistic emphasis of the course, and to its flexible multimedia course materials.

*A more detailed discussion of aims is given in the Resource Book for this course and in the letter to the Student on Appendix page A3.

The Project Physics Course Today.   Using the last of the experimental versions of the course developed by Harvard Project Physics as a starting point, and taking into account the evaluation results from the try-outs, the three original collaborators set out to develop the version suitable for large-scale publication. We take particular pleasure in acknowledging the assistance of Dr. Andrew Ahlgren of the University of Minnesota. Dr. Ahlgren was invaluable because of his skill as a physics instructor, his editorial talent, his versatility and energy, and above all, his commitment to the goals of Harvard Project Physics.

We would also especially like to thank Ms. Joan Laws whose administrative skills, dependability, and thoughtfulness contributed so much to our work. The publisher, Holt, Rinehart and Winston, Inc. of New York, provided the coordination, editorial support, and general backing necessary to the large undertaking of preparing the final version of all components of the Project Physics Course, including texts, laboratory apparatus, films, etc. Damon-Educational Division located in Westwood, Massachusetts, worked closely with us to improve the engineering design of the authorized laboratory apparatus and to see that it was properly integrated into the program.

Since their last use in experimental form, all of the instructional materials have been more closely integrated and rewritten in final form. The course now consists of a large variety of coordinated learning materials of which this textbook is only one; in addition there are readers, handbooks, programmed instruction booklets, film loops, documentary films, transparencies, apparatus and various materials for the instructor. With the aid of these materials and the guidance of the instructor, with the student's own interest and effort, every student can look forward to a successful and worthwhile experience.

In the years ahead, the learning materials of the Project Physics Course will be revised as often as is necessary to remove remaining ambiguities, clarify instructions, and to continue to make the materials more interesting and relevant to the students. We therefore urge all who use this course to send to us (in care of Holt, Rinehart and Winston, Inc., 383 Madison Avenue, New York, New York 10017) any criticisms or suggestions they may have. And now—welcome to the study of physics!

F. James Rutherford
Gerald Holton
Fletcher G. Watson

Contents PROJECT PHYSICS — TEXT

PROJECT PHYSICS

1

Concepts of Motion

Things to Do and Use

Experiments

Activities

Film Loops

Programmed Instruction Booklets

Sound Films (16mm)

Reader Articles

Transparencies

Contents TEXT, UNIT 1

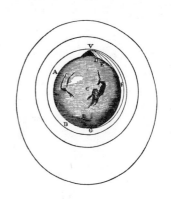

Physicist Enrico Fermi (1901–1954) at different stages of his career in Italy and America. Mrs. Laura Fermi is shown in the photograph at the top left of the page.

Concepts of Motion

PROLOGUE   It is January 1934 in the city of Paris. A husband and wife are at work in a university laboratory. They are exposing a piece of ordinary aluminum to a stream of tiny charged bits of matter called alpha particles. Stated so simply, this hardly sounds like an important event. But let us look more closely, for it is important indeed.

Never mind the technical details. Don't let them get in the way of the story. It all began as something of a family affair. The husband and wife are the French physicists Frédéric Joliot and Irène Curie. The alpha particles they are using in their experiment are shooting from a piece of naturally radioactive metal. This metal is polonium, first identified 36 years before by Irène's parents, Pierre and Marie Curie, the discoverers of radium. What Frédéric and Irène have found is that when the common aluminum is bombarded by alpha particles, it too becomes radioactive for a while.

This is a surprise. Until this moment, nothing like this—a familiar, everyday substance becoming artificially radioactive—has ever been observed. But physicists in the laboratory cannot force new phenomena on nature. They can only show more clearly what nature is like. We know now that this type of radioactivity occurs quite often. It happens, for example, in stars and in our atmosphere when it is bombarded by cosmic rays.

The news was exciting to scientists and traveled rapidly, though it made few, if any, newspaper headlines. Enrico Fermi, a young physicist at the University of Rome, became intrigued by the possibility of repeating the experiment of Frédéric and Irène. But Fermi added an important alteration. The story is told in the book *Atoms in the Family* by Enrico Fermi's wife, Laura. She writes:

> . . . he decided he would try to produce artificial radioactivity
> with neutrons [instead of alpha particles]. Having no electric
> charge, neutrons are neither attracted by electrons nor repelled

by nuclei; their path inside matter is much longer than that of alpha particles; their speed and energy remain higher; their chances of hitting a nucleus with full impact are much greater.

Usually a physicist is guided by some theory in setting up an experiment. This time, no good theory had yet been developed. Only through actual experiment could one tell whether or not neutrons could trigger artificial radioactivity in the target nuclei. Fermi, already an outstanding theoretical physicist at age 33, decided to design some experiments that could settle the issue. His first task was to obtain instruments suitable for detecting the particles emitted by radioactive materials. The best such laboratory instruments by far were Geiger counters. But in 1934, Geiger counters were still relatively new and not readily available. Therefore, Fermi built his own.

The counters were soon in operation detecting the radiation from radioactive materials. But Fermi also needed a source of neutrons. This he made by enclosing beryllium powder and the radioactive gas radon in a glass tube. Alpha particles from the radon, striking the beryllium, caused it to emit neutrons, which passed freely through the glass tube.

All quotations in the Prologue are from Laura Fermi, *Atoms in the Family: My Life With Enrico Fermi,* University of Chicago Press, Chicago, 1954 (available as a paperback book in the Phoenix Books series). Fermi was one of the major physicists of the twentieth century.

Now Enrico was ready for the first experiments. Being a man of method, he did not start by bombarding substances at random, but proceeded in order, starting from the lightest element, hydrogen, and following the periodic table of elements. Hydrogen gave no results: when he bombarded water with neutrons, nothing happened. He tried lithium next, but again without luck. He went on to beryllium, then to boron, to carbon, to nitrogen. None were activated. Enrico wavered, discouraged, and was on the point of giving up his researches, but his stubbornness made him refuse to yield. He would try one more element. That oxygen would not become radioactive he knew already, for his first bombardment had been on water. So he irradiated fluorine. Hurrah! He was rewarded. Fluorine was strongly activated, and so were other elements that came after fluorine in the periodic table.

This field of investigation appeared so fruitful that Enrico not only enlisted the help of Emilio Segré and of Edoardo Amaldi but felt justified in sending a cable to Rasetti [a colleague in Morocco], to inform him of the experiments and advise him to come home at once. A short while later a chemist, Oscar D'Agostino, joined the group, and systematic investigation was carried on at a fast pace.

With the help of his co-workers, Fermi pursued his experiments with high spirit, as Laura Fermi's account shows:

Follow the story rather than worrying about the techniques of the experiment.

. . . Irradiated substances were tested for radioactivity with Geiger counters. The radiation emitted by the neutron source would have disturbed the measurements had it reached the counters. Therefore, the room where substances were irradiated and the room with the counters were at the two ends of a long corridor.

Sometimes the radioactivity produced in an element was of short duration, and after less than a minute it could no longer be detected. Then haste was essential, and the time to cover the length of the corridor had to be reduced by swift running. Amaldi and Fermi prided themselves on being the fastest runners, and theirs was the task of speeding short-lived substances from one end of the corridor to the other. They always raced, and Enrico claims that he could run faster than Edoardo. . . .

And then, one morning in October 1934, a fateful discovery was made. Two of Fermi's co-workers were irradiating a hollow cylinder of silver to make it artificially radioactive. They were using neutrons from a source placed at the center of the cylinder. They found that the amount of radioactivity induced in the silver depended on other objects that happened to be present in the room!

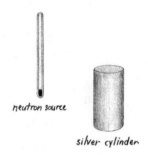

neutron source

silver cylinder

. . . The objects around the cylinder seemed to influence its activity. If the cylinder had been on a wooden table while being irradiated, its activity was greater than if it had been on a piece of metal.

By now the whole group's interest has been aroused, and everybody was participating in the work. They placed the neutron source outside the cylinder and interposed objects between them. A plate of lead made the activity increase slightly. Lead is a heavy substance. "Let's try a light one next," Fermi said, "for instance, paraffin." The most plentiful element in paraffin is hydrogen. The experiment with paraffin was performed on the morning of October 22.

They took a big block of paraffin, dug a cavity in it, put the neutron source inside the cavity, irradiated the silver cylinder, and brought it to a geiger counter to measure its activity. The counter clicked madly. The halls of the physics building resounded with loud exclamations: "Fantastic! Incredible! Black Magic!" Paraffin increased the artificially induced radioactivity of silver up to one hundred times.

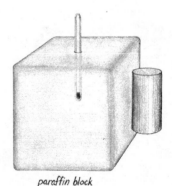

paraffin block

By the time Fermi came back from lunch, he had already found a theory to account for the strange action of the paraffin.

Paraffin contains a great deal of hydrogen. Hydrogen nuclei are protons, particles having the same mass as neutrons. When the source is enclosed in a paraffin block, the neutrons hit the protons in the paraffin before reaching the silver nuclei. In the collision with a proton, a neutron loses part of its energy, in the same manner as a billiard ball is slowed down when it hits a

Because of Fermi's earlier experiments, they knew the water would not become artifically radioactive. However, they now reasoned that it would slow down neutrons and so allow silver to become more strongly radioactive.

ball of its same size whereas it loses little speed if it is reflected off a much heavier ball, or a solid wall. Before emerging from the paraffin, a neutron will have collided with many protons in succession, and its velocity will be greatly reduced. This *slow* neutron will have a much better chance of being captured by a silver nucleus than a fast one, much as a slow golf ball has a better chance of making a hole than one which zooms fast and may bypass it.

If Enrico's explanations were correct, any other substance containing a large proportion of hydrogen should have the same effect as paraffin. "Let's try and see what a considerable quantity of water does to the silver activity," Enrico said on the same afternoon.

There was no better place to find a "considerable quantity of water" than the goldfish fountain. . . in the garden behind the laboratory. . .

In that fountain the physicists had sailed certain small toy boats that had suddenly invaded the Italian market. Each little craft bore a tiny candle on its deck. When the candles were lighted, the boats sped and puffed on the water like real motorboats. They were delightful. And the young men, who had never been able to resist the charm of a new toy, had spent much time watching them run in the fountain.

It was natural that, when in need of a considerable amount of water, Fermi and his friends should think of that fountain. On that afternoon of October 22, they rushed their source of neutrons and their silver cylinder to that fountain, and they placed both under water. The goldfish, I am sure, retained their calm and dignity, despite the neutron shower, more than did the crowd outside. The men's excitement was fed on the results of this experiment. It confirmed Fermi's theory. Water also increased the artificial radioactivity of silver many times.

Fermi and his co-workers had learned that slowed-down neutrons can produce much stronger effects in making certain atoms radioactive than can fast neutrons. This discovery turned out to be a crucial step toward further discoveries which, years later, led Fermi and others to the controlled production of atomic energy from uranium.

We will return to the study of nuclear physics later in the course. We described Fermi's discovery of slow neutrons here, not to instruct you now on the details of the nucleus, but to present a quick impression of scientists in action. Not every discovery in science is made in just the way Fermi and his co-workers made this one. Nevertheless, the episode does illustrate many of the major themes or characteristics of modern science. Some of these themes were mentioned in the Preface, and summaries of how they apply to this particular case are given below. Look for these themes also as you go through this course; they appear over and over again in many varied situations.

Progress in science over the years is the result of the work of many people in many lands. They may work alone, in pairs or small groups, or in large research teams. No matter how different the individual way of

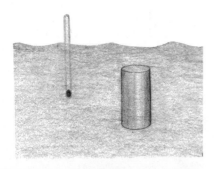

The same process by which neutrons were slowed down in the fountain is used in today's large nuclear reactors. An example is the "pool" research reactor pictured above.

working, no matter where scientists work, each expects to share ideas and results with other scientists who will try to confirm and add to the findings. As important as such cooperation is, the most essential ingredient of science is individual thought and creativity.

Fermi and his associates refused to give up in the face of discouraging results. They showed imagination in the invention of theories and experiments. They remained alert to the appearance of unexpected results and resourceful in using the material resources at hand. Moreover, they found joy in discovering something new and important. These distinctly humane traits are of value in pursuing scientific work no less than elsewhere in life.

Scientists build on what has been found out and reported by other scientists in the past. Yet every advance in science raises new scientific questions. The work of science is not to produce some day a finished book that can be closed once and for all. Rather, it is to carry investigation and imagination on into fields whose importance and interest had not been realized before.

Some work in science depends upon painstaking observation and measurement. The results sometimes stimulate new ideas and sometimes reveal the need to change or even completely discard existing theories. Measurement itself, however, is usually guided by a theory. One does not gather data just for their own sake.

All these are characteristics of science as a whole and not of physics alone. This being a physics text, you may well ask, "Yes, but just what *is* physics?" The question is fair enough, yet there is no simple answer. Physics can be thought of as an organized body of tested ideas about the physical world. Information about this world is accumulating ever more rapidly. The great achievement of physics has been to find a fairly small number of basic principles which help to organize and to make sense of certain parts of this flood of information. This course will deal with some, but not nearly all, of the ideas that together make up the content of physics. The purpose of this course is to provide you with the opportunity to become familiar with some of these ideas, to witness their birth and development, and to share in the pleasure that comes from using them to view the world in a new light.

Physics is more than just a body of laws and facts. Physics is a unique activity of each physicist. It is a continuing activity—a process of search that sometimes leads to discovery. Look in on different physicists at work and you will see differences in problems being studied, in apparatus being used, in individual style, and in much more. Fermi has provided us with one example, but as the course proceeds we will encounter other, sometimes very different examples. By the end of this course, you will have dealt with many of the ideas and activities which together make up physics. You will not just have learned about it—you will have actually done some physics.

Science gives us no final answers. But it has come upon wondrous things, and some of them may renew our childhood delight in the miracle that is around us.

The Project Physics Course has made two documentary films that you might like to see. One is called *The World of Enrico Fermi* and includes the discovery described here. The other is entitled *People and Particles* and shows what it is like to be working now on a research problem in elementary particle physics.

Our place in space

Physics deals with those laws of the universe that apply everywhere—from the largest to the smallest.

	ORDER OF MAGNITUDE
Distance to the furthest observed galaxy	10^{26} meters
Distance to the nearest galaxy	10^{22}
Distance to the nearest star	10^{17}
Distance to the sun	10^{11}
Diameter of the earth	10^{7}
One mile	10^{3}
Human height	10^{0}
Finger breadth	10^{-2}
Paper thickness	10^{-4}
Large bacteria	10^{-5}
Small virus	10^{-8}
Diameter of atom	10^{-10}
Diameter of nucleus	10^{-14}

A globular star cluster

Atomic sites in tungsten

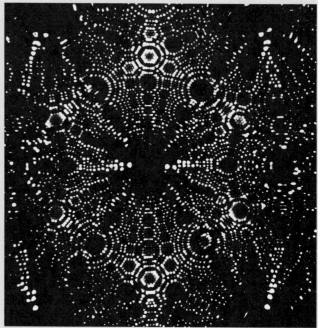

The estimated size of the universe now is of the order of 100 million, million, million, million times a man's height (man's height × 10,000,000, 000,000,000,000,000,000).

The smallest known constituent units of the universe are less in size than a hundreth of a millionth of a millionth of a man's height (man's height × 0.000,000,000,000,01).

Our place in time

Physicists study phenomena in the extremes of time-space and the whole region between the longest and shortest.

	ORDER OF MAGNITUDE
Age of universe	10^{17} seconds
Precession of the earth's axis	10^{12}
Human life span	10^{9}
One year	10^{7}
One day	10^{5}
Light from sun to earth	10^{3}
Time between heartbeats	10^{0}
One beat of fly's wings	10^{-3}
Duration of strobe flash	10^{-5}
Short laser pulse	10^{-9}
Time for light to cross an atom	10^{-18}
Shortest-lived subatomic particles	10^{-23}

Particle tracks in a bubble chamber

Fossilized trilobites

The history of the universe has been traced back as far into the past as a hundred million times the length of a man's life (man's life × 100,000,000).

Events have been recorded that last only a few millionths of a millionth of a millionth of a millionth of a man's heartbeat (man's heartbeat × 0.000,000,000,000,000,000,000,001).

It is hard to resist the temptation to say more about these intriguing extremes; however, this is not where physics started. Physics started with the human-sized world—the world of horse-drawn chariots, of falling rain, and of flying arrows. It is with the physics of phenomena on this scale that we shall begin.

Study for "Dynamism of a Cyclist" (1913) by Umberto Boccioni. Courtesy Yale University Art Gallery.

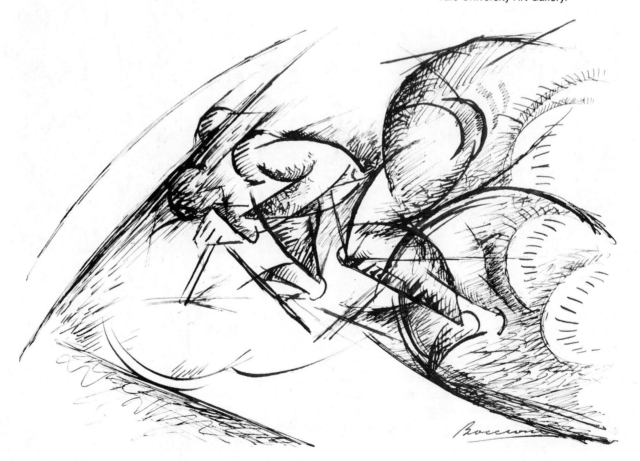

CHAPTER ONE

The Language of Motion

1.1 The motion of things

The world is filled with things in motion: things as small as dust and as large as galaxies, all continually moving. Your textbook may seem to be lying quietly on the desk, but each of its atoms is constantly vibrating. The "still" air around it consists of molecules tumbling wildly, at various speeds, most of them moving as fast as rifle bullets. Light beams dart through the room, covering the distance from wall to wall in about a hundred-millionth of a second, and making about ten million vibrations during that time. Even the whole earth, our majestic spaceship, is moving at about 18 miles per second around the sun.

There is an old maxim: "To be ignorant of motion is to be ignorant of nature." Of course we cannot investigate all motions, even those of "only" earthly objects. So, from this swirling, whirling, vibrating world of ours let us choose just one moving object for our attention. It should be something interesting but typical and, above all, something manageable. Then let us describe its motion.

But where shall we start? A machine, such as a rocket or a car? Though made and controlled by humans, machines and their parts move in fast and complicated ways. We really ought to start with something slower and simpler, something that our eyes can follow in detail. Then how about a bird in flight? Or a leaf falling from a tree?

Surely, in all of nature there is no motion more ordinary than that of a leaf fluttering down from a branch. Can we describe how it falls or explain why it falls? Think about it: you will quickly realize that, while the motion may be "natural," it is very complicated. The leaf twists and turns, sails right and left, back and forth, as it floats down. Even a motion as ordinary as this may turn out, on closer examination, to be more complicated than the motion of machines. And even if we could describe it in detail, what would we gain? No two leaves fall in quite the same

way. Therefore, each leaf seems to require its own detailed description. This individuality is typical of most events we see occurring in nature.

And so we face a problem. We want to describe motion, but the motions we encounter under ordinary circumstances appear too complex. What shall we do? The answer is that we should go, at least for a while, into the physics laboratory. The laboratory is the place to separate the simple ingredients that make up all complex natural phenomena and to make those phenomena more easily visible to our limited human senses.

See the articles "Motion in Words" and "Representation of Movement" in *Project Physics Reader 1*.

1.2 A motion experiment that does not quite work

Having abandoned the fall of a leaf as the way to start on the physics of motion, we select a clearly simpler case. A billiard ball, hit squarely in the center, speeds easily across a table top in a straight line. An even simpler motion (simpler because there is no rolling) can be obtained: Place a disk of what is called "dry ice" (really frozen carbon dioxide) on a smooth floor and give it a gentle push. (Take care not to touch the extremely cold disk with bare hands for more than a brief moment!) The disk will move slowly and with very little friction, supported on its own vapor. We did this in front of a camera to get a photograph that would "freeze" the action for easier measurement later. While the dry-ice disk was moving, the shutter of the camera was kept open; the resulting time-exposure shows the path taken by the disk.

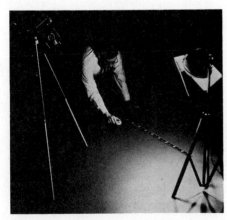

Laboratory setup

Time exposure of the disk in motion

Close-up of a dry-ice disk

What can we learn about the disk's motion by examining the photograph? Our question is easy enough to answer: as nearly as we can judge by placing a ruler on the photograph, the disk moved in a straight line. This is a very useful result, and we will see later that it is really quite surprising. It shows how simple a situation can be made in the laboratory; the kinds of motion one ordinarily sees are almost never that simple. But did the disk move steadily, or did it slow down? From this photograph we cannot tell. Let us improve our experiment. Before we do so, however, we must decide just how we plan to measure the speed.

Why not use something like an automobile speedometer? A speedometer can tell us directly the speed at which a car is moving at any time. Everyone knows how to read that most familiar of all meters, even though few of us have a clear notion of how it works. Think of how speeds are expressed. We say, for example, that a car is moving at 60 *miles per hour*. This means that if the car continues to move with the same speed it had at the instant the speed reading was taken, the car would move a distance of 60 miles in a time interval of 1.0 hour. Or we could say that the car would move 1.0 mile in 1/60 of an hour, or 6.0 miles in 1/10 of an hour. In fact, we could use *any* distance and time intervals for which the ratio of distance to time is 60 miles per hour.

Unfortunately, an automobile speedometer cannot be hooked to a disk of dry ice, or to a bullet, or to many other objects. (See SG 1.2.) However, there is a way to measure speeds in most cases that would interest us.

As a clue, think of what you could do if the speedometer in a car were broken and you still wanted to know your speed as you moved along a turnpike. You could do one of two things (the result is the same in either case). You could count the number of mile markers passed in one hour (or some known fraction of it) and find the average speed by getting the ratio of miles and hours. Or, you could determine the fraction of an hour it takes to go from one mile marker to the next (or to another marker a known number of miles away) and again find the average speed as a ratio of miles to hours.

Either method gives, of course, only the *average* speed for the interval during which speed is measured. That is not the same as *instantaneous* speed—the speed given at any given instant as a speedometer might register it. But it is good enough for a start. After we get average speeds clear, we will see a simple way of finding instantaneous speeds.

To find the average speed of an object, we measure the distance it moves and the time it takes to move that distance. Then we divide the distance by the time. The speed comes out in miles per hour, or feet per second, or meters per second, depending upon the units used to measure the distance and time. With this plan of attack, we return to the experiment with the dry-ice disk. Our task now is to find the speed of the disk as it moves along its straight-line path. If we can do it for the disk, we can do it for many other objects as well.

The speed of an object is, of course, how fast it moves from one place to another. A more formal way to say the same thing is: *Speed is the time rate of change of position.* The term "displacement" is often used to refer to the straight-line distance between the beginning and end points in the change in position of a moving object. We will use this term in connection with vectors in Chapter 3, and more often still with wave motion in Chapter 12.

From time to time you will be referred to items in the *Study Guide,* a few pages found at the end of each chapter. Usually the letters SG plus a number will indicate this. See SG 1.1 on page 31 for more information on how to study for this course and on the use of the Study Guide.

Note: There will usually be one or more brief questions at the end of each section in a text chapter. Q1, below, is the first. Use these to check

on your progress. Answer the questions *before* continuing to the next
section. Check your answers to these End-of-Section questions at the back
of the book starting on Appendix page A-25. Whenever you find you did
not get the correct answer, study through the section again. And of
course, if anything is still unclear after you have tried to study it on your
own or together with other students, then ask your instructor.

Q1 Why is it impossible to determine the speed of the dry ice disk in
the time-exposure photograph on page 11?

1.3 A better experiment

To find speed, we need to be able to measure both distance and time.
So let's repeat the experiment with the dry-ice disk after first placing a
meter stick (100 cm) on the table parallel to the expected path of the disk.
This is the photograph we obtain:

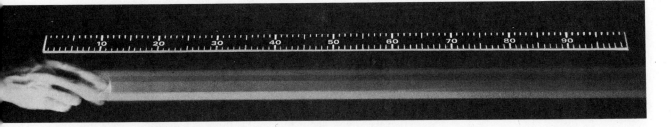

We now have a way of measuring the distance traveled by the disk.
But we still need a way to measure the time it takes the disk to travel a
given distance.

This can be done in various ways, but there is a fine trick that you
can try in the laboratory. The camera shutter is again kept open and
everything else is the same as before, except that the only source of light
in the darkened room comes from a stroboscopic lamp. This lamp
produces bright flashes of light at intervals which we can set as we
please. Each pulse or flash of light lasts for only about 10 millionths of a
second (10 microseconds). Therefore, the moving disk appears in a series
of separate, sharp exposures, rather than as a continuous blur. The
photograph below was made by using such a stroboscopic lamp flashing
10 times per second, after the disk had been gently pushed as before.

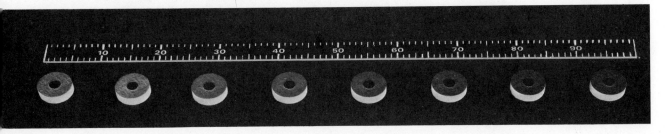

Now we're getting somewhere. Our special setup enables us to record accurately a series of positions of the moving object. The meter stick helps us to measure the distance moved by the front edge of the disk between one light flash and the next. The time interval between images is, of course, equal to the time interval between stroboscopic lamp flashes (0.10 second in these photos).

We can now determine the speed of the disk at the beginning and end of its photographed path. The front edge of the first clear image of the disk at the left is 6 cm from the zero mark on the meter stick. The front edge of the second image from the left is at the 19-cm position. The distance traveled during that time was the difference between those two positions, or 13 cm. The corresponding time interval was 0.10 second. Therefore, the speed at the start must have been 13 cm/0.10 sec, or 130 cm/sec.

Now look at the two images of the disk farthest to the right in the photograph. Here, too, the distance traveled during 0.10 sec was 13 cm. Thus the speed at the right end was 13 cm/0.10 sec, or 130 cm/sec.

The disk's motion was not measurably slower at the right end than at the left end. Its speed was 130 cm/sec near the beginning of the path and 130 cm/sec near the end of the path. However, this does not yet prove that the speed was constant all the way. We might well suspect that it was, and we can easily check to find out. Since the *time* intervals between images are equal, the speeds will be equal if the *distance* intervals are equal to one another. Is the distance between images always 13 cm? Did the speed stay constant, as far as you can tell from the measurement?

When you think about this result, there is something really unusual in it. Cars, planes, and ships do not move in neat, straight lines with precisely constant speed even when using power. Yet this disk did it, coasting along on its own, without anything to keep it moving. You might consider this a rare event which would not happen again. In any case, *you* should try the experiment. The equipment you will need includes cameras, strobe lamps (or mechanical strobes, which work just as well), and low-friction disks of one sort or another. Repeat the experiment several times with different initial speeds. Then compare your results with those we found above.

You may have a serious reservation about the experiment. You might ask: "How do you know that the disk didn't slow down an amount too small to be detected by your measurements?" We can only answer that we don't know. All measurements involve some uncertainty, though one which can usually be estimated. With a meter stick we can measure distances reliably to the nearest 0.1 cm. If we had been able to measure to the nearest 0.01 cm or 0.001 cm, we might have detected some slowing down. But if we again found no change in speed, you could still raise the same objection. There is no way out of this. We must simply admit that *no* physical measurements are ever perfectly precise. So it is wise to leave open to question the results of any set of measurements and the findings based on them if increased precision could reveal other results.

Let us briefly review the results of our experiment. We devised a way to measure the successive positions of a moving dry ice disk at known time intervals. From this we calculated first the distance intervals and

Uncertainty of measurement is taken up in detail in the *Handbook,* particularly in Experiment 1-3.

See the articles "Motion in Words" and "Representation of Movement" in the *Project Physics Reader 1.*

then the speed between selected positions. We soon discovered that
(within the limits of precision of our measurements) the speed did not
change. Objects that move in such a manner are said to have *uniform
speed* or *constant speed*. We know now how to measure uniform speed.
But, of course, actual motions are seldom uniform. What about the more
usual case of *non*uniform speed? That is our next concern.

Some practice problems dealing
with constant speed are given in
Study Guide 1.3 (a, b, c, and d).

Q2   Suppose the circles below represent the successive positions of a
moving object as photographed stroboscopically. Did the object move with
uniform speed? How do you know?

Q3   Describe uniform speed without referring to dry-ice disks and
strobe photography or to *any* particular object or technique of
measurement.

1.4 Leslie's "50" and the meaning of average speed

Consider the situation at a swimming meet. At the end of each race,
the name of the winner is announced—the swimmer with the shortest
time. But in any given race—say the 100-yard backstroke—every swimmer
goes the same distance. Therefore the swimmer with the shortest time is
also the one having the highest average speed while covering the
measured distance. The ratio of the distance traveled to the elapsed time
is the measure of average speed. This relationship is expressed in the
following equation:

$$\text{average speed} = \frac{\text{distance traveled}}{\text{elapsed time}}$$

What information does a knowledge of the average speed give us? We can
answer this question by studying a real example.

Leslie is not the fastest girl freestyle swimmer in the world, but
Olympic speed is not necessary for our purpose. Leslie was timed while
swimming two lengths of an indoor pool. The pool is 25.0 yards long, and
it took her 56.1 seconds to swim the two lengths. Thus her average speed
over the whole 50-yard distance-was

2.7 ft/sec is the equivalent of 1.8
miles per hour. No great speed! A
sailfish can do over 40 mph. But
man is a land animal. For short
distances he can run better than
20 mph.

$$\frac{50.0 \text{ yd}}{56.1 \text{ sec}} = 0.89 \text{ yd/sec, or nearly } 2.7 \text{ ft/sec}$$

Did Leslie swim the 50 yards at uniform (or constant) speed? If not,
which length did she cover more quickly? What was her greatest speed?
Her least speed? How fast was she moving when she passed the 10-yard,
or 18-yard, or 45-yard mark? These are useful things to know when
training for a meet. But so far we do not have a way to answer any of
these questions. The value 0.89 yd/sec probably comes closer than any
other *one* value to describing the whole event.

To compare Leslie's speed at different parts of the swim, we must observe the times and distances covered as we did in experimenting with the dry-ice disk. That is why we arranged the event as shown in the photograph below.

Observers stationed at 5-yard intervals from the 0 mark along the length of the pool started their stopwatches when the starting signal was given. Each observer had two watches. He stopped one watch as Leslie passed his mark going down the pool, and stopped the other as she passed on her return trip. The data are tabulated next to the photograph of this experiment.

d	t
0.0 yd	0.0 sec
5.0	2.5
10.0	5.5
15.0	11.0
20.0	16.0
25.0	22.0
30.0	26.5
35.0	32.0
40.0	39.5
45.0	47.5
50.0	56.0

From these data we can determine Leslie's average speed for the first 25 yards and for the last 25 yards separately.

$$\text{Average speed for the } \textit{first} \text{ 25 yards} = \frac{\text{distance traveled}}{\text{elapsed time}}$$

$$= \frac{25.0 \text{ yd}}{22.0 \text{ sec}}$$

$$= 1.10 \text{ yd/sec}$$

$$\text{Average speed for the } \textit{last} \text{ 25 yards} = \frac{\text{distance traveled}}{\text{elapsed time}}$$

$$= \frac{25.0 \text{ yd}}{56.0 \text{ sec} - 22.0 \text{ sec}}$$

$$= \frac{25.0 \text{ yd}}{34.0 \text{ sec}} = 0.735 \text{ yd/sec}$$

It is now clear that Leslie did not swim with uniform speed. She swam the first length much faster (1.10 yd/sec) than the second length (0.74 yd/sec). Notice that the overall average speed (0.89 yd/sec) does not describe either lap very well. Here and elsewhere in our study of motion, the more we refine our measurements to look at detail, the more variation we find.

In a moment we will continue our analysis of the data we have obtained for Leslie's swim. This analysis is important because the concepts we are developing for this everyday type of motion will be needed later to discuss other motions, ranging from that of planets to that of atoms. But, now let us introduce some shorthand notation to simplify our definition of average speed,

$$\text{average speed} = \frac{\text{distance traveled}}{\text{elapsed time}}$$

A more concise statement that says exactly the same thing is

$$v_{\text{av}} = \frac{\Delta d}{\Delta t}$$

In this equation v_{av} is the symbol for the average speed, Δd is the symbol for change in position, and Δt is the symbol for an elapsed interval of time. The symbol Δ is the fourth letter in the Greek alphabet and is called delta. When Δ precedes another symbol, it means "the change in. . ." Thus, Δd does *not* mean "Δ multiplied by d." Rather, it means "the change in d" or "the distance interval." Likewise, Δt stands for "the change in t" or "the time interval."

We can now go back to the data and compute Leslie's average speed for each 5-yard interval, from beginning to end. This calculation is easily made, especially if we reorganize our data as shown in the table on page 19. The values of v_{av} calculated at 5-yard intervals for the first lap are entered in the right-hand column. (The values for the second lap are left for you to complete.)

Much more detail is emerging from the picture. Looking at the speed column, we see that Leslie's speed was greatest, as expected, near the start. Her racing jump into the water gave her extra speed at the beginning. In the middle of her first length she swam at a fairly steady rate, and she slowed down coming into the turn. Use your own figures to see what happened after the turn.

Although we have determined Leslie's speeds at various intervals along the path, we are still dealing with *average* speeds. The intervals are smaller—5 yards rather than the entire 50. But we do not know the details of what happened *within* any of the 5-yard intervals. Thus, we know that Leslie's average speed between the 15- and 20-yard marks was 1.0 yd/sec. But we don't know yet how to compute her speed at the very instant and point when she was, say, 18 yards or 20 yards from the start. Even so, the average speed for the 5-yard interval between the 15- and the 20-yard marks is probably a better estimate of her speed as she went through the 18-yard mark than is the average speed for the whole 50 yards, or for either 25-yard length. We will come back to this problem of determining "speed at a particular instant and point" in Sec. 1.7.

   Q4 Define the concept *average speed.*

   Q5 If you have not already completed the table on page 19, do so now before going on to the next section.

Practice problems on average speed can be found in Study Guide 1.3 (e, f, g, and h). Study Guide 1.4, 1.5, 1.6, and 1.7 offer somewhat more challenging problems. Some suggestions for average speeds to measure are listed in Study Guide 1.8 and 1.9. An interesting activity is suggested in Study Guide 1.10.

1.5 Graphing motion and finding the slope

What can we learn about motion by graphing the data rather than just writing down the figures in a table? Let us find out by preparing a distance-versus-time graph, using the data from Leslie's 50-yard swim. As shown in the first graph on the next page, all we really know are the data points. Each point on the graph shows the time when Leslie reached a particular position along her path. In the second graph, straight dotted lines have been drawn to connect these points. We don't actually know what the values are between the data points. Thus, the straight-line connections are just a very simple way of suggesting what the overall graph might look like. In fact, the straight lines are not likely to give a very good approximation, because they indicate some very abrupt changes of speed. If we believe that Leslie changed speed only gradually, we can get a better approximation by drawing the smoothest curve possible through the data points. One experimenter's idea of a smooth curve is shown in the last graph.

Now let us "read" the last graph. Notice that the line is steepest at the start. This means that a comparatively large change in position occurred during the first seconds. In other words, Leslie got off to a fast start. The steepness of the graph line is an indication of how fast she was moving. From 10 yards to 20 yards the line appears to be straight, becoming neither more or less steep. This means that her speed in the stretch was constant. Reading the graph further, we see that she slowed down noticeably just before the 25-yard mark, but gained speed right after the turn. The steepness decreases gradually from the 30-yard mark to the finish—Leslie was slowing down. There was no final spurt over the last 5 yards.

Looked at in this way, a graph provides us at a glance with a visual representation of motion. But this kind of representation does not help us if we want to know actual values of Leslie's speed at various times. For this, we need a way of measuring the steepness of the graph line. Here we can turn to mathematics for help, as we often shall.

There is an old method in geometry for solving just this problem. The steepness of a graph at any point is related to the change in vertical direction (Δy) and the change in horizontal direction (Δx). By definition, the ratio of these two changes ($\Delta y/\Delta x$) is the slope:

$$\text{slope} = \frac{\Delta y}{\Delta x}$$

Slope is a widely used mathematical concept. It can be used to indicate the steepness of a line in any graph. In a distance-time graph, like the one for Leslie's swim, the position, or distance from the start, is usually plotted on the vertical axis (d replaces y) and time on the horizontal axis (t replaces x). Therefore, in such a graph, the slope of a straight line is given by

$$\text{slope} = \frac{\Delta d}{\Delta t}$$

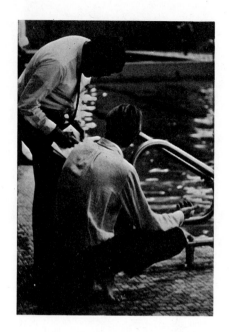

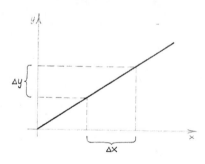

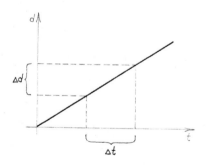

d	t	Δd	Δt	$\dfrac{\Delta d}{\Delta t}$
0.0 yd	0.0 sec			
		5.0 yd	2.5 sec	2.0 yd/sec
5.0	2.5			
		5.0	3.0	1.7
10.0	5.5			
		5.0	5.5	0.9
15.0	11.0			
		5.0	5.0	1.0
20.0	16.0			
		5.0	6.0	0.8
25.0	22.0			
		5.0	4.5	etc.
30.0	26.5			
		5.0	5.5	
35.0	32.0			
		5.0	etc.	
40.0	39.5			
		5.0		
45.0	47.5			
		5.0		
50.0	56.0			

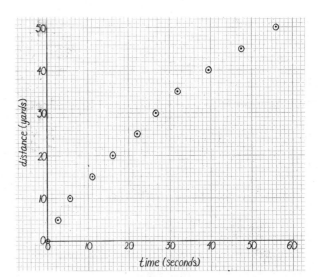

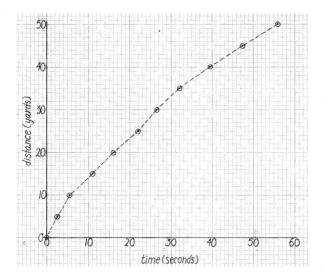

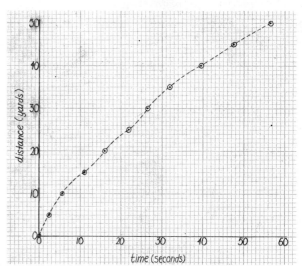

Above are shown four ways of representing Leslie's swim: a table of data, a plot of the data points, broken straight-line segments that connect the points, and a smooth curve that connects the points.

If this concept is new to you or if you wish to review it, turn now to Study Guide 1.11 before continuing here.

But this reminds us of the definition of average speed, $v_{av} = \Delta d/\Delta t$. In fact, we see that v_{av} is numerically equal to the slope! In other words, the slope of any straight-line part of a graph of distance versus time gives a measure of the average speed of the object during that interval. When we measure slope on a graph, we do basically the same thing that highway engineers do when they specify the steepness of a road. They simply measure the rise in the road and divide that rise by the horizontal distance one must go in order to achieve the rise. The only difference between this and what we have done is that the highway engineers are concerned with an actual physical slope. Thus, on a graph of their data, the vertical axis and horizontal axis both show *distance*. We, on the other hand, are using the *mathematical concept* of a slope as a way of expressing *distance* measured against *time*.

We can get a numerical value quickly and directly for the slope of each straight-line segment in the graph on page 19. This will give us the value of the average speed for each of the 5-yard intervals between data points. For example, we used our data table to calculate Leslie's average speed between the 5- and 10-yard markers as 1.4 yd/sec. She moved 5 yards on the vertical (distance) axis during a lapse of 3.5 seconds on the horizontal (time) axis. Therefore, the slope of the line connecting the 5-yard and 10-yard points is equal to 5 yards divided by 3.5 seconds, or 1.4 yd/sec.

The slope, as we have defined it here, is not exactly the same thing as the steepness of the line on the graph paper. Suppose we had chosen a different scale for either the distance or time axis, making the graph twice as tall or twice as wide. Then the apparent steepness of the entire graph would be different. The slope, however, is measured by the ratio of the distance and time units. A Δd of 10 meters in a Δt of 5 seconds gives a ratio of 2 m/sec, no matter how much space on the drawing or graph is used to represent meters and seconds.

But the graph is more than just a "picture" of the values in the table. We can now ask questions that cannot be answered directly from the original data: What was Leslie's speed 10 seconds after the start? What was her speed as she crossed the 37-yard mark? We can answer questions like these by finding the slope of a fairly straight portion of the graph line near the point of interest. Two examples are worked out on the graph at the bottom of page 20. For each example, Δt was chosen to be a 4-second interval—from 2 seconds before the point in question to 2 seconds after it. Then the Δd for that Δt was measured.

You can check the reasonableness of using the graph in this way by

The 4-sec value for t is just for convenience; some other value could have been used. Or, we could have chosen a value for Δd and then measured the corresponding Δt.

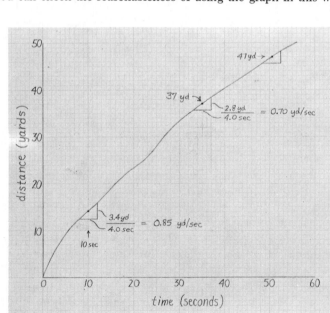

comparing the results with the values listed in the table on page 19. For example, the speed near the 10-second mark is found from the graph to be about 3.4 yd/4.0 sec = 0.85 yd/sec. This is somewhat less than the value of 0.9 yd/sec given in the table for the average speed between 6 and 11 seconds. And this is just what we would expect, because we can see that the smooth-curve graph does become slightly less steep around the 10-second point. If the smooth curve really describes Leslie's swimming better than the straight-line graph does, then we can get more information out of the graph than we put into it.

Q6 Turn back to page 13 and draw a distance-time graph for the motion of the dry-ice disk.

Q7 Which of the two graphs below has the greater slope?

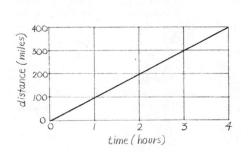

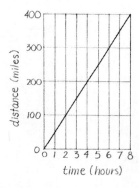

Q8 Where was Leslie swimming most rapidly? Where was she swimming most slowly?

Q9 From the graph, find Leslie's speed at the 47-yard mark. From the table on page 19, calculate her average speed over the last 5 yards. How do the two values compare?

1.6 Time out for a warning

Graphs are useful—but they can also be misleading. You must always be aware of the limitations of any graph you use. The only actual *data* in a graph are the plotted points. There is a limit to the precision with which the points can be plotted, and a limit to how precisely they can be read from the graph.

The placement of a line through a series of data points, as in the graph on page 19, depends on personal judgment and interpretation. The process of estimating values *between* data points is called *interpolation*. That is essentially what you are doing when you draw a line between data points. Even more risky than interpolation is *extrapolation*, where the graph line is extended to provide estimated points *beyond* the known data.

The description of a high-altitude balloon experiment carried out in Lexington, Massachusetts, nicely illustrates the danger of extrapolation. A cluster of helium-filled balloons carried cosmic ray detectors high above

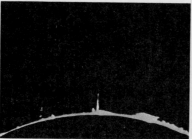

19 minutes 17 minutes 27 minutes

The Language of Motion

These photographs show a stormy outburst of incandescent gas at the edge of the sun, a developing chive plant and a glacier. From these pictures and the time intervals given between pictures, you can determine the average speeds (1) of the growth of the solar flare with respect to the sun's surface (radius of sun is about 432,000 mi), (2) of the growth of one of the chive shoots with respect to the graph paper behind it (large squares are one inch), (3) of the moving glacier with respect to its "banks."

17 hours 33 hours

4 years

the earth's surface. From time to time observers measured the altitude of
the cluster. The graph on the right shows the data for the first hour and a
half. After the first 20 minutes the balloons seem to be rising in a cluster
with unchanging speed. The average speed can be calculated from the
slope: speed of ascent = $\Delta d/\Delta t$ = 27,000 ft/30 min = 900 ft/min. Now,
suppose we were asked how high the balloons would be at the very end of
the experiment (500 min). We might be tempted to extrapolate, either by
extending the graph or by computing from the speed. In either case we
would obtain about 500 min × 900 ft/min = 450,000 ft, which is over 90
miles high! Would we be right? Turn to SG 1.12 to see for yourself. (The
point is that mathematical aids, including graphs, can be a splendid help,
but only within the limits set by physical realities.)

Q10 What is the difference between extrapolation and interpolation?
Q11 Which estimate from the graph would you expect to be less
accurate: Leslie's speed as she crossed the 30-yard mark, or her speed at
the end of an additional lap?

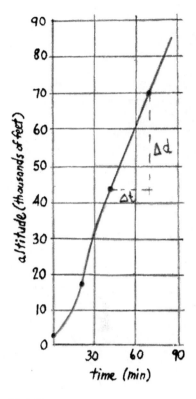

SG 1.13

1.7 Instantaneous speed

Now let us wrap up the chief lessons of this first chapter. In Sec. 1.5
we saw that distance-time graphs could be very helpful in describing
motion. Near the end of the section, we spoke briefly of specific needs at
particular points along the path ("the 14-yard mark") and at particular
instants of time ("the instant 10 seconds after the start"). You probably
were bothered by this manner of talking, since at the same time we
admitted that the only kind of speed we can actually measure is *average*
speed. To find average speed we need a ratio of distance *intervals* and
time *intervals*. A particular point on the path, however, does not have any
interval. Nevertheless, it does make sense to speak about the speed at a
point. We will summarize the reasons for using "speed" in this way, and
see how well we can get away with it.

You remember that our answer to the question (page 20), "How fast
was Leslie swimming at time t = 10 sec?" was 0.85 yd/sec. We obtained
that answer by finding the slope of a small portion of the curve around
the point **P** when t = 10 sec. That section of the curve is reproduced in
the margin here. Notice that the part of the curve we used appears to be
nearly a straight line. As the table under the graph shows, the value of
the slope for each interval changes very little as we decrease the time
interval Δt. Now imagine that we closed in on the point where t = 10 sec
until the amount of curve remaining became vanishingly small. Can we
safely assume that the slope of that infinitesimally small part of the curve
is the same as the slope of the straight line of which it seems to be a

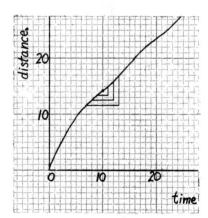

Δt	Δd	$\Delta d / \Delta t$
6.0 sec	5.4 yd	0.90 yd/sec
4.0	3.4	0.85
2.0	1.7	0.85

part? We think so. That is why we took the slope of the straight line from
$t = 8$ sec to $t = 12$ sec, and *called* it the speed *at* the midpoint, $t = 10$
sec. The correct term for this value is "the instantaneous speed" at $t = 10$
sec.

To estimate Leslie's instantaneous speed at a particular time, we
actually measured the average speed over a 4.0-sec interval. We then
made the assumption that we have described. We decided that the
instantaneous speed at a particular instant has the same value as the
average speed $\Delta d/\Delta t$ if two conditions are met: First, the particular instant
must be included in Δt. Second, the ratio $\Delta d/\Delta t$ must cover a small
enough part of the curve, one that is nearly a straight-line segment.
Under this condition, the ratio will not change noticeably when we
compute it again over a still smaller time interval.

A second concrete example will help here. In the oldest known study
of its kind, the French scientist de Montbeillard periodically recorded the
height of his son during the years 1759-1777. A graph of height versus
age for his son was published and is shown at the lower left.

From the graph, we can compute the average growth rate, or average
speed of growth (v_{av}) over the entire 18-year interval, or over any shorter
time interval within that period. Suppose, however, we wanted to know
how fast the boy was growing just as he reached his fifteenth birthday.
The answer becomes evident if we enlarge the graph in the vicinity of the
fifteenth year. His height at age 15 is indicated as point **P,** and the other
letters indicate instants of time on either side of **P.** The boy's average

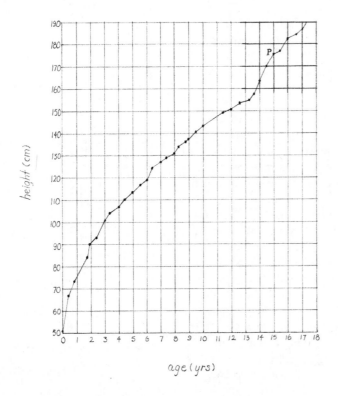

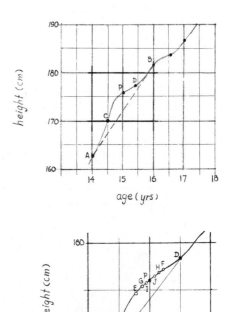

growth rate over a two-year interval is given by the slope of the line **AB.**
Over a one-year interval this average growth rate is given by the slope
CD. (See the third graph at the bottom of the previous page.) The slope of
EF gives the average growth rate over six months, etc. The four lines,
AB, CD, EF, and **GH,** are not parallel to each other and so their slopes
are different. However, the difference in slope gets smaller and smaller. It
is large when we compare **AB** and **CD,** less if we compare **CD** and **EF,**
and still less between **EF** and **GH.** For intervals less than $\Delta t = 1$ year,
the lines become parallel to each other and gradually merge into the
curve. For very small intervals, you can find the slope by drawing a
straight line *tangent* to this curve at **P.** This method involves placing a
ruler parallel to line **GH** at **P** and extending it on both sides, as shown in
SG 1.11.

The values of the slopes of the straight-line segments in the two right
hand graphs at the bottom of the previous page have been computed for
the corresponding time intervals. These values appear in the table in the
margin at the right. We note that values of v_{av} calculated for shorter and
shorter time intervals approach closer and closer to 6.0 cm/yr. In fact, for
any time interval less than 2 months, v_{av} will be 6.0 cm/yr within the
limits of accuracy of measuring height. Thus we can say that, on his
fifteenth birthday, young de Montbeillard was growing at a rate of 6.0
cm/yr. At that instant in his life, $t = 15.0$ yr, this was his instantaneous
growth rate. (We might also express it as *instantaneous speed* of his head
with respect to his feet!)

Average speed over a time interval Δt, we have said, is the ratio of
distance traveled to elapsed time. In symbols,

Line between points	Δt	Δd	Growth rate $v_{av} = \dfrac{\Delta d}{\Delta t}$
AB	2 yr	19.0 cm	9.5 cm/year
CD	1 yr	8.0	8.0
EF	6 mo	3.5	7.0
GH	4 mo	2.0	6.0
IJ	2 mo	1.0	6.0

If you have taken a course in calculus, you will of course have seen simpler and more rigorous ways of defining the instantaneous value of a quantity that is changing.

$$v_{av} = \frac{\Delta d}{\Delta t}$$

SG 1.14

We now have added the definition of *instantaneous* speed at a given
instant t: It is the final, limiting value approached by the average speeds
when we compute v_{av} for smaller and smaller time intervals including the
instant t. In almost all physical situations, such a limiting value can be
accurately and quickly estimated by the method described on the previous
page.

From now on we will use the letter v (without the subscript $_{av}$) to
represent instantaneous speed defined in this way. You may wonder why
we have used the letter "v" instead of "s" for speed. The reason is that
speed is closely related to velocity. We use the term "velocity" to mean
speed in a specified direction (such as *50 mph to the north*) and represent
it by the symbol $\vec{v}$. When direction is not specified and only the
magnitude (*50 mph*) is of interest, we remove the arrow and just use the
letter v. This symbol represents only the *magnitude* of the velocity—and
that is the "speed." We will discuss this distinction between speed and
velocity in more detail in later sections. We also will learn why velocity is
the more important concept in physics.

1. Paris street scene, 1839. A daguerro-type made by Louis Daguerre himself.

2. American street scene, 1859

3. Boys on skateboards

Photography 1839 to the Present

1.   Note the lone figure in the otherwise empty street. He was getting his shoes shined. The other pedestrians did not remain in one place long enough to have their images recorded. With exposure times several minutes long, the outlook for the possibility of portraiture was gloomy.

2.   However, by 1859, due to improvements in photographic emulsions and lenses, it was not only possible to photograph a person at rest, but one could capture a bustling crowd of people, horses and carriages. Note the slight blur of the jaywalker's legs.

3.   Today, one can "stop" action with an ordinary camera.

4.   A new medium—the motion picture. In 1873 a group of California sportsmen called in the photographer Eadweard Muybridge to settle the question, "Does a galloping horse ever have all four feet off the ground at once?" Five years later he answered the question with these photos. The five pictures were taken with five cameras lined up along the track, each camera being triggered when the horse broke a string which tripped the shutter. The motion of the horse can be restructured by making a flip pad of the pictures.

   With the perfection of flexible film, only one camera was needed to take many pictures in rapid succession. By 1895, there were motion picture parlors throughout the United States. Twenty-four frames each second were sufficient to give the viewer the illusion of motion.

4. Muybridge's series, 1878

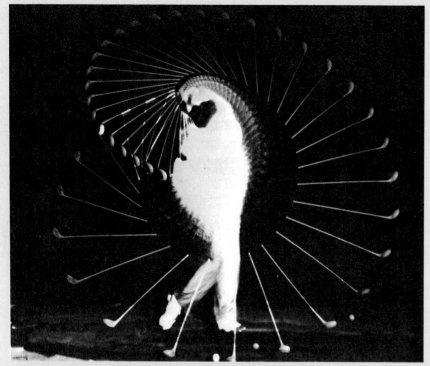

5. Stroboscopic photo of golfer's swing. (See the article "The Dynamics of a Golf Club" in Project Physics *Reader 1*.)

5.   A light can be flashed successfully at a controlled rate and a multiple exposure (similar to the strobe photos in this text) can be made. In this photo of a golfer, the light flashed 100 times each second.

6.   It took another ninety years after the time the crowded street was photographed before a bullet in flight could be "stopped." This remarkable picture was made by Harold Edgerton of MIT, using a brilliant electric spark which lasted for about one millionth of a second.

7.   An interesting offshoot of motion pictures is the high-speed motion picture. In the frames of the milk drop series shown below, 1000 pictures were taken each second (by Harold Edgerton). The film was whipped past the open camera shutter while the milk was illuminated with a flashing light (similar to the one used in photographing the golfer) synchronized with the film. When the film is projected at the rate of 24 frames each second, action which took place in 1 second is spread out over 42 seconds.

It is clear that the eye alone could not have seen the elegant details of this event. This is precisely why photography of various kinds is used in the laboratory.

6. Bullet cutting through a playing card.

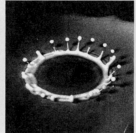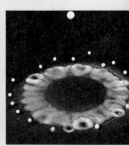

7. Action shown in high-speed film of milk drop.

See SG 1.17, 1.18, and 1.19 for problems that check your understanding of the chapter up to this point.

Q12 (a) Define instantaneous speed, first in words, and then in symbols. (b) What was the value of young de Montbeillard's instantaneous growth rate on his fifteenth birthday, expressed in cm/hr?

Q13 Explain the difference in meaning between average speed and instantaneous speed.

1.8 Acceleration—by comparison

You can tell from the photograph of a rolling baseball at the bottom of this page that it was changing speed—accelerating. The increasing distances between the images of the ball give you this information. But how can you tell how *much* acceleration the ball has?

To answer this question we have to learn the definition of acceleration. But the definition itself is simple. Our real task is to learn how to *use* it in situations like the one below. For the time being, we will define acceleration as *rate of change of speed*. Later this definition will have to be modified somewhat when we encounter motion in which change in *direction* becomes important. But for now we are dealing only with straight-line motion. So we can equate the rate of change of speed with acceleration.

Some of the effects of acceleration are familiar to everyone. It is acceleration, not speed, that you notice when an elevator suddenly starts up or slows down. The flutter in one's stomach comes only during the speeding up and slowing down. It is not felt during most of the ride, when the elevator is moving at a steady speed. Likewise, the excitement of the roller coaster and other rides at amusement parks result from their unexpected accelerations. Speed by itself does not cause these sensations. If it did, we would feel them during a smooth plane ride at 650 mph, or during the continuous motion of the earth around the sun at 65,000 mph.

Simply stated, speed is a relationship between two objects. One object is taken to be the reference object while the other moves with respect to it. Some examples are the speed of the earth with respect to the stars, the speed of the swimmer with respect to the pool edge, the speed of the top of the growing boy's head with respect to his feet. In a perfectly smooth-riding train, we could tell that we were moving at a high speed only by seeing the scenery whizzing by. We would have just the same experience if the train were somehow fixed and the earth, rails, etc., were to whiz by in the other direction. And if we "lost the reference object" (by pulling down the shades, say) we could not tell whether we were moving or not.

Unless noted otherwise, "rate of change" will always mean "rate of change with respect to time."

In contrast, we "feel" accelerations. We do not need to look out the train window to realize that the engineer has suddenly started the train, or has slammed on the brakes. We might be pushed against the seat, or the luggage might fly from the rack.

All this suggests a profound physical difference between motion at constant speed and motion with acceleration. It is best to learn about acceleration at first hand (in the laboratory and through the film loops). But we can summarize the main ideas here. For the moment let us focus on the similarities between the concepts of speed and acceleration. For motion in a straight line:

The rate of *change of position* is called *speed*.	The rate of *change of speed* is called *acceleration*.

This similarity of form is very helpful. It enables us to use what we have just learned about the concept of speed as a guide for using the concept of acceleration. For example, we have learned that the slope of a line of a *distance*-time graph is a measure of *instantaneous speed*. Similarly, the slope of a *speed*-time graph is a measure of *instantaneous acceleration*.

This section concludes with a list of six statements about motion along a straight line. The list has two purposes: (1) to help you review some of the main ideas about speed presented in this chapter, and (2) to present the corresponding ideas about acceleration. For this reason, each statement about speed is immediately followed by a parallel statement about acceleration.

1. *Speed* is the rate of change of position. *Acceleration* is the rate of change of speed.

2. *Speed* is expressed in units of distance/time. *Acceleration* is expressed in units of speed/time.

3. *Average speed* over any time interval is the ratio of the change of position Δd and the time interval Δt:

$$v_{av} = \frac{\Delta d}{\Delta t}$$

Average acceleration over any time interval is the ratio of the change of speed Δv and the time interval Δt:

$$a_{av} = \frac{\Delta v}{\Delta t}$$

4. *Instantaneous speed* is the value approached by the average speed as Δt is made smaller and smaller. *Instantaneous acceleration* is the value approached by the average acceleration as Δt is made smaller and smaller.

5. On a *distance*-time graph, the *instantaneous speed* at any instant is the slope of the straight line tangent to the curve at the point of interest. On a *speed*-time graph, the *instantaneous acceleration* at any instant is the slope of the straight line tangent to the curve at the point of interest.

6. For the particular case of *constant speed,* the distance-time graph is a straight line. Therefore, the instantaneous speed has the same value

For example, if an airplane changes its speed from 500 mph to 550 mph in 10 minutes, its average acceleration would be

$$\frac{\Delta v}{\Delta t} = \frac{550 \text{ mi/hr} - 500 \text{ mi/hr}}{10 \text{ min}}$$

$$= \frac{50 \text{ mi/hr}}{10 \text{ min}}$$

$$= \frac{5 \text{ mi/hr}}{\text{min}}$$

That is, its speed changed at a rate of 5 mph per minute. (If the speed was decreasing, the value of the acceleration would be negative.)

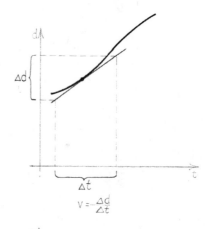

$$v = \frac{\Delta d}{\Delta t}$$

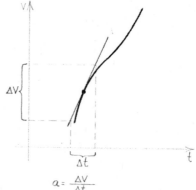

$$a = \frac{\Delta v}{\Delta t}$$

Constant speed and constant acceleration are often called "uniform" speed and "uniform" acceleration. In the rest of this course, we will use the terms interchangeably.

SG 1.20 provides an opportunity to work with distance-time and speed-time graphs and to see their relationship to one another. Transparencies T3 and T4 may be helpful also.

at every point on the graph. Further, this value is equal to the average speed computed for the whole trip. For the particular case of *constant acceleration,* the speed-time graph is a straight line. Therefore, the instantaneous acceleration has the same value at every point on the graph. Further, this value is equal to the average acceleration computed for the whole trip. When speed is constant, its value can be found from any corresponding Δd and Δt. When acceleration is constant, its value can be found from any corresponding Δv and Δt. (This is useful to remember because constant acceleration is the kind of motion we encounter most often in the following chapters.)

We now have most of the tools needed to get into some real physics problems. Our first such problem will involve the accelerated motion of bodies caused by gravitational attraction. It was by studying the motion of falling objects that Galileo, in the early 1600's first shed light on the nature of accelerated motion. His work remains a wonderful example of how scientific theory, mathematics, and actual measurements can be combined to develop physical concepts. More than that, Galileo's work opened one of the earliest and most important battles of the scientific revolution. The specific ideas he introduced are even today fundamental to the science of *mechanics,* the study of bodies in motion.

Q14 What is the average acceleration of an airplane which goes from 0 to 60 mph in 5 seconds?

Q15 What is your average acceleration if, while walking, you change your speed from 4.0 mph to 2.0 mph in an interval of 15 minutes? Is your answer affected by how your change of speed is distributed over the 15 minutes?

SG 1.21 to 1.23 are review problems for this chapter. Some of these will test how thoroughly you grasp the language used for describing straight-line motion.

1.1   This book is probably different in many ways from textbooks you have had in other courses. Therefore we feel it might help to make some suggestions about how to use it.

  1. Do not write in this book, of course, unless it is your own personal copy and you intend to retain it after you have completed the course. However, if you are indeed fortunate enough to be in a situation which permits you to mark freely in the book, we encourage you to do so. You will note that there are wide margins. One of our reasons for leaving that much space is to enable you to record questions or statements as they occur to you when you are studying the material. Mark passages that you do not understand so that you can seek help from your instructor.

  2. If you may not write in the textbook itself, try keeping a notebook keyed to the text chapters. In this study notebook jot down the kinds of remarks, questions and answers that you would otherwise write in the textbook as suggested above. Also, you ought to write down the questions raised in your mind by the other learning materials you will use, by the experiments you do, by demonstrations or other observations, and by discussions you may have with fellow students and others with whom you talk physics. Most students find such an informal notebook to be enormously useful when studying, or when seeking help from their instructors (or, for that matter, from advanced students, scientists they may know, or anyone else whose understanding of physics they have confidence in).

  3. Always try to answer the end-of-section review questions yourself first and then check your answers (Appendix, page A-25). If your answer agrees with the one in the book, it is a good sign that you understand the main ideas in that section—although it is true that you can sometimes get the right answer for the wrong reason, and also that there may sometimes be other answers as good as (or better than!) those given in the book.

  4. There are many different kinds of items in the Study Guide at the end of each chapter. Brief answers to some are given on Appendix page A-36. It is not intended that you should do every item. Sometimes we include material in the Study Guide which we think will especially interest only some students. Notice also that there are several kinds of problems. Some are intended to give practice in the use of a particular concept, while others are designed to help you bring together several related concepts. Still other problems are intended to challenge those students who particularly like to work with numbers.

  5. This text is only one of the learning materials of the Project Physics course. The course includes several other materials such as film loops, programmed instruction booklets, and transparencies. Use those. Be sure to familiarize yourself also with the *Handbook*, which describes outside activities and laboratory experiments, and with the *Reader*, in which we

have collected interesting articles related to physics. Each of these learning aids makes its own contribution to an understanding of physics, and all are designed to be used together.

The Project Physics learning materials particularly appropriate for Chapter 1 include:

Experiments (in the *Handbook*)
  Naked Eye Astronomy
  Regularity and Time
  Variations in Data
  Measuring Uniform Motion

Reader Articles
  Motion in Words
  Representation of Motion
  Motion Dynamics of a Golf Club
  Bad Physics in Athletic
    Measurements

Transparencies
  Analyzing a Stroboscopic Photograph
  Stroboscopic Measurements
  Graphs of Various Motions
  Instantaneous Speed
  Instantaneous Rate of Change

In addition the following Project Physics materials can be used with Unit 1 in general:

Reader Articles
  The Value of Science
  Close Reasoning
  How to Solve It
  Four Pieces of Advice
  to Young People
  On Being the Right Size
  The Vision of Our Age
  Becoming a Physicist
  Chart of the Future

1.2   One type of automobile speedometer is a small electric generator driven by a flexible cable run off the drive shaft. The current produced increases with the rate at which the generator is turned by the drive shaft. The speedometer needle indicates the current. Until the speedometer is calibrated it cannot indicate actual speeds in miles per hour. Try answering the questions below. If you have trouble you may want to try again after you have studied through Sec. 1.7.

(a) How would you calibrate the speedometer in a car if the company had forgotten to do the job?

(b) If you replaced the 24″-diameter rear wheels with 28″-diameter wheels, what would your actual speed be if the speedometer read 50 mph?

(c) Would the speedometer read too high or too low if you loaded down the rear end of your car and had the tire pressure too low?

(d) Does the operation of the speedometer itself affect the motion of the car?

(e) How would you test to see if a bicycle speedometer affects the speed of a bike?

(f) Can you invent a speedometer that has no effect on the motion of the vehicle that carried it?

1.3   Some practice problems:

	SITUATION	FIND
a	Speed uniform, distance = 72 cm, time = 12 sec	Speed
b	Speed uniform at 45 miles per hour	Distance traveled in 20 minutes
c	Speed uniform at 36 ft/min	Time to move 9.0 feet
d	$d_1 = 0$ $t_1 = 0$ $d_2 = 15$ cm $t_2 = 5.0$ sec $d_3 = 30$ cm $t_3 = 10$ sec	Speed and position at 8.0 sec
e	You drive 240 miles in 6.0 hr	Average speed
f	Same as e	Speed and position after 3.0 hr
g	Average speed is 76 cm/sec, computed over a distance of 418 cm	Time taken
h	Average speed is 44 m/sec, computed over time interval of 0.20 sec	Distance moved

1.4   A tsunami caused by an earthquake occurring near Alaska in 1946 consisted of several sea waves which were found to travel at the average speed of 490 mph. The first of the waves reached Hawaii 4 hrs and 34 min after the earthquake occurred. From these data, calculate how far the origin of the tsunami was from Hawaii.

1.5   Light and radio waves travel through a vacuum in a straight line at a speed of very nearly 3×10^8 m/sec.

(a) How long is a "light year" (the *distance* light travels in a year)?

(b) The nearest star, *Alpha Centauri,* is 4.06×10^{16} m distant from us. If this star possesses planets on which highly intelligent beings live, how soon, at the earliest, could we expect to receive a reply after sending them a radio or light signal strong enough to be received there?

1.6   If you traveled one mile at a speed of 1000 miles per hour and another mile at a speed of 1 mile per hour, your average speed would *not* be 1000 mph + 1 mph/2 or 500.5 mph. What *would* be your average speed? (Hint: What is the total distance and total time?)

1.7   What is your average speed in each of these cases?

(a) You run 100 m at a speed of 5.0 m/sec and then you walk 100 m at a speed of 1.0 m/sec.

(b) You run for 100 sec at a speed of 5.0 m/sec and then you walk for 100 sec at a speed of 1.0 m/sec.

1.8   Design and describe experiments to enable you to make estimates of the average speeds for some of the following objects in motion.

(a) A baseball thrown from outfield to home plate

(b) The wind

(c) A cloud

(d) A raindrop

(e) A hand moving back and forth as fast as possible

(f) The tip of a swinging baseball bat

(g) A person walking on level ground, upstairs, downstairs

(h) A bird flying

(i) An ant walking

(j) A camera shutter opening and closing

(k) An eye blinking

(l) A whisker growing

(m) The center of a vibrating guitar string

1.9   What problems arise when you attempt to measure the speed of light? Can you design an experiment to measure the speed of light?

1.10   Sometime, when you are a passenger in an automobile, compare the speed as read from the speedometer with the speed calculated from $\Delta d/\Delta t$. Explain any differences. Refer again to SG1.2. (For other activities see your Project Physics *Handbook*.)

1.11 Take a look at the graph of y versus x shown below:

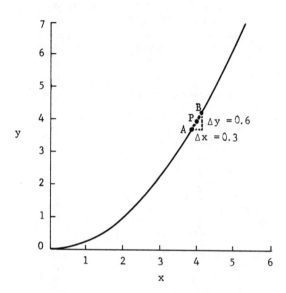

Although in this particular graph the steepness of the line increases as x increases, the method presented below would also hold for a curve of any other shape. One way to indicate the steepness of the line at a point **P** is by means of its "slope." The numerical value of the slope at a point **P** is obtained by the following procedure (diagrammed above): At a very short distance along the line from point **P** to either side of it, mark 2 points, **A** and **B**. Choose these points so close to **P** that although they also lie on the curve, the line **APB** is a straight line as nearly as one can determine with a ruler. Measure Δy (the change in y) in going from **A** to **B**. In this example $y = 0.6$. Measure Δx (the corresponding change in x) in going from **A** to **B**. Δx here is 0.3. The slope of the segment **AB** is defined as the ratio of Δy to Δx of the short straight-line-segment **APB**. By definition, the slope of the curve *at point* **P** is taken to be equal to the slope of the straight-line-segment **APB**.

$$\text{slope} = \frac{\Delta y}{\Delta x}$$

In this example,

$$\text{slope} = \frac{\Delta y}{\Delta x} = \frac{0.6}{0.3} = 2$$

Q. What are the dimensions or units for the slope?

A. The dimensions are just those of y/x. For example, if y represents a distance in meters and x represents a time in seconds, then the units for slope will be meters per second (or m/sec).

Q. In practice, how close must **A** and **B** be to point **P**? (Close is not a very precise adjective. Baltimore is close to Washington if you are flying

over both by jet. If you are walking, it is not close.)

A. Choose **A** and **B** near enough to point **P** so that a straight line drawn carefully to connect **A** and **B** also goes through point **P**.

Q. Suppose **A** and **B** are so close together that you cannot adequately read Δx or Δy from your graph. How would you try to calculate the slope?

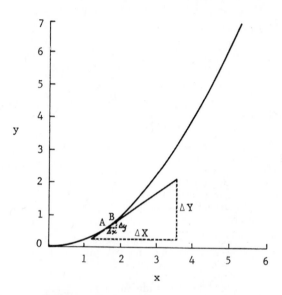

A. Extend the straight line **AB** in both directions, as shown in the figure, as far as you wish, and compute its slope. What you are then doing is putting a *tangent line* to the curve at the chosen point between **A** and **B**. Notice that the small triangle is similar to the large triangle, and, therefore

$$\Delta y/\Delta x = \Delta Y/\Delta X$$

Problem:
(a) Determine the slope of this graph of distance versus time (y in meters, t in seconds) at four different points or instants, namely when $t = 1, 2, 3,$ and 4 seconds.
(b) Find the instantaneous speed at these 4 points, and plot a graph of speeds vs. time.

1.12 (Answer to question in text, page 23.)
Indeed the prediction based upon the first hour and a half would be vastly wrong. A prediction based on an extrapolation from the first $1\frac{1}{2}$ hour's observation neglects all the factors which limit the maximum height obtainable by such a cluster of balloons, such as the bursting of some of the balloons, the change in air pressure and density with height and many others. Actually, at the end of 500 minutes the cluster was not 450,000 feet high but had come down again, as the distance-time graph for the entire experiment shows. See top of next page. For another extrapolation problem, see SG 1.13.

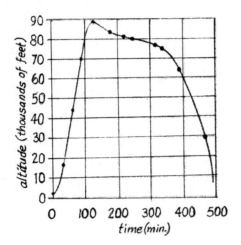

1.13 In the figure above, find the local time at which the sounding balloon was rising most rapidly with respect to the ground below it, and give the values for the instantaneous speed at that time. Then mark with an x those points on the graph where the instantaneous speed of rising was zero.

1.14 World's 400-meter swimming records in minutes and seconds for men and women (numbers in parentheses are ages):

1926	4:57.0	Johnny Weissmuller (18)
	5:53.2	Gertrude Ederle (17)
1936	4:46.4	Syozo Makino (17)
	5:28.5	Helene Madison (18)
1946	4:46.4	(1936 record unbroken)
	5:00.1	R. Hveger (18)
1956	4:33.3	Hironoshin Furuhashi (23)
	4:47.2	Lorraine Crapp (18)
1966	4:11.1	Frank Weigand (23)
	4:38.0	Martha Randall (18)

By about how many meters would Martha Randall have beaten Johnny Weissmuller if they had raced each other? Could you predict the 1976 records for the 400-meter race by extrapolating the graphs of world's records vs. dates up to the year 1976?

1.15 Discuss the following quotation from Mark Twain's *Life on the Mississippi* (1875) as an example of extrapolation. "In the space of one hundred and seventy-six years the Lower Mississippi has shortened itself two hundred and forty-two miles. That is an average of a trifle over one mile and a third per year. Therefore, any calm person, who is not blind or idiotic, can see that in the old Colitic Silurian Period, just a million years ago next November, the Lower Mississippi River was upward of one million three hundred thousand miles long, and stuck out over the Gulf of Mexico like a fishing rod. And by the same token any person can see that seven hundred and forty-two years from now the Lower Mississippi will be only a mile and three-quarters long, and Cairo and New Orleans will have joined their streets together, and be plodding comfortably along under a single

mayor and a mutual board of aldermen. There is something fascinating about science. One gets such wholesale returns of conjecture out of such trifling investment of fact."

1.16 How can we justify defining instantaneous speed as we have on p. 25? How can we be sure the definition is right?

1.17 Using the graph on p. 20 find the instantaneous speeds v at several points (0, 10, 20, 30, 40, and 50 sec, and near 0, or at other points of your choice) by finding the slopes of lines tangent to the curve at each of those points. Make a graph of v vs. t. Use your graph to describe her swim.

1.18 Turn back to p. 28. At the bottom of this page there is a multiple-exposure photograph of a baseball rolling to the right. The time interval between successive flashes was 0.20 sec. The distance between marks on the meter stick was 1 centimeter. You might tabulate your measurements of the ball's progress between flashes and construct a distance-time graph. From the distance-time graph, you can determine the instantaneous speed at several instants and construct a speed-time graph. You can check your results by referring to the answer page at the end of this unit.

1.19 Careful analysis of a stroboscopic photograph of a moving object yielded information which was plotted on the graph below. By placing your ruler tangent to the curve at appropriate points estimate the following:

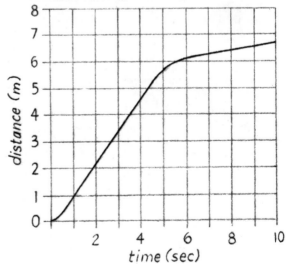

(a) At what moment or interval was the speed greatest? What was the value of the speed at that time?
(b) At what moment or in which interval was the speed least? What was it at that time?
(c) What was the speed at time $t = 5.0$ sec?
(d) What was the speed at time $t = 0.5$ sec?
(e) How far did the object move from time $t = 7.0$ sec to $t = 9.5$ sec?

1.20 The data below show the instantaneous speed in a test run of a car starting from rest. Plot the speed-vs-time graph, then derive data from it and plot the acceleration-vs-time graph.

(a) What is the speed at $t = 2.5$ sec?

(b) What is the maximum acceleration?

Time (sec)	Speed (m/sec)	Time (sec)	Speed (m/sec)
0.0	0.0	6.0	27.3
1.0	6.3	7.0	29.5
2.0	11.6	8.0	31.3
3.0	16.5	9.0	33.1
4.0	20.5	10.0	34.9
5.0	24.1		

1.21 The electron beam in a typical TV set sweeps out a complete picture in 1/30 sec and each picture is composed of 525 lines. If the width of the screen is 20 inches, what is the speed of that beam horizontally across the screen?

1.22 Suppose you must measure the instantaneous speed of a bullet as it leaves the barrel of a rifle. Explain how you might do this.

1.23 Discuss the motion of the horse in the following series of photographs by Muybridge. The time interval between exposures is 0.045 sec.

Portrait of Galileo by Ottavio Leoni, a contemporary of Galileo.

CHAPTER TWO

Free Fall—
Galileo Describes Motion

2.1 The Aristotelian theory of motion

SG 2.1

In this chapter we will follow the development of an important piece of basic research: Galieo's study of freely falling bodies. The phenomenon of free fall is interesting in itself. But our emphasis will be on the way Galileo, one of the first modern scientists, presented his argument. His view of the world, way of thinking, use of mathematics, and reliance upon experimental tests set the style for modern science. These aspects of his work, therefore, are as important to us as the actual results of his investigation.

To understand the nature and importance of Galileo's work, we must first examine the previous system of physical thought which his ideas eventually replaced. Medieval physical science, as Galileo learned it at the University of Pisa, made a sharp distinction between objects on the earth and those in the sky. All *terrestrial* matter, matter on or near the earth, was believed to contain a mixture of four "elements": Earth, Water, Air, and Fire. These elements were not thought of as identical with the natural materials for which they were named. Ordinary water, for example, was thought to be a mixture of all four elements, but mostly the element Water. Each of the four elements was thought to have a natural place in the terrestrial region. The highest place was allotted to Fire. Beneath Fire was Air, then Water, and finally, in the lowest position, Earth. Each was thought to seek its own place. Thus Fire, if placed below its natural position, would tend to rise through Air. Similarly, Air would tend to rise through Water, whereas Earth would tend to fall through both Air and Water. The movement of any real object depended on its particular mixture of these four elements, and on where it was in relation to the natural places of these elements. When water boiled, for example, the

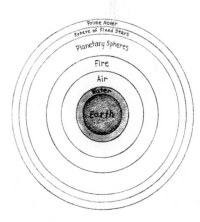

A sketch of a medieval world-system.

A good deal of common-sense
experience supports this natural-
place view. See SG 2.2

element Water would be joined by the element Fire, whose higher natural place would cause the mixture to rise as steam. A stone, on the other hand, was composed mainly of the element Earth. Therefore, a stone would fall when released and would pass through Fire, Air, and Water until it came to rest on the ground, its natural place.

Medieval thinkers also believed that stars, planets, and other *celestial* (heavenly) bodies differed in composition and behavior from objects on or near the earth. Celestial bodies were believed to contain none of the four ordinary elements, but to consist solely of a fifth element, the *quintessence*. The difference in composition required a different physics. Thus the natural motion of celestial objects was thought to be neither rising nor falling, but an endless revolving in circles around the center of the universe. That center was considered to be identical with the center of the earth. Heavenly bodies, although moving, were at all times in their natural places. In this way, heavenly bodies differed from terrestrial objects, which displayed natural motion only as they returned to their natural places from which they had been displaced.

From *quinta essentia*, meaning fifth essence. In earlier Greek writings the term for it was *aether* (also written *ether*).

This theory, so widely held in Galileo's time, had originated almost 2,000 years before, in the fourth century B.C. We find it stated clearly in the writings of the Greek philosopher Aristotle. (See the time chart on the opposite page.) This physical science, built on order, class, place, and purpose, seemed to fit well with many everyday observations. It was particularly believable in societies like those in which Aristotle and Galileo lived, where ideas of rank and order dominated human affairs. Moreover, these ideas about matter and motion were part of an all-embracing universal scheme, or *cosmology*. In this cosmology, Aristotle sought to relate ideas which today are discussed separately under such headings as science, poetry, politics, ethics, and theology.

Not very much is known of Aristotle's physical appearance or life. It is thought that he was born in 384 B.C. in the Greek province of Macedonia. His father was the physician to the King of Macedonia, so Aristotle's early childhood was spent in an environment of court life. He completed his education in Athens and later returned to Macedonia to become the private tutor to Alexander the Great. In 335 B.C., Aristotle came back to Athens and founded the Lyceum, a school and center of research.

The painting entitled "School of Athens," was done by Raphael in the beginning of the sixteenth century. It reflects a central aspect of the Renaissance, the rebirth of interest in classical Greek culture. The central figures are Plato (on the left, pointing to the heavens) and Aristotle (pointing to the ground).

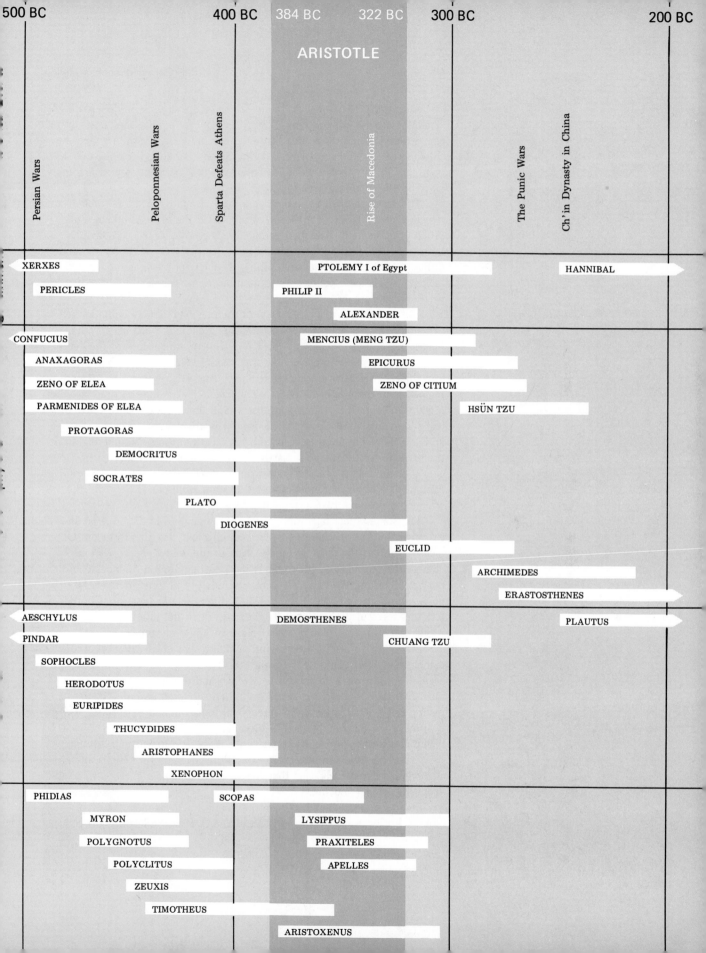

After the decline of the ancient Greek civilization, Aristotle's writings remained almost unknown in Western Europe for 1,500 years. They were rediscovered in the thirteenth century A.D. and soon began to shape the thinking of Christian scholars and theologians. Aristotle became such a dominant influence in the late Middle Ages that he was referred to simply as "The Philosopher."

The work of Aristotle makes up almost an encyclopedia of ancient Greek thought. Some of it merely summarized the work of others, but much of it seems to have been created by Aristotle himself. Today it is hard to believe that one man could have been so well informed on such different subjects as logic, philosophy, theology, physics, astronomy, biology, psychology, politics, and literature. Some scholars doubt that it was all the work of one person.

Unfortunately, Aristotle's physical theories had serious limitations. (This does not, of course, detract from his great achievements in other fields.) According to Aristotle, the fall of a heavy object toward the center of the earth is an example of "natural" motion. He evidently thought that any object, after release, quickly reaches some final speed of fall which it maintains to the end of its path. What factors determine the final speed of a falling object? It is a common observation that a rock falls faster than a leaf. Therefore, Aristotle reasoned, weight is a factor that governs the speed of fall. This fitted in well with his idea that the *cause* of weight was the presence of the element Earth, whose natural motion was to the center of the earth. Thus a heavier object, having a greater content of Earth, has a stronger tendency to fall to its natural place. In turn, this stronger tendency creates a greater speed of falling.

The same object falls more slowly in water than in air, so Aristotle reasoned that the resistance of the medium must also affect motion. Other factors, such as the color or temperature of the falling object, also might change the rate of fall. But Aristotle decided that such influences could not be important. He concluded that the rate of fall must increase in proportion to the weight of the object and decrease in proportion to the resisting force of the medium. The actual rate of fall in any particular case would be found by dividing the weight by the resistance.

Aristotle also discussed "violent" motion—that is, any motion of an object other than going freely toward its "natural place." Such motion, he argued, must always be caused by a *force,* and the speed of the motion must increase as the force increases. When the force is removed, the motion must stop. This theory agrees with our common experience, say in pushing a chair or a table across the floor. It doesn't work quite so well for objects thrown through the air, since they keep moving for a while even after we have stopped exerting a force on them. To explain this kind of motion, Aristotle proposed that the air itself somehow exerts a force that keeps the object moving.

Later scientists suggested certain changes in Aristotle's theory of motion. For example, in the fifth century A.D. John Philoponus of

Aristotle: rate of fall is proportional to weight divided by resistance.

SG 2.3

Alexandria argued that the speed of an object in natural motion should be found by *subtracting* the resistance of the medium from the weight of the object. (Aristotle, you recall, recommended *dividing* by the resistance.) Philoponus claimed that his experimental work supported his theory, though he did not report the details. He simply said that he dropped two weights, one twice as heavy as the other, and observed that the heavy one did not reach the ground in half the time taken by the light one.

John Philoponus: rate of fall is proportional to weight *minus* resistance.

SG 2.4

There were still other difficulties with Aristotle's theory of motion. However, the knowledge that his teachings had faults did little to lessen their influence in the universities of France and Italy during the fifteenth and sixteenth centuries. Aristotle's theory of motion did, after all, fit much of ordinary experience in a general—if qualitative—way. Besides, the study of motion through space was of great interest to only a few scholars, just as it had been only a very small part of Aristotle's own work.

Qualitative refers to quality— the *sort* of thing that happens. *Quantitative* refers to quantity— the measurement or prediction of *numerical* values. This distinction will appear often in the course.

Two other influences stood in the way of major changes in the theory of motion. First, Aristotle believed that mathematics was of little value in describing terrestrial phenomena. Second, he put great emphasis upon direct, qualitative observation as the basis for forming theories. Simple qualitative observation was very useful in Aristotle's biological studies. But as it turned out, real progress in physics began only when scientists recognized the value of mathematical prediction and detailed measurement.

A number of scholars in the fifteenth and sixteenth centuries took part in this change to a new way of doing science. But of all these, Galileo was by far the best known and most successful. He showed how to describe mathematically the motions of simple, ordinary objects—falling stones and balls rolling on an incline. His work paved the way for other scholars to describe and explain the motion of everything from pebbles to planets. It also began the intellectual revolution that led to what we now consider modern science.

Q1 Describe two ways in which, according to the Aristotelian view, terrestrial and celestial bodies differ from each other.

Q2 Which of these statements would be accepted in the fifteenth and sixteenth centuries by persons who believed in the Aristotelian system of thought?
  (a) Ideas of motion should fit in with poetry, politics, theology, and other aspects of human thought and activity.
  (b) Heavy objects fall faster than light ones.
  (c) Except for motion toward their natural location, objects will not move unless acted on violently by a force.
  (d) Mathematics and precise measurement are especially important in developing a useful theory of motion.

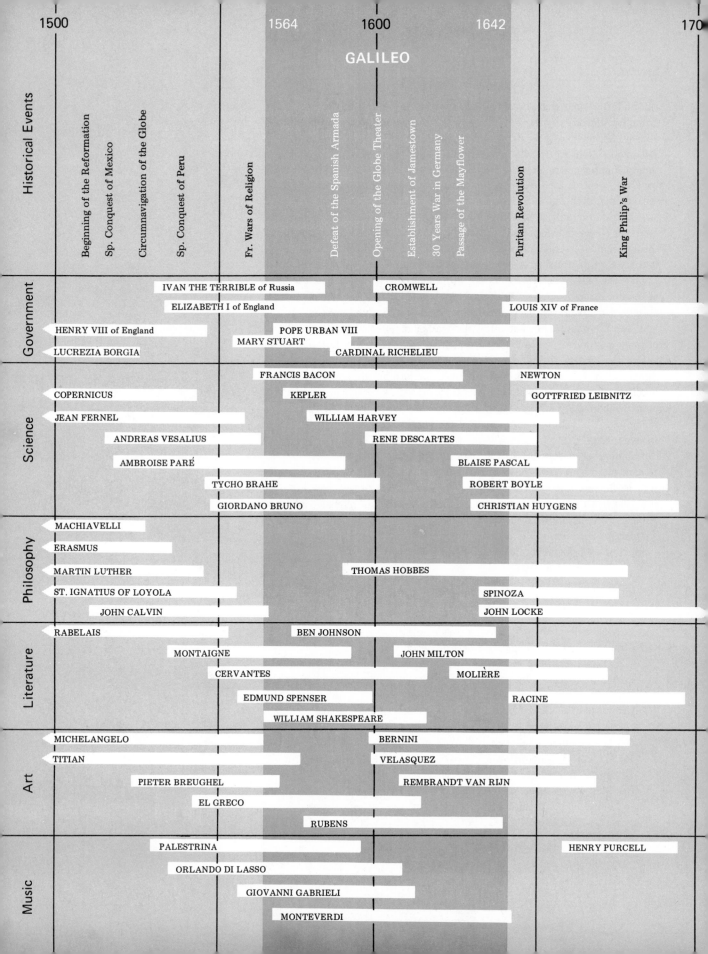

2.2 Galileo and his times

Galileo Galilei was born in Pisa in 1564—the year of Michelangelo's death and Shakespeare's birth. Galileo was the son of a noble family from Florence, and he acquired his father's active interest in poetry, music, and the classics. His scientific inventiveness also began to show itself early. For example, as a young medical student, he constructed a simple pendulum-type timing device for the accurate measurement of pulse rates.

After reading the classical Greek philosopher-scientists Euclid and Archimedes, Galileo changed his interest from medicine to physical science. He quickly became known for his unusual scientific ability. At the age of 26, he was appointed Professor of Mathematics at Pisa. There he showed an independence of spirit unmellowed by tact or patience. Soon after his appointment, he began to challenge the opinions of older professors, many of whom became his enemies. He left Pisa before his term was completed, apparently forced out by financial difficulties and by his enraged opponents. Later, at Padua in the Republic of Venice, he began his work in astronomy. His support of the sun-centered theory of the universe brought him additional enemies, but it also brought him immortal fame. We will deal with that part of his work in Unit 2.

A generous offer of the Grand Duke drew Galileo back to his native province of Tuscany in 1610. He became Court Mathematician and Philosopher, a title which he chose himself. From then until his death at 78, despite illness, family troubles, occasional poverty, and quarrels with his enemies, he continued his research, teaching, and writing.

Italy about 1600

2.3 Galileo's *Two New Sciences*

Mechanics is the study of the behavior of matter under the influence of forces. Galileo's early writings on this subject follow the standard medieval theories of physics, although he was aware of some of the shortcomings of those theories. During his mature years his chief interest was in astronomy. However, his important astronomical book, *Dialogue on the Two Great World Systems* (1632), was condemned by the Inquisition. Forbidden to teach the "new" astronomy, Galileo decided to concentrate again on mechanics. This work led to his book *Discourses and Mathematical Demonstrations Concerning Two New Sciences Pertaining to Mechanics and Local Motion* (1638), usually referred to as *Two New Sciences*. This book signaled the beginning of the end of the medieval theory of mechanics and of the entire Aristotelian cosmology.

Galileo was old, sick, and nearly blind at the time he wrote *Two New Sciences*. Yet, as in all his writings, his style is lively and delightful. As he had in the *Two Chief World Systems,* he presented his ideas in the form of a conversation among three speakers: *Simplicio* competently represents

Title page of *Dialogue on Two Great World Systems* (1632).

DISCORSI
E
DIMOSTRAZIONI
MATEMATICHE,
intorno à due nuoue fcienze
Attenenti alla
MECANICA & i MOVIMENTI LOCALI,
del Signor
GALILEO GALILEI LINCEO,
Filofofo e Matematico primario del Sereniffimo
Grand Duca di Tofcana.

Con vna Appendice del centro di grauità d'alcuni Solidi.

IN LEIDA,
Appreffo gli Elfevirii. M. D. C. XXXVIII.

Title page of *Discourses and Mathematical Demonstrations Concerning Two New Sciences Pertaining to Mechanics and Local Motion* (1638).

SG 2.5

DEL GALILEO. 63
Vacuo non fi farebbe il moto, la pofizion del vacuo affolutamente prefa, e non in relazione al moto, non vien deftrutta, mà per dire quel che per auuentura potrebber rifpondere quegli antichi, acciò meglio fi fcorga, quanto concluda la dimoftrazione d' Ariftotele, mi par che fi potrebbe andar contro à gli affunti di quello, negandogli amendue. E quanto al primo: io grandemente dubito, che Ariftotele non fperimentaffe mai quanto fia vero, che due pietre vna più graue dell' altra dieci volte lafciate nel medefimo inftante cader da vn altezza, v. gr. di cento braccia fuffer talmente differenti nelle lor velocità, che all' arrivo della maggior in terra l' altra fi trouaffe non hauere nè anco fcefo dieci braccia.
Simp. Si vede pure dalle fue parole, ch' ei fi moftra d' hauerlo fperimentato, perche ei dice: Veggiamo il più graue: hor quel vederfi accenna l' hauerne fatta l' efperienza.
Sagr. Mà io S. Simp. che n' hò fatto la proua, vi afficuro, che vna palla d' artiglieria, che pefi cento, o dugento, e anco più libbre, non anticiperà di vn palmo folamente l' arriuo in terra della palla d' un mofchetto, che ne pefi vna mezza, venendo anco dall' altezza di dugento braccia.
Salu. Mà fenz' altre efperienze con breue, e concludente dimoftrazione poffiamo chiaramente prouare non effer vero, che vn mobile più graue fi muoua più velocemente d' un' altro men graue, intendendo di mobili dell' iftefffa materia; & in fomma di quelli de i quali parla Ariftotele. Però ditemi S. Simp. fe voi ammettete, che di ciafcheduno corpo graue cadente fia vna da natura determinata velocità; fi che l' accrefcergliela, ò diminuirgliela non fi poffa fe non con vfargli violenza, ò opporgli qualche impedimento.
Simp. Non fi può dubitare, che l' ifteffo mobile nell' ifteffo mezzo habbia vna ftatuita, e da natura determinata velocità, la quale non fe gli poffa accrefcere fe non con nuouo impeto conferitogli, ò diminuirgliela faluo che con qualche impedimento che lo ritardi.
Salu. Quando dunque noi haueffimo due mobili, le naturali
velo-

A page from the original Italian edition of *Two New Sciences*, showing statements that are translated in this text.

the Aristotelian view; *Salviati* presents the new views of Galileo; and *Sagredo* is a man of good will and open mind, eager to learn. Eventually, of course, Salviati leads his companions to Galileo's views. Let us listen to Galileo's three speakers as they discuss the problem of free fall:

Salviati: I greatly doubt that Aristotle ever tested by experiment whether it is true that two stones, one weighing ten times as much as the other, if allowed to fall at the same instant from a height of, say, 100 cubits, would so differ in speed that when the heavier had reached the ground, the other would not have fallen more than 10 cubits. [A "cubit" is about 20 inches.]

Simplicio: His language would indicate that he had tried the experiment, because he says: *We see the heavier;* now the word *see* shows that he had made the experiment.

Sagredo: But, I, Simplicio, who have made the test can assure you that a cannon ball weighing one or two hundred pounds, or even more, will not reach the ground by as much as a span [hand-breadth] ahead of a musket ball weighing only half a pound, provided both are dropped from a height of 200 cubits.

Here, perhaps, one might expect a detailed report on an experiment done by Galileo or one of his students. Instead, Galileo uses a "thought experiment"—an analysis of what would happen in an imaginary experiment—to cast doubt on Aristotle's theory of motion:

Salviati: But, even without further experiment, it is possible to prove clearly, by means of a short and conclusive argument, that a heavier body does not move more rapidly than a lighter one provided both bodies are of the same material and in short such as those mentioned by Aristotle. But tell me, Simplicio, whether you admit that each falling body acquires a definite speed fixed by nature, a velocity which cannot be increased or diminished except by the use of violence or resistance?

Simplicio: There can be no doubt but that one and the same body moving in a single medium has a fixed velocity which is determined by nature and which cannot be increased except by the addition of impetus or diminished except by some resistance which retards it.

Salviati: If then we take two bodies whose natural speeds are different, it is clear that on uniting the two, the more rapid one will be partly retarded by the slower, and the slower will be somewhat hastened by the swifter. Do you not agree with me in this opinion?

Simplicio: You are unquestionably right.

Salviati: But if this is true, and if a large stone moves with a speed of, say, eight, while a smaller moves with a speed of

four, then when they are united, the system will move with a
speed less than eight; but the two stones when tied together
make a stone larger than that which before moved with a
speed of eight. Hence the heavier body moves with less speed
than the lighter one; an effect which is contrary to your
supposition. Thus you see how, from your assumption that the
heavier body moves more rapidly than the lighter one, I infer
that the heavier body moves more slowly.

Simplicio: I am all at sea. . . . This is, indeed, quite beyond my
comprehension. . . .

SG 2.6

Simplicio retreats in confusion when Salviati shows that the
Aristotelian theory of fall contradicts itself. But while Simplicio cannot
refute Galileo's logic, his own eyes tell him that a heavy object *does* fall
faster than a light object:

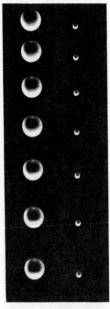

> *Simplicio:* Your discussion is really admirable; yet I do not find
> it easy to believe that a birdshot falls as swiftly as a cannon
> ball.
>
> *Salviati:* Why not say a grain of sand as rapidly as a
> grindstone? But, Simplicio, I trust you will not follow the
> example of many others who divert the discussion from its
> main intent and fasten upon some statement of mine that
> lacks a hairsbreadth of the truth, and under this hair hide the
> fault of another that is as big as a ship's cable. Aristotle says
> that "an iron ball of one hundred pounds falling from a height
> of 100 cubits reaches the ground before a one-pound ball has
> fallen a single cubit." I say that they arrive at the same time.
> You find, on making the experiment, that the larger outstrips
> the smaller by two fingerbreadths. . . . Now you would not
> hide behind these two fingers the 99 cubits of Aristotle, nor
> would you mention my small error and at the same time pass
> over in silence his very large one.

This is a clear statement of an important principle: even in careful
observation of a common natural event, a very minor effect may distract
the observer's attention. As a result, he fails to see a much more important
regularity. Different bodies falling in air from the same height, it is true,
may *not* reach the ground at exactly the same time. However, the
important point is not that the times of arrival are *slightly different*, but
that they are *very nearly the same!* Galileo regarded the failure of the
bodies to arrive at exactly the same time as a minor effect which could be
explained with a better understanding of motion in free fall. He himself
correctly attributed the observed results to differences in the effect of air
resistance on bodies of different size and weight. A few years after his
death, the invention of the vacuum pump allowed others to show that
Galileo was right. In one experiment, for example, a feather and a heavy
gold coin were dropped from the same height at the same time inside a

A stroboscopic photograph of two
freely falling balls of unequal weight.
The balls were released simultaneously. The time interval between
images is 1/30 sec.

The phrase "free fall" as now used in physics generally refers to fall when the only force acting is gravity; that is, when air friction is negligible.

One of the arguments against the existence of a vacuum was deduced in Aristotle's theory as follows: if the final speed of fall is proportional to the weight divided by the resistance, then, since the resistance in an assumed vacuum would be zero, the final speed of fall of all bodies must be infinite in a vacuum. But such a result was regarded as absurd, so the assumption of a vacuum was believed to be shown to be impossible.

container pumped almost empty of air. With the effect of air resistance eliminated, the different bodies fell at the same rate and struck the bottom of the container at the same instant. Long after Galileo, scientists learned how to express the laws of air resistance in mathematical form. With this knowledge, one can understand exactly why and by how much a light object will fall behind a heavier one.

Learning what to ignore has been almost as important in the growth of science as learning what to take into account. In the case of falling bodies, Galileo's explanation depended on his being able to imagine how an object would fall if there were no air resistance. His explanation seems simple today, when we know about vacuum pumps. But in Galileo's time it was difficult to accept. For most people, as for Aristotle, common sense said that air resistance is always present in nature. Thus a feather and a coin could never fall at the same rate. Why talk about motions in a vacuum, when a vacuum could not be shown to exist? Physics, said Aristotle and his followers, should deal with the world all around us that we can readily observe. It should not bother with imaginary situations which might never be seen or which, like the vacuum, were considered impossible.

Aristotle's physics had dominated Europe since the thirteenth century. To many scientists, it seemed to offer the most reasonable method for describing natural phenomena. To overthrow such a firmly established doctrine required much more than writing reasonable arguments. It even required more than clear experimental proof such as dropping heavy and light objects from a tall building. (Galileo is often said to have done this from the top of the Leaning Tower of Pisa, but probably did not.) It demanded Galileo's unusual combination of mathematical talent, experimental skill, literary style, and tireless campaigning to discredit Aristotle's theories, and thus to begin the era of modern physics.

A chief reason for Galileo's success was that he attacked the Aristotelian theory at its weakest point. He showed that we can deal better with the world around us if we realize that it is not so simple as the Aristotelians thought it to be. On the contrary, even the most ordinary events are usually quite complex. For example, in observing falling bodies you see the effects of both the law of fall and the law of air resistance. To understand what you see, you should start from a simpler case, such as fall without resistance. Of course, you may be able to "see" such an event only in your mind or as a mathematical model. Or you might turn to an experiment in the laboratory. Here the usual conditions of observation can be changed, and you can discover how each different effect results from a different physical cause. Only when you understand the separate physical laws that govern these individual effects should you try to understand the event as a whole. This basic approach is sometimes called "reductionism." Reductionism does not claim that it is the path to all truths. It merely holds that it is the quickest and surest method for understanding physical phenomena.

Q3 If a nail and a toothpick are dropped at the same time from the same height, they do not reach the ground at exactly the same instant.

(Try it with these or similar objects.) How would Aristotelian theory explain this? What was Galileo's explanation?

2.4 Why study the motion of freely falling bodies?

In Galileo's attack on the Aristotelian cosmology, few details were actually new. However, his approach and his findings together provided the first workable presentation of the science of motion. Galileo realized that understanding free-fall motion is the key to understanding all observable motions of all bodies in nature. To know *which* was the key phenomenon to study was a gift of genius. But Galileo in many ways simply worked as do scientists in general. His approach to the problem of motion makes a good "case" to follow as an introduction to strategies of inquiry that are still used in science.

We have just mentioned several reasons why we study in detail Galileo's attack on the problem of free fall. Galileo himself recognized another reason—that the study of motion which he proposed was only the starting phase of a mighty field of discovery:

> My purpose is to set forth a very new science dealing with a very ancient subject. There is, in nature, perhaps nothing older than motion, concerning which the books written by philosophers are neither few nor small; nevertheless, I have discovered some properties of it that are worth knowing that have not hitherto been either observed or demonstrated. Some superficial observations have been made, as for instance, that the natural motion of a heavy falling body is continuously accelerated; but to just what extent this acceleration occurs has not yet been announced. . . .
>
> Other facts, not few in number or less worth knowing I have succeeded in proving; and, what I consider more important, there have been opened up to this vast and most excellent science, of which my work is merely the beginning, ways and means by which other minds more acute than mine will explore its remote corners.

2.5 Galileo chooses a definition of uniform acceleration

Two New Sciences deals directly with the motion of freely falling bodies. In studying the following paragraphs from it, we must be alert to Galileo's overall plan. First he discusses the mathematics of a possible, simple type of motion. (We now call this motion *uniform acceleration* or *constant acceleration*.) Then he proposes that heavy bodies actually fall with just this kind of motion. Next, on the basis of this proposal, he makes certain predictions about balls rolling down an incline. Finally, he shows that experiments bear out these predictions.

By Aristotelian cosmology is meant the whole interlocking set of ideas about the structure of the physical universe and the behavior of all the objects in it. This was briefly mentioned in Sec. 2.1. Other aspects of it will be presented in Unit 2.

In fact, more than mere "superficial observations" had been made long before Galileo set to work. For example, Nicolas Oresme and others at the University of Paris had by 1330 discovered the same distance-time relationship for falling bodies that Galileo was to announce in the *Two New Sciences*. Some of their reasoning is discussed in SG 2.7.

It will help you to have a plan clearly in mind as you progress through the rest of this chapter. As you study each succeeding section, ask yourself whether Galileo is
—presenting a definition
—stating an assumption (or hypothesis)
—deducing predictions from his hypothesis
—experimentally testing the predictions

The first part of Galileo's presentation is a thorough discussion of motion with uniform speed, similar to our discussion in Chapter 1. This leads to the second part, where we find Salviati saying:

> We pass now to . . . naturally accelerated motion, such as that generally experienced by heavy falling bodies.
>
> . . . in the investigation of naturally accelerated motion we were led, by hand as it were, in following the habit and custom of nature herself, in all her various other processes, to employ only those means which are most common, simple and easy . . .
>
> When, therefore, I observe a stone initially at rest falling from an elevated position and continually acquiring new increments of speed, why should I not believe that such increases take place in a manner which is exceedingly simple and rather obvious to everybody? If now we examine the matter carefully we find no addition or increment more simple than that which repeats itself always in the same manner. This we readily understand when we consider the intimate relationship between time and motion; for just as uniformity of motion is defined by and conceived through equal times and equal spaces (thus we call a motion uniform when equal distances are traversed during equal time-intervals), so also we may, in a similar manner, through equal time-intervals, conceive additions of speed as taking place without complication. . . .
>
> Hence the definition of motion which we are about to discuss may be stated as follows:
>
> *A motion is said to be uniformly accelerated when, starting from rest, it acquires during equal time-intervals, equal increments of speed.*
>
> *Sagredo:* Although I can offer no rational objection to this or indeed to any other definition devised by any author whosoever, since all definitions are arbitrary, I may nevertheless without defense be allowed to doubt whether such a definition as the foregoing, established in an abstract manner, corresponds to and describes that kind of accelerated motion which we meet in nature in the case of freely falling bodies. . . .

Here Sagredo questions whether Galileo's arbitrary definition of acceleration actually corresponds to the way objects fall. Is acceleration, as defined, really useful in describing their observed change of motion? Sagredo wonders about a further point, so far not raised by Galileo:

> From these considerations perhaps we can obtain an answer to a question that has been argued by philosophers, namely, what is the *cause* of the acceleration of the natural motion of heavy bodies. . . .

But Salviati, the spokesman of Galileo, rejects the ancient tendency to investigate phenomena by looking first for their causes. It is pointless, he declares, to ask about the cause of any motion until an accurate description of it exists:

This is sometimes known as the Rule of Parsimony: unless forced to do otherwise, assume the simplest possible hypothesis to explain natural events.

Rephrasing Galileo and using *our* symbols: for motion with uniform speed *v*, the ratio $\Delta d/\Delta t$ is constant. Similarly, recall that for accelerated motion, as we saw in Chapter 1, we defined uniform acceleration as

$$a = \frac{\Delta v}{\Delta t} = \text{constant}$$

Other ways of expressing this relationship are discussed in SG 2.8 and 2.9.

Salviati: The present does not seem to be the proper time to investigate the cause of the acceleration of natural motion concerning which various opinions have been expressed by philosophers, some explaining it by attraction to the center, others by repulsion between the very small parts of the body, while still others attribute it to a certain stress in the surrounding medium which closes in behind the falling body and drives it from one of its positions to another. Now, all these fantasies, and others, too, ought to be examined; but it is not really worth while. At present it is the purpose of our Author merely to investigate and to demonstrate some of the properties of accelerated motion, whatever the cause of this acceleration may be.

Here Salviati refers to the Aristotelian assumption that air propels an object moving through it (see Sec. 2.1).

Galileo has now introduced two distinct propositions: (1) "uniform" acceleration means that equal increases of speed Δv occur in equal time intervals Δt; and (2) things actually fall that way.

Let us first look more closely at Galileo's proposed definition. Is this the only possible way of defining uniform acceleration? Not at all! Galileo says that at one time he thought it would be more useful to define uniform acceleration in terms of speed increase in proportion to distance traveled Δd, rather than to time Δt. Notice that both definitions met Galileo's requirement of simplicity. (In fact, both definitions had been discussed since early in the fourteenth century.) Furthermore, both definitions seem to match our common sense idea of acceleration. When we say that a body is "accelerating," we seem to imply "the farther it goes, the faster it goes" as well as "the longer time it goes, the faster it goes." How should we choose between these two ways of putting it? Which definition will be more useful in describing nature?

This is where experimentation becomes important. Galileo chose to define uniform acceleration as the motion in which the change in speed Δv is proportional to elapsed time Δt. He then demonstrated that his definition matches the real behavior of moving bodies, in laboratory situations as well as in ordinary "un-arranged" experience. As you will see later, he made the right choice. But he was not able to prove his case by direct or obvious means, as you will also see.

Q4 Describe uniform speed without referring to dry-ice disks and strobe photography or to *any* particular object or technique of measurement.

Q5 Express Galileo's definition of uniformly accelerated motion in words and in the form of an equation.

Q6 What two conditions did Galileo want his definition of uniform acceleration to meet?

2.6 Galileo cannot test his hypothesis directly

After Galileo defined uniform acceleration in terms that matched the way he *believed* freely falling objects behaved, his next task was to show that his definition actually was useful for describing observed motions.

Suppose we drop a heavy object from several different heights—say, from windows on different floors of a building. We want to check whether the final speed increases in proportion to the time the object falls. That is, we want to know whether $\Delta v \propto \Delta t$, or in other words, whether $\Delta v / \Delta t$ is constant. In each trial we must observe the time of fall and the speed just before the object strikes the ground. But there's the rub. Even with modern instruments, it would be very difficult to make a *direct measurement* of the speed reached by an object just before striking the ground. Furthermore, the entire time intervals of fall (less than 3 seconds from the top of a 10-story building) is shorter than Galileo could have measured accurately with the clocks available to him. So a direct test of whether $\Delta v / \Delta t$ is constant was not possible for Galileo.

The symbol $\propto$ means "directly proportional to."

SG 2.10

Q7 Which of these statements accurately explains why Galileo could not test directly whether the final speed reached by a freely falling object is proportional to the time of fall?
  (a) His definition was wrong.
  (b) He could not measure the speed attained by an object just before it hit the ground.
  (c) There existed no instruments for measuring time.
  (d) He could not measure ordinary distances accurately enough.
  (e) Experimentation was not permitted in Italy.

2.7 Looking for logical consequences of Galileo's hypothesis

Galileo's inability to make *direct* measurements to test his hypothesis—that $\Delta v / \Delta t$ is constant in free fall—did not stop him. He turned to mathematics to derive from this hypothesis some other relationship that *could* be checked by measurements with equipment available to him. We will see that in a few steps he came much closer to a relationship he could use to check his hypothesis.

Large distances and large time intervals are, of course, easier to measure than the very small values of Δd and Δt needed to find the final speed just before a falling body hits. So Galileo tried to determine, by reasoning, how total distance of fall would increase with total time of fall if objects did fall with uniform acceleration. You already know how to find the total distance from total time for motion at constant *speed*. Now we will derive a new equation that relates total distance of fall to total time of fall for motion at constant *acceleration*. In doing so we will not follow Galileo's own calculations exactly, but the results will be the same. First, we recall the definition of average speed as the distance traveled Δd divided by the elapsed time Δt:

$$v_{\text{av}} = \frac{\Delta d}{\Delta t}$$

From this general definition we can compute the average speed from measurement of Δd and Δt, whether Δd and Δt are small or large. We can rewrite the equation as

$$\Delta d \;=\; v_{av} \,\times\, \Delta t$$

This equation, still being really a definition of v_{av}, is always true. For the special case for motion at a constant speed v, then $v_{av} = v$ and therefore, $\Delta d = v \times \Delta t$. Suppose the value of v is known—for example, when a car is driven with a steady reading of 60 mph on the speedometer. Then we can use this equation to figure out how far (Δd) the car would go in any given time interval (Δt). But in uniformly accelerated motion the speed is continually *changing*—so what value can we use for v_{av}?

The answer involves just a bit of algebra and some reasonable assumptions. Galileo reasoned (as others had before him) that for any quantity that changes uniformly, *the average value is just halfway between the beginning value and the final value.* For uniformly accelerated motion starting from rest, $v_{\text{initial}} = 0$. Thus, our rule tells us that the average speed is halfway between 0 and v_{final}; that is, $v_{av} = \frac{1}{2} v_{\text{final}}$. If this reasoning is correct, it follows that

$$\Delta d \;=\; \tfrac{1}{2}\, v_{\text{final}} \,\times\, \Delta t$$

for uniformly accelerated motion starting from rest.

This relation could not be tested directly either, because the equation still contains a speed factor. What we need is an equation relating total distance and total time, without any need to measure speed.

Now we look at Galileo's definition of uniform acceleration: $a = \Delta v / \Delta t$. We can rewrite this relationship in the form $\Delta v = a \times \Delta t$. The value of Δv is just $v_{\text{final}} - v_{\text{initial}}$; and $v_{\text{initial}} = 0$ for motion that begins from rest. Therefore we can write

$$\Delta v = a \times \Delta t$$
$$v_{\text{final}} - v_{\text{initial}} = a \times \Delta t$$
$$v_{\text{final}} = a \times \Delta t$$

Now we can substitute this expression for v_{final} into the equation for Δd above. Thus *if* the motion starts from rest, and *if* it is uniformly accelerated (and *if* the average rule is correct, as we have assumed) we can write

$$\Delta d = \tfrac{1}{2} v_{\text{final}} \times \Delta t$$
$$\quad = \tfrac{1}{2}(a \times \Delta t) \times \Delta t$$

Or, regrouping terms,

$$\Delta d = \tfrac{1}{2} a (\Delta t)^2$$

This is the kind of relation Galileo was seeking. It relates total distance Δd to total time Δt, without involving any speed term.

Before finishing, though, we will simplify the symbols in the equation to make it easier to use. If we measure distance and time from the

More generally the average speed would be

$$v_{av} = \frac{v_{\text{initial}} + v_{\text{final}}}{2}$$

SG 2.11, 2.12

position and the instant that the motion starts, then $d_{initial} = 0$ and $t_{initial} = 0$. Thus the intervals Δd and Δt have the values given by d_{final} and t_{final}. We then can write the equation above more simply as

SG 2.13, 2.14

$$d_{final} = \tfrac{1}{2} a t^2_{final}$$

Remember that this is a very specialized equation. It gives the total distance fallen as a function of total time of fall; but it does so *only* if the motion starts from rest ($v_{initial} = 0$), if the acceleration is uniform ($a = constant$), and if time and distance are measured from the start ($t_{initial} = 0$ and $d_{initial} = 0$).

Galileo reached the same conclusion, though he did not use algebraic forms to express it. Since we are dealing only with the special situation in which acceleration a is constant, the quantity $\tfrac{1}{2}a$ is constant also. Therefore we can write our conclusion in the form of a proportion: in uniform acceleration from rest, the distance traveled is proportional to the square of the time elapsed, or

$$d_{final} \propto t^2_{final}$$

For example, if a uniformly accelerating car starting from rest moves 10 m in the first second, in *twice* the time it would move *four* times as far, or 40 m in the first two seconds. In the first *three* seconds it would move *nine* times as far—or 90 m.

Another way to express this relation is to say that the ratio d_{final} to t^2_{final} has a constant value, that is,

SG 2.15

$$\frac{d_{final}}{t^2_{final}} = constant$$

Because we will use the expression d_{final}/t^2_{final} many times, it is simpler to write it as d/t^2—it is understood that d and t mean total distance and time interval of motion, starting from rest.

Thus we reach a logical result of Galileo's original proposal for defining uniform acceleration. We can express this result as follows: If an object accelerates uniformly from rest, the ratio d/t^2 should be constant. Conversely, any motion for which this ratio of d and t^2 is constant for different distances and their corresponding times is a case of *uniform acceleration* as defined by Galileo.

Of course, we still must test the hypothesis that freely falling bodies actually *do* exhibit just such motion. Earlier, we confessed that we were unable to test directly whether $\Delta v/\Delta t$ has a constant value. But we have just shown that a constant value of $\Delta v/\Delta t$ means there will be a constant ratio of d_{final} to t^2_{final}. The values for total time and distance of fall d_{final} are easier to measure than the values for short intervals Δd and Δt needed to find Δv. However, even measuring the total time of fall presented a difficult task in Galileo's time. So, instead of a *direct* test of his hypothesis, Galileo went one step further and deduced a clever *indirect* test.

Q8 Why was the equation $d = \tfrac{1}{2}at^2$ more promising for Galileo than $a = \Delta v/\Delta t$ in testing his hypothesis?

Q9 If you simply combined the two equations $\Delta d = v\,\Delta t$ and $\Delta v = a\,\Delta t$ it looks as if one might get the results $\Delta d = a\,\Delta t^2$. What is wrong with doing this?

2.8 Galileo turns to an indirect test

Realizing that direct measurements involving a rapidly and freely falling body would not be accurate, Galileo decided to test an object that was moving less rapidly. He proposed a new hypothesis: if *a freely falling body has constant acceleration, then a perfectly round ball rolling down a perfectly smooth inclined plane will also have a constant, though smaller, acceleration.* Thus Galileo claimed that if d/t^2 is constant for a body falling freely from rest, this ratio will also be constant, although smaller, for a ball rolling from rest down a straight inclined plane.

Here is how Salviati described Galileo's own experimental test in *Two New Sciences:*

A piece of wooden moulding or scantling, about 12 cubits long, half a cubit wide, and three finger-breadths thick, was taken; on its edge was cut a channel a little more than one finger in breadth; having made this groove very straight, smooth, and polished, and having lined it with parchment, also as smooth and polished as possible, we rolled along it a hard, smooth, and very round bronze ball. Having placed this board in a sloping position, by lifting one end some one or two cubits above the other, we rolled the ball, as I was just saying, along the channel, noting, in a manner presently to be described, the time required to make the descent. We repeated this experiment more than once in order to measure the time with an accuracy such that the deviation between two observations never exceeded one-tenth of a pulse beat. Having performed this operation and having assured ourselves of its reliability, we now rolled the ball only one-quarter of the length of the channel; and having measured the time of its descent, we found it precisely one-half of the former. Next we tried other distances, comparing the time for the whole length with that for the half, or with that for two-thirds, or three-fourths, or indeed for any fraction; in such experiments, repeated a full hundred times, we always found that the spaces traversed were to each other as the squares of the times, and this was true for all inclinations of the . . . channel along which we rolled the ball . . . .

Note the careful description of the experimental apparatus. Today an experimenter would add to his verbal description any detailed drawings, schematic layouts or photographs needed to make it possible for other competent scientists to duplicate the experiment.

This picture painted in 1841 by G. Bezzuoli, attempts to reconstruct an experiment Galileo is alleged to have made during his time as lecturer at Pisa. Off to the left and right are men of ill will: the blasé Prince Giovanni de Medici (Galileo had shown a dredging-machine invented by the prince to be unusable) and Galileo's scientific opponents. These were leading men of the universities; they are shown here bending over a book of Aristotle, where it is written in black and white that bodies of unequal weight fall with different speeds. Galileo, the tallest figure left of center in the picture, is surrounded by a group of students and followers.

Galileo has packed a great deal of information into these lines. He describes his procedures and apparatus clearly enough to allow others to repeat the experiment for themselves if they wish. He indicates that consistent measurements can be made. Finally, he restates the two chief experimental results which he believes support his free-fall hypothesis. Let us examine the results carefully.

(a) First, he found that when a ball rolled down the incline, the ratio of the distance covered to the square of the corresponding time was always the same. For example, if d_1, d_2, and d_3 represent distances measured from the same starting point on the incline, and t_1, t_2, and t_3 represent the times taken to roll down these distances, then

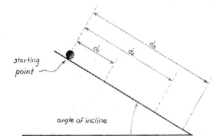

$$\frac{d_1}{t_1^2} = \frac{d_2}{t_2^2} = \frac{d_3}{t_3^2}$$

In general, for each angle of incline, the value of d/t^2 was constant. Galileo did not present his experimental data in the full detail which since has become the custom. However, others have repeated his experiment and have obtained results which parallel his. (See data in SG 2.16.) You can perform this experiment yourself with the help of one or two other students. (The photograph on the opposite page shows students doing the experiment with the aid of a water clock. The accompanying graph shows some of their results.)

(b) Galileo's second experimental finding relates to what happened when the angle of inclination of the plane was changed. Whenever the angle changed, the ratio d/t^2 took on a new value, although for any one angle it remained constant regardless of distance of roll. Galileo confirmed this by repeating the experiment "a full hundred times" for each of the many different angles. After finding that the ratio d/t^2 was constant for each angle at which t could be measured conveniently, Galileo was willing to extrapolate. He concluded that the ratio d/t^2 is a constant even for steeper angles, where the ball moves too fast for accurate measurement of t. Now, finally, Galileo was ready to solve the problem that had started the whole argument: He reasoned that when the angle of inclination became 90°, the ball would move straight down as a *freely falling object*. By his reasoning, d/t^2 would still be constant even in that extreme case, although he couldn't say *what* the numerical value was.

Galileo already had deduced that a constant value of d/t^2 was characteristic of uniform acceleration. By extrapolation, he could conclude at last that free fall was uniformly accelerated motion.

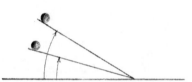

For each angle, the acceleration is found to be a constant.

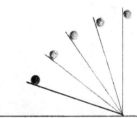

Spheres rolling down planes of increasingly steep inclination. At 90° the inclined plane situation matches free fall. (Actually, the ball will start slipping instead of rolling long before the angle has become that large.)

Q10 In testing his hypothesis that free-fall motion is uniformly accelerated, Galileo made the unproved *assumption* that (check one or more):
    (a) d/t^2 is constant.
    (b) the acceleration has the same value for all angles of inclination of the plane.

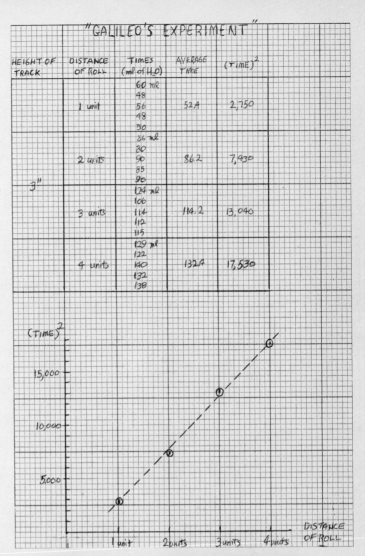

"GALILEO'S EXPERIMENT"

HEIGHT OF TRACK	DISTANCE OF ROLL	TIMES (ml of H_2O)	AVERAGE TIME	$(TIME)^2$
3"	1 unit	60 ml 48 56 48 50	52.4	2,750
	2 units	86 ml 80 90 85 90	86.2	7,930
	3 units	124 ml 106 114 112 115	114.2	13,040
	4 units	129 ml 122 140 132 138	132.4	17,530

$(TIME)^2$ vs DISTANCE OF ROLL

15,000 — 10,000 — 5,000 — 1 unit, 2 units, 3 units, 4 units

Galileo's technique for measuring time is discussed in the next section.

(c) the results for small angles of inclination can be extrapolated to large angles.

(d) the speed of the ball is constant as it rolls.

(e) the acceleration of the rolling ball is constant if the acceleration in free fall is constant, though the value of the two constants is not the same.

Q11 Which of the following statements best summarizes the work of Galileo on free fall when air friction is not a factor? (Be prepared to defend your choice.) Galileo:

(a) proved that all objects fall at exactly the same speed regardless of their weight.

(b) proved that for any freely falling object the ratio d/t^2 is constant for any distance of fall.

(c) proved that an object rolling down a smooth incline accelerates in the same way, although more slowly than, the same object falling freely.

(d) supported indirectly his assertion that the speed of an object falling freely from rest is proportional to the elapsed time.

(e) made it clear that until a vacuum could be produced, it would not be possible to settle the free-fall question once and for all.

For problems that will check and extend your understanding of uniform acceleration. See SG 2.17 through 2.24.

2.9 Doubts about Galileo's procedure

This whole process of reasoning and experiment looks long and involved on first reading, and you may have some doubts concerning it. For example, was Galileo's measurement of time precise enough to establish the constancy of d/t^2 even for a slowly rolling object? In his book, Galileo tries to reassure possible critics by providing a detailed description of his experimental arrangement:

> For the measurement of time, we employed a large vessel of water placed in an elevated position; to the bottom of this vessel was soldered a pipe of small diameter giving a thin jet of water, which we collected in a small cup during the time of each descent, whether for the whole length of the channel or for a part of its length; the water thus collected was weighed on a very accurate balance; the differences and ratios of these weights gave us the differences and ratios of the time intervals, and this with such accuracy that, although the operation was repeated many, many times, there was no appreciable discrepancy in the results.

The water clock described by Galileo was not invented by him. Indeed, water clocks existed in China as early as the sixth century B.C., and probably were used in Babylonia and India even earlier. In the early sixteenth century a good water clock was the most accurate instrument available for measuring short time intervals. It remained so until shortly after Galileo's death, when the work of Christian Huygens and others led

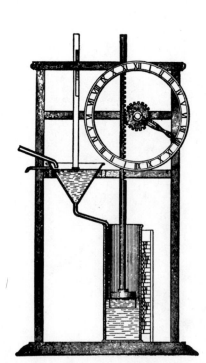

Early water clock

to practical pendulum clocks. When better clocks became available, Galileo's results on inclined-plane motion were confirmed.

Another reason for questioning Galileo's results involves the great difference between free-fall and rolling motion on a slight incline. Galileo does not report what angles he used in his experiment. However, as you may have found out from doing a similar experiment, the angles must be kept rather small. As the angle increases, the speed of the ball soon becomes so great that it is difficult to measure the times involved. The largest usable angle reported in a recent repetition of Galileo's experiment was only 6°. (See SG 2.15.) It is not likely that Galileo worked with much larger angles. This means that his extrapolation to free fall (90° incline) is a large one. A cautious person, or one not already convinced of Galileo's argument, might well doubt its value.

There is still another reason for questioning Galileo's results. As the angle of incline is increased, there comes a point where the ball starts to slide as well as roll. This change in behavior could mean that the motion is very different at large angles. Galileo does not discuss these cases. It is surprising that he apparently did not repeat the experiment with blocks which would slide, rather than roll. If he had, he would have found that for sliding motion the ratio d/t^2 is also a constant, although having a different numerical value than for rolling at the same angle.

SG 2.25

Q12 Which of the following statements could be regarded as major reasons for doubting the value of Galileo's procedure?
(a) His measurement of time was not accurate enough.
(b) He used too large an angle of inclination in his experiment.
(c) It is not clear that his results apply when the ball can slide as well as roll.
(d) In Galileo's experiment the ball was rolling, and therefore he could not extrapolate to the case of free fall where the ball did not roll.
(e) d/t^2 was not constant for a sliding object.

2.10 Consequences of Galileo's work on motion

Galileo seems to have understood that one cannot get the correct numerical value for the acceleration of a body in free fall simply by extrapolating through increasingly large angles of incline. He did not attempt to calculate a numerical value for the acceleration of freely falling bodies. For his purposes it was enough that he could support the hypothesis that the acceleration is *constant* for any given body, whether rolling or falling. This is the first of Galileo's findings, and it has been fully borne out by all following tests.

Second, spheres of different weights allowed to roll down an inclined plane set at a given angle, have the same acceleration. We do not know how much experimental evidence Galileo himself had for this conclusion,

We now know by measurement that the magnitude of the acceleration of gravity, symbol a_g, is about 9.8 m/sec per sec, or 32 ft/sec per sec, at the earth's surface. The Project Physics *Handbook* contains five different experiments for finding a value of a_g. (For many problems, the approximate value 10 m/sec/sec is satisfactory.)

but it agrees with his observations for freely falling objects. It also agrees with the "thought experiment" by which he argued that bodies of different weights fall at the same rate (aside from the effects of air resistance). His results clearly contradicted what one would have expected on the basis of Aristotle's theory of motion.

SG 2.26

Third, Galileo developed a mathematical theory of accelerated motion from which other predictions about motion could be derived. We will mention just one example here, which will turn out to be very useful in Unit 3. Recall that Galileo chose to define acceleration as the rate at which the speed changes with time. He then found by experiment that falling bodies actually do experience equal changes of speed in equal times, and *not* in equal distances. Still, the idea of something changing by equal amounts in equal distances has an appealing simplicity. One might ask if there isn't some quantity that *does* change in that way during uniform acceleration. In fact, there is. It follows without any new assumptions that, during uniform acceleration from rest, the *square* of the speed changes by equal amounts in equal distances. There is a mathematical equation which expresses this result: if $v_{initial} = 0$, and $a = constant$, then

You can derive this equation. (See SG 2.27)

$$v^2_{final} = 2ad_{final}$$

In words: if an object moves from rest with uniform acceleration, the square of its speed at any point is equal to twice the product of its acceleration and the distance it has moved. (We will see the importance of this relation in Unit 3.)

SG 2.28, 2.29

These results of Galileo's work were most important to the development of physics. But they could scarcely have brought about a revolution in science by themselves. No sensible scholar in the seventeenth century would have given up his belief in Aristotelian cosmology only because some of its predictions had been disproved. Still, Galileo's work on free-fall motion helped to prepare the way for a new kind of physics, and indeed a new cosmology, by planting the seeds of doubt about the basic assumptions of Aristotelian science. For example, when it was recognized that all bodies fall with equal acceleration if air friction is minor, the whole Aristotelian explanation of falling motion (Sec. 2.1) broke down.

The most disputed scientific problem during Galileo's lifetime was not in mechanics but in astronomy. A central question in cosmology was whether the earth or the sun was the center of the universe. Galileo supported the view that the earth and other planets revolved around the sun, a view entirely contrary to Aristotelian cosmology. But to support such a view required a physical theory of why and how the earth itself moved. Galileo's work on free fall and other motions turned out to be just what was needed to begin constructing such a theory. His work did not have its full effect, however, until it had been combined with the studies of forces and motion by the English scientist Isaac Newton. But as Newton acknowledged, Galileo was the pioneer. (In the next chapter we will consider Newton's work on force and motion. In Chapter 8, we will take up its application to the motions in the heavens, as well as the revolution it caused in science.)

Galileo's work on motion introduced a new and important method of doing scientific research. This method is as effective today as when Galileo demonstrated it. The basis of this procedure is a cycle, repeated as often as necessary, entirely or in part, until a satisfactory theory has emerged. The cycle roughly follows this form: general observation → hypothesis → mathematical analysis or deduction from hypothesis → experimental test of deduction → revision of hypothesis in light of test, and so forth.

While the mathematical steps are determined mainly by "cold logic," this is not so for the other parts of the process. A variety of paths of thought can lead to a hypothesis in the first place. A new hypothesis might come from an inspired hunch based on general knowledge of the experimental facts. Or it might come from a desire for mathematically simple statements, or from modifying a previous hypothesis that failed. Moreover, there are no general rules about exactly how well experimental data must agree with predictions based on theory. In some areas of science, a theory is expected to be accurate to better than 1/1000th of one percent. In other areas, or at an early stage of any new work, one might be delighted with an error of only 50 percent. Finally note that while experiment has an important place in this process, it is not the only or even the main element. On the contrary, experiments are worthwhile only in combination with the other steps in the process.

SG 2.30

The general cycle of observation, hypothesis, deduction, test, revision, etc., so skillfully demonstrated by Galileo in the seventeenth century, commonly appears in the work of scientists today. Though there is no such thing as *the* scientific method, some form of this cycle is almost always present in scientific research. It is used not out of respect for Galileo as a towering figure in the history of science, but because it works so well so much of the time. What is too frequently underplayed is the sheer creativity that enters into each of these phases. There are no fixed rules for doing any one of them, or for how to move from one to the next.

Galileo himself was aware of the value of both the results and the methods of his pioneering work. He concluded his treatment of accelerated motion by putting the following words into the mouths of the characters in his book:

> *Salviati:* . . . we may say the door is now opened, for the first time, to a new method fraught with numerous and wonderful results which in future years will command the attention of other minds.

> *Sagredo:* I really believe that . . . the principles which are set forth in this little treatise will, when taken up by speculative minds, lead to another more remarkable result; and it is to be believed that it will be so on account of the nobility of the subject, which is superior to any other in nature.

During this long and laborious day, I have enjoyed these simple theorems more than their proofs, many of which, for their complete comprehension, would require more than an hour each; this study, if you will be good enough to leave the book in my hands, is one which I mean to take up at my leisure after we have read the remaining portion which deals with the motion of projectiles; and this if agreeable to you we shall take up tomorrow.

Salviati: I shall not fail to be with you.

Many details of physics, mathematics and history have appeared in this chapter. For a review of the most important ideas, see SG 2.31, 2.32, and 2.33.

Q13 Which one of the following was *not* a result of Galileo's work on motion?
   (a) The correct numerical value of the acceleration in free fall was obtained by extrapolating the results for larger and larger angles of inclination.
   (b) If an object starts from rest and moves with uniform acceleration a through a distance d, then the square of its speed will be proportional to d.
   (c) Bodies rolling on a smooth inclined plane are uniformly accelerated (according to Galileo's definition of acceleration).

2.1 Note that at the beginning of each chapter in this book there is a list of the section titles. This is a sort of road map you can refer to from time to time as you study the chapter. It is important, expecially in a chapter such as this one, to know how the part you are studying relates to what preceded it and to have some idea of where it is leading. For this same reason, you will find it very helpful at first to skim through the entire chapter, reading it rapidly and not stopping to puzzle out parts that you do not quickly understand. Then you should return to the beginning of the chapter and work your way through it carefully, section by section. Remember also to use the end-of-section questions to check your progress.

The Project Physics learning materials particularly appropriate for Chapter 2 include:

Experiments
A Seventeenth-Century Experiment
Twentieth Century Version of Galileo's
Experiment
Measuring the Acceleration Due to
Gravity, a_g

Reader Article
On the Scientific Method

Film Loops
Acceleration Due to Gravity – Method I
Acceleration Due to Gravity – Method II

Transparency
Derivation of $d = v_i t + \frac{1}{2}at^2$

2.2 Aristotle's theory of motion seems to be supported to a great extent by common sense experience. For example, water bubbles up through earth at springs. When sufficient fire is added to water by heating it, the resulting mixture of elements (what we call steam) rises through the air. Can you think of other examples?

2.3 Drop sheets of paper with various degrees of "crumpling." Try to crumple a sheet of paper tight enough that it will fall at the same rate as a tennis ball. Can you explain the results with Aristotle's theory?

2.4 Compare Aristotle's hypothesis about falling rate (weight divided by resistance) with Philoponus' (weight minus resistance) for some extreme cases: a very heavy body with no resistance, a very light body with great resistance. Do the two hypotheses suggest very different results?

2.5 Consider Aristotle's statement "A given weight moves [falls] a given distance in a given time; a weight which is as great and more moves the same distances in less time, the times being in inverse proportion to the weights. For instance,

if one weight is twice another, it will take half as long over a given movement." (*De Caelo*)

Indicate what Simplicio and Salviati each would predict for the falling motion in these cases:

(a) A 2-pound rock falls from a cliff and, while dropping, breaks into two equal pieces.
(b) A hundred-pound rock is dropped at the same time as one hundred 1-pound pieces of the same type of rock.
(c) A hundred 1-pound pieces of rock, falling from a height, drop into a draw-string sack which closes, pulls loose and falls.

2.6 Tie two objects of greatly different weight (like a book and a pencil) together with a piece of string. Drop the combination with different orientations of objects. Watch the string. In a few sentences summarize your results.

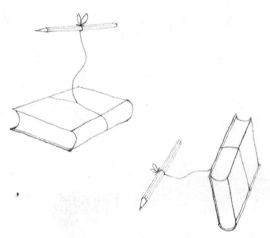

2.7 A good deal of work preceded that of Galileo on the topic of motion. In the period 1280-1340, mathematicians at Merton College, Oxford, carefully considered different quantities that change with the passage of time. One result that had profound influence was a general theorem known as the "Merton Theorem" or "Mean Speed Rule."

This theorem might be restated in our language and applied to uniform acceleration as follows: the distance an object goes during some time while its speed is changing uniformly is the same distance it would go if it went at the average speed the whole time.

(a) First show that the total distance traveled at a constant speed can be expressed as the area under the graph line on a speed-time graph. ("Area" must be found in speed units × time units.)
(b) Assume that this area represents the total distance even when the speed is not constant. Draw a speed vs. time graph for uniformly increasing speed and shade in the area under the graph line.

(c) Prove the "Merton Rule" by showing that the area is equal to the area under a constant-speed line at the average speed.

2.8 According to Galileo, uniform acceleration means equal Δv's in equal Δt's. Which of the following are other ways of expressing the same idea?
(a) Δv is proportional to Δt
(b) $\Delta v / \Delta t = $ constant
(c) the speed-time graph is a straight line
(d) v is proportional to t

2.9 In the *Two New Sciences* Galileo states, ". . . for so far as I know, no one has yet pointed out that the distances traversed, during equal intervals of time, by a body falling from rest, stand to one another in the same ratio as the odd numbers beginning with unity [namely 1:3:5:7 . . .] . . . ."
The area beneath the curve in a speed-time graph represents the distance traveled during some time interval. Using that idea, give a proof that the distances an object falls in successive equal time intervals will be in the ratios of the odd numbers.

2.10 Using whatever modern equipment you wish, describe how you could find an accurate value for the speed of a falling object just before striking the ground.

2.11 Show that the expression
$$v_{ar} = \frac{v_{\text{initial}} + v_{\text{final}}}{2}$$
is equivalent to the "Merton Rule" discussed in SG 2.7.

2.12 For any quantity that *changes uniformly*, the average is the sum of the initial and final values divided by two. Try it out for any quantity you may choose — for example: what is the average age in a group of five people having individually the ages of 15, 16, 17, 18, and 19 years? What is your average earning power over five years if it grows steadily from $8000 per year at the start to $12000 per year at the end?

2.13 Several special assumptions have been made in arriving at the equation $d = \frac{1}{2}at^2$. What is the "unwritten text" behind it?

2.14 Lt. Col. John L. Stapp achieved a speed of 632 mph (284 m/sec) in an experimental rocket sled at the Holloman Air Base Development Center, Alamogordo, New Mexico, on March 19, 1954. Running on rails and propelled by nine rockets, the sled reached its top speed within 5 seconds. Stapp survived a maximum acceleration of 22 g's in slowing to rest during a time interval of $1\frac{1}{2}$ seconds (one g is an acceleration equal in magnitude to that due to gravity; 22 g's means $22 \times a_g$.)
(a) Find the average acceleration in reaching maximum speed.
(b) How far did the sled travel before attaining maximum speed?

(c) Find the *average* acceleration while stopping.

2.15 Derive the expression $d/t^2 = constant$ from the expression $d = \frac{1}{2}at^2$.

2.16 Table 2.1 reports results from a recent repetition of Galileo's experiment in which the angle of inclination was 3.73° (*Science*, *133*, 19-23, June 6, 1961). A water clock with a constant-level reservoir was used.

TABLE 2.1

DISTANCE (ft)	TIME (measured in milliliters of water)	d/t^2
15	90	0.00185
13	84	0.00183
10	72	0.00192
7	62	0.00182
5	52	0.00185
3	40	0.00187
1	23.5	0.00182

Do these data really support Galileo's assertion that d/t^2 is constant? Explain your conclusion.

2.17 Indicate whether the following statements are true or false when applied to the strobe photo below:

(a) The speed of the ball is greater at the bottom than at the top.
(b) This could be a freely falling object. (Make measurements on photograph.)
(c) This could be a ball thrown straight upward.
(d) If (b) is true, the speed increases with time because of the acceleration due to gravity.
(e) If (c) is true, the speed decreases with time because of the effect of gravity; this effect could still be called acceleration due to gravity.

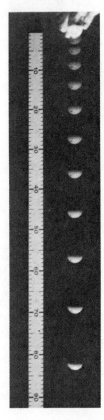

2.18(a) Show by means of equations that Galileo's statement in SG 2.9 follows from $d/t^2 =$ constant for free fall from rest.
  (b) The time interval between strobe flashes was 0.35 sec. Use this information to make a rough graph of d vs. t, also one of v vs. t, and find the acceleration of the ball.

2.19 The photograph in the figure below is of a ball thrown upward. The acceleration due to gravity increases the speed of the ball as it goes down from its highest point (like any free-falling object), if air friction is negligible. But the acceleration due to gravity, which does not change, acts also while the ball is still on its way up, and for that portion of the path causes the ball to slow down as it rises to the top point, C.

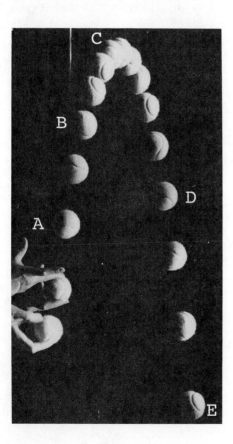

Stroboscopic photograph of a ball thrown into the air.

When there is both up and down motion, it will help to adopt a sign convention, an arbitrary but consistent set of rules, similar to designating the height of a place with respect to sea level. To identify distances measured *above* the point of initial release, give them *positive* values, for example, the distance at **B** or at **D**, measured from

the release level, is about $+60$ cm and $+37$ cm, respectively. If measured *below* the release level, give them *negative* values; for example, **E** is at -23 cm. Also, assign a positive value to the speed of an object on its way up to the top (about $+3$ m/sec at **A**) and a negative value to a speed a body has *on the way down* after reaching the top (about -2 m/sec at **D** and -6 m/sec at **E**).
  (a) Fill in the table with $+$ and $-$ signs.

AT POSITION	SIGN GIVEN TO VALUE OF	
	d	v
A		
B		
C		
D		
E		

  (b) Show that it follows from this convention and from the definition of $a = \Delta v/\Delta t$ that the value or sign given to the acceleration due to gravity is *negative*, and for both parts of the path.
  (c) What would the sign of acceleration due to gravity be in each case if we had chosen the $+$ and $-$ sign conventions just the other way, that is, associating $-$ with up, $+$ with down?

2.20 Draw a set of points (as they would appear in a strobe photo) to show the successive positions of an object that by our convention in SG 2.19 had a positive acceleration, that is, "upward." Can you think of any way to produce such an event physically?

2.21 Memorizing equations will not save you from having to think your way through a problem. You must decide if, when and how to use equations. This means analyzing the problem to make certain you understand *what information is given* and *what is to be found*. Test yourself on the following problem. Assume that the acceleration due to gravity is nearly enough equal to 10 m/sec/sec.
  Problem: A stone is dropped from rest from the top of a high cliff.
  (a) How far has it fallen after 1 second?
  (b) What is the stone's speed after 1 second of fall?
  (c) How far does the stone fall during the second second? (That is, from the end of the first second to the end of the second second.)

2.22 From the definition for a, show it follows directly that $v_{\text{final}} = v_{\text{initial}} + at$ for motion with constant acceleration. Using this relation, and the sign convention in SG 2.19, answer the questions below. (Assume $a_g = 10$ m/sec/sec.) An object is thrown straight upward with an initial speed of 20 m/sec.
  (a) What is its speed after 1.0 sec?
  (b) How far did it go in this first second?

(c) How long did the object take to reach its maximum height?

(d) How high is this maximum height?

(e) When it descends, what is its final speed as it passes the throwing point?

If you have no trouble with this, you may wish to try problems SG 2.23 and 2.24.

2.23 A batter hits a pop fly that travels straight upwards. The ball leaves his bat with an initial speed of 40 m/sec. (Assume $a_g = 10$ m/sec/sec)

(a) What is the speed of the ball at the end of 2 seconds?

(b) What is its speed at the end of 6 seconds?

(c) When does the ball reach its highest point?

(d) How high is this highest point?

(e) What is the speed of the ball at the end of 10 seconds? (Graph this series of speeds.)

(f) What is its speed just before it is caught by the catcher?

2.24 A ball starts up an inclined plane with a speed of 4 m/sec, and comes to a halt after 2 seconds.

(a) What acceleration does the ball experience?

(b) What is the average speed of the ball during this interval?

(c) What is the ball's speed after 1 second?

(d) How far up the slope will the ball travel?

(e) What will be the speed of the ball 3 seconds after starting up the slope?

(f) What is the total time for a round trip to the top and back to the start?

2.25 As Director of Research in your class, you receive the following research proposals from physics students wishing to improve upon Galileo's free-fall experiment. Would you recommend support for any of them? If you reject a proposal, you should make it clear why you do so.

(a) "Historians believe that Galileo never dropped objects from the Leaning Tower of Pisa. But such an experiment is more direct and more fun than inclined plane experiments, and of course, now that accurate stopwatches are available, it can be carried out much better than in Galileo's time. The experiment involves dropping, one by one, different size spheres made of copper, steel, and glass from the top of the Leaning Tower and finding how long it takes each one to reach the ground. Knowing d (the height of the tower) and time of fall t, I will substitute in the equation $d = \frac{1}{2}at^2$ to see if the acceleration a has the same value for each sphere."

(b) "An iron shot will be dropped from the roof of a 4-story building. As the shot falls, it passes a window at each story. At each window there will be a student who starts his stopwatch upon hearing a signal that the shot has been released, and stops the watch as the shot passes his window.

Also, each student records the speed of the shot as it passes. From his own data, each student will compute the ratio v/t. I expect that all four students will obtain the same numerical value of the ratio."

(c) "Galileo's inclined planes dilute motion all right, but the trouble is that there is no reason to suppose that a ball rolling down a board is behaving like a ball falling straight downward. A better way to accomplish this is to use light, fluffy, cotton balls. These will not fall as rapidly as metal spheres, and therefore it would be possible to measure the time of the fall t for different distances. The ratio d/t^2 could be determined for different distances to see if it remained constant. The compactness of the cotton ball could then be changed to see if a different value was obtained for the ratio."

2.26 A student on the planet Arret in another solar system dropped an object in order to determine the acceleration due to gravity at that place. The following data are recorded (in local units):

TIME (in surgs)	DISTANCE (in welfs)	TIME (in surgs)	DISTANCE (in welfs)
0.0	0.0	2.2	10.41
0.5	0.54	2.4	12.39
1.0	2.15	2.6	14.54
1.5	4.84	2.8	16.86
2.0	8.60	3.0	19.33

(a) What is the acceleration due to gravity on the planet Arret, expressed in welfs/surg²?

(b) A visitor from Earth finds that one welf is equal to about 6.33 cm and that one surg is equivalent to 0.167 sec. What would this tell us about Arret?

2.27 (a) Derive the relation $v^2 = 2ad$ from the equations $d = \frac{1}{2}at^2$ and $v = at$. What special conditions must be satisfied for the relation to be true?

(b) Show that if a ball is thrown straight upward with an initial speed v it will rise to a height

$$h = \frac{v^2}{2a_g}$$

2.28 Sometimes it is helpful to have a special equation relating certain variables. For example, for constant acceleration a, the final speed v_f is related to initial speed v_i and distance traveled d by

$$v_f{}^2 = v_i{}^2 + 2ad$$

Try to derive this equation from some others you are familiar with.

2.29 Use a graph like the one sketched below, and the idea that the area under the graph line in a speed-time graph gives a value for the distance traveled, to derive the equation

$$d = v_i t + \tfrac{1}{2}at^2$$

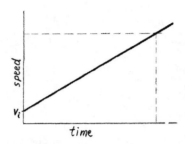

2.30 List the steps by which Galileo progressed from his first definition of uniformly accelerated motion to his final confirmation that this definition is useful in describing the motion of a freely falling body. Identify each step as a hypothesis, deduction, observation, or computation, etc. What limitations and idealizations appear in the argument?

2.31 In these first two chapters we have been concerned with motion in a straight line. We have dealt with distance, time, speed and acceleration, and with the relationships among them. Surprisingly, most of the results of our discussion can be summarized in the three equations listed below.

$$v_{av} = \frac{\Delta d}{\Delta t} \qquad a_{av} = \frac{\Delta v}{\Delta t} \qquad d = \tfrac{1}{2}at^2$$

The last of these equations can be applied only to those cases where the acceleration is constant. Because these three equations are so useful, they are worth remembering (together with the limitation on their use).

(a) State each of the three equations in words.
(b) Make up a *simple* problem to demonstrate the use of each equation. (For example: How long will it take a jet plane to travel 3200 miles if it averages 600 mi/hr?) Then work out the solution just to be sure the problem can be solved.
(c) Derive the set of equations which apply *whether or not* the initial speed is zero.

2.32 Show to what extent the steps taken by Galileo on the problem of free fall, as described in Sections 2.5 through 2.8, follow the general cycle in the scientific process.

2.33 What is wrong with the following common statements? "The Aristotelians did not observe nature. They took their knowledge out of old books which were mostly wrong. Galileo showed it was wrong to trust authority in science. He did experiments and showed everyone directly that the old ideas on free fall motion were in error. He thereby started science, and also gave us the scientific method."

CHAPTER THREE

The Birth of Dynamics—
Newton Explains Motion

3.1 "Explanation" and the laws of motion

Kinematics is the study of *how* objects move, but not of *why* they move. Galileo investigated many topics in kinematics with insight, originality, and energy. The most valuable part of that work dealt with special types of motion, such as free fall. In a clear and consistent way, he showed how to describe the motion of objects with the aid of mathematical ideas.

Galileo had written that "the present does not seem to be the proper time to investigate the cause of the acceleration of natural motion . . . ." When Isaac Newton began his studies of motion in the second half of the seventeenth century, that statement was no longer appropriate. Indeed, because Galileo had been so effective in describing motion, Newton could turn his attention to *dynamics*. Dynamics is the study of *why* an object moves the way it does—why it starts to move instead of remaining at rest, why it speeds up or moves on a curved path, and why it comes to a stop.

How does dynamics differ from kinematics? As we have seen in the two earlier chapters, kinematics deals with the description of motion. For example, we might describe the motion of a stone dropped from a cliff. To do so, we can write an equation showing how the distance *d* through which the stone has dropped is related to the time *t* the stone has been falling. We can find the acceleration and the final speed reached during any chosen time interval. But when we have completed our description of the stone's motion, we are still not satisfied. Why, we might ask, does the stone accelerate rather than fall with a constant speed? Why does it accelerate uniformly as long as air friction does not interfere? To answer these questions, we must understand the concepts of *force* and *mass;* and in answering, we are doing *dynamics*. Dynamics goes beyond kinematics by taking into account the *cause* of a motion.

SG 3.1

Some kinematics concepts: position, time, speed, acceleration.
Some dynamics concepts: mass, force, momentum (Ch. 9), energy (Ch. 10).

In our study of kinematics in Chapters 1 and 2, we recognized that an object may:

(a) remain at rest; (b) move uniformly in a straight line; (c) speed up during straight-line motion; (d) slow down during straight-line motion. Because the last two situations are examples of acceleration, we actually could reduce the list to:

(a) rest; (b) uniform motion; and (c) acceleration.

In Chapter 4 we will take up motion also along *curved* paths.

Rest, uniform motion, and acceleration are therefore the phenomena we will try to explain. But the word "explain" must be used with care. To the physicist, an event is "explained" when it is shown to be a logical consequence of a law the physicist has reason to believe is true. In other words, a physicist with faith in a general law "explains" an event by showing that it is consistent (in agreement) with the law. An infinite number of separate, different-looking events occur constantly all around us and within us. In a sense, the physicist's job is to show how each of these events results necessarily from certain general rules which describe the way the world operates. This approach to "explanation" is made possible by the fact that the number of general laws of physics is surprisingly small. In this chapter we will discuss three such laws. Together with the mathematical schemes of Chapters 1 and 2 for describing motion, they will enable us to understand practically all motions that we can easily observe. Adding one more law, the law of universal gravitation (Unit 2), we can explain the motions of stars, planets, comets, and satellites. In fact, throughout physics one sees again and again that nature has a marvelous simplicity.

Newton's First Law: Every object continues in its state of rest or of uniform motion in a straight line unless acted upon by an unbalanced force.

To explain rest, uniform motion, and acceleration of any object, we must be able to answer such questions as these: Why does a vase placed on a table remain stationary? If a dry-ice disk resting on a smooth, level surface is given a brief push, why does it move with uniform speed in a straight line? Why does it neither slow down quickly nor curve to the right or left? We can answer these and almost all other specific questions about motion either directly or indirectly from Isaac Newton's three general "Laws of Motion." These laws appear in his famous book, *Philosophiae Naturalis Principia Mathematica (Mathematical Principles of Natural Philosophy,* 1687), usually referred to simply as *The Principia.* They remain among the most basic laws in physics today.

Newton's Second Law: The acceleration of an object is directly proportional to, and in the same direction as, the unbalanced force acting on it, and inversely proportional to the mass of the object.

We will examine Newton's three laws of motion one by one. If your Latin is fairly good, try to translate them from the original. A modern, English version of Newton's text of these laws appears in the margin at the left.

Newton's Third Law: To every action there is always opposed an equal reaction; or, mutual actions of two bodies upon each other are always equal and in opposite directions.

Before taking up Newton's ideas, let us see how other scientists of Newton's time, or earlier, might have answered questions about motion. One reason for doing this now is that many people who have not studied physics still tend to think a bit like pre-Newtonians! Let us look at what must be overcome.

Q1 A baseball is thrown straight upward. Which of these questions about the baseball's motion are kinematic and which dynamic?

[12]

AXIOMATA
SIVE
LEGES MOTUS

Lex. I.

Corpus omne perseverare in statu suo quiescendi vel movendi uniformiter in directum, nisi quatenus a viribus impressis cogitur statum illum mutare.

PRojectilia perseverant in motibus suis nisi quatenus a resistentia aeris retardantur & vi gravitatis impelluntur deorsum. Trochus, cujus partes cohaerendo perpetuo retrahunt sese a motibus rectilineis, non cessat rotari nisi quatenus ab aere retardatur. Majora autem Planetarum & Cometarum corpora motus suos & progressivos & circulares in spatiis minus resistentibus factos conservant diutius.

Lex. II.

Mutationem motus proportionalem esse vi motrici impressae, & fieri secundum lineam rectam qua vis illa imprimitur.

Si vis aliqua motum quemvis generet, dupla duplum, tripla triplum generabit, sive simul & semel, sive gradatim & successive impressa fuerit. Et hic motus quoniam in eandem semper plagam cum vi generatrice determinatur, si corpus antea movebatur, motui ejus vel conspiranti additur, vel contrario subducitur, vel obliquo oblique adjicitur, & cum eo secundum utriusq; determinationem componitur.

Lex. III.

[13]
Lex. III.

Actioni contrariam semper & aequalem esse reactionem: sive corporum duorum actiones in se mutuo semper esse aequales & in partes contrarias dirigi.

Quicquid premit vel trahit alterum, tantundem ab eo premitur vel trahitur. Siquis lapidem digito premit, premitur & hujus digitus a lapide. Si equus lapidem funi alligatum trahit, retrahetur etiam & equus aequaliter in lapidem: nam funis utrinq; distentus eodem relaxandi se conatu urgebit Equum versus lapidem, ac lapidem versus equum, tantumq; impediet progressum unius quantum promovet progressum alterius. Si corpus aliquod in corpus aliud impingens, motum ejus vi sua quomodocunq; mutaverit, idem quoque vicissim in motu proprio eandem mutationem in partem contrariam vi alterius (ob aequalitatem pressionis mutuae) subibit. His actionibus aequales fiunt mutationes non velocitatum sed motuum, (scilicet in corporibus non aliunde impeditis:) Mutationes enim velocitatum, in contrarias itidem partes factae, quia motus aequaliter mutantur, sunt corporibus reciproce proportionales.

Corol. I.

Corpus viribus conjunctis diagonalem parallelogrammi eodem tempore describere, quo latera separatis.

Si corpus dato tempore, vi sola M, ferretur ab A ad B, & vi sola N, ab A ad C, compleatur parallelogrammum ABDC, & vi utraq; ferretur id eodem tempore ab A ad D. Nam quoniam vis N agit secundum lineam AC ipsi BD parallelam, haec vis nihil mutabit velocitatem accedendi ad lineam illam BD a vi altera genitam. Accedet igitur corpus eodem tempore ad lineam BD sive vis N imprimatur, sive non, atq; adeo in fine illius temporis reperietur alicubi in linea illa

(a) How high will the ball go before coming to a stop and starting downward?

(b) How long will it take to reach that highest point?

(c) What would be the effect of throwing it upward twice as hard?

(d) Which takes longer, the trip up or the trip down?

(e) Why does the acceleration remain the same whether the ball is moving up or down?

3.2 The Aristotelian explanation of motion

The idea of force played a central role in the dynamics of Aristotle twenty centuries before Newton. You will recall from Chapter 2 that in Aristotle's physics there were two types of motion—"natural" motion and "violent" motion. For example, a falling stone was thought to be in "natural" motion (towards its natural place). On the other hand, a stone being steadily lifted was thought to be in "violent" motion (away from its natural place). To maintain this uniform violent motion, a force had to be continuously applied. Anyone lifting a large stone is very much aware of this force as he strains to hoist the stone higher.

The Aristotelian ideas agreed with many common-sense observations. But there were also difficulties. Take a specific example—an arrow shot into the air. It cannot be in violent motion without a mover, or something pushing it. Aristotelian physics required that the arrow be constantly propelled by a force. If this propelling force were removed, the arrow should immediately stop its flight and fall directly to the ground in "natural" motion.

But, of course, an arrow does not fall to the ground as soon as it loses direct contact with the bowstring. What, then, is the force that propels the arrow? Here, the Aristotelians offered a clever suggestion: the motion of the arrow through the air is maintained by the air itself! As the arrow starts to move, the air in front of it is pushed aside. Naturally, more air rushes in to fill the space being vacated by the arrow. This rush of air behind the arrow keeps it in flight.

More adequate ideas to explain motion from our present point of view were developed before the mid-seventeenth century. But in every case, a force was considered necessary to sustain uniform motion. The explanation of uniform motion depended on finding the force, and that was not always easy. There were also other problems. For example, a falling acorn or stone does not move with uniform speed—it accelerates. How is acceleration explained? Some Aristotelians thought that the speeding up of a falling object was connected with its approaching arrival at its natural place, the earth. In other words, a falling object was thought to be like a tired horse that starts to gallop as it nears the barn. Others claimed that when an object falls, the weight of the air above it increases, pushing it harder. Meanwhile, the column of air below it decreases, thus offering less resistance to its fall.

Keeping an object in motion at uniform speed.

SG 3.2

When a falling object finally reaches the ground, as close to the center of the earth as it can get, it stops. And there, in its "natural place," it remains. Rest, being regarded as the natural state of objects on earth, required no further explanation. The three phenomena—rest, uniform motion, and acceleration—could thus be explained more or less reasonably by an Aristotelian. But now let us examine the Newtonian explanation of the same phenomena. The key to this approach is a clear understanding of the concept of force.

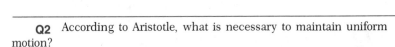

Q2   According to Aristotle, what is necessary to maintain uniform motion?

Q3   Give an Aristotelian explanation of a dry-ice disk's uniform motion across a table top.

3.3 Forces in equilibrium

Our common-sense idea of force is closely linked with our own muscular activity. We know that a sustained effort is required to lift and support a heavy stone. When we push a lawn mower, row a boat, split a log, or knead bread dough, our muscles let us know that we are applying a force to some object. Force and motion and muscular activity are naturally associated in our minds. When we think of changing the shape of an object, or moving it, or changing its motion, we automatically think of the muscular sensation of applying a force to the object. We shall see that many—but not all—of our everyday, common-sense ideas about force are useful in physics.

We know, without having to think about it, that forces can make things move. But forces can also hold things still. The cable supporting the main span of the Golden Gate Bridge is under the influence of mighty forces, yet it remains at rest. Apparently, more is required to start motion than just any application of forces.

Of course, this is not surprising. We have all seen children quarrelling over a toy. If each child pulls with determination in his own direction, the toy may go nowhere. On the other hand, the tide of battle may shift if one of the children suddenly makes an extra effort, or if two children cooperate and pull side by side against a third.

Likewise, in the tug-of-war between the two teams shown above, large forces are exerted on each side, but the rope remains at rest. We might say that the forces "balance" or "cancel." A physicist would say that the rope was *in equilibrium*. That is, the sum of all forces applied to one side of the rope is just as large, though acting in opposite directions, as the sum of forces applied to the other side. Equally well, the physicist might say the *net force* on the rope is zero. Thus, a body in equilibrium cannot start to move. It starts to move only when a new, "unbalanced" force is added, destroying the equilibrium.

In all these examples, both the magnitude (size or amount) of the forces and their directions are important. The effect of a force depends on the direction in which it is applied. We can represent both the sizes and directions of forces in a sketch by using arrows. The direction in which an arrow points represents the direction in which the force acts. The length of the arrow represents how large the force is. For example, a 10-lb force is shown by an arrow twice as long as a 5-lb force.

Now we discover a surprising result. If we know separately each of the forces applied to any object at rest, we can predict whether it will remain at rest. It is as simple as this: An object acted on by forces is in equilibrium and remains at rest only if the arrows representing the forces all total zero.

How does one "total" arrows? By means of a simple technique. Take the tug-of-war as an example. Let us call the force applied by the team

We start with commonly used units for force, but will soon change to units more suitable for scientific work.

(a)

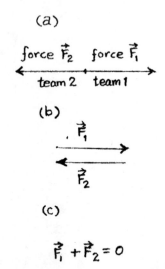

There are **several ways of expressing** the idea of **unbalanced force:** *net force, resultant force, total force, vector sum of forces.* All mean the same thing.

pulling to the right $\vec{F}_1$. (The arrow over the $\vec{F}$ indicates that we are dealing with a quantity for which direction is important.) The force applied to the rope by the second team is then called $\vec{F}_2$. Figure (a) in the margin shows the two arrows corresponding to the two forces, each applied to the same rope, but in opposite directions. Let us assume that these forces, $\vec{F}_1$ and $\vec{F}_2$, were accurately and separately measured. For example, we might let each team in turn pull on a spring balance as hard as it can. We can then draw the arrows for $\vec{F}_1$ and $\vec{F}_2$ carefully to a chosen scale, such as 1 in = 1,000 lb. Thus, a 750-lb force in either direction would be represented by an arrow 3/4 inch in length. Next, we take the arrows $\vec{F}_1$ and $\vec{F}_2$ and draw them again in the correct directions and to the chosen scale. This time, however, we put them "head to tail" as in Figure (b). Thus we might draw $\vec{F}_1$ first, and then draw $\vec{F}_2$ with the tail of $\vec{F}_2$ starting from the head of $\vec{F}_1$. (Since they would of course overlap in this example, we have drawn them slightly apart in Figure (b) to show them both clearly.) The technique is this: If the head end of the second arrow falls exactly on the tail end of the first, then we know that the effects of $\vec{F}_1$ and $\vec{F}_2$ balance each other. The two forces, equally large, and acting in opposite directions, total zero. If they did not, the excess of one force over the other would be the *net force,* and the rope would accelerate instead of being at rest.

To be sure, this was an obvious case. But the "head-to-tail" method, using drawings, also works in cases that are not so simple. For example, apply the same procedure to a boat that is secured by three ropes attached to different moorings. Suppose $\vec{F}_1$, in this case, is a force of 24 lb, $\vec{F}_2$ is 22 lb, and $\vec{F}_3$ is 19 lb, each in the direction shown in the sketch below. (A

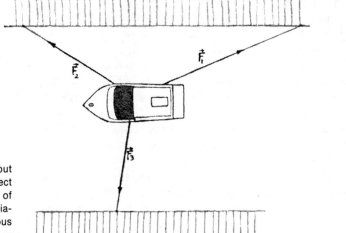

We are defining equilibrium without worrying about whether the object will rotate. For example: The sum of the forces on the plank in the diagram below is zero, but it is obvious that the plank will rotate.

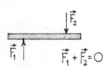

good scale for the magnitude of the forces here is 0.1 cm = 1 lb of force.) Is the boat in equilibrium when it is acted on by the forces? Yes, if the forces add up to zero. Let's see. With rule and protractor we can draw the arrows to scale and in exactly the right directions. Adding $\vec{F}_1$, $\vec{F}_2$, and $\vec{F}_3$

head to tail, we see that the head of the last arrow falls on the tail of the first. (See the force arrow addition to the right of the sketch of the moored boat.) Yes, the forces cancel; they total zero; the net force = 0. Therefore the object (the boat) is in equilibrium. This method tells us when an object is in equilibrium, no matter how many different forces are acting on it.

SG 3.3

We can now summarize our understanding of the state of rest as follows: If an object remains at rest, the sum of all forces acting on it must be zero. Rest is an example of the condition of equilibrium, the state in which all forces on the object are balanced.

An interesting case of equilibrium, very different from the disputed toy or rope, is part of the "free fall" of a skydiver. In fact, the fall is "free" only at the beginning. The force of air friction increases with speed. This upward frictional force on the skydiver is soon great enough to balance the force of gravity downward. Under these conditions, the diver falls with constant speed, much like a badminton bird or falling leaf. The sensation is not of falling but, except for the wind, the same as lying on a soft bed. During part of a dive from an airplane you can be as much in equilibrium as lying in bed! In both cases the net force acting on you is zero.

Q4 A vase is standing at rest on a table. What forces would you say are acting on the vase? Show how each force acts (to some scale) by means of an arrow. Can you show that the sum of the forces is zero?

Q5 In which of these cases are the forces balanced?

Q6 Does an object have to be at rest to be in equilibrium?

3.4 About vectors

Our method for representing forces by arrows really works. (We can call it the "graphical method.") With it we can predict whether the forces balance and will leave the object in equilibrium or whether any net force is left over, causing the object to accelerate. Why can we use arrows in this way? The reason involves the precise mathematical definitions of displacement and of force. But you can demonstrate for yourself the reliability of the addition rule by doing a few experiments. For example, you could attach three spring scales to a ring. Have three persons pull on the scales with forces that just balance, keeping the ring at rest. While they are pulling, read the magnitudes of the forces on the scales and mark the directions of the pulls. Then make a sketch with arrows representing the forces, using a convenient scale, and see whether they total zero. Many different experiments of this kind ought all to show a net force equal to zero.

It is not obvious that forces should behave like arrows. But arrows drawn on paper happen to be useful for calculating how forces add. (If they were not, we simply would look for other symbols that did work.) Forces belong in a class of concepts called *vector quantities*, or just *vectors* for short. Some characteristics of vectors are easy to represent by arrows. In particular, vector quantities have *magnitude,* which we can represent by the length of an arrow drawn to scale. They also have *direction*, which can be shown by the direction of an arrow. By experiment, we find that vectors can be *added* in such a way that the total effect of two or more can be represented by the head-to-tail addition of arrows. This total effect is called the *vector resultant.*

In the example of the tug-of-war, we determined the total effect of equally large, opposing forces. If two forces act in the *same* direction, the resultant force is found in much the same way, as shown below.

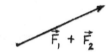

If two forces act at some angle to each other, the same type of sketch is still useful. For example, suppose two forces of equal magnitude are applied to an object at rest but free to move. One force is directed due east and the other due north. The object will accelerate in the northeast direction, the direction of the resultant force. (See sketch in the margin.) The magnitude of the acceleration is proportional to the magnitude of the resultant force, shown by the length of the arrow representing the resultant.

The same adding procedure works for forces of any magnitude and acting at any angle to each other. Suppose one force is directed due east and a somewhat larger force is directed northeast. The resultant vector sum can be found as shown below.

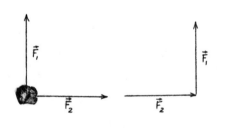

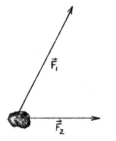
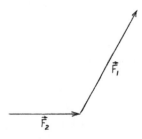
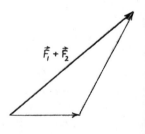

To summarize, we can now define a vector quantity. It is a quantity which has both direction and magnitude. Vectors can be added by constructing a head-to-tail arrangement of vector arrows (graphical method), or by an equivalent technique known as the parallelogram method which is briefly explained in the marginal note at the right. (Vectors also have other properties which you will study if you take further physics courses.) By this definition, many important concepts in physics are vectors—for example, displacement, velocity, and acceleration. Some other physical concepts, including volume, distance, and speed, do not require that we specify a direction, and so are not vectors. Such quantities are called *scalar quantities*. When you add 10 liters of water to 10 liters of water, the result is always 20 liters; direction has nothing to do with this result. Similarly, the term *speed* has no directional meaning; it is simply the *magnitude* of the velocity vector. Speed is shown by the *length* of the vector arrow, without regard to its direction. By contrast, suppose you add two forces of 10 lb each. The resultant force may be anywhere between 0 and 20 lb, depending on the *direction* of the two individual forces.

In Section 1.8 we defined acceleration as the rate of change of speed. That was only partly correct because it was incomplete. We must also consider changes in the *direction* of motion as well. Acceleration is best defined as the rate of change of *velocity,* where velocity is a vector having both magnitude and direction. In symbols this definition may be written

$$\vec{a}_{\text{av}} = \frac{\Delta \vec{v}}{\Delta t}$$

where $\Delta \vec{v}$ is the change in velocity. Velocity can change in two ways: by changing its magnitude (speed), and by changing its direction. In other words, an object is accelerating when it speeds up, or slows down, or changes direction. We will explore this definition and its important uses more fully in later sections.

Q7 List three properties of vector quantities.

Q8 How does the new definition of acceleration given above differ from the one used in Chapter 1?

3.5 Newton's first law of motion

You probably were surprised when you first watched a moving dry-ice disk or some other nearly frictionless object. Remember how smoothly it glided along after the slightest shove? How it showed no sign of slowing down or speeding up? From our everyday experience, we automatically think that some force is constantly needed to keep an object moving. But the disk does not act according to our common sense Aristotelian expectations. It is always surprising to see this for the first time.

In fact, the disk is behaving quite naturally. If the forces of friction

Any vector quantity is indicated by a letter with an arrow over it; for example, $\vec{F}$, $\vec{a}$, or $\vec{v}$.

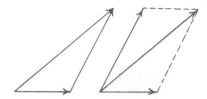

You can equally well use a graphical construction called the "parallelogram method." It looks different from the "head-to-tail" method, but is really exactly the same. In the parallelogram construction, the vectors to be added are represented by arrows joined tail-to-tail instead of head-to-head, and the resultant is obtained by completing the diagonal of the parallelogram. (See SG 3.4.)

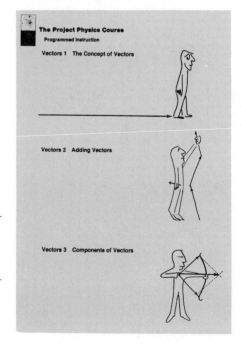

The Project Physics Course
Programmed Instruction

Vectors 1   The Concept of Vectors

Vectors 2   Adding Vectors

Vectors 3   Components of Vectors

We shall use vectors frequently. To learn more about them you can use the Project Physics Programmed Instruction booklets on vectors. See also *Reader 1* article "Introduction to Vectors."

were absent, a gentle push would send tables and chairs gliding across the floor like dry-ice disks. Newton's first law directly challenges the Aristotelian idea of what is "natural." It declares that the state of rest and the state of uniform, unaccelerated motion in a straight line are equally natural. Only the existence of some force, friction for example, keeps a moving object from moving *forever!* Newton's first law of motion can be stated in modern language as follows:

> Every object continues in its state of rest or of uniform rectilinear (straight-line) motion unless acted upon by an unbalanced force. Conversely, if an object is at rest or in uniform rectilinear motion, the unbalanced force acting upon it must be zero.

In order to understand the motion of an object, we must take into account all the forces acting on it. If *all* forces (including friction) are in balance, the body will be moving at constant $\vec{v}$.

Although Newton was the first to express this idea as a general law, Galileo had made similar statements fifty years before. Of course, neither Galileo nor Newton had dry-ice disks or similar devices. Therefore, they were unable to observe motion in which friction had been reduced so greatly. Instead, Galileo devised a thought experiment in which he imagined the friction to be zero.

This thought experiment was based on an actual observation. If a pendulum bob on the end of a string is pulled back and released from rest, it will swing through an arc and rise to very nearly its starting height. Indeed, as Galileo showed, the pendulum bob will rise almost to its starting level even if a peg is used to change the path as shown in the illustration below.

Because constant velocity means both constant speed and constant direction, we can write Newton's first law more concisely:

$$\vec{v} = \text{constant}$$

if and only if

$$\vec{F}_{\text{net}} = 0$$

This statement includes the condition of rest, since rest is a special case of unchanging velocity — the case where $\vec{v} = 0$.

SG 3.5

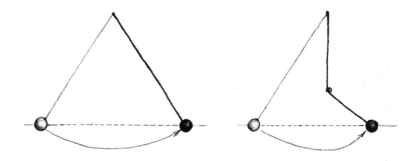

From this observation Galileo went on to his thought experiment. He predicted that a ball released from a height on a frictionless ramp would roll up to the same height on a similar facing ramp. Consider the diagram at the top of the next page. As the ramp on the right is changed from position (a) to (b) and then to (c), the ball must roll farther in each case to reach its original height. It slows down more gradually as the angle of the incline decreases. If the second ramp is exactly *level* as shown in (d), the ball can *never* reach its original height. Therefore, Galileo believed, the

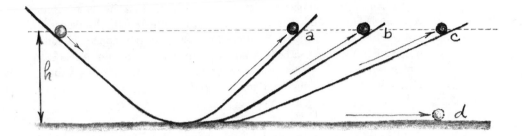

ball on this frictionless surface would roll on in a straight line and at an unchanged speed forever. This could be taken to mean the same as Newton's first law. Indeed, some historians of science do give credit to Galileo for having come up with this law first. Other historians, however, point out that Galileo thought of the "rolling on forever" as "staying at a constant height above the earth." He did not think of it as "moving in a straight line through space."

This tendency of objects to maintain their state of rest or of uniform motion is sometimes called "the principle of inertia." Newton's first law is therefore sometimes referred to as the "law of inertia." *Inertia* is a property of all objects. Material bodies have, so to speak, a stubborn streak concerning their state of motion. Once in motion, they continue to move with unchanging velocity (unchanging speed and direction) unless acted on by some unbalanced external force. If at rest, they remain at rest. This tendency is what makes seat belts so necessary when a car stops very suddenly. It also explains why a car may not follow an icy road around a turn, but travel a straighter path into a field or fence. The greater the inertia of an object, the greater its resistance to a change in its state of motion. Hence, the greater is the force needed to produce a change in the state of its motion. For example, it is more difficult to start a train or a ship and to bring it up to speed than to keep it going once it is moving at the desired speed. (In the absence of friction, it would keep moving without any applied force at all.) But for the same reason it is difficult to bring it to a stop, and passengers and cargo keep going forward if the vehicle is suddenly braked.

Newton's first law tells us that if an object is moving with a constant speed in a straight line, the forces acting on it must be balanced. That is, the object is in equilibrium. Does this mean that in Newtonian physics the state of rest and the state of uniform motion are equivalent? It does indeed! When we know that a body is in equilibrium, we know only that $\vec{v}$ = constant. Whether the value of this constant is zero or not depends in any case on our frame of reference for measuring the magnitude of $\vec{v}$. We can say whether it is at rest or is moving with constant $\vec{v}$ larger than zero only by reference to some other body.

Take, for example, a tug-of-war. The two teams are sitting on the deck of a barge that is drifting with uniform velocity down a lazy river. Two observers—one on the same barge and one on the shore—report on the incident, each as viewed from his own frame of reference. The observer on the barge reports that the forces on the rope are balanced and

Inside the laboratory there is no detectable difference between a straight (horizontal) line and a constant height above the earth. But on a larger scale, Galileo's eternal rolling would become motion in a circle around the earth. Newton made clear what is really important: that in the absence of the earth's gravitational pull or other external forces, the ball's undisturbed path would extend straight out into space.

that it is at rest. The observer on the shore reports that the forces on the rope are balanced and that it is in uniform motion. Which observer is right? They are both right; Newton's first law of motion applies to both observations. Whether a body is at rest or in uniform motion depends on which reference frame is used to observe the event. In both cases the forces on the object involved are balanced.

Q9 What is the net force on the body in each of the four cases sketched in the margin of the opposite page?

Q10 What may have been a difference between Newton's concept of inertia and Galileo's?

3.6 The significance of the first law

Newton's laws involve many deep philosophical concepts. (See SG 3.7.) But the laws are easy to use; and we can see the importance of Newton's first law without going into any complex ideas. For convenience let us list the important insights the first law provides.

1. It presents the idea of inertia as a basic property of all material objects. Inertia is the tendency of an object to maintain its state of rest or uniform motion.
2. It points up the equivalence of a state of rest for an object and a state of uniform motion in a straight line. In both states the net force is zero.
3. It raises the whole issue of frame of reference. An object stationary for one observer might be in motion for another observer. Therefore, if the ideas of rest or uniform motion are to have any meaning, the frame of reference used must be specified.
4. It claims to be a universal law. It emphasizes that a single scheme can deal with motion anywhere in the universe. For the first time, no distinction is made between events on the earth and in other parts of the universe. The same law applies to objects on earth as well as on the moon, the planets, and the stars. And it applies to balls, dry-ice disks, magnets, atomic nuclei, electrons—everything!
5. The first law describes the behavior of objects when no unbalanced force acts on them. Thus, it sets the stage for the question: Exactly what happens when an unbalanced force *does* act on an object?

Of course, the idea of inertia does not *explain why* bodies resist change in their state of motion. It is simply a term that helps us to talk about this basic, experimentally observed fact of nature. (See SG 3.6 and 3.7.)

The correct reference frame to use in our physics turns out to be any reference frame that is at rest or in uniform rectilinear motion with respect to the stars. The rotating earth is, therefore, strictly speaking not allowable as a Newtonian reference frame; but for most purposes the earth rotates so little during an experiment that the rotation can be neglected. (See SG 3.8.)

SG 3.9

SG 3.10

3.7 Newton's second law of motion

In Section 3.1 we stated that a theory of dynamics must account for rest, uniform motion, and acceleration. So far we have met two of our three objectives: the explanation of rest and of uniform motion. In terms of the first law, the states of rest and uniform motion are equivalent. That is, they are simply different ways of describing the state of equilibrium —that state in which no unbalanced force acts on an object.

The last section concluded with a list of insights provided by the first law. You may have noticed that no quantitative (mathematical) relationship was established between force and inertia. Newton's second law of motion enables us to reach our third objective—the explanation of acceleration. It also provides a quantitative expression, an equation for the relationship between force and inertia. We will study separately the ways in which force and inertia enter into the second law. Later in this section we will look more closely at how force and inertia are measured. But first we will take some time to be sure that Newton's statement is clear. First we will consider a situation in which different forces act on the same object. Then we will take up a situation in which the same force acts on different objects.

Force and Acceleration. To emphasize the force aspect, Newton's second law can be stated as follows:

> The net, unbalanced force acting on an object is directly proportional to, and in the same direction as, the acceleration of the object.

More briefly, this law can be written as: "Acceleration of a body is proportional to the net force on it." If we let $\vec{F}_{net}$ stand for the net force and $\vec{a}$ stand for acceleration, we can write this relationship as:

$$\vec{a} \propto \vec{F}_{net}$$

Both $\vec{a}$ and $\vec{F}_{net}$ are vectors. The statement that they are proportional includes the understanding that they also point in the same direction.

To say that one quantity is proportional to another is to make a precise mathematical statement. Here it means that if a given net force ($\vec{F}_{net}$) causes an object to move with a certain acceleration ($\vec{a}$), then a new force equal to twice the previous force ($2\vec{F}_{net}$) will cause the same object to have a new acceleration equal to twice the earlier acceleration ($2\vec{a}$). Similarly, three times the previous net force will cause three times the acceleration, and so on. Using symbols, this principle can be expressed by a statement like the following:

If a force $\vec{F}_{net}$ will cause $\quad \vec{a}$, then a force equal to
$\quad\quad 2\vec{F}_{net}$ will cause $\quad 2\vec{a}$
$\quad\quad 3\vec{F}_{net}$ will cause $\quad 3\vec{a}$
$\quad\quad \tfrac{1}{2}\vec{F}_{net}$ will cause $\quad \tfrac{1}{2}\vec{a}$
$\quad\quad 5.2\vec{F}_{net}$ will cause $5.2\vec{a}$
and so on.

One can readily imagine a rough experiment to test this law. Take a nearly frictionless dry-ice disk on a flat table, attach a spring balance, and pull with a steady force so that it accelerates continuously. The pull registered by the balance is the net force since it is the only unbalanced

Apple falling—negligible friction

Feather falling at nearly constant speed

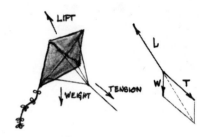

Kite held suspended in the wind

Man running against the wind

force acting. Measure the forces and the corresponding accelerations in various tries, then compare the values of $\vec{F}_{net}$ and $\vec{a}$. We will look into this method in detail in the next section.

Mass and Acceleration. Now we can consider the inertia aspect of the second law, the effect of the same net force acting on different objects. In discussing the first law, we defined inertia as the resistance of an object to any change in its velocity. We know from experience and observation that some objects have greater inertia than others. For instance, suppose you were to throw a baseball and then put a shot with your full effort. You know that the baseball would be accelerated more and hence would reach a greater speed than the shot. Thus, the acceleration given a body depends as much on the body as it does on the force applied to it. The concept of the amount of inertia a body has is expressed by the term *mass*.

Mass is a familiar word, but it becomes useful in physics only if it is not confused with some of its everyday, common-sense meanings. For example, mass is often used as a synonym for weight. But although mass and weight are closely related, they are not at all the same thing. Weight is a force, the force with which gravity is acting on an object. Mass, on the other hand, is a measure of an object's resistance to acceleration. It is true that on or near the surface of the earth, objects that are hard to accelerate are also heavy, and we will return to this relationship in Section 3.8.

SG 3.11

If you apply the same force to several objects of different mass, their accelerations will not be the same. Newton stated that the resulting acceleration of each object is inversely proportional to its mass. Using the symbol m for mass (a scalar quantity), and the symbol a for the magnitude of the vector acceleration $\vec{a}$, we can write "a is inversely proportional to m." Mathematically, this expression is the same as "a is proportional to $1/m$," or

What does it mean to say that mass is a scalar quantity?

$$a \propto \frac{1}{m}$$

This equation means that if a certain force gives an object a certain acceleration, then the same force will cause an object having twice the mass to have one-half the acceleration. An object having three times the mass will have one-third the acceleration, an object of one-fifth the mass will have five times the acceleration, and so on. Thus, for example, a truck takes much longer to reach the same cruising speed when it is full than when it is nearly empty. Using symbols, we can express this relationship as follows:

> If a given force $\vec{F}_{net}$ is applied, and an object
> of mass m experiences a, then an object
> of mass $2m$ will experience $\frac{1}{2}a$,
> of mass $3m$ will experience $\frac{1}{3}a$,
> of mass $\frac{1}{5}m$ will experience $5a$,
> of mass $2.5m$ will experience $0.4a$,
> and so on.

These statements can be demonstrated by experiment. Can you suggest
how it might be done?

The roles played by force and mass in Newton's second law can be
combined in a single statement:

> The acceleration of an object is directly proportional to, and in
> the same direction as, the unbalanced force acting on it, and it
> is inversely proportional to the mass of the object.

The ideas expressed in this long statement can be summarized by the
equation

$$\vec{a} = \frac{\vec{F}_{net}}{m}$$

SG 3.12, 3.13

This equation is one possible way of expressing Newton's second law of
motion. The same relationship may of course be written equally correctly
in the form

$$\vec{F}_{net} = m\vec{a}$$

In either form, this is probably the most basic equation in all of
Newtonian mechanics. Like the first law, the second has a very wide
range of application. It does not matter whether the force is mechanical or
electric or magnetic, whether the mass is that of a star or a nuclear
particle, whether the acceleration is large or small. We can use the law in
the simplest problems and in the most difficult ones. By measuring the
acceleration which an unknown net force gives a body of *known mass,* we
can compute a numerical value for the force from the equation $\vec{F}_{net} = m\vec{a}$.
Or, by measuring the acceleration that a *known net force* gives a body of
unknown mass, we can compute a numerical value for the mass from the
equation $m = \vec{F}_{net}/a$. Clearly, we must be able to *measure* two of the
three quantities in order to be able to *compute* the other.

Units of mass and force. Before we can make such measurements,
however, we must establish units for mass and force. Further, these units
must be consistent with the units for acceleration, which we already have
defined in terms of standards of length and time—for example, meters per
second per second.

One way to define such units is to choose some convenient object,
perhaps a piece of corrosion-free metal, as the universal standard of mass.
We can assign to this object a mass of one unit. Once this unit has been
selected, we can proceed to develop a measure of force.

We are free to choose any object as a standard of mass. But ideally it
should be very stable, easy to reproduce, and of reasonably convenient
size. Such a standard object has, in fact, been agreed on by the scientific
community. By international agreement, the primary standard of mass is a
cylinder of platinum-iridium alloy. The cylinder is kept at the International
Bureau of Weights and Measures near Paris. The mass of this platinum

1 kg corresponds to the mass of
about 1 liter of water, or about
2.2 lb (more precisely 2.205 lb).
The 1/1000th part of 1 kg is 1 gram
(1 g).

cylinder is *defined* as exactly *1 kilogram* (abbreviated 1 kg). (A similar agreement has established a universal standard of length.) Accurately made copies of this international primary standard of mass are kept in the various standards laboratories throughout the world. Further copies have been made from these for distribution to manufacturers and research laboratories.

SG 3.14

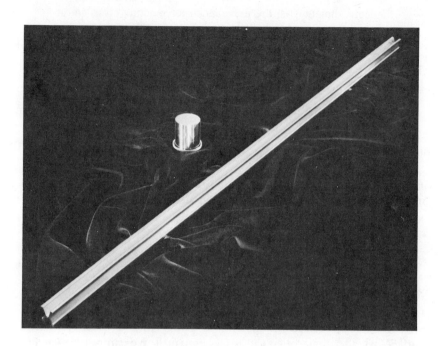

The standard kilogram and meter at the U.S. Bureau of Standards.

SG 3.15, 3.16

SG 3.17, 3.18

Now we can answer the question of how "push" or "pull" should be regarded as one unit of force. We *define* 1 unit of force as a force which, when acting alone, causes an object with a mass of 1 kilogram to accelerate at the rate of exactly 1 meter/second/second.

Imagine an experiment in which the standard 1-kg object is pulled with a spring balance in a horizontal direction across a level, frictionless surface. The pull is regulated to make the 1-kg object accelerate at exactly 1 m/sec. The required force will *by definition* be one unit in magnitude:

In this equation we use only the magnitudes—the direction is not part of the definition of the unit of force.

$$F_{net} = 1 \text{ kg} \times 1 \text{ m/sec}^2 = 1 \text{ kg m/sec}^2$$

The units of acceleration "m/sec per second" can be written as "m/sec/sec" or "m/sec²". The sec² means that division by time units occurs twice, not something like "square time."

Thus, 1 kg m/sec² of force is that quantity of force which causes an object with a mass of 1 kg to accelerate 1 m/sec².

The unit kg m/sec² has been given a shorter name, the *newton* (abbreviated as N). The newton is a *derived* unit. It is defined in terms of a particular relationship between the *m*eter, the *k*ilogram, and the *s*econd. Thus the newton is part of the *mks* system of units, which is used almost universally in modern scientific work.

In a sense, then, there is a "hidden text" in Newton's second law. It involves both definitions and experimental facts. Textbooks do not all agree on how best to present the relation of definition and experiment in Newton's second law. Indeed, Newton himself may have not thought it through entirely. However, as a system of ideas, and no matter how it is analyzed, it was powerful in leading to many discoveries in physics.

Newton did not "discover" the concepts of force and mass. But he did recognize that these concepts were basic to an understanding of motion. He clarified these concepts, and found a way to express them in numerical values, and so made a science of dynamics possible.

SG 3.19–3.23

Q11 Which three fundamental units of distance, mass, and time are used to define the unit of force?

Q12 A net force of 10 N gives an object a constant acceleration of 4 m/sec². What is the mass of the object?

Q13 True or false? Newton's second law holds only when frictional forces are absent.

Q14 A 2-kg object, shoved across the floor with a speed of 10 m/sec, slides to rest in 5 sec. What was the magnitude of the force producing this acceleration?

Q15 Complete the table in the margin which lists some accelerations resulting from applying equal forces to objects of different mass.

MASS	ACCELERATION
m	30 m/sec²
$2m$	15 m/sec²
$3m$	
$1/5m$	
$0.5m$	
$45m$	
	3 m/sec²
	75 m/sec²

3.8 Mass, weight, and free fall

The idea of force in physics includes much more than muscular pushes and pulls. Whenever we observe an acceleration, we know that there is a force acting. Forces need not be "mechanical" (exerted by contact only). They can also result from gravitational, electric, magnetic, or other actions. Newton's laws hold true for all forces.

The force of gravity acts between objects even without direct contact. Such objects may be separated by only a few feet of air, as is the case with the earth and a falling stone. Or they may be separated by many miles of empty space, as are artificial satellites and the earth.

We will use the symbol $\vec{F}_g$ for gravitational force. The magnitude of the gravitational pull $\vec{F}_g$ is roughly the same anywhere on the surface of the earth for a given object. When we wish to be very precise, we must take into account the facts that the earth is not exactly spherical, and that there are irregularities in the makeup of the earth's crust. These factors cause slight differences—up to ½%—in the gravitational force on the same object at different places on the earth. An object having a constant mass of 1 kg will experience a gravitational force of 9.812 newtons in London, but only 9.796 newtons in Denver, Colorado. Geologists make use of these variations in locating oil and other mineral deposits.

The term *weight* is often used in everyday conversation as if it meant the same thing as mass. In physics, we define the weight of an object as the *gravitational force acting on the body*. Weight is a vector quantity, as are all forces. Your weight is the downward force our planet exerts on you whether you stand or sit, fly or fall, orbit the earth in a space vehicle or merely stand on a scale to "weigh" yourself.

Think for a moment what a scale does. The spring in it compresses until it exerts on you an upward force strong enough to hold you up. So what the scale registers is really the force with which it pushes up on your feet. When you and the scale stand still and are not accelerating, the scale must be pushing up on your feet with a force equal in magnitude to your weight. That is why you are in equilibrium—the sum of the forces on you is zero.

Now imagine for a moment a ridiculous but instructive thought experiment. As you stand on the scale, the floor (which, while sagging slightly, has been pushing up on the scale) suddenly gives way. You and the scale drop into a deep well in free fall. At every instant, your fall speed and the scale's fall speed will be equal, since you fall with the same acceleration. Your feet now touch the scale only barely (if at all). You look at the dial and see that the scale registers zero. This does not mean you have lost your weight—that could only happen if the earth suddenly disappeared, or if you were suddenly removed to deep space. No, $\vec{F}_g$ still acts on you as before, accelerating you downward. But since the scale is accelerating *with* you, you are no longer pushing down on it, nor is it pushing up on you.

You can get a fairly good idea of the difference between the properties of weight and mass by holding a big book. First, lay the book on your hand; you feel the weight of the book acting down. Next, grasp the book and shake it back and forth sideward. You still feel the weight downward, but you also feel how hard it is to accelerate the book back and forth. This resistance to acceleration is the book's mass. You could "cancel" the sensation of the book's *weight* by hanging the book on a string. But the sensation of its *inertia* as you shake it would remain the same. This is only a crude demonstration. More elaborate experiments would show, however, that weight can change without any change of mass. Thus when an astronaut on the moon's surface uses a big camera, he finds it much easier to hold than on earth. In terms of the moon's gravity, the camera's *weight* is only ⅙ of its weight on earth. But its *mass* or inertia is not less, so it is as hard to swing the camera around suddenly into a new position on the moon as it is on earth.

Consider SG 3.14 again.

We can now understand more clearly the results of Galileo's experiment on falling objects. Galileo showed that any given object (at a given locality) falls with uniform acceleration, $\vec{a}_g$. What is responsible for its uniform acceleration? A constant net force. In this case of free fall, this net force is just $\vec{F}_g$. Now Newton's second law expresses the relationship between this force and the resulting acceleration. Applying the equation $\vec{F}_{net} = m\vec{a}$ to this case, where $\vec{F}_{net} = \vec{F}_g$ and $\vec{a} = \vec{a}_g$, we can write

Many books use the symbol g instead of a_y.

$$\vec{F}_g = m\vec{a}_g$$

We can, of course, rewrite this equation as

$$\vec{a}_g = \frac{\vec{F}_g}{m}$$

From Newton's second law, we can now see why the acceleration of a body in free fall is constant. The reason is that, for an object of given mass m, the gravitational force $\vec{F}_g$ over normal distances of fall is nearly constant.

Galileo, however, did more than claim that every object falls with *constant* acceleration: he found that at any one place *all* objects fall with the *same* uniform acceleration. We now know that at the earth's surface this acceleration has the value of 9.8 m/sec². Regardless of the mass m or weight $\vec{F}_g$, all bodies in free fall (in the same locality) have the same acceleration a_g.

Does this agree with the relation $\vec{a}_g = \vec{F}_g / m$? It does so *only* if $\vec{F}_g$ is directly proportional to mass m for every object. In other words, if m is doubled, $\vec{F}_g$ must double; if m is tripled, $\vec{F}_g$ must triple. This is an important result indeed. Weight and mass are entirely different concepts. *Weight* is the gravitational *force* on an object (hence weight is a vector). *Mass* is a measure of the resistance of an object to change in its motion, a measure of *inertia* (hence mass is a scalar). Yet we have seen that different objects fall freely with the same acceleration in any given locality. Thus, in the same locality, the magnitudes of these two quite different quantities are proportional.

SG 3.25 –3.28

Q16 An astronaut is orbiting the earth in a space vehicle. The acceleration due to gravity at that distance is half its value on the surface of the earth. Which of the following are true?
   (a) His weight is zero.
   (b) His mass is zero.
   (c) His weight is half its original value.
   (d) His mass is half its original value.
   (e) His weight remains the same.
   (f) His mass remains the same.

Q17 A girl jumps from a table top. When she is halfway between the table top and the floor, which of the statements in Q16 are true?

3.9 Newton's third law of motion

In his first law, Newton described the behavior of objects when they are in a state of equilibrium; that is, when the net force acting on them is zero. His second law explained how their motion changes when the net force is not zero. Newton's third law added a new and surprising insight about forces.

Consider this problem: In a 100-meter dash, an athlete goes from rest to nearly top speed in less than a second. We could measure his mass before he makes the dash, and we could use high-speed photography to measure his initial acceleration. With his mass and acceleration known, we could use $\vec{F}_{net} = m\vec{a}$ to find the force acting on him during the initial acceleration. But where does the force come from? It must have something to do with the runner himself. Is it possible for him to exert a force on himself as a whole? Can he, for example, ever lift himself by his own bootstraps?

Newton's third law of motion helps us to understand just such puzzling situations. First, let us see what the third law claims. In Newton's words:

> To every action there is always opposed an equal reaction: or, mutual actions of two bodies upon each other are always equal and directed to contrary parts.

This is a word-for-word translation from the *Principia*. It is generally agreed, however, that we may substitute the expression *force on one object* for the word *action,* and the expression *equally large force on another object* for the words *equal reaction.* Read it over with this change.

The most startling idea in this statement is that forces always exist in mirror-twin pairs, and on two different objects. Indeed, the idea of a single force acting without another force acting somewhere else is without any meaning whatsoever. On this point Newton wrote: "Whatever draws or presses another is as much drawn or pressed by that other. If you press a stone with your finger, the finger is also pressed by the stone." This statement suggests that forces always arise as a result of mutual actions ("interactions") between objects. If object A pushes or pulls on B, then at the same time object B pushes or pulls with precisely equal force on A. These paired pulls and pushes are always equal in magnitude, opposite in direction, *and on two different objects.*

SG 3.29

Let us apply this idea to the athlete. We now see that his act of pushing with his feet back against the ground (one may call it here the *action*) also involves a push of the ground forward on him (one can call it the *reaction*). It is this reaction that propels him forward. In this and all other cases it really makes no difference which force we call the action and which the reaction, because they occur at exactly the same time. The action does not "cause" the reaction—if the earth could not "push back" on his feet, the athlete could not push on the earth in the first place. Instead, he would slide around as on slippery ice. Action and reaction coexist. You can't have one without the other. And most important, the two forces are not acting on the same body. In a way, they are like debt and credit: One is impossible without the other; they are equally large but of opposite sign; and they happen to two different objects.

Any body A that affects body B must itself be affected by B—equally and oppositely. We can use the efficient shorthand of algebra to express the idea that, whenever bodies A and B interact,

$$\vec{F}_{AB} = -\vec{F}_{BA}$$

This equation clearly sums up Newton's third law: Whenever two bodies

He is, to be sure, pushing against the ground — but that is a force acting *on the ground*.

interact, the forces they exert on each other are equal in magnitude and opposite in direction.

Every day we see hundreds of examples of this law at work. A boat is propelled by the water that pushes forward on the oar while the oar pushes back on the water. A car is set in motion by the push of the ground on the tires as they push back on the ground; when friction is not sufficient, the push on the tires cannot start the car forward. While accelerating a bullet forward, a rifle experiences a recoil "kick." A balloon shoots forward while the air spurts out from it in the opposite direction. Many such effects are not easily observed. For example, when an apple falls, pulled down by its attraction to the earth, i.e., by its weight, the earth in turn accelerates upward slightly, pulled up by the attraction of the earth to the apple.

Now, note what the third law does *not* say—this, too, is important. The third law speaks of *forces,* not of the effects these forces produce. Thus, in the last example, the earth accelerates upward as the apple falls down. The force on each is equally large. But the accelerations produced by the forces are quite different. The mass of the earth is enormous, and so the earth's upward acceleration is far too small to notice. The third law also does not describe how the push or pull is applied, whether by contact or by magnetic action or by electrical action. Nor does the law require that the force be either an attraction or repulsion. The third law in fact does not depend on any particular kind of force. It applies equally to resting objects and to moving objects, to accelerating objects as well as to objects in uniform motion. It applies whether or not there is friction present. This universal nature of the third law makes it extremely valuable in physics.

In the collision between the ball and the club, the force the ball exerts on the club is equal and opposite to the force the club exerts on the ball. Both the club and the ball get deformed by the forces acting on them.

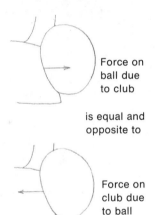

Force on ball due to club

is equal and opposite to

Force on club due to ball

force on earth   force on moon

The force on the moon due to the earth is equal and opposite to the force on the earth due to the moon.

Q18 According to Newton's third law, what are the four general characteristics of forces?

Q19 Identify the forces that act according to Newton's third law when a horse accelerates; when a swimmer moves at constant speed.

Q20 A piece of fishing line breaks if the force exerted on it is greater than 500 N. Will the line break if two people at opposite ends of the line pull on it, each with a force of 300 N?

Q21 State Newton's three laws of motion as clearly as you can in your own words.

SG 3.30-3.32

3.10 Using Newton's laws of motion

We have discussed each of Newton's three laws of motion in some detail. The first law emphasizes the modern point of view in the study of motion. It states that what requires explanation is not motion itself, but *change* of motion. The first law stresses that one must account for why an object speeds up or slows down or changes direction. The second law asserts that the rate of change of velocity of an object is related to both the mass of the object and the net force applied to it. In fact, the very meanings of force and mass are shown by the second law to be closely related to each other. The third law describes a relationship between interacting objects.

Despite their individual importance, Newton's three laws are most powerful when they are used together. The mechanics based on Newton's laws was very successful. Indeed, until the late nineteenth century it seemed that the entire universe must be understood as "matter in motion." Let us examine two specific examples that illustrate the use of these laws.

Example 1

On September 12, 1966, a dramatic experiment based on Newton's second law was carried out high over the earth. In this experiment, the mass of an orbiting Agena rocket case was determined by accelerating it with a push from a Gemini spacecraft. After the Gemini spacecraft made contact with the Agena rocket case, the thrusters on the Gemini were fired for 7.0 sec. These thrusters were set to give an average thrusting force of 890 N. The change in velocity of the spacecraft and rocket case was found to be 0.93 m/sec. The mass of the Gemini spacecraft was known to be about 3,400 kg. The question to be answered was: What is the mass of the Agena?

(Actually, the mass of the Agena had already been measured independently. The purpose of the experiment was to develop a method for finding the unknown mass of a foreign satellite in orbit.)

In this case, a known force of magnitude 890 N was acting on two objects in contact, with a total mass of m_{total}, where

$$m_{total} = m_{Gemini} + m_{Agena}$$

$$= 3400 \text{ kg} + m_{Agena}$$

The magnitude of the average acceleration produced by the thrust is found as follows:

$$a = \frac{\Delta v}{\Delta t}$$

$$= \frac{0.93 \text{ m/sec}}{7.0 \text{ sec}}$$

$$= 0.13 \text{ m/sec}^2$$

Newton's second law gives us the relation

$$F = m_{\text{total}} \times a$$

or

$$= (m_{\text{Agena}} + 3\ 400 \text{ kg}) \times a$$

Solving for m_{Agena} gives

$$m_{\text{Agena}} = \frac{F}{a} - 3\ 400 \text{ kg} = \frac{890 \text{ N}}{0.13 \text{ m/sec}} - 3\ 400 \text{ kg}$$

$$= 6\ 900 \text{ kg} - 3\ 400 \text{ kg}$$

$$= 3\ 500 \text{ kg}$$

The actual mass of the Agena, as previously determined, was about 3,660 kg. The method for finding the mass by pushing the Agena while in orbit therefore gave a result that was accurate to within 5%. This accuracy was well within the margin of error expected in making the measurement.

Example 2

Imagine taking a ride on an elevator: (A) At first it is at rest on the ground floor; (B) it accelerates upward uniformly at 1m/sec/sec for a few seconds; then (C) it continues to go up at a constant speed of 5 m/sec. Suppose a 100-kg man (whose weight would therefore be about 1,000 newtons) is standing in the elevator. With what force is the elevator floor pushing up on him during (A), (B), and (C)?

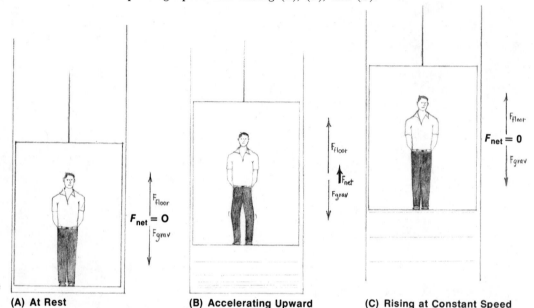

(A) At Rest   **(B) Accelerating Upward**   **(C) Rising at Constant Speed**

Parts (A) and (C) are the same in terms of dynamics: Since the man is not accelerating, the net force on him must be zero. So the floor must be pushing up on him just as hard as gravity is pulling him down. The gravitational force on him, his weight, is 1,000 N. So the floor must be exerting an upward force of 1,000 newtons.

Part (B): Since the man is accelerating upward, there must be a net force upward on him. The unbalanced force is

$$F_{net} = ma_{up}$$
$$= 100 \text{ kg} \times 2 \text{ m/sec/sec}$$
$$= 200 \text{ N}$$

Clearly, the floor must be pushing up on him with a force 200 N greater than what is required just to balance his weight. Therefore the total force upward on him is 1,200 N.

SG 3.33 is an elaboration of a similar example. For a difficult, worked-out example see SG 3.34.

3.11 Nature's basic forces

Our study of Newton's laws of motion has increased our understanding of objects at rest, moving uniformly, and accelerating.

However, we have learned much more in the process. Newton's first law alerted us to the importance of frames of reference. In fact, an understanding of the relationship between descriptions of the same event seen from different frames of reference was the necessary first step toward the theory of relativity.

Newton's second law shows the fundamental importance of the concept of force. It says, in effect, "When you observe acceleration, find the force!" This is how we were first made aware of gravitational force as an explanation of Galileo's kinematics. We discovered that, at a given place, $\vec{a}_g$ is constant for all objects. And since $\vec{a} = \vec{F}_g/m$ by Newton's second law, we concluded that the magnitude of $\vec{F}_g$ is always proportional to m.

But this is only a halfway solution. Now we want to know more. Why is $\vec{F}_g$ proportional to m for all bodies at a given place? How does $\vec{F}_g$ change for a given body as it is moved to places more distant from the earth? Is there a law connecting $\vec{F}_g$, m and distance—a "force law"? As Unit 2 will show, there is indeed. Knowing that force law, we can understand all gravitational interactions among objects.

Gravitational attraction is not the only basic force by which objects interact. However, there appear to be very few such basic forces. In fact, physicists now believe that everything we observe in nature results from only four basic types of interactions. In terms of our present understanding, *all* events of nature—from those among subnuclear particles to those among vast galaxies—involve one or more of only these few types of forces. There is, of course, nothing sacred about the number four. New discoveries or new insights into present theories might increase or reduce the number. For example, two (or more) of the basic forces might someday be seen as arising from even more basic force.

The first of the four interactions is the gravitational force. This force becomes important only on a relatively large scale, when tremendous numbers of atoms of matter are involved. Between individual atoms, gravitational force is extremely weak. But it is this very weak force that literally holds the universe together. The second interaction involves electric and magnetic processes and is most important on the atomic and molecular scale. It is chiefly the electromagnetic force that holds together objects in the size range between an atom and a mountain.

We know the force laws governing gravitational and electromagnetic interactions. Therefore, these interactions are fairly well "understood." But we know considerably less about the two remaining basic interactions. They are the subject of much research today. The third interaction (the so-called "strong" interaction) somehow holds the particles of the nucleus together. The fourth interaction (the so-called "weak" interaction) governs certain reactions among subnuclear particles.

We do, of course, have other *names* for forces, but each of these belongs to one of the basic types. One of the most common is the "frictional" force. Friction is thought to be an electrical interaction. That is, the atoms on the surfaces of the objects sliding or rubbing against each other are believed to interact electrically.

Refer to K. Ford's: *The World of Elementary Particles* for brief discussion of four forces.

Einstein spent most of the latter half of his life seeking a theory that would express gravitational and electromagnetic effects in a unified way. A satisfactory "unified field theory" is still being sought.

We will encounter these ideas again. The gravitational force is covered in Unit 2, the electrical and magnetic forces in Units 4 and 5, and the forces between nuclear particles in the Supplemental Unit entitled *The Nucleus*. In all of these cases, all objects subjected to a force behave in agreement with Newton's laws of motion, no matter what kind of force is involved.

The knowledge that there are so few basic interactions is both surprising and encouraging. It is surprising because, at first glance, the events all around us seem so varied and complex. It is encouraging because it makes our elusive goal—an understanding of the events of nature—look more attainable.

"The Starry Night," by Vincent Van Gogh. The intuitive feeling that all of nature's phenomena are interlinked on a grand scale is shared by scientists as well as artists.

3.1 The Project Physics learning materials particularly appropriate for Chapter 3 include the following:

Experiments
Newton's Second Law
Mass and Weight

Activities
Checker Snapping
Beaker and Hammer
Pulls and Jerks
Experiencing Newton's Second Law
Make One of These Accelerometers

Reader Articles
Introduction to Vectors
Newton's Laws of Dynamics
The Scientific Revolution
How the Scientific Revolution of the 17th
    Century Affected Other Branches of
    Thought

Film Loops
Vector Addition – Velocity of a Boat

3.2 The Aristotelian explanation of motion should not be dismissed lightly. Great intellects of the Renaissance period, such as Leonardo da Vinci, who among other things designed devices for launching projectiles, did not challenge such explanations. One reason for the longevity of these ideas is that they are so closely aligned with our common sense ideas.

In what ways do your common-sense notions of motion agree with the Aristotelian ones?

3.3 Three ants are struggling with a crumb. One ant pulls toward the east with a force of 8 units. Another pulls toward the north with a force of 6 units, and the third pulls in a direction 30° south of west with a force of 12 units.
(a) Using the "head-to-tail" construction of arrows, find whether the forces balance, or whether there is a net (unbalanced) force on the crumb.
(b) If there is a net force, you can find its direction and magnitude by measuring the line drawn from the tail of the first arrow to the head of the last arrow. What is its magnitude and direction?

3.4 Show why the parallelogram method of adding arrows is geometrically equivalent to the head-to-tail method.

3.5 There are many familiar situations in which the net force on a body is zero, and yet the body moves with a constant velocity. One example of such "dynamic equilibrium" is an automobile traveling at constant speed on a straight road: the force the road exerts on the tires is just balanced by the force of air friction. If the gas pedal is depressed further, the tires will push against the road harder and the road will push against the tires harder; so the car will accelerate forward – until the air friction builds up enough to balance the greater drive force. Give another example of a body moving with constant velocity under balanced forces. Specify the source of each force on the body and, as in the automobile example, explain how these forces could be changed to affect the body's motion.

3.6 (a) You exert a force on a box, but it does not move. How would you explain this? How might an Aristotelian explain it?
(b) Suppose now that you exert a greater force and the box moves. Explain this from your (Newtonian) point of view and from an Aristotelian point of view.
(c) You stop pushing on the box and it quickly comes to rest. Explain this from both the Newtonian and the Aristotelian points of view.

3.7 There are at least two drawbacks to an experimental test of Newton's law of inertia.
(a) How can you really be sure that there is no unbalanced force acting on the object, even if you see that the object moves uniformly in a straight line? We can answer that we are sure because the object does continue to move uniformly in a straight line. But this answer is merely a restatement of the first law, which we wanted to prove by experiment. Surely we cannot use the first law to verify the first law! But we are not really caught in a circular argument. Practically, we can expect to find forces on an object only when other objects are in contact with it, or somewhere near it. The influences may be of unfamiliar kinds, and we may have to stretch what we mean by "near"; but whenever a force is detected we look for the source of the influence. If all known influences on an object were balanced, and yet it didn't move uniformly, we would suspect an unknown influence and track it down – and we would find it. At least, that's how it has always turned out so far. As a practical example, consider the demonstration involving low friction pucks on a level surface. Without using Newton's first law, how could you be sure the surface was level?
(b) What is meant by a straight line?

3.8 (a) Assume that the floor of a laboratory could be made perfectly horizontal and perfectly smooth. A dry-ice puck is placed on the floor and given a small push. Predict the way in which the puck would move. How would this motion differ if the whole laboratory were moving uniformly during the experiment? How would it differ if the whole laboratory were accelerating along a straight line? If the puck were seen to move in a curved path along the floor, how would you explain this?
(b) A man gently starts a dry-ice puck in motion while both are on a rotating

platform. What will he report to be the motion he observes as the platform keeps rotating? How will he explain what he sees if he believes he can use Newton's first law to understand observations made in a rotating reference frame? Will he be right or wrong?

3.9 In terms of Newton's first law, explain:
(a) Why people in a moving car lurch forward when the car suddenly slows down;
(b) What happens to the passengers of a car that makes a sharp, quick turn;
(c) When a coin is put on a phonograph turntable and the motor started, does the coin fly off when the turntable reaches a certain speed? Why doesn't it fly off sooner?

3.10 (a) A balloon-like object stands before you, not moving, suspended in mid-air. What can you say about the forces that may be acting on it? Suddenly it moves off in a curved path. Give two different explanations. How can you test which is right?
(b) Consider anew the motion of a falling leaf (Chapter 1). How do Newton's laws control the motion of the leaf?

3.11 In an actual experiment on applying the same force to different masses, how would you know it was the "same force"?

3.12 Several proportionalities can be combined into an equation only if care is taken about the units in which the factors are expressed. When we wrote $\Delta d = v \times \Delta t$ in Chapter 1, we chose *meters* as units for *d*, *seconds* as units for *t*, and then made sure that the equation came out right by using meters/second as units for *v*. In other words, we let the equation *define* the unit for *v*. If we had already chosen some *other* units for *v*, say miles per hour, then we would have had to write instead something like

$$\Delta d = k \times v\Delta t$$

where *k* is a constant factor that matches up the units of *d*, *t*, and *v*.
What value would *k* have if *d* were measured in *miles*, *t* in *seconds*, and *v* in *miles per hour*?
Writing $\vec{a} = \vec{F}_{net}/m$ before we have defined units of *F* and *m* is not the very best mathematical procedure. To be perfectly correct in expressing Newton's law, we would have had to write:

$$\vec{a} = k \times \frac{\vec{F}_{net}}{m}$$

where *k* is a constant factor that would match up whatever units we choose for *a*, *F*, and *m*. In fact, we will take the easiest way out and let the equation define the units of *F* in terms of the units we choose for *a* and *m*, so the equation comes out right without using *k*. (Or if you prefer to say it that way, we choose units so that $k = 1$.)

3.13 A body is accelerated by an unbalanced force. If

the magnitude of the net force is doubled and the mass of the body is reduced to one-third of the original value, what will be the ratio of the second acceleration to the first?

3.14 What does a laboratory balance measure — mass or weight? What about a spring balance? (Hint: consider what would happen to readings on each if they were on the moon instead of the earth.) You might want to consider this question again after reading Sec. 3.8.

3.15 Describe as a thought experiment how you could calibrate a spring balance in force units. If you actually tried to do the experiments, what practical difficulties would you expect?

3.16 "Hooke's law" says that the force exerted by a stretched or compressed spring is directly proportional to the amount of the compression or extension. As Robert Hooke put it in announcing his discovery:

> . . . the power of any spring is in the same proportion with the tension thereof: that is, if one power stretch or bend it one space, two will bend it two, three will bend it three, and so forward. Now as the theory is very short, so the way of trying it is very easie.

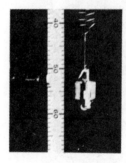 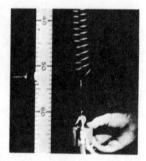

If Hooke says it's "easie," then it might well be so. You can probably think immediately of how to test this law using springs and weights. (a) Try designing such an experiment; then after checking with your instructor, carry it out. What limitations do you find to Hooke's law? (b) How could you use Hooke's law to simplify the calibration procedure asked for in SG 3.15?

3.17 Refer to the discussion in SG 3.12. Show that $k = 1$ when we define a newton as we do on p. 83.

3.18 When units for different terms in a relation are defined completely independently from one another, the numerical value of the constant must be found experimentally. (Later in this course you will see how finding the value of *k* in certain relations was very important in the development of physics.) Say, for example, that we had decided to measure force in "tugs," defining a tug as the force required to stretch a standard rubber band one inch. How could we go about finding k?

3.19 Complete this table:

	NET FORCE	MASS	RESULTING ACCELERATION
a	1.0 N	1.0 kg	1.0 m/sec²
b	24.0	2.0	12.0
c		3.0	8.0
d		74.0	0.2
e		0.0066	130.0
f	72.0		8.0
g	3.6		12.0
h	1.3		6.4
i	30.0	10.0	
j	0.5	0.20	
k	120.0	48.0	

3.20 A rocket-sled has a mass of 4440 kg and is propelled by a solid-propellent rocket motor of 890,000-N thrust which burns for 3.9 seconds.
(a) What is the sled's average acceleration and maximum speed?
(b) This sled has a maximum acceleration of 30 g ($= 30\ a_g$). How can that be, considering the data given?
(c) If the sled travels a distance of 1530 m while attaining a top speed of 860 m/sec (how did it attain *that* high a speed?), what is its average acceleration?

3.21 If you have small carts with smoothly moving wheels available, here is one way of doing an experiment to demonstrate the *inverse proportionality* between acceleration and mass:
(a) Add load blocks to one or the other of two carts until the carts balance when placed on opposite platforms of a laboratory balance. Balance a third cart with one of the first pair. Each cart now has the same mass m. (State two main assumptions involved here.)
(b) Accelerate one cart on a level surface, using a rubber band; that is, pull the cart with the rubber band, keeping the rubber band stretched a known constant amount so that it supplies a constant force. Any other method can be used that will assure

you that, within reason, the same force is being applied each time. Record the position of the cart at equal time intervals by means of stroboscopic photography.
(c) Repeat the last step in all details, but use two carts hooked together. Repeat again using all three carts hooked together. In all three cases it is crucial that the applied force be essentially the same.
(d) Determine the value of acceleration for masses of m (1 cart), $2m$ (2 carts), and $3m$ (3 carts).
(e) Prepare a graph of a vs. m, of a vs. $1/m$, and of $1/a$ vs. m. Comment on your results.

3.22 Describe in detail the steps you would take in an idealized experiment to determine the unknown mass m of a certain object (in kilograms) if you were given nothing but a frictionless horizontal plane, a 1-kg standard, an uncalibrated spring balance, a meter stick, and a stopwatch.

3.23 A block is dragged with *constant velocity* along a *rough* horizontal table top by means of a spring balance horizontally attached to the block. The balance shows a reading of 0.40 N at this and any other constant velocity. This means that the retarding frictional force between block and table is 0.40 N. Compute the mass of the block.
Now the block is pulled harder and given a constant acceleration of 0.85 m/sec²; the balance is found to read 2.1 N. Compute the mass of the block.

3.24 We have claimed that any body in free fall is "weightless" because any weight-measuring device falling with it would read zero. This is not an entirely satisfactory explanation, because you feel a definite sensation during free fall that is exactly the same sensation you would feel if you were truly without weight—say deep in space far from any star or planet. (The sensation you feel on jumping off a roof or a diving board, or when someone pulls a chair out from under you.) Can you explain why your insides react in the same way to lack of weight and to free fall?

3.25 Explain the statement that while the mass of an object is the same everywhere, its weight may vary from place to place.

3.26 (a) A replica of the standard kilogram is constructed in Paris and then sent to the National Bureau of Standards near Washington. D.C. Assuming that this secondary standard is not damaged in transit, what is

(i) its mass in Washington?
(ii) its weight in Paris and in Washington? (In Paris, $a_g = 9.81$ m/sec²; in Washington, $a_g = 9.80$ m/sec².)

(b) What is the change in your own weight as you go from Paris to Washington?

3.27 (a) Find your mass in kg, and your weight in newtons.

(b) How much force is needed to accelerate you 1 m/sec²? How many kilograms can you lift? How many newtons of force must you exert to do this?

3.28 Why is it often said that astronauts in orbit around a planet or satellite are weightless?

3.29 Quite apart from pushing down on the ground owing to his own weight, a runner pushes on the earth with the sole of his shoe in a horizontal direction and the earth pushes with an equal and opposite force on the sole of the shoe. This latter force has an accelerating effect on the runner, but what does the force acting on the earth do to the earth? From Newton's second law we would conclude that such an unbalanced force would accelerate the earth. The mass of the earth is very great, however, so the acceleration caused by the runner is very small. A reasonable value for the average acceleration of a runner when he starts is 5m/sec/sec, and a reasonable value for his mass would be 60 kg. The mass of the earth is approximately 60×10^{23} kg.

(a) What acceleration of the earth would the runner cause?

(b) If the acceleration lasts for 2 seconds, what speed will the runner have reached?

(c) What speed will the earth have reached?

3.30 In terms of Newton's third law, assess the following statements:

(a) You are standing perfectly still on the ground; therefore you and the earth exert equal and opposite forces on each other.

(b) The reason that a propeller airplane cannot fly above the atmosphere is that there is no air to push one way while the plane goes the other.

(c) Object A rests on object B. The mass of object A is 100 times as great as that of object B, but even so, the force A exerts on B is no greater than the force of B on A.

3.31 Consider a tractor pulling a heavy log in a straight line. On the basis of Newton's third law,

one might argue that the log pulls back on the tractor just as strongly as the tractor pulls the log. But why, then, does the tractor move? (Make a large drawing of the tractor, rope, log, and the earth, and enter all the forces acting on each.)

3.32 Consider the system consisting of a 1.0-kg ball and the earth. The ball is dropped from a short distance above the ground and falls freely. Assuming that the mass of the earth is approximately 6.0×10^{24} kg,

(a) make a vector diagram illustrating the important forces acting on each member of the system.

(b) calculate the acceleration of the earth in this interaction.

(c) find the ratio of the magnitude of the ball's acceleration to that of the earth's acceleration (a_b/a_e).

(d) make a vector diagram as in (a) but showing the situation when the ball has come to rest after hitting the ground.

3.33 (a) A 75-kg man stands in an elevator. What force does the floor exert on him when the elevator

(i) starts moving upward with an acceleration of 1.5 m/sec²?

(ii) moves upward with a constant speed of 2.0 m/sec?

(iii) starts accelerating downward at 1.5 m/sec²?

(b) If the man were standing on a bathroom (spring) scale during his ride, what readings would the scale have under conditions (i), (ii), and (iii) above?

(c) It is sometimes said that the "apparent weight" changes when the elevator accelerates. What could this mean? Does the weight really change?

3.34 Useful hints for solving problems about the motion of an object and the forces acting on it:

(a) make a light sketch of the physical situation.

(b) in heavy line. indicate the limits of the particular object you are interested in, and draw all the forces acting on that object. (For each force acting on it, it will be exerting an opposite force on something else—but we don't care about those.)

(c) find the vector sum of all these forces, for example, by graphical construction.

(d) using Newton's second law, set this sum, $\vec{F}_{net}$, equal to $m\vec{a}$.

(e) solve the equation for the unknown quantity.

(f) put in the numerical values you know and calculate the answer.

Example:

A ketchup bottle whose mass is 1.0 kg rests on a table. If the friction force between the table and the bottle is a constant 3 newtons, what horizontal pull is required to accelerate the bottle from rest to a speed of 6 m/sec in 2 sec?

First, sketch the situation:

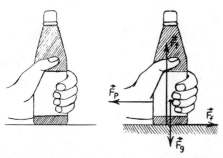

Second, draw in arrows to represent all the forces acting on the object of interest. There will be the horizontal pull $\vec{F}_p$, the friction $\vec{F}_f$, the gravitational pull $\vec{F}_g$ (the bottle's weight), and the upward force $\vec{F}_t$ exerted by the table. (There is, of course, also a force acting down on the table, but we don't care about that—we're interested only in the forces acting *on the bottle*.) Next, draw the arrows alone. In this sketch all the forces can be considered to be acting on the center of mass of the object.

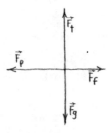

Because the bottle is not accelerating up or down, we know there is no net force up or down— so $\vec{F}_t$ must just balance $\vec{F}_g$. So the net force acting on the bottle is just the vector sum of $\vec{F}_p$ and $\vec{F}_f$. Using the usual tip-to-tail addition:

As the last arrow diagram shows, the horizontal pull must be greater than the force required for acceleration by an amount equal to the friction. We already know $\vec{F}_f$. We can find $\vec{F}_{net}$ from Newton's second law if we know the mass and acceleration of the bottle, since $\vec{F}_{net} = m\vec{a}$. The net force required to accelerate the case is found from Newton's second law:

$$\vec{F}_{net} = m\vec{a}$$

The mass m is given as 1.0 kg. The acceleration involved in going from rest to 6.0 m/sec in 2 seconds is

$$a = \frac{\Delta v}{\Delta t} = \frac{6.0 \text{ m/sec}}{2 \text{ sec}} = 3.0 \text{ m/sec/sec}$$

So the net force required is

$$F_{net} = 1.0 \text{ kg} \times 3.0 \text{ m/sec/sec}$$
$$= 3.0 \text{ kg m/sec/sec}$$
$$= 3.0 \text{ newtons}$$

If we consider toward the right to be the positive direction, F_{net} is 3.0 newtons and F_f, which is directed to the left, is −3.0 newtons.

$$\vec{F}_{net} = \vec{F}_p + \vec{F}_f$$
$$3.0\text{N} = \vec{F}_p + (-3.0\text{N})$$
$$\vec{F}_p = 3.0\text{N} + 3.0\text{N}$$
$$\vec{F}_p = 6.0\text{N}$$

If you prefer not to use + and − signs, you can work directly from your final diagram and use only the magnitudes of the forces:

from which the magnitude of F_p is obviously 6.0N.

3.35 Using the same convention as in 3.34, as is universally done, we can assign positive values to any vector quantity in a chosen direction (say, to the right, or upward), and negative values to the vector quantities of the same kind pointing in the opposite direction (say, to the left, or downward). For example, in Leslie's 50-yd swim in Chapter 1, her velocity can be assigned positive values while she swam to the right in the first 25 yards, and negative values while she swam to the left in the next 25 yards. Therefore, a graph of her velocity against time will have the curve above the horizontal axis for the first part, and below the axis (negative values) for the second part.

Use the solution to Problem 1.15 in which you found the instantaneous *speed* at several points, and plot the values of the instantaneous *velocity* during this swim.

3.36 The graph on page 20 of Chapter 1 showed Leslie's *distance* as a function of time. Now, however, make a graph of her instantaneous *displacement*—a vector quantity which gives the distance between the object and its starting point, measured along a straight line from the starting point to the object. (Note therefore that her displacement at the end of the swim is zero!)

3.37 Just before reaching the end of her first lap, Leslie was swimming at a velocity $\vec{v}_1$ of 0.8 yd/sec to the right. Two seconds later she had turned around and was swimming with a velocity $\vec{v}_2$ of 1.0 yd/sec to the left. From Section 3.5 we recall that the average acceleration, considered as a vector, is given by $\vec{a}_{av} = \Delta \vec{v}/\Delta t$. Here, $\Delta \vec{v}$ is the change of velocity, which may be symbolized by $(\vec{v}_2 - \vec{v}_1)$. Using the convention that positive values can be given to motion to the right, and negative values to motion to the left, find the $\vec{a}_{av}$ during the two-second interval. Represent the result also by means of an arrow (with its scale).

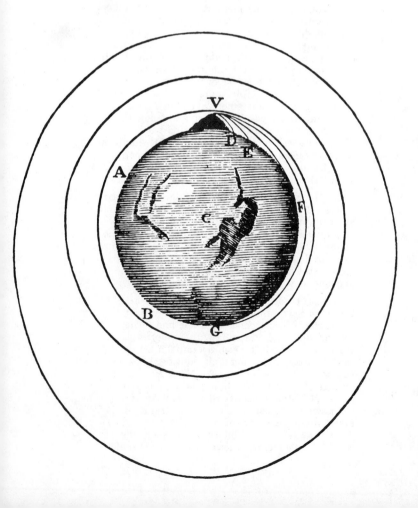

". . . the greater the velocity . . . with which [a stone] is projected, the farther it goes before it falls to the earth. We may therefore suppose the velocity to be so increased, that it would describe an arc of 1, 2, 5, 10, 100, 1000 miles before it arrived at the earth, till at last, exceeding the limits of the earth, it should pass into space without touching it."—Newton's *System of the World*

CHAPTER FOUR

Understanding Motion

In his science-fiction novels of more than a hundred years ago, the French author Jules Verne (1828-1905) launched three spacemen to the moon by means of a gigantic charge fixed in a steel pipe deep in the earth.

SG 4.1

4.1 A trip to the moon

Imagine a Saturn rocket taking off from its launching pad at Cape Kennedy. It climbs above the earth, passing through the atmosphere and beyond. Successive stages of the rocket shut off, finally leave a capsule hurtling through the near vacuum of space. Approximately 65 hours after takeoff, the capsule reaches its destination 240,000 miles away. It circles the moon and descends to its target—the center of the lunar crater Copernicus.

The complexity of such a voyage is enormous. To direct and guide the flight, a great number and variety of factors must be taken into account. The atmospheric drag in the early part of the flight depends upon the rocket's speed and altitude. The engine thrust changes with time. The gravitational pulls of the sun, the earth, and the moon change as the capsule changes its position relative to them. The rocket's mass changes as it burns fuel. Moreover, it is launched from a spinning earth, which in turn is circling the sun. Meanwhile, the target—the moon—is moving around the earth at a speed of about 2,300 miles per hour relative to the earth.

Yet, like almost any complex motion, the flight can be broken down into small portions, each of which is relatively simple. What we have learned in earlier chapters will be useful in this task.

In simplified form, the earth-moon trip can be divided into eight parts or steps:

Step 1. The rocket accelerates vertically upward from the surface of the earth. The force acting on the rocket is not really constant, and the mass of the rocket decreases as the fuel burns. The value of the acceleration at any instant can be computed by using Newton's second law. The value is given by the ratio of net force (thrust minus weight) at that instant to the mass at that instant.

Step 2. The rocket, still accelerating, follows a curved path as it is "injected" into an orbit about the earth.

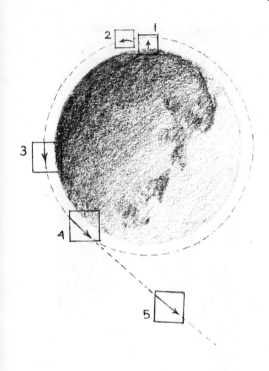

Step 3.   In an orbit 115 miles above the earth's surface, the capsule moves in a nearly circular arc. Its speed is constant at 17,380 mi/hr.

Step 4.   The rocket engines are fired again, increasing the capsule's speed so that it follows a much less curved path into space. (The minimum speed necessary to escape the earth completely is 24,670 mi/hr.)

Step 5.   In the flight between the earth and moon, occasional short bursts from the capsule's rockets keep it precisely on course. Between these correction thrusts, the capsule moves under the influence of the gravitational forces of earth, moon, and sun. We know from Newton's first law that the capsule would move with constant velocity if it were not for these forces.

Step 6.   On nearing the moon, the rocket engines are fired again to give the capsule the correct velocity to "inject" into a circular orbit around the moon.

Step 7.   The capsule moves with a constant speed of about 1 m/sec in a nearly circular path 50 miles above the moon's surface.

Step 8.   The rockets are fired in the direction of motion to reduce the speed. The capsule then accelerates downward as it falls toward the surface of the moon. It follows an arcing path toward a landing in the crater Copernicus. (Just before impact, the rocket engines fire a final time to reduce speed of fall and prevent a hard landing.)

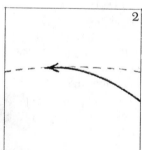
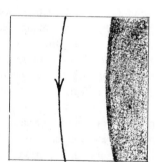
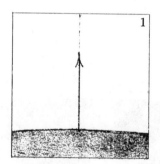
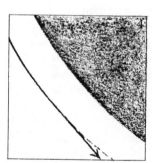

SG 4.2   Motion along a straight line (as in Steps 1 and 5) is easy enough to describe. But let us analyze in greater detail other parts of this trip. Motion in a circular arc, as in Steps 3 and 7, and projectile motion, as in Step 8, are two important cases.

How can we go about making this analysis? Following the example of Galileo and Newton, we can learn about motions beyond our reach, even on the moon or in the farthest parts of the universe, by studying motions near at hand. If physics is the same everywhere, the path of a lunar capsule moving as in Step 8 can be understood by studying a bullet fired from a horizontal rifle.

4.2 Projectile motion

Imagine an experiment in which a rifle is mounted on a tower with its barrel parallel to the ground. The ground over which the bullet will travel is level for a great distance. At the instant a bullet leaves the rifle, an identical bullet is dropped from the height of the rifle's barrel. This second bullet has no horizontal motion relative to the ground; it goes only straight down. Which bullet will reach the ground first?

We do not need to know anything about the speed of the bullet or the height of the tower in order to answer this question. Consider first the motion of the second bullet, the one that is dropped. As a freely falling object, it accelerates toward the ground with constant acceleration. As it falls, the elapsed time interval Δt and the corresponding downward displacement Δy are related by the equation

$$\Delta y = \tfrac{1}{2} a_g \Delta t^2$$

where a_g is the acceleration due to gravity at that location. Following usual practice, let us now drop the Δ symbols but keep in mind that y and t stand for displacement and time interval respectively. So we can write the last equation as

$$y = \tfrac{1}{2} a_g t^2$$

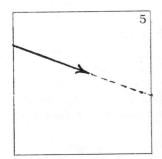

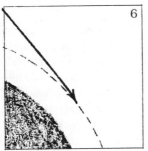

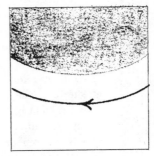

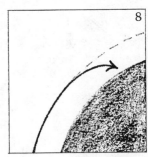

Now consider the bullet that is fired horizontally from the rifle. When the gun fires, the bullet is driven by the force of expanding gases. It accelerates very rapidly until it reaches the muzzle of the rifle. On reaching the muzzle the gases escape and no longer push the bullet. At that moment, however, the bullet has a large horizontal speed, v_x. The air slows the bullet slightly, but we will ignore that fact and imagine an ideal case with no air friction. As long as air friction is ignored, there is no horizontal force acting on the projectile. Therefore, the horizontal speed will remain constant. From the instant the bullet leaves the muzzle, its

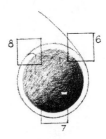

horizontal motion is described by the following equation involving the horizontal displacement Δx:

$$\Delta x = v_x \Delta t$$

or again dropping the Δ's,

$$x = v_x t$$

So much for the forward part of the motion of the bullet. There is, however, another part that becomes more and more important as t increases. From the moment the bullet leaves the gun, it falls toward the earth while it moves forward, like any other unsupported body. Can we use the same equation to describe its fall that we used to describe the fall of the dropped bullet? And how will falling affect the bullet's horizontal motion? These questions raise a more fundamental one which goes beyond just the behavior of the bullets in this experiment: namely, is the vertical motion of an object affected by its horizontal motion? Or vice versa?

To answer these questions, we can carry out a real experiment similar to our thought experiment. We can use a special laboratory device which fires a ball horizontally and at the same moment releases a second ball to fall freely. We set up our apparatus so that both balls are the same height above a level floor and release them at exactly the same time. Although the motion of the balls may be too rapid to follow with the eye, our ears will tell us that they do in fact reach the floor at the same time. This result suggests that the vertical motion of the projected ball is unaffected by its horizontal motion.

In the margin is a stroboscopic photograph of this experiment. Equally spaced horizontal lines aid our examination of the two motions. Look first at the ball on the left, the one which was released without any horizontal motion. We can see that it accelerates because it moves a greater distance between successive flashes of the strobe's light. Careful measurement of the photograph shows that the acceleration is constant, within the uncertainty of our measurements.

Now, compare the vertical positions of the second ball, fired horizontally, with the vertical positions of the ball which is falling freely. The horizontal lines show that the distances of fall are the same for corresponding time intervals. The two balls obey the same law for motion in a vertical direction. That is, at every instant they both have the same constant acceleration a_g, the same downward velocity, and the same vertical displacement. The experiment therefore supports the idea that the vertical motion is the same whether or not the ball has a horizontal motion also. The horizontal motion does not affect the vertical motion.

We can also use the strobe photo to see if the vertical motion of the projectile affects its horizontal velocity. We do this by measuring the *horizontal* distance between images. We find that the horizontal distances are practically equal. Since the time intervals between images are equal,

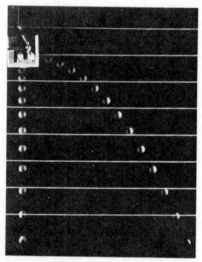

The two balls in this stroboscopic photograph were released simultaneously. The one on the left was simply· dropped from rest position; the one on the right was given an initial velocity in the horizontal direction.

we can conclude that the horizontal velocity v_x is constant. So we can conclude that the vertical motion does not affect the horizontal motion.

The experiment shows that the vertical and horizontal parts, or *components*, of the motion are independent of each other. This experiment can be repeated from different heights and with different horizontal velocities, but the results lead to the same conclusion.

SG 4.3

The independence of horizontal and vertical motions has important consequences. For example, it allows us to predict the displacement and the velocity of a projectile at any time during its flight. We need merely to consider the horizontal and vertical aspects of the motion *separately,* and then add the results by the vector method. We can predict the magnitude of the components of displacement x and $y,$ and the components of velocity v_x and v_y at any instant by applying the appropriate equations. For the horizontal component of motion, the equations are

SG 4.4

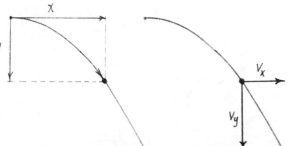

$$v_x = constant$$

and

$$x = v_x t$$

and for the vertical component of motion,

$$v_y = a_g t$$

$$y = \tfrac{1}{2} a_g t^2$$

Q1 If a body falls from rest with acceleration a_g, with what acceleration will it fall if it has an initial horizontal speed v_x?

4.3 What is the path of a projectile?

It is easy to see that a thrown object, such as a rock, follows a curved path. But it is not so easy to see just what kind of curve it traces. Arcs of circles, ellipses, parabolas, hyperbolas, and cycloids (to name only a few geometric figures) all provide likely-looking curved paths.

The early scientists gained better knowledge about the path of a projectile when they applied mathematics to the problem. This was done by deriving the equation that expresses the shape of the path. Only a few steps are involved. First let us list equations we already know for a projectile launched horizontally:

$$x = v_x t$$

and

$$y = \tfrac{1}{2} a_g t^2$$

We could plot the shape of the path or *trajectory* as it is often called in physics, if we had an equation that gave the value of y for each value of x. We could find the fall distance y for any horizontal distance x by combining these two equations in a way that eliminates the time variable. Solving the equation $x = v_x t$ for t we get

$$t = \frac{x}{v_x}$$

Because t means the same in both equations, we can substitute x/v_x for t in the equation for y:

$$y = \tfrac{1}{2} a_g t^2$$

and thus,

$$y = \tfrac{1}{2} a_g \left(\frac{x}{v_x} \right)^2$$

This last equation is a specialized equation of the kind that need not be memorized. It contains two variables of interest, x and y. It also contains three constant quantities: the number $\tfrac{1}{2}$, the uniform acceleration of free fall a_g, and the horizontal speed v_x which we take to be constant for any one flight, from launching to the end. Bringing these constants together between one set of parentheses, we can write the equation as

$$y = \left(\frac{a_g}{2 v_x^2} \right) x^2$$

Letting k stand for the constant $(a_g/2v^2 x)$:

$$y = k x^2$$

This equation shows a fairly simple relationship between x and y for the trajectory. We can translate it as follows: the distance a projectile falls away from a straight path is proportional to the square of the distance it moves sideways. For example, when the projectile goes twice as far horizontally from the launching point, it drops vertically four times as far.

The mathematical curve represented by this relationship between x and y is called a *parabola*. Galileo deduced the parabolic shape of trajectories by an argument similar to the one we used. (Even projectiles not launched horizontally—as in the photographs on pages 103 and 123—have parabolic trajectories.) This discovery greatly simplified the study of projectile motion, because the geometry of the parabola had been established centuries earlier by Greek mathematicians.

Here we find a clue to one of the important strategies in modern science. Whenever possible, we express the features of a phenomenon quantitatively and put the relations between them into equation form. Then we can use the rules of mathematics to shift and substitute terms, opening the way to unexpected insights.

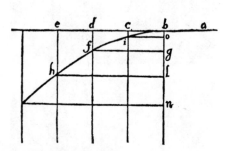

Drawing of a parabolic trajectory from Galileo's *Two New Sciences*.

SG 4.5-4.7

Galileo insisted that *"the proper language of nature is mathematics."* That is, we can better understand natural phenomena by translating our qualitative experiences into quantitative terms. For example, we have found that trajectories have a parabolic shape. So now we can apply all we know about the mathematics of parabolas to describe—and predict—trajectories. Physicists often draw on previously developed parts of pure mathematics to express or extend their knowledge of natural phenomena. Sometimes, as in the case of Newton's inventing calculus, they have to develop new areas of mathematics. The physical scientist often uses methods from another branch of science, in addition to mathematics, to solve a particular problem. For example, Galileo used the already known mathematics of parabolas to deal with actual projectile motions. In the same way, the modern sound engineer solves problems in acoustics with the aid of ideas and mathematical techniques developed by electrical engineers. Ideas and concepts can often be extended from one specialty to another, with fruitful results.

We can now apply our theory of projectile motion to the free motion of the space capsule toward the moon's surface. Let us assume that the lunar orbit is a low one, so that the acceleration due to gravity between the orbit and the surface is almost constant. If the rocket engines are fired forward, in the direction of motion, the capsule's speed will decrease and it will begin to fall closer to the surface. After firing, the reduced horizontal speed remains constant, so the capsule falls toward the surface on a parabolic path. Spaceflight engineers apply ideas like these to land a space capsule on a desired moon target. (See SG 4.23.)

"Philosophy is written in this grand book, the universe, which stands continually open to our gaze. But the book cannot be understood unless one first learns to comprehend the language and read the letters in which it is composed. It is written in the language of mathematics, and its characters are triangles, circles, and other geometric figures, without which it is humanly impossible to understand a single word of it." (Galileo, cited in *Discoveries and Opinions of Galileo, translated by Stillman Drake,* Anchor Books, pp. 237-238.)

Q2 Which of the conditions below must hold in order for the relationship $y = kx^2$ to describe the path of a projectile?
(a) a_g is a constant   (b) a_g depends on t (c) a_g is straight down
(d) v_x depends on t (e) air friction is negligible

4.4 Moving frames of reference—Galilean relativity

Galileo's work on projectiles leads to thinking about reference frames. As you will see in Unit 2, Galileo strongly supported the idea that the proper reference frame for discussing motions in our planetary system is one fixed to the sun, not the earth. From that point of view, the earth both revolves around the sun and rotates on its own axis. For many scientists of Galileo's time, this idea was impossible to accept, and they thought they could prove their case. If the earth rotated, they said, a stone dropped from a tower would not land directly at the tower's base. For if the earth rotates once a day, the tower would move onward hundreds of feet for every second the stone is falling. Hence the stone would be left behind while falling through the air and so would land far away from the base of the tower. But this is *not* what happens. As nearly as one can tell, the stone lands directly below the point of release. Therefore, many of

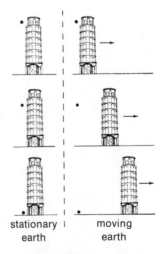

stationary   moving
earth   earth

The critics of Galileo claimed that if the earth moved, a dropped stone would be left behind and land beyond the foot of the tower.

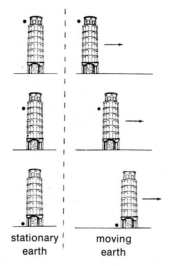

stationary | moving
earth | earth

Galileo argues that the falling stone continued to share the motion of the earth, so that an observer on earth could not tell whether or not the earth moved by watching the stone.

At high speeds, air drag will affect the results considerably. The situation is still indistinguishable from a car at rest—but in a high wind!

Galileo's critics believed that the tower and the earth could not possibly be in motion.

To answer these arguments, Galileo used the same example. But he used it to support his *own* view. During the time of fall, Galileo said, the tower and the ground supporting it move forward together with the same uniform velocity. While the stone is held at the top of the tower, it has the same horizontal velocity as the tower. Releasing the stone allows it to gain vertical speed. But by the principle of independence of v_x and v_y discussed in Section 4.2, this vertical component does not diminish any horizontal speed the stone had on being released. In other words, the falling stone behaves like any other projectile: the horizontal and vertical components of its motion are independent of each other. And since the stone and tower continue to have the same v_x throughout, the stone will not be left behind as it falls. Therefore, no matter what the speed of the earth, the stone will land at the foot of the tower. So the fact that falling stones are not left behind does *not* prove that the earth is standing still.

Similarly, Galileo said, an object released from a crow's nest at the top of a ship's mast lands at the foot of the mast, whether the ship is standing still or moving with constant velocity in calm water. This was actually tested by experiment in 1642 (and is also the subject of three Project Physics film loops). Many everyday observations support this view. For example, when you drop or throw a book in a bus or train or plane that is moving with constant velocity, you see the book move just as it would if the vehicle were standing still. Or again, if an object is projected vertically *upward* from inside an open car moving at constant velocity, it will fall back into the car. A person in the car sees the same thing happen whether the car is moving at constant velocity or standing still.

These and other observations lead to a valuable generalization: If Newton's laws hold in any one laboratory, then they will hold equally well in any other laboratory (or "reference frame") moving at constant velocity with respect to the first. This generalization is called the *Galilean relativity principle*. It holds true for all "classical" mechanical phenomena—that is, phenomena where the relative velocities are in the range from almost negligible up to millions of miles per hour.

Even if the laws of mechanics are the same for all reference frames moving with constant velocity with respect to each other, a problem still arises. Namely, there is no way to find the *speed* of one's *own* reference frame from any mechanical experiment done *within* that frame. Nor can one pick out any one reference frame as the "true" frame—the one that is, say, at absolute rest. Thus there can be no such thing as the "absolute" velocity of a body. All measured velocities are only *relative*.

What about observations of phenomena outside of one's own frame of reference? Certainly some outside phenomena appear differently to observers in different reference frames. For example, the observed velocity of an airplane will have a different value when measured from the earth and from a moving ship. But other quantities such as mass, acceleration, and time interval have the *same* values when measured from different reference frames moving with constant velocity with respect to one another. Moreover, certain *relationships* among such measurements will be the same for these different reference frames. Newton's laws of motion are examples of such "invariant" relationships, and so are all the laws of mechanics that follow from them.

Notice that the relativity principle, even in this restricted, classical form, does not say "everything is relative." On the contrary, it asks us to look for relationships that do *not* change when we transfer our attention from one frame to another.

When relative speeds become a noticeable fraction of the speed of light (almost a billion mph), some deviations from this simple relativity principle begin to appear. We will consider some of them in Unit 5.

Q3 If the laws of mechanics are found to be the same in two reference frames, what must be true of the motions of those frames?

SG 4.8-4.10

4.5 Circular motion

A projectile launched horizontally from a tall tower strikes the earth at a point determined by three factors. These factors are the speed of the projectile, the height of the tower, and the acceleration due to the force of gravity. As the projectile's launch speed is increased, it strikes the earth at points farther and farther from the tower's base. Eventually, then, we would have to consider a fourth factor: that the earth is not flat but curved. If the launch speed were increased even more, the projectile would strike the earth at points even farther from the tower, and at last would rush around the earth in a nearly circular orbit. (See the quotation from Newton, page 98.) At this orbiting speed, the fall of the projectile away from the forward, straight-line motion is matched by the curvature of the earth's surface. Therefore, the projectile stays at a constant distance above the surface.

What horizontal launch speed is required to put an object into a circular orbit about the earth or the moon? We will be able to answer this question quite easily after we have learned about circular motion.

The simplest kind of circular motion is *uniform* circular motion, that is, motion in a circle at constant speed. If you are in a car that goes around a perfectly circular track so that at every instant the speedometer reading is forty miles per hour, you are in uniform circular motion. But this is not the case if the track is of any shape other than circular, or if your speed changes at any point.

How can we find out if an object in circular motion is moving at constant speed? We can apply the same test we used in deciding whether or not an object traveling in a straight line does so with constant speed. That is, we measure the instantaneous speed at many different moments and see whether the values are the same. If the speed is constant, we can describe the circular motion of any object by means of two numbers: the

In discussing circular motion it is useful to keep clearly in mind a distinction between *revolution* and *rotation*. We define these terms differently: revolution is the act of traveling along a circular or elliptical path; rotation is the act of spinning rather than traveling. A point on the rim of a phonograph turntable travels a long way; it is *revolving* about the axis of the turntable. But the turntable as a unit does not move from place to place: it merely *rotates*. In some situations both processes occur simultaneously; for example, the earth rotates about its own axis, while it also revolves (in a nearly circular path) around the sun.

radius R of the circle, and the speed v along the path. For regularly repeated circular motion, we can use a quantity more easily measured than speed. We can take either the time required by an object to make one complete revolution, or the number of revolutions the object completes in a unit of time. The time required for an object to complete one revolution in a circular path is called the *period* of the motion. The period is usually denoted by the capital letter T. The number of revolutions completed by the same object in a unit time interval is called the *frequency* of the motion. Frequency will be denoted by the letter *f*.

As an example, we will use these terms to describe a car moving with uniform speed on a circular track. Let us suppose the car takes 20 seconds to make one lap around the track. Thus, $T = 20$ seconds. On the other hand, the car makes three laps in one minute. Thus, $f = 3$ revolutions per minute, or $f = 1/20$ revolution per second. The relationship between frequency and period (*when the same time unit is used*) is $f = 1/T$. If the period of the car is 20 sec/rev, then the frequency is given by

$$f = \frac{1}{20 \dfrac{\text{sec}}{\text{rev}}} = \frac{1}{20} \frac{\text{rev}}{\text{sec}}$$

All units are a matter of convenience. Radius may be expressed in terms of centimeters, kilometers, miles, or any other distance unit. Period may be expressed in seconds, minutes, years, or any other time unit. Frequency may be expressed as "per second," "per minute," "per year," and so on. The most widely used units of radius, period, and frequency in scientific work are, respectively, meter, second, and per second.

Table 4.1 Comparison of the frequency and period for various kinds of circular motion. Note the differences between units.

PHENOMENON	PERIOD T		FREQUENCY f
Electron in circular accelerator	10^{-6}	sec	10^6 per sec
Ultra-centrifuge	0.00033	sec	3000 per sec
Hoover Dam turbine	0.33	sec	3 per sec
Rotation of earth	24	hours	0.0007 per min
Moon around the earth	27	days	0.0015 per hour
Earth about the sun	365	days	0.0027 per day

If we know the frequency of revolution f and the radius R of the path, we can compute the speed v of any object in uniform circular motion without difficulty. The distance traveled in one revolution is simply the perimeter of the circular path, that is, $2\pi R$. The time for one revolution is by definition the period T. For uniform motion along any path, it is always true that

$$\text{speed} = \frac{\text{distance traveled}}{\text{time elapsed}}$$

Hence, by substitution we get

$$v = \frac{2\pi R}{T}$$

To express this equation for circular motion in terms of the frequency f,

Note: always use t for time, T for period, and in general stick to symbols as given.

1/20 revolution per second can be written 0.05 rev/sec, or more briefly, just 0.05 sec^{-1}. (In this last expression the symbol sec^{-1} stands for 1/sec, or "per second.")

SG 4.11

The term "revolutions" is not assigned any units because it is a pure number, a count. There is no need for a standard as there is for distance, mass, and time. So, the unit for frequency is usually given without "rev." This looks strange, but one gets used to it—and it is not very important, because it is merely a matter of terminology, not a fact of physics.

we rewrite it as

$$v = 2\pi R \times \frac{1}{T}$$

Now, since by definition

$$f = \frac{1}{T}$$

we can write

$$v = 2\pi R \times f$$

If the body is in *uniform* circular motion, the speed computed by this equation is both the instantaneous speed and the average speed. If the motion is not uniform, the formula gives only the *average* speed. But the *instantaneous* speed for any point on the circle can be determined if we find $\Delta d/\Delta t$ from measurements of very small portions of the path.

Let us now see how we best can use the last equation above. We can, for example, calculate the speed of the tip of a helicopter rotor blade in its motion around the central shaft. On one model, the main rotor has a diameter of 7.50 m and a frequency of 480 revolutions /minute under standard conditions. Thus $R = 3.75$ m, and so

$$v = 2\pi R f$$
$$v = 2 \ (3.14) \ (3.75) \ (8.00) \ \text{m/sec}$$
$$v = 189 \ \text{m/sec}$$

or about 420 mi/hr.

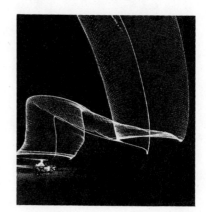

SG 4.12 a to f

Q4 If a phonograph turntable is running at 33.3 revolutions per minute,

    (a) What is its period (in minutes)?

    (b) What is its period (in seconds)?

    (c) What is its frequency in cycles per second?

Q5 What is the period of the minute hand of an ordinary clock? If the hand is 3.0 cm long, what is the speed of the tip of the minute hand?

Q6 The terms *frequency* and *period* can also be used for any other regularly, repetitive phenomenon. For example, if your heart beats 80 times per minute, what are the frequency and period for your pulse?

4.6 Centripetal acceleration and centripetal force

Let us assume that a stone on the end of a string is whirling about with uniform circular motion in a horizontal plane. The speed of the stone is constant. The velocity, however, is always changing. Velocity is a vector quantity which includes both speed and direction. Up to this point we have dealt with accelerations in which only the speed was changing. In uniform circular motion the speed of the revolving object remains the same, while the direction of motion changes continually. The top figure in

the margin shows the whirling stone at three successive moments in its revolution. At any instant, the direction of the velocity vector is tangent to the curving path. Notice that the stone's *speed,* represented by the *length* of the velocity arrow, does not change. But its *direction* does change from moment to moment. Since acceleration is defined as a change in velocity per unit time, the stone is then in fact accelerating.

But to produce an acceleration, a net force is needed. In the case of the whirling stone, a force is exerted on the stone by the string. If we ignore the weight of the stone and air resistance, this force is the net force. If the string were suddenly cut, the stone would go flying off with the velocity it had at the instant that the string was cut. Its path would start off on a tangent to the circular path. But as long as the string holds, the stone is forced to move in the circular path.

The direction of this force which is holding the stone in its circular path is along the string. Thus the force vector always points toward the center of rotation. This kind of force—always directed toward the center of rotation—is called *centripetal* force.

From Newton's second law we know that net force and corresponding acceleration are in the same direction. Therefore, the acceleration vector is also directed toward the center. We shall call this acceleration *centripetal* acceleration, and give it the symbol $\vec{a}_c$. Any object moving along a circular path has a centripetal acceleration.

$\vec{a}_c$ and $\vec{F}_c$ are parallel, but $\vec{v}$ is perpendicular to $\vec{a}_c$ and $\vec{F}_c$. Note that usually one should *not* draw different kinds of vector quantities on the same drawing.

The adjective centripetal means literally "moving, or directed, toward the center."

In uniform circular motion, the instantaneous velocity and the centripetal force at any instant of time are perpendicular, one being along the tangent, the other along the radius. So instantaneous velocity and the acceleration are also always at right angles.

We know now the direction of centripetal acceleration. What is its magnitude? We can derive an expression for a_c from the definition of acceleration $\vec{a}_c = \Delta v/\Delta t$. The details for such a derivation are given on the next page. The result shows that $\vec{a}_c$ depends on $\vec{v}$ and R. In fact, the magnitude of a_c is given by

$$a_c = \frac{v^2}{R}$$

Derivation of the equation $a_c = \dfrac{v^2}{R}$

Assume that a stone on the end of a string is moving uniformly in a circle of radius R. We can find the relationship between a_c, v, and R by treating a small part of the circular path as a combination of tangential motion and acceleration toward the center. To follow the circular path, the stone must accelerate toward the center through a distance h in the *same time* that it would move through a tangential distance d. The stone, with speed v, would travel a tangential distance d given by $d = v\Delta t$. In the same time Δt, the stone, with acceleration a_c, would travel toward the center through a distance h given by $h = \tfrac{1}{2}a_c\Delta t^2$. (We can use this last equation because at $t = 0$, the stone's velocity toward the center is zero.)

We can now apply the Pythagorean Theorem to the triangle in the figure below.

$$R^2 + d^2 = (R + h)^2$$
$$= R^2 + 2Rh + h^2$$

When we subtract R^2 from each side of the equation we are left with

$$d^2 = 2Rh + h^2$$

We can simplify this expression by making an approximation: since h is very small compared to R, h^2 will be very small compared to Rh. And since we must choose Δt to be vanishingly small to get the instantaneous acceleration, h^2 will become vanishingly small compared to Rh. So we neglect h^2 and write

$$d^2 = 2Rh$$

Also, we know $d = v\Delta t$ and $h = \tfrac{1}{2}a_c\Delta t^2$, so we can substitute for d^2 and for h accordingly. Thus

$$(v\Delta t)^2 = 2R \cdot \tfrac{1}{2}a_c(\Delta t)^2$$
$$v^2(\Delta t)^2 = Ra_c(\Delta t)^2$$
$$v^2 = Ra_c$$

or

or
$$a_c = \frac{v^2}{R}$$

The approximation becomes better and better as Δt becomes smaller and smaller. In other words, v^2/R gives the magnitude of the *instantaneous* centripetal acceleration for a body moving on a circular arc of radius R. For uniform circular motion, v^2/R gives the magnitude of the centripetal acceleration at every point of the path. (Of course it does not have to be a stone on a string. It can be a small particle on the rim of a rotating wheel, or a house on the rotating earth, or a coin sitting on a rotating phonograph disk, or a car in a curve on the road, or an electron in its path through a magnetic field.)

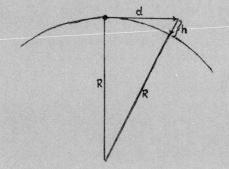

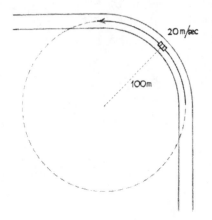

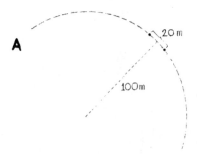

This is about 4/10 of a_g, and could be called an acceleration of "0.4g."

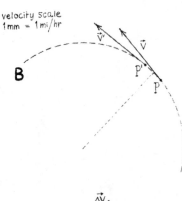

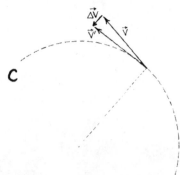

Let us verify this relationship with a numerical example. As sketched in the diagram in the margin, a car goes around a circular curve of radius $R = 100$ m at a uniform speed of $v = 20$ m/sec. What is the car's centripetal acceleration a_c toward the center of curvature? By the equation derived on the next page:

$$a_c = \frac{v^2}{R}$$

$$= \frac{\left(20\,\frac{m}{sec}\right)^2}{100\,m}$$

$$= \frac{400\,\frac{m^2}{sec^2}}{100\,m}$$

$$= 4.0\,\frac{m}{sec^2}$$

Does this make sense? We can check the result by going back to the basic vector definition of acceleration: $\vec{a}_{av} = \Delta\vec{v}/\Delta t$. We will need a scale drawing of the car's velocity vector at two instants a short time Δt apart. Then we can measure the change in velocity $\Delta\vec{v}$ between these points, and divide the magnitude of $\Delta\vec{v}$ by Δt to get $\vec{a}_{av}$ over the interval.

Consider a time interval of $\Delta t = 1$ second. Since the car is moving at 20 m/sec, its position will change 20 m during Δt. Two positions **P** and **P′**, separated by 20 m, are marked in Diagram A.

Now, draw arrows representing velocity vectors. If we choose a scale of 1 cm = 10 m/sec, the velocity vector for the car will be represented by an arrow 2 cm long. These are drawn at **P** and **P′** in Diagram B.

Now, put these two arrows together tail to tail as in Diagram C. It is easy to see what the change in the velocity vector has been during Δt. Notice that if $\Delta\vec{v}$ were drawn halfway between **P** and **P′**, it would point directly toward the center of the curve. So the average acceleration between **P** and **P′** is indeed directed centripetally. The $\Delta\vec{v}$ arrow in the diagram is 0.40 cm long, so it represents a velocity change of 4.0 m/sec. This change occurred during $\Delta t = 1$ second, so the rate of change is 4.0 m/sec/sec. This is the same value we found by using $a_c = v^2/R$!

The relation $a_c = v^2/R$ agrees completely with the mechanics we have developed in Unit 1. We can show this by doing some experiments to measure the centripetal force required to keep an object moving in a circle. Let us return to our example of the car. If its mass were 1,000 kg, we could find the centripetal force acting on it as follows:

$$F_c = m \times a_c$$

$$= 1\,000\,kg \times 4.0\,\frac{m}{sec^2}$$

$$= 4\,000\,kg\,\frac{m}{sec^2} = 4\,000\,N \text{ (or about 1,800 pounds)}$$

This force would be directed toward the center of curvature of the road. That is, it would always be sideways to the direction the car is moving. This force is exerted on the tires by the road. If the road is wet or icy, and cannot exert the force of 4,000 N sideways on the tires, the centripetal acceleration will be less than 4.0 m/sec. Then the car will follow a less curved path as sketched in Diagram D. In situations where the car's path is less curved than the road, we would say the car "left the road." Of course, it might be just as appropriate to say the road left the car.

The sideways force exerted on tires by a road is not easy to measure. But the *Project Physics Handbook* suggests several ways for you to check experimentally whether the relations $F_c = ma_c$ or $F_c = mv^2/R$ are in fact useful.

For uniform motion in repeated cycles, it often is easier to measure the frequency f or period T than to measure v directly. (See the marginal note at the right.)

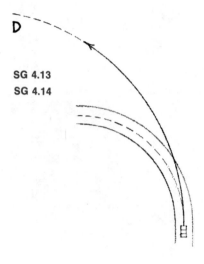

D

SG 4.13
SG 4.14

Q7 In which of the following cases can a body have an acceleration?
(a)   moves with constant speed
(b)   moves in a circle with constant radius
(c)   moves with constant velocity

Q8 In what direction would a piece from a rapidly spinning fly-wheel go if it suddenly shattered?

Q9 A car of mass m going at speed v enters a curve of radius R. What is the force required to keep the car curving with the road?

Q10 A rock of mass m is being whirled overhead at 1 revolution/second on a string of length R. What is the force which the string must be exerting?

We can substitute the relation $v = 2\pi Rf$ or $v = 2\pi R/T$ (derived in Chapter 3 for uniform circular motion) into the equation for a_c:

SG 4.12 g, h
SG 4.15-4.18

$$a_c = \frac{v^2}{R} \qquad\qquad a_c = \frac{v^2}{R}$$

$$= \frac{(2\pi Rf)^2}{R} \qquad = \frac{\left(\dfrac{2\pi R}{T}\right)^2}{R}$$

$$= \frac{4\pi^2 R^2 f^2}{R} \qquad = \frac{\dfrac{4\pi^2 R^2}{T^2}}{R}$$

$$= 4\pi^2 Rf^2 \qquad\quad = \frac{4\pi^2 R}{T^2}$$

These two resulting expressions for a_c are entirely equivalent.

4.7   The motion of earth satellites

Nature and technology provide many examples of objects in uniform circular motion. The wheel has been a main characteristic of our civilization, first appearing on crude carts and later forming essential parts of complex machines. The historical importance of rotary motion in the development of modern technology has been described by the historian V. Gordon Childe in *The History of Technology*:

> Rotating machines for performing repetitive operations, driven by water, by thermal power, or by electrical energy, were the most decisive factors of the industrial revolution, and, from the first steamship till the invention of the jet plane, it is the application of rotary motion to transport that has revolutionized communications. The use of rotary machines, as of any other human tools, has been cumulative and progressive. The inventors of the eighteenth and nineteenth centuries were merely extending the applications of rotary motion that had been devised in previous generations, reaching back thousands of years into the prehistoric past. . . .

As you will see in Unit 2, there is another rotational motion that has concerned man throughout recorded history. This motion is the orbiting of planets around the sun, and of the moon around the earth.

SG 4.19

The kinematics and dynamics for *any* uniform circular motion are the same. Therefore, you can apply what you have learned so far to the motion of artificial earth satellites in circular (or nearly circular) paths. A typical illustration is Alouette I, Canada's first satellite, which was launched into a nearly circular orbit in 1962.

Tracking stations located in many places around the world maintain a record of any satellite's position in the sky. From the position data, the satellite's period of revolution and its distance above the earth at any time are found. By means of such tracking, we know that Alouette I moves at an average height of 630 miles above sea level. It takes 105.4 minutes to complete one revolution.

We can now quickly calculate the orbital speed and the centripetal acceleration of Alouette I. The relation $v = 2\pi R/T$ gives us the speed of any object moving uniformly in a circle if we know its period T and its distance R from the center of its path. In this case, the center of the path is the center of the earth. So, adding 630 miles to the earth's radius of 3,963 miles, we get $R = 4,594$ miles. Thus,

$$
\begin{aligned}
v &= \frac{2\pi R}{T} \\
&= \frac{2\pi \times 4593 \text{ mi}}{105.4 \text{ min}} \\
&= \frac{28,860 \text{ mi}}{105.4 \text{ min}} \\
&= 274 \text{ mi/min}
\end{aligned}
$$

The same equation ($v + 2\pi R/T$) can be used to find the speed of any satellite in nearly or fully circular orbit, for example, that of our moon. The average distance from the center of the moon is approximately 2.39×10^5 mi, and the moon takes an average of 27 days, 7 hr, 43 min to complete one revolution around the earth with respect to the fixed stars. Thus

$$
v = \frac{2\pi(239 \times 10^5) \text{ mi}}{3.93 \times 10^4 \text{ min}}
$$

$$
= 38.2 \text{ min/min}
$$

or about 2,290 mi/hr.

or roughly 16,400 mi/hr.

To calculate the centripetal acceleration of Alouette I, we can use this value of v along with the relationship $a_c = v^2/R$. Thus

$$
\begin{aligned}
a_c &= \frac{v^2}{R} \\
&= \frac{(274 \text{ mi/min})^2}{4,594 \text{ mi}} \\
&= 16.3 \text{ mi/min}^2
\end{aligned}
$$

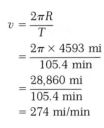

which is about 7.3 m/sec². (We could just as well have used the values of R and T directly in the relationship $a_c = 4\pi^2 R/T^2$.)

SG 4.20
SG 4.21

What is the origin of the force that gives rise to this acceleration? We will not make a good case for our answer until Chapter 8, but you surely know already that it is due to the earth's attraction. Evidently the centripetal acceleration a_c of the satellite is just the gravitational acceleration a_g at that height. (Note that a_g at this height has a value about 25% less than a_g very near the earth's surface.)

Earlier we asked the question, "What speed is required for an object to stay in a circular orbit about the earth?" You can answer this question now for an orbit 630 miles above the earth's surface. To get a general answer, you need to know how the acceleration due to gravity changes with distance. In Chapter 8 we will come back to the problem of injection speeds for orbits.

The same kind of analysis applies to an orbit around the moon. For example, consider the first manned orbit of the moon (Apollo 8, in 1968). The mission control group wanted to put the capsule into a circular orbit 70 miles above the lunar surface. They believed that the acceleration due to the moon's gravity at that height would be $a_g = 1.43$ m/sec². What direction and speed would they have to give the capsule to inject it into lunar orbit?

The direction problem is fairly easy. To stay at a constant height above the surface, the capsule would have to be moving horizontally at the instant the orbit correction was completed. So injection would have to occur just when the capsule was moving on a tangent, 70 miles up, as shown in the sketch in the margin. What speed (relative to the moon, of course) would the capsule have to be given? The circular orbit has a radius 70 miles greater than the radius of the moon, which is 1,080 miles. So $R = 1,080$ mi $+ 70$ mi $= 1,150$ mi or 1.85×10^6 meters. The centripetal acceleration is just the acceleration caused by gravity, which was thought to be 1.43 m/sec², so

Chariot. Alberto Giacometti, 1950.

$$a_c = a_g$$
$$\frac{v^2}{R} = a_g$$
$$v^2 = R a_g$$
$$v = \sqrt{R a_g}$$
$$= \sqrt{(1.85 \times 10^6 \text{m}) \times 1.43 \, \frac{\text{m}}{\text{sec}^2}}$$
$$= \sqrt{2.65 \text{ m} \times 10^6 \, \frac{\text{m}}{\text{sec}^2}}$$
$$= 1.63 \times 10^3 \, \frac{\text{m}}{\text{sec}}$$

The necessary speed for an orbit at 70 miles above the surface is 1,630 m/sec (about 3,600 mi/hr). Knowing the capsule's speed, ground control could calculate the speed changes needed to reach 1,630 m/sec. Knowing the thrust force of the engines and the mass of the capsule, they could calculate the time of thrust required to make this speed change.

SG 4.22 - 4.24

Because the injection thrust is not applied instantaneously, the details are actually far more difficult to calculate.

Q11 What information was necessary to calculate the speed for an orbit 70 miles above the moon's surface?

Table 4.2 Some information on early selected artificial satellites.

NAME	LAUNCH DATE	WEIGHT (lb)	PERIOD (min)	HEIGHT (miles) Perigee-Apogee	REMARKS (including purpose)
Sputnik 1 1957 (USSR)	Oct. 4, 1957	184	96.2	142-588	First earth satellite. Internal temperature, pressure inside satellite.
Explorer 7 1958 (USA)	Jan. 31, 1958	30.8	114.8	224-1,573	Cosmic rays, micrometeorites, internal and shell temperatures, discovery of first Van Allen belts.
Lunik 3 1959 (USSR)	Oct. 4, 1959	959	22,300	30,000-291,000	Transmitted photographs of far side of moon.
Vostok 1 1961 (USSR)	Apr. 12, 1961	10,416	89.34	109-188	First manned orbital flight (Major Yuri Gagarin; one orbit)
Midas 3 1961 (USA)	July 12, 1961	3,500	161.5	2,129-2,153	Almost circular orbit.
Telestar 1 1962 (USA)	July 10, 1962	170	157.8	593-3,503	Successful transmission across the Atlantic: telephony, phototelegraphy, and television.
Alouette 1 1962 (USA-Canada)	Sept. 29, 1962	319	105.4	620-640	Joint project between NASA and Canadian Defense Research Board; measurement in ionosphere.
Luna 4 1963-08 (USSR)	Apr. 2, 1963	3,135	42,000	56,000-435,000	Passed 5,300 miles from moon; very large orbit.
Vostok 6 1963-23 (USSR)	June 16, 1963	"about 5 tons"	88.34	106-134	First orbital flight by a woman; (Valentina Terishkiva; 48 orbits)
Syncom 2 1963-31 (USA)	July 26, 1963	86	1,460.4	22,187-22,192	Successfully placed in near-synchronous orbit (stays above same spot on earth).

4.8 What about other motions? Retrospect and prospect

So far we have described straight-line motion, projectile motion, and uniform circular motion. But we have considered only examples where the acceleration was constant—in magnitude if not in direction—or very nearly constant. There is another basic kind of motion that is equally common and important in physics. In this kind of motion the acceleration is always changing. A common example is seen in playground swings, or in vibrating guitar strings. Such back and forth motion, or *oscillation,* about a center position occurs when there is a force always directed toward the center position. When a guitar string is pulled aside, for example, a force arises which tends to restore the string to its undisturbed center position. If it is pulled to the other side, a similar restoring force arises in the opposite direction.

In very common types of such motion, the restoring force is

proportional, or nearly proportional, to how far the object is displaced. This is true for the guitar string, if the displacements are not too large. Pulling the string aside 2 mm produces twice the restoring force that pulling it aside 1 mm does. Oscillation with a restoring force proportional to the displacement is called *simple harmonic motion*. The mathematics for describing simple harmonic motion is relatively simple, and many phenomena, from pendulum motion to the vibration of atoms, have aspects that are very close to simple harmonic motion. Consequently, the analysis of simple harmonic motion is used very widely in physics. The *Project Physics Handbook* describes a variety of activities you can do to become familiar with oscillations and their description.

The dynamics discussed in this chapter will cover most motions that interest us. It provides a good start toward understanding apparently very complicated motions such as water ripples on a pond, a person running, the swaying of a tall building or bridge in the wind, a small particle zig-zagging through still air, an amoeba seen under a microscope, or a high-speed nuclear particle moving in the field of a magnet. The methods we have developed in this Unit give us means for dealing with any kind of motion whatsoever, on earth or anywhere in the universe.

SG 4.25
SG 4.26

When we considered the forces needed to produce motion, Newton's laws supplied us with the answers. Later, we will discuss other motions ranging from motion of the planets to the motion of an alpha particle passing near a nucleus inside an atom. And we will continue to find in Newton's laws the tools for determining the magnitude and direction of the forces acting in each case.

If we know the magnitude and direction of the forces acting on an object, we can determine what its change in motion will be. If we also know the present position, velocity, and mass of an object, we can reconstruct how it moved in the past and predict how it will move in the future under these forces. Thus Newton's laws provide a nearly unlimited view of forces and motion. It is not surprising that Newtonian mechanics became a model for many other sciences: here seemed to be a method for understanding all motions, no matter how mysterious they appeared to be.

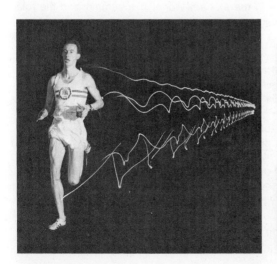

EPILOGUE   The purpose of this Unit was to deal with the fundamental concepts of motion. We decided to start by analyzing very simple kinds of motion. After learning the "ABC's" of physics, we expected to be able to turn our attention to some of the more complex features of the world. To what extent were our expectations fulfilled?

We did find that a relatively few basic concepts gave us a fairly solid understanding of motion. We found that we could describe many motions of objects by using the concepts of distance, displacement, time, speed, velocity, and acceleration. To these concepts we added force and mass and the relationships expressed in Newton's three laws of motion. With this knowledge, we found we could understand most observed motion in an effective way. The surprising thing is that these concepts of motion, which were developed in very restricted circumstances, can in fact be so widely applied. For example, our discussion of motion in the laboratory centered around the use of sliding dry-ice disks and steel balls rolling down inclined planes. These are not objects ordinarily found moving around in the everyday "natural" world. Yet we found that the ideas obtained from those specialized experiments led to an understanding of objects falling near the earth's surface, of projectiles, and of objects moving in circular paths. We started by analyzing the motion of a disk of dry ice moving across a smooth surface. We ended up analyzing the motion of a space capsule as it circles the moon and descends to its surface.

We have made quite a lot of progress in analyzing complex motions. On the other hand, we cannot be certain that we have here all the tools needed to understand all the phenomena that interest us. In Unit 3 we will add to our stock of fundamental concepts a few additional ones, particularly those of momentum, work, and energy. They will help us when we turn our attention from interactions involving a relatively few objects of easily measured size, to interactions involving countless numbers of submicroscopic objects—molecules and atoms.

In this Unit we have dealt mainly with concepts that owe their greatest debts to Galileo, Newton, and their followers. If space had permitted, we should also have included the contributions of René Descartes and the Dutch scientist Christian Huyghens. The mathematician and philosopher A. N. Whitehead, in *Science and the Modern World,* has summarized the role of these four men and the importance of the concepts we have been studying as follows:

> This subject of the formation of the three laws of motion and of the law of gravitation [which we shall take up in Unit 2] deserves critical attention. The whole development of thought occupied exactly two generations. It commenced with Galileo and ended with Newton's *Principia;* and Newton was born in the year that Galileo died. Also the lives of Descartes and Huyghens fall within the period occupied by these great terminal figures. The issue of the combined labours of these four men has some right to be considered as the greatest single intellectual success which mankind has achieved.

The laws of motion that Whitehead mentions were the subject of this Unit. They were important most of all because they suddenly allowed a new understanding of celestial motion. For at least twenty centuries man had been trying to reduce the complex motions of the stars, sun, moon, and planets to an orderly system. The genius of Galileo and Newton lay in their studying the nature of motion as it occurs on earth, and then assuming that the same laws would apply to objects in the heavens beyond man's reach.

Unit 2 is an account of the centuries of preparation that paved the way for the great success of this idea. We will trace the line of thought, starting with the formulation of the problem of planetary motion by the ancient Greeks. We will continue through the work of Copernicus, Tycho Brahe, Kepler, and Galileo to provide a planetary model and the laws of planetary motion. And finally we will discover Newton's magnificent synthesis of terrestrial and celestial physics through his Law of Universal Gravitation.

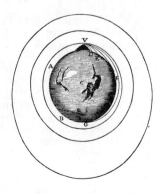

4.1 The Project Physics learning materials particularly appropriate for Chapter 4 include the following:

Experiments

  Curves of Trajectories
  Prediction of Trajectories
  Centripetal Force
  Centripetal Force on a Turntable

Activities

  Projectile Motion Demonstration
  Speed of a Stream of Water
  Photographing a Waterdrop Parabola
  Ballistic Cart Projectiles
  Motion in a Rotating Reference Frame
  Penny and Coat Hanger
  Measuring Unknown Frequencies

Reader Articles

  Galileo's Discussion of Projectile Motion
  Newton's Laws of Dynamics
  Rigid Body
  Fun in Space

Film Loops

  A Matter of Relative Motion
  Galilean Relativity—Ball Dropped from Mast of Ship
  Galilean Relativity—Object Dropped from Aircraft
  Galilean Relativity—Projectile Fired vertically
  Analysis of Hurdle Race I
  Analysis of Hurdle Race II

4.2 The thrust developed by a Saturn Apollo rocket is 7,370,000 newtons (approximately 1,650,000 lbs.) and its mass is 540,000 kg. What is the acceleration of the vehicle relative to the earth's surface at lift off? How long would it take for the vehicle to rise 50 meters?

  The acceleration of the vehicle increases greatly with time (it is 47 m/sec² at first stage burnout) even though the thrust force does not increase appreciably. Explain why the acceleration increases.

4.3 A hunter points his gun barrel directly at a monkey in a distant palm tree. Will the bullet follow the line of sight along the barrel? If the animal, startled by the flash, drops out of the branches at the very instant of firing, will it then be hit by the bullet? Explain.

4.4 The displacement $\vec{d}$ of an object is a vector giving the straightline distance from the beginning to the end of an actual path; $\vec{d}$ can be thought of as made up of a horizontal (x) and a vertical (y) component of displacement; that is, $\vec{d} = \vec{x} + \vec{y}$ (added vectorially).

  In a trajectory, x, y, and the total displacement d can be thought of as the magnitudes of the sides of right triangles. So can v_x, v_y and the magnitude of the velocity v.

  (a) Find an expression for d in terms of x and y.

(b) Find an expression for v in terms of v_x and v_y
(c) Rewrite the expression for d and v in terms of v_x, a_g, and t.

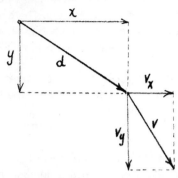

4.5 If you like algebra, try this general proof.

  If a body is launched with speed v at some angle other than 0°, it will initially have both a horizontal speed v_x and a vertical speed v_y. The equation for its horizontal displacement is $x = v_x t$, as before. But the equation for its vertical displacement has an additional term: $y = v_y t + \frac{1}{2}a_g t^2$. Show that the trajectory is still parabolic in shape.

4.6 A lunch pail is accidently kicked off a steel beam on a skyscraper under construction. Suppose the initial horizontal speed v_x is 1.0 m/sec. Where is the pail (displacement), and what is its speed and direction (velocity) 0.5 sec after launching?

4.7 In Galileo's drawing on page 104, the distances bc, cd, de, etc. are equal. What is the relationship among the distances bo, og, gl, and ln?

4.8 You are inside a van that is moving with a constant velocity. You drop a ball.

  (a) What would be the ball's path relative to the van?
  (b) Sketch its path relative to a person driving past the van at a high uniform speed.
  (c) Sketch its path relative to a person standing on the road.

  You are inside a moving van that is accelerating uniformly in a straight line. When the van is traveling at 10mph (and still accelerating) you drop a ball from near the roof of the van onto the floor.

  (d) What would be the ball's path relative to the van?
  (e) Sketch its path relative to a person driving past the van at a high uniform speed.
  (f) Sketch its path relative to a person standing on the road.

4.9 Two persons watch the same object move. One says it accelerates straight downward, but the other claims it falls along a curved path. Describe conditions under which each would be reporting correctly what he sees.

4.10 An airplane has a gun that fires bullets straight ahead at the speed of 600 mph when tested on the ground while the plane is stationary.

The plane takes off and flies due east at 600 mph. Which of the following describes what the pilot of the plane will see? In defending your answers, refer to the Galilean relativity principle:

(a) When fired directly ahead the bullets move eastward at a speed of 1200 mph.

(b) When fired in the opposite direction, the bullets dropped vertically downward.

(c) If fired vertically downward, the bullets move eastward at 600 mph. while they fall.

Specify the frames of reference from which (a), (b), and (c) are the correct observations.

4.11 Many commercial record turntables are designed to rotate at frequencies of 16⅔ rpm (called transcription speed), 33⅓ rpm (long playing), 45 rpm (pop singles), and 78 rpm (old fashioned). What is the period corresponding to each of these frequencies?

4.12 Two blinkies are resting on a rotating turntable and are photographed in a setup as shown in the figure below. The outer blinky has a frequency of 9.4 flashes/sec and is located 15.0 cm from the center. For the inner blinky, the values are 9.1 flashes/sec and 10.6 cm.

(a) What is the period of the turntable?

(b) What is the frequency of rotation of the turntable? Is this a standard phonograph speed?

(c) What is the speed of the turntable at the position of the outer blinky?

(d) What is the speed of the turntable at the position of the inner blinky?

(e) What is the speed of the turntable at the very center?

(f) What is the *angular speed* of each blinky—that is, the rate of rotation measured in degrees/sec? Are they equal?

(g) What is the centripetal acceleration experienced by the inner blinky?

(h) What is the centripetal acceleration experienced by the outer blinky?

(i) If the turntable went faster and faster, which would leave the turntable first, and why?

4.13 Passengers on the right side of the car in a left turn have the sensation of being "thrown against the door." Explain what actually happens to the passengers in terms of force and acceleration.

4.14 The tires of the turning car in the example on page 112 were being pushed sideways by the road with a total force of 1800 lb. Of course the tires would be pushing on the road with a total force of 1800 lb also. (a) What happens if the road is covered with loose sand or gravel? (b) How would softer (lower pressure) tires help? (c) How would banking the road (that is, tilting the surface toward the center of the curve) help? (Hint: consider the extreme case of banking in the bob-sled photo on p. 110.)

4.15 Using a full sheet of paper, make and complete a table like the one below.

NAME OF CONCEPT	SYMBOL	DEFINITION	EXAMPLE
		Length of a path between any two points, as measured along the path.	
			Straight line distance and direction from Detroit to Chicago.
	v		
Instantaneous speed			
			An airplane flying west at 400 mph at constant altitude.
		Time rate of change of velocity.	
	a_g		
Centripetal acceleration			
			The drive shaft of some automobiles turns 600 rpm in low gear.
		The time it takes to make one complete revolution.	

4.16   Our sun is located at a point in our galaxy about 30,000 light years (1 light year = 9.46×10^{12} km) from the galactic center. It is thought to be revolving around the center at a linear speed of approximately 250 km/sec.
   (a) What is the sun's centripetal acceleration with respect to the center of the galaxy?
   (b) The sun's mass can be taken to be 1.98×10^{30} kg; what centripetal force is required to keep the sun moving in a circular orbit about the galactic center?
   (c) Compare the centripetal force in (b) with that necessary to keep the earth in orbit about the sun. (The earth's mass is 5.98×10^{24} kg and its average distance from the sun is 1.495×10^8 km.)

4.17   The hammer thrower in the photograph below is exerting a large centripetal force to keep the hammer moving fast in a circle, and applies it to the hammer through a connecting wire. The mass of the 16-pound hammer is 7.27 kg. (a) Estimate the radius of the circle and the period, and calculate a rough value for the amount of force required just to keep it moving in a circle. (b) What other components are there to the total force he exerts on the hammer?

4.18   Contrast rectilinear motion, projectile motion, and uniform circular motion by
   (a) defining each.
   (b) giving examples.
   (c) describing the relation between velocity and acceleration in each case.

4.19   These questions are asked with reference to Table 4.2 on page 116.
   (a) Which satellite has the most nearly circular orbit?
   (b) Which satellite has the most eccentric orbit? How did you arrive at your answer?
   (c) Which has the longest period?
   (d) How does the position of Syncom 2 relative to a point on earth change over one day?

4.20   If the earth had no atmosphere, what would be the period of a satellite skimming just above the earth's surface? What would its speed be?

4.21   Explain why it is impossible to have an earth satellite orbit the earth in 80 minutes. Does this mean that it is impossible for any object to go around the earth in less than 80 minutes?

4.22   What was the period of the "70 mi" Apollo 8 lunar orbit?

4.23   Knowing a_g near the moon's surface, and the orbital speed in an orbit near the moon's surface, we can now work an example of Part 8 of the earth-moon trip described in Sec 4.1. The Apollo 8 capsule was orbiting about 100 kilometers above the surface. The value of a_g near the moon's surface is about 1.5 m/sec².

   If the capsule's rocket engines are fired in the direction of its motion, it will slow down. Consider the situation in which the rockets fire long enough to reduce the capsule's horizontal speed to 100 m/sec².
   (a) About how long will the fall to the moon's surface take?
   (b) About how far will it have moved horizontally during the fall?
   (c) About how far in advance of the landing target might the "braking" maneuver be performed?

4.24   Assume that a capsule is approaching the moon along the right trajectory, so that it will be moving tangent to the desired orbit. Given the speed v_o necessary for orbit and the current speed v, how long should the engine with thrust F fire to give the capsule of mass m the right speed?

4.25   The intention of the first four chapters has been to describe "simple" motions and to progress to the description of more "complex" motions. Put each of the following examples under the heading "simplest motion," "more complex," or "very complex." Be prepared to say why you place any one example as you did and state any assumptions you made.
   (a) helicopter shown on p. 109
   (b) "human cannon ball" in flight
   (c) car going from 40 mph to a complete stop
   (d) tree growing
   (e) child riding a Ferris wheel
   (f) rock dropped 3 mi.
   (g) person standing on a moving escalator
   (h) climber ascending Mt. Everest
   (i) person walking
   (j) leaf falling from a tree

4.26   Write a short essay on the physics involved in the motions shown in one of the four pictures on the opposite page, using the ideas on motion from Unit 1.

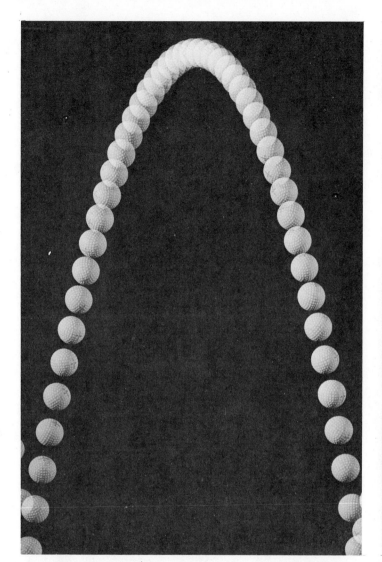

PROJECT PHYSICS

2

Motion in the Heavens

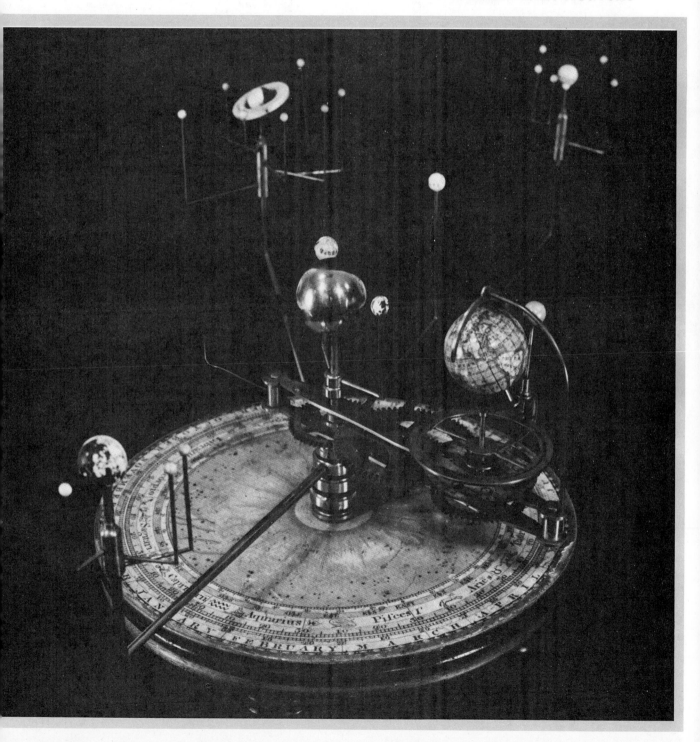

Experiments

2-1 Naked-Eye Astronomy
2-2 Size of the Earth
2-3 The Distance to the Moon
2-4 The Height of Piton, a Mountain on the Moon
2-5 Retrograde Motion
2-6 The Shape of the Earth's Orbit
2-7 Using Lenses to Make a Telescope
2-8 The Orbit of Mars
2-9 Inclination of Mars' Orbit
2-10 The Orbit of Mercury
2-11 Stepwise Approximation to an Orbit
2-12 Model of the Orbit of Halley's Comet

Activities

Making Angular Measurements
Epicycles and Retrograde Motion
Celestial Sphere Model
How Long is a Sidereal Day?
Scale Model of the Solar System
Build a Sundial
Plot an Analemma
Stonehenge
Moon Crater Names
Literature
Frames of Reference
Demonstrating Satellite Orbits
Galileo
Conic-Sections Models
Challenging Problem: Finding Earth-Sun Distance from Venus Photos
Measuring Irregular Areas
Other Comet Orbits
Drawing a Parabolic Orbit
Forces on a Pendulum
Trial of Copernicus
Discovery of Neptune and Pluto
Haiku
Resource Letter SL - 1 on Science and Literature

Film Loops

L10 Retrograde Motion—Geocentric Model
L11 Retrograde Motion—Heliocentric Model
L12 Jupiter Satellite Orbit
L13 Program Orbit I
L14 Program Orbit II
L15 Central Forces—Iterated Blows (computer program)
L16 Kepler's Laws (computer program)
L17 Unusual Orbits

Transparencies

T13 Stellar Motion
T14 The Celestial Sphere
T15 Retrograde Motion
T16 Eccentrics and Equants
T17 Orbit Parameters
T18 Motion Under Central Forces

Reader Articles

1 *Opening Scenes*
by Fred Hoyle
2 *Roll Call*
by Isaac Asimov
3 *A Night at the Observatory*
by Henry S. F. Cooper, Jr.
4 *Preface to De Revolutionibus*
by Nicolaus Copernicus
5 *The Starry Messenger*
by Galileo Galilei
6 *Kepler's Celestial Music*
by I. Bernard Cohen
7 *Kepler*
by Gerald Holton
8 *Kepler on Mars*
by Johannes Kepler
9 *Newton and the Principia*
by C. C. Gillispie
10 *The Laws of Motion,* and *Proposition One*
by Isaac Newton
11 *The Garden of Epicurus*
by Anatole France
12 *Universal Gravitation*
by Richard P. Feynman, Robert B. Leighton and Matthew Sands
13 *An Appreciation of the Earth*
by Stephen H. Dole
14 *Mariners 6 and 7 Television Pictures: Preliminary Analysis*
by R. B. Leighton and others
15 *The Boy Who Redeemed His Father's Name*
by Terry Morris
16 *The Great Comet of 1965*
by Owen Gingerich
17 *Gravity Experiments*
by R. H. Dicke, P. G. Roll and J. Weber
18 *Space the Unconquerable*
by Arthur C. Clarke
19 *Is There Intelligent Life Beyond the Earth?*
by I. S. Shklovskii and Carl Sagan
20 *The Stars Within Twenty-Two Light Years That Could Have Habitable Planets*
by Stephen Dole
21 *Scientific Study of Unidentified Flying Objects*
from the Condon Report with an Introduction by Walter Sullivan
22 *The Life-Story of a Galaxy*
by Margaret Burbidge
23 *Expansion of the Universe*
by Hermann Bondi
24 *Negative Mass*
by Banesh Hoffmann
25 *Four Poetic Fragments about Astronomy*
by William Shakespeare, Samuel Butler, John Ciardi and Francis Jammes
26 *The Dyson Sphere*
by I. S. Shklovskii and Carl Sagan

Contents TEXT, UNIT 2

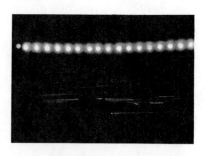

The Aztec calendar, carved over 100 years before our calendar was adopted, divides the year into eighteen months of twenty days each.

Motion in the Heavens

PROLOGUE Astronomy, the oldest science, deals with objects now known to lie vast distances from us. To early observers, the sun, moon, planets, and stars did not seem to be so far away. Yet always, even today, the majesty of celestial events has fired our imagination and curiosity. The ancients noted the great variety of objects visible in the sky, the regularity of their motions, the strangely slow changes in their position and brightness. This whole mysterious pattern of motions required some reason, some cause, some explanation.

Happily, the stars and planets appear to the eye as very well defined pinpoints of light. They are easy to observe and follow precisely, unlike most other naturally occurring phenomena. The sky therefore provided the natural "laboratory" for beginning a science based on the ability to abstract, measure, and simplify.

The early chapters of this unit deal with the discovery of the causes and meanings of observed celestial motions. We begin with prehistoric attempts to explain such observations by translating them into myths and tales. We end with the Scientific Revolution of the seventeenth century, which gave us the explanations that hold to this day. These explanations also provided a whole new set of methods for solving problems in a scientific manner.

Astronomical events affected not only the imagination of the ancients, but had a practical effect on everyday life. The working day began when the sun rose and ended when the sun set. Before electric lighting, human activity was dominated by the presence or absence of daylight and the sun's warmth, which changed season by season.

Of all time units commonly used, "one day" is probably the most basic and surely the most ancient. For counting longer intervals, a "moon" or month was an obvious unit. Over the centuries, clocks were devised to subdivide days into smaller units, and calendars were invented to record

Even in modern times outdoorsmen use the sun by day and the stars by night as a clock. Directions are indicated by the sun at rising and setting time, and true south can be determined from the position of the sun at noon. The Pole Star gives a bearing on true north after dark. The sun's position can also be used as a crude calendar. Its noontime altitude varies with the seasons.

the passage of days into years.

When the early nomadic tribes settled down to live in villages some 10,000 years ago, they became dependent upon agriculture for their food. They needed a calendar for planning their plowing and sowing. Throughout recorded history, most of the world's population has been involved in agriculture and so has depended on a calendar. If seeds were planted too early, they might rot in the ground, or the young shoots might be killed by a frost. If they were planted too late, the crops would not ripen before winter came. Therefore, a knowledge of the best times for planting and harvesting was important for survival. Because religious festivals were often related to the seasons, the job of making and improving the calendar often fell to priests. Such improvements required observation of the sun, planets, and stars. The first astronomers, therefore, were probably priests.

Practical needs and imagination acted together to give astronomy an early importance. Many of the great buildings of ancient times were constructed and situated with a clear awareness of astronomy. The great pyramids of Egypt, tombs of the Pharaohs, have sides that run due north-south and east-west. The awesome circles of giant stones at Stonehenge in England appear to have been arranged about 2000 B.C. to permit accurate observations of the positions of the sun and moon. The Mayans and the Incas in America, as well as the ancient civilizations of India and

Stonehenge, England, apparently a prehistoric observatory.

China put enormous effort into buildings from which they could measure changes in position of the sun, moon, and planets. At least as early as 1000 B.C. the Babylonians and Egyptians had developed considerable ability in timekeeping. Their recorded observations are still being unearthed.

Thus, for thousands of years, the motions of the heavenly bodies were carefully observed and recorded. In all science, no other field has had such a long accumulation of data as astronomy.

But our debt is greatest to the Greeks, who began trying to deal in a new way with what they saw. The Greeks recognized the contrast between the apparently haphazard and short-lived motions of objects on earth and the unending cycles of the heavens. About 600 B.C. they began to ask a new question: How can we explain these cyclic events in the sky in a simple way? What order and sense can we make of them? The Greeks' answers, discussed in Chapter 5, had an important effect on science. For example, the writings of Aristotle (about 330 B.C.) became widely studied and accepted in Western Europe after 1200 A.D. They were important factors in the scientific revolution that followed.

After the conquests of Alexander the Great, the center of Greek thought and science shifted to Egypt. At the new city of Alexandria, founded in 332 B.C., a great museum similar to a modern research institute was created. It flourished for many centuries. But as Greek civilization gradually declined, the practical-minded Romans captured Egypt, and interest in science died out. In 640 A.D., Alexandria was captured by the Muslims as they swept along the southern shore of the Mediterranean Sea and moved northward through Spain to the Pyrenees. Along the way they seized and preserved many libraries of Greek documents, some of which were later translated into Arabic and carefully studied. During the following centuries, Muslim scientists made new and better observations of the heavens. However, they made no major changes in the explanations or theories of the Greeks.

In Western Europe during this period, the works of the Greeks were largely forgotten. Eventually Europeans rediscovered them through Arabic translations found in Spain after the Muslims were forced out. By 1130 A.D., complete manuscripts of at least one of Aristotle's books were known in Italy and France. After the founding of the University of Bologna in the late 1100's, and of the University of Paris around 1200, many other writings of Aristotle were acquired. Scholars studied these writings both in Paris and at the new English universities, Oxford and Cambridge.

During the next century, the Dominican monk Thomas Aquinas blended major elements of Greek thought and Christian theology into a single philosophy. His work was widely studied and accepted in Western Europe for several centuries. In achieving this synthesis, Aquinas accepted the physics and astronomy of Aristotle. Because the science was blended with theology, any questioning of the science seemed also to question the theology. Thus for a time there was little effective criticism of the Aristotelian science.

The Renaissance movement, which spread out across Europe from Italy, brought new art and music. It also brought new ideas about the universe and humanity's place in it. Curiosity and a questioning attitude became acceptable, even prized. Scholars acquired a new confidence in

The positions of Jupiter from 132 B.C. to 60 B.C. are recorded on this section of Babylonian clay tablet, now in the British Museum.

In the twelfth century, the Muslim scholar Ibn Rashd had attempted a similar union of Aristotelianism and Islam.

their ability to learn about the world. Among those whose work introduced the new age were Columbus and Vasco da Gama, Gutenberg and da Vinci, Michelangelo and Raphael, Erasmus and Vesalius, Luther, Calvin, and Henry VIII. (The chart in Chapter 6 shows their life spans.) Within this emerging Renaissance culture lived Niklas Koppernik, later called Copernicus, whose re-examination of astronomical theories is discussed in Chapter 6.

Further improvements in astronomical theory were made in the seventeenth century by Kepler, mainly through mathematical reasoning, and by Galileo through his observations and writings. These contributions are discussed in Chapter 7. In Chapter 8 we take up Newton's work in the second half of the seventeenth century. Newton's genius extended ideas about motion on earth to explain motion in the heavens—a magnificent synthesis of terrestrial and celestial dynamics. These men, and others like them in other sciences such as anatomy and physiology, literally changed the world. The results they obtained and the ways in which they went about their work had effects so far-reaching that we generally refer to them as the *Scientific Revolution*.

Great scientific advances can, and often do, affect ideas outside

Louis XIV visiting the French Academy of Sciences, which he founded in the middle of the seventeenth century. Seen through the right-hand window is the Paris Observatory, then under construction.

science. For example, Newton's work helped to create a new feeling of self-confidence. It seemed possible to understand all things in the heavens and on the earth. This great change in attitude was a major characteristic of the eighteenth century, which has been called the Age of Reason. To a degree, what we think today and how we run our affairs are still affected by scientific discoveries made centuries ago.

Broad changes in thought developed at the start of the Renaissance and grew for nearly a century, from the work of Copernicus to that of Newton. In a sense, this era of invention resembles the sweeping changes which have occurred during the past hundred years. This recent period might extend from the publication of Darwin's *Origin of Species* in 1859 to the first controlled release of nuclear energy in 1942. Within this interval lived such great scientists as Mendel and Pasteur, Planck and Einstein, Rutherford and Fermi. The ideas they and others introduced into science have become increasingly important. These scientific ideas are just as much a part of our time as the ideas and works of people such as Roosevelt and Ghandi, Martin Luther King and Pope John XXIII, Marx and Lenin, Freud and Dewey, Picasso and Stravinsky, Shaw and Joyce. If we understand how science influenced the people of past centuries, we can better understand how science influences our thought and lives today. This is clearly one of the basic aims of this course.

In sum, the material treated in this unit is historical as well as scientific. But, even today, it remains of great importance to anyone interested in understanding science. The reasons for presenting the science of astronomy in its historical framework include the following:

ON

THE ORIGIN OF SPECIES

BY MEANS OF NATURAL SELECTION,

OR THE

PRESERVATION OF FAVOURED RACES IN THE STRUGGLE
FOR LIFE.

By CHARLES DARWIN, M.A.,

FELLOW OF THE ROYAL, GEOLOGICAL, LINNÆAN, ETC., SOCIETIES;
AUTHOR OF 'JOURNAL OF RESEARCHES DURING H. M. S. BEAGLE'S VOYAGE
ROUND THE WORLD.'

LONDON:
JOHN MURRAY, ALBEMARLE STREET.
1859.

The right of Translation is reserved.

> The results that were finally obtained still hold true and rank among the oldest ideas used every day in scientific work. The characteristics of all scientific work are clearly visible. We can see the role of assumptions, of experiment and observations, of mathematical theory. We can note the social mechanisms for cooperation, teaching, and disputing. And we can appreciate the possibility of having one's scientific findings become part of the accepted knowledge of the time.

> There is an interesting conflict between the rival theories used to explain the same set of astronomical observations. It exhibits characteristics that all such disputes have in common down to our day. Thus, it helps us to see clearly what standards may be used to judge one theory against another.

> This subject matter includes the main reasons for the rise of science as we understand it now. The story of the Scientific Revolution and its many effects outside science itself is as necessary to understanding our current age of science as is the story of the American Revolution to an understanding of America today.

Midnight sun photographed at five minute intervals over the Ross Sea in Antarctica.

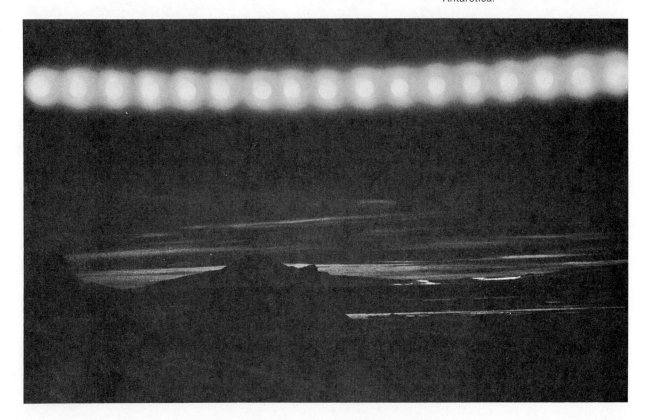

CHAPTER FIVE

Where is the Earth?—
The Greeks' Answers

5.1 Motions of the sun and stars

SG 5.1

The facts of everyday astronomy, the celestial events themselves, are the same now as in the times of the ancient Greeks. You can observe with your unaided eyes most of what these early scientists saw and recorded. You can discover some of the long-known cycles and rhythms: the seasonal changes of the sun's height at noon, the monthly phases of the moon, and the glorious spectacle of the slowly turning night sky. If we wished only to forecast eclipses, planetary positions, and the seasons, we could, like the Babylonians and Egyptians, focus our attention on recording the details of the cycles and rhythms. Suppose, however, like the Greeks, we wish to *explain* these cycles. Then we must also use our data to construct some sort of simple model or theory with which we can predict the observed variations. Before we explore several theories proposed in the past, let us review the *major observations* which the theories tried to explain: the motions of the sun, moon, planets, and stars.

The most basic celestial cycle as seen from our earth is, of course, that of day and night. Each day the sun rises above the local horizon on the eastern side of the sky and sets on the western side. The sun follows an arc across the sky, as is sketched in part (a) of the diagram at the top of the next page. At noon, halfway between sunrise and sunset, the sun is highest above the horizon. Every day, it follows a similar path from sunrise to sunset. Indeed all the objects in the sky show this pattern of daily motion. They all rise in the east, reach a high point, and drop lower in the west. (However, some stars never actually sink below the horizon.)

As the seasons change, so do the details of the sun's path across the sky. In our Northern Hemisphere during winter, the sun rises and sets more to the south. Its altitude at noon is lower, and so its run across the sky lasts for a shorter period of time. In summer the sun rises and sets more toward the north. Its height at noon is greater, and its track across the sky lasts a longer time. The whole cycle takes a little less than $365\frac{1}{4}$ days.

The motions of these bodies, essentially the same as they were thousands of years ago, are not difficult to observe—you should make a point of doing so. The *Handbook* has many suggestions for observing the sky, both with the naked eye and with a small telescope.

This description is for observers in the Northern Hemisphere. For observers south of the equator, exchange "north" and "south."

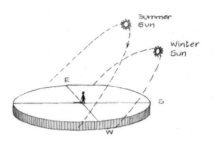

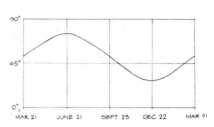

(a) Path of the sun through the sky for one day of summer and one day of winter.

(b) Noon altitude of the sun as seen from St. Louis, Missouri, throughout the year.

SG 5.2

SG 5.3

This year-long cycle north and south is the basis for the seasonal or "solar" year. Apparently the ancient Egyptians once thought that the year had 360 days, but they later added five feast days to have a year of 365 days. This longer year agreed better with their observations of the seasons. Now we know that the solar year is 365.24220 days long. The decimal fraction 0.24220 raises a problem for the calendar maker, who works with whole days. If you used a calendar of just 365 days, after four years New Year's Day would come early by one day. In a century you would be in error by almost a month. In a few centuries the date called January 1 would come in the summertime! In ancient times extra days or even whole months were inserted from time to time to keep a calendar of 365 days in fair agreement with the seasons.

To reduce the number of leap days from 100 to 97 in 400 years, century years not divisible by 400 were omitted as leap years. Thus the year 1900 was not a leap year, but the year 2000 will be a leap year.

Such a makeshift calendar is, however, hardly satisfactory. In 45 B.C. Julius Caesar decreed a new 365-day calendar (the Julian calendar) with one extra whole day (a "leap day") inserted each fourth year. Over many years, the average would therefore be $365\frac{1}{4}$ days per year. This calendar was used for centuries, during which the small difference between $\frac{1}{4}$ and 0.24220 added up to several days. Finally, in 1582 A.D. Pope Gregory announced a new calendar (the Gregorian calendar). This had only 97 leap days in 400 years, and the new approximation has lasted satisfactorily to this day without revision.

You have noticed that a few stars are bright and many are faint. The brighter stars may seem to be larger, but if you look at them through binoculars, they still appear as points of light. Some bright stars show colors, but most appear whitish. People have grouped many of the brighter stars into patterns, called constellations. Examples include the familiar Big Dipper and Orion.

SG 5.4

You may have also noticed a particular pattern of stars overhead, then several hours later noticed it low in the west. What was happening? More detailed observation, say by taking a time-exposure photograph, would show that the entire bowl of stars had moved from east to west. New stars had risen in the east and others had set in the west. As seen from the Northern Hemisphere, during the night the stars appear to move counterclockwise around a point in the sky called the north celestial pole. This

A combination trail and star photograph of the constellation Orion. The camera shutter was opened for several hours while the stars moved across the sky (leaving trails on the photographic plate). Then the camera was closed for a few minutes and reopened while the camera was driven to follow the stars.

Time exposure showing star trails around the north celestial pole. The diagonal line was caused by the rapid passage of an artificial earth satellite.

You can use a protractor to determine the duration of the exposure; the stars move about 15° per hour.

stationary point is near the fairly bright star Polaris (see the photograph at the top of this page).

Some star patterns, such as Orion (the Hunter) and Cygnus (the Swan—also called the Northern Cross), were described and named thousands of years ago. Since the star patterns described by the ancients still fit, we can conclude that the star positions change very little, if at all, over the centuries. This constancy of relative positions has led to the term "fixed stars."

Thus, we observe in the heavens unchanging relationships over the centuries and smooth, orderly motions each day. But, although the daily

SG 5.5

See "The Garden of Epicurus" in *Reader 2.*

URSA MAJOR

URSA MINOR

CASSIOPEIA

CYGNUS

LYRA

ORION

A very easy but precise way to time
the motions of the stars is explained
in the *Handbook*.

The differences between the two
frames of reference—the horizon
and the fixed stars—are the basis
for establishing a position on the
earth, as in navigation.

rising and setting cycles of the sun and stars are similar, they are not
identical. Unlike the sun's path, the paths of the stars do not vary in
altitude from season to season. Also, stars do not have quite the same
rhythm of rising and setting as the sun, but go a little faster. Some
constellations seen high in the sky soon after sunset appear low in the
west at the same time several weeks later. As measured by sun-time, the
stars set about four minutes earlier each day.

Thus far, we have described the positions and motions of the sun and
stars in relation to the observer's horizon. But different observers have
different horizons. Therefore, we can not use the horizon as an
unchanging frame of reference from which all observers will see the same
positions and motions in the sky. However, the fixed stars provide a frame
of reference which *is* the same for all observers. The positions of these
stars relative to one another do not change as the observer moves over the
earth. Also, their daily motions are simple circles with almost no changes
during a year or through the years. For this reason, we usually describe
positions in the heavens in terms of a frame of reference defined by the
stars.

Such a description of the sun's motion must include the daily crossing
of the sky, the daily difference in rising and setting times, and the
seasonal change in noon altitude. We have already seen that, as measured
by sun-time, each star sets about four minutes earlier each day than it did
the previous day; it goes ahead of the sun toward the west. We can just
as well say that, measured by star-time, the sun sets about four minutes
later each day. That is, the sun appears gradually to *slip behind* the daily
east-to-west motion of the stars. In other words, the sun moves very slowly
east against a background of "fixed" stars.

The difference in noon altitude of the sun during the year
corresponds to a drift of the sun's path north and south on the
background of stars. In the first diagram below, the middle portion of the
sky is represented by a band around the earth. The sun's yearly path
against this background of stars is represented by the dark line. If we cut
and flatten out this band, as shown in the second and third diagrams, we
get a chart of the sun's path during the year. (The 0° line is the *celestial
equator,* an imaginary line in the sky directly above the earth's equator.)
The sun's path against the background of the stars is called the *ecliptic.*
Its drift north and south of the celestial equator is about $23\frac{1}{2}°$. We also
need to define one point on the ecliptic so we can locate the sun or other
celestial objects along it. For centuries this point has been the place
where the sun crosses the equator from south to north—about March 21.
This point is called the "vernal (spring) equinox." It is the zero point from
which positions among the stars usually are measured.

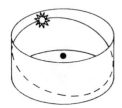
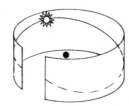
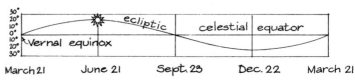

Thus, there are three apparent motions of the sun: (1) its daily westward motion across the sky, (2) its yearly drift eastward among the stars, (3) its yearly cycle of north-south drift in noon altitude. These phenomena are all the more fascinating because they repeat without fail and precisely. We will try to explain these cyclic events by devising a simple model to represent them.

Q1 If you told time by the stars, would the sun set earlier or later each day?

Q2 For what practical purposes were calendars needed?

Q3 What are the observed motions of the sun during one year?

These end-of-section questions are intended to help you check your understanding before going on to the next section.

5.2 Motions of the moon

The moon shares the general east-to-west daily motion of the sun and stars. But the moon slips eastward against the background of the stars faster than the sun does. Each night the moon rises nearly one hour later. When the moon rises in the east at sunset (opposite the sun in the sky) it is a bright, full disc (full moon). Each day after that, it rises later and appears less round. Finally it wanes to a thin crescent low in the sky at dawn. After about fourteen days, the moon is passing near the sun in the sky and rising with it. During this time (new moon) we cannot see the moon at all. After the new moon, we first see the moon as a thin crescent low in the western sky at sunset. As the moon moves rapidly eastward from the sun, its crescent fattens to a half disc. Within another week it reaches full moon again. After each full moon the cycle repeats.

A "half moon" occurs one-quarter of the way through the monthly cycle, and is therefore called "first quarter" by astronomers. The full moon occurs half way through the cycle, and another "half moon" occurs at "third quarter."

26 days after new moon.

17 days after new moon.

3 days after new moon.

As early as 380 B.C., the Greek philosopher Plato recognized that the phases of the moon could be explained by thinking of the moon as a globe reflecting sunlight and moving around the earth in about 29 days. Because the moon appears so big and moves so rapidly compared to the stars, people in early times thought that it must be quite close to the earth.

The moon's path around the sky is close to the yearly path of the sun. That is, the moon is always near the ecliptic. But the moon's path tilts a bit with respect to the sun's path. If it did not, the moon would come exactly in front of the sun at every new moon, causing an eclipse of the sun. It would be exactly opposite the sun at every full moon, moving into the earth's shadow and causing an eclipse of the moon.

The motions of the moon have been studied with great care for centuries, partly because of interest in predicting eclipses. These motions are very complicated. The precise prediction of the moon's position is an exacting test for any theory of motion in the heavens.

SG 5.6

Q4 Draw a rough diagram to show the relative positions of the sun, earth, and moon during each of the moon's four phases.

Q5 Why don't eclipses occur each month?

5.3 The "wandering" stars

Without a telescope we can see, in addition to the sun and moon, five rather bright objects which move among the stars. These are the "wanderers," or planets: Mercury, Venus, Mars, Jupiter, and Saturn. With the aid of telescopes, three more planets have been discovered: Uranus, Neptune, and Pluto. None of these three were known until nearly a century after the time of Isaac Newton. Like the sun and moon, all the planets rise daily in the east and set in the west. Also like the sun and moon, the planets generally move slowly eastward among the stars. But they have another remarkable and puzzling motion of their own. At certain times, each planet stops moving eastward among the stars and for some months loops back westward. This westward or "wrong-way" motion is called *retrograde motion*. The retrograde loops made by Mercury, Mars, and Saturn during one year are plotted on the opposite page.

Saturn, Jupiter, and Mars at one time or another may be anywhere in the sky. However, their paths always follow very near the ecliptic. The retrograde motion of one of these three planets occurs when it is nearly opposite the sun (that is, halfway across the sky at midnight). Mercury and Venus, however, have limits to how far away from the sun they can

When a planet is observed directly opposite from the sun, the planet is said to be *in opposition*. Retrograde motions of Mars, Jupiter, and Saturn are observed about the time they are in opposition.

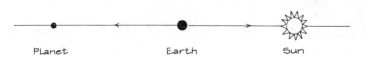

Planet   Earth   Sun

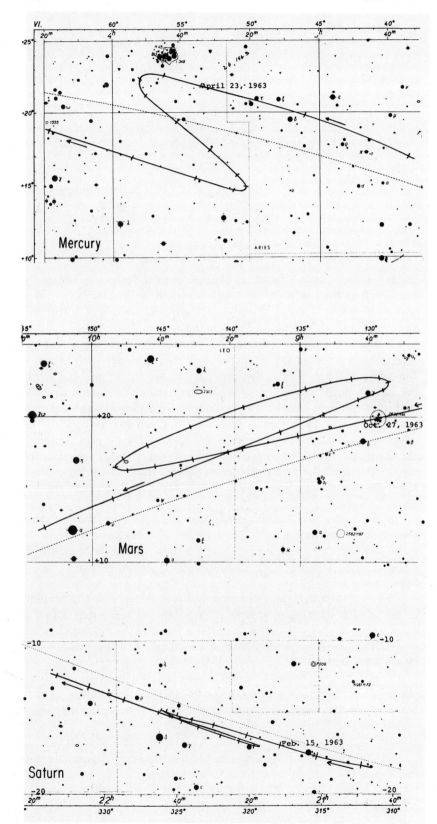

The retrograde motions of Mercury (marked at 5-day intervals), Mars (at 10-day intervals), and Saturn (at 20-day intervals) in 1963, plotted on a star chart. The dotted line is the annual path of the sun, called the ecliptic.

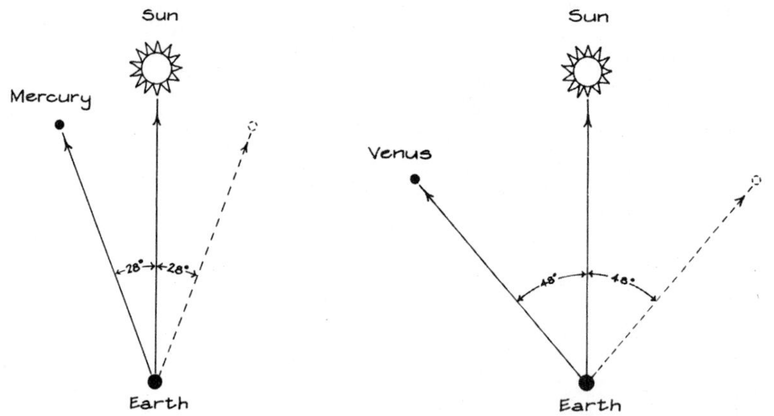

The maximum angles from the sun at which we observe Mercury and Venus. Both planets can, at times, be observed at sunset or at sunrise. Mercury is never observed to be more than 28° from the sun, and Venus is never more than 48° from the sun.

SG 5.7

**Typical Retrograde
Motions of the Planets**

PLANET	DAYS	WESTWARD DISPLACEMENT
Mercury	34	15°
Venus	43	19°
Mars	83	22°
Jupiter	118	10°
Saturn	139	7°
Uranus	152	4°
Neptune	160	3°
Pluto	156	2°

Aristotle: rate of fall is proportional to weight divided by distance.

be. As the above figures show, the greatest angular distance in either direction from the sun is 28° for Mercury and 48° for Venus. The retrograde motion of Venus or Mercury begins after the planet is farther east of the sun and visible in the evening sky.

The planets change considerably in brightness. When Venus first appears in the evening sky as the "evening star," it is only fairly bright. During the following four to five months, it moves farther eastward from the sun. Gradually it becomes so bright that it often can be seen in daytime if the air is clear. A few weeks later, Venus scoots westward toward the sun. It fades rapidly, passes the sun, and soon reappears in the morning sky before sunrise as the "morning star." Then it goes through the same pattern, but in the opposite order: bright at first, then gradually fading. Mercury follows much the same pattern. But because Mercury is seen only near the sun (that is, only during twilight), its changes are difficult to observe.

Mars, Jupiter, and Saturn are brightest about the time that they are in retrograde motion and opposite the sun. Yet over many years their maximum brightness differs. The change is most obvious for Mars; the planet is brightest when it is opposite the sun during August or September.

We have seen that the sun, moon, and planets generally slip behind as the celestial sphere goes around us each day, and hence they appear to move eastward among the stars. It is also a fact that the moon and planets (except Pluto) are always found within a band only 8° wide on either side of the sun's path.

These, then, are some of the main observations of celestial phenomena. All of them were known to the ancients. In their day as in ours, the puzzling regularities and variations seemed to cry out for some explanation.

Q6 In what part of the sky must you look to see the planets Mercury and Venus?

Q7 In what part of the sky would you look to see the planet that is in opposition to the sun?

Q8 When do Mercury and Venus show retrograde motion?
Q9 When do Mars, Jupiter, and Saturn show retrograde motion?
Q10 Can Mars, Jupiter, and Saturn appear any place in the sky?

5.4 Plato's problem

In the fourth century B.C., Greek philosophers asked a new question:
How can we explain the cycles of changes observed in the sky? What
model can consistently and accurately account for all celestial motions?
Plato sought a theory to explain what was seen, or, as he phrased it, "to
save the appearances." The Greeks were among the first people to desire
clear, rational explanations for natural events. Their attitude was an
important step toward science as we know it today.

How did the Greeks begin their explanation of celestial motion? What
were their assumptions?

Any answers to these questions must be partly guesswork. Many
scholars over the centuries have devoted themselves to the study of Greek
thought. But the documents on which our knowledge of the Greeks is
based are mostly copies of copies and translations of translations. Many
errors and omissions occur. In some cases all we have are reports from
later writers on what certain philosophers did or said. These accounts may
be distorted or incomplete. The historian's task is difficult. Most of the
original Greek writings were on papyrus or cloth scrolls which have
decayed through the ages. Wars and plundering and burning have also
destroyed many important documents. Especially tragic was the burning of
the famous library of Alexandria in Egypt, which contained several
hundred thousand documents. (It was burned three times: in part by
Caesar's troops in 47 B.C.; in the fourth century A.D. by Christians; and
about 640 A.D. by early Muslims when they overran the country.) The
general picture of Greek culture is fairly clear. But many interesting
details are missing.

The approach to celestial motion taken by the Greeks and their
intellectual followers for many centuries was outlined by Plato in the
fourth century B.C. He defined the problem to his students in terms of
order and status. The stars, he said, represent eternal, divine, unchanging
beings. They move at a uniform speed around the earth in the most
regular and perfect of all paths, an endless circle. But the sun, moon, and
planets wander across the sky by complex paths, including even
retrograde motions. Yet, being heavenly bodies, surely they too are really
moving in a way that suits their high status. Their motions, if not in a
perfect circle, must therefore be in some combination of perfect circles.
What combinations of circular motions at uniform speed could account for
these strange variations?

Notice that the problem deals only with the changing *apparent* positions
of the sun, moon, and planets. The planets appear to be only points of
light moving against the background of stars. From two observations at

Several centuries later, a more
mature Islamic culture led to
extensive study and scholarly
commentary on the remains of
Greek thought. Several centuries
later still, a more mature Christian
culture used the ideas preserved by
the Muslims to evolve early parts of
modern science.

different times we obtain a rate of motion: a value of so many degrees per day. The problem then is to find a "mechanism," some combination of motions that reproduces the observed angular motions and leads to accurate predictions. The ancient astronomers had no evidence about the distance of the planets from the earth. All they had were directions, dates, and rates of angular motion. They did know that the changes in brightness of the planets were related to their positions with respect to the sun. But these changes in brightness were not included in Plato's problem.

Plato and many other Greek philosophers assumed that there were only a few basic "elements." Mixed together, these few elements gave rise to the great variety of materials observed in the world. Not everyone agreed as to what these elements were. But gradually four were accepted as explaining all phenomena taking place on earth. These elements were Fire, Air, Water, and Earth. All substances found on earth were supposed to contain various mixtures of these elements. These different mixtures allowed a wide range of properties. (See Unit 1, Chapter 2.) Perfection could only exist in the heavens, which were separate from the earth, and were the home of the gods. Just as motions in the heavens must be eternal and perfect, the unchanging heavenly objects could not contain elements normally found on or near the earth. Hence, they were supposed to consist of a changeless fifth element (or *quintessence*) of their own—the *ether*.

Plato's problem in explaining the motion of planets remained the most important problem in astronomy for nearly two thousand years. In later chapters we will explore the different interpretations developed by Kepler, Galileo, and Newton. But in order to appreciate these men's efforts we must first examine the solutions offered by the Greeks to Plato's problem. Let us confess right away that for their time these solutions were useful, intelligent, and indeed beautiful.

In Latin the ether became *quinta essentia* (fifth element), whence our "quintessence."

Q11   What was Plato's problem of planetary motion?

Q12   Why is our knowledge of Greek science incomplete?

Q13   Why did the Greeks feel that they should use only uniform circular motion to explain celestial phenomena?

5.5 The Greek idea of "explanation"

Plato's statement of this historic problem of planetary motion illustrates three major contributions of the Greek philosophers. With slight changes, these concepts are still basic to our understanding of the nature of physical theories:

1. A theory should be based on simple ideas. Plato regarded it not merely as simple, but also as self-evident, that heavenly bodies must move uniformly along circular paths. Only in recent centuries have we learned that such common-sense beliefs may be misleading. While unproved

assumptions at the outset, they must be examined closely and never accepted without reservation. As we will see often in this course, it has been very difficult to identify hidden assumptions in science. Yet in many cases, when the assumptions were identified and questioned, entirely new theories followed.

2. Physical theory must agree with the measured results of observation of *phenomena,* such as the motions of the planets. Our purpose in making a theory is to discover the uniformity of behavior, the hidden simplicity underlying apparent irregularities. For organizing our observations, the language of numbers and geometry is useful. This use of mathematics, widely accepted today, originated in part with the Pythagoreans. This group of mathematicians lived in southern Italy about 500 B.C. They believed that "all things are numbers." However, the use of mathematics and measurement in science became important only later. Plato stressed the fundamental role of numerical data only in his astronomy, while Aristotle largely avoided detailed measurements. This was unfortunate because, as the Prologue reported, Aristotle greatly influenced later scholars. His arguments, which gave little attention to the idea of measurement of change as a tool of knowledge, were adopted centuries afterward by such important philosophers as Thomas Aquinas.

3. To "explain" complex phenomena means to develop or invent a physical model, or a geometrical or other mathematical construction. This model must show the same features as the phenomena to be explained. For example, if one actually constructs a model of interlocking spheres, a point on one of the spheres must have the same motions as the planet which the point represents.

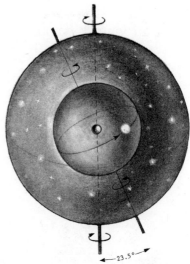

The annual north-south (seasonal) motion of the sun was explained by having the sun on a sphere whose axis was tilted $23\frac{1}{2}°$ from the axis of the eternal sphere of the stars.

5.6 The first earth-centered solution

The Greeks observed that the earth was large, solid, and permanent. Meanwhile the heavens seemed to be populated by small, remote objects that were continually in motion. What was more natural than to conclude that our big, heavy earth was the steady, unmoving center of the universe? Such an earth-centered viewpoint is called *geocentric.* From this viewpoint the daily motion of the stars could be explained easily: the stars were attached to, or were holes in, a large, dark, spherical shell surrounding the earth. They were all at the same distance from us. Daily, this celestial sphere turned once on an axis through the earth. As a result, all the stars fixed on it moved in circular paths around the pole of rotation. Thus, a simple model of a rotating celestial sphere and a stationary earth could explain the daily motions of the stars.

The three observed motions of the sun required a somewhat more complex model. To explain the sun's motion with respect to the stars, a separate, invisible shell was imagined. This shell carried the sun around the earth. It was fixed to the celestial sphere and shared its daily motion. But it also had a slow, opposite motion of its own, amounting to one 360° cycle per year.

A geocentric cosmological scheme. The earth is fixed at the center of concentric rotating spheres. The sphere of the moon *(lune)* separates the terrestrial region (composed of concentric shells of the four elements Earth, Water, Air, and Fire) from the celestial region. In the latter are the concentric spheres carrying Mercury, Venus, Sun, Mars, Jupiter, Saturn, and the stars. To simplify the diagram, only one sphere is shown for each planet. (From the DeGolyer copy of Petrus Apianus' *Cosmographia*, 1551.)

The yearly north-south motion of the sun was accounted for by tilting the axis of its sphere. This adjustment matched the tilt of the sun's path from the axis of the dome of stars.

The motions of the visible planets—Mercury, Venus, Mars, Jupiter, and Saturn—were more difficult to explain. They share generally the daily motion of the stars, but they also have peculiar motions of their own. Saturn moves most slowly among the stars, revolving once in 30 years. Therefore, its sphere was assumed to be largest and closest to the stars. Inside the sphere for Saturn were spheres carrying the faster-moving Jupiter (12 years) and Mars (687 days). Since they all require more than a year for a complete trip among the stars, these three planets were believed to lie beyond the sphere of the sun. Venus, Mercury, and the moon were placed between the sun and the earth. The fast-moving moon was assumed to reflect sunlight and to be closest to the earth.

This imaginary system of transparent shells or spheres provided a rough "machine" for explaining the general motions of heavenly objects. By choosing the sizes of the spheres and their rates and direction of motions, one could roughly match the model with the observations. If additional observations revealed other cyclic variations, more spheres could be added to adjust the model.

Plato's friend Eudoxus concluded that 26 spheres would account for the general pattern of motions. Later Aristotle added 29 more. (An interesting description of this general system of cosmology appears in the *Divine Comedy*, written by the poet Dante about 1300 A.D. This was shortly after Aristotle's writings became known in Europe.) Yet even Aristotle knew that this system did not quite match the observations. Moreover, it did not explain the observed changes in brightness of the planets.

You may feel that Greek science was bad science because it was different from our own, or because it was less accurate. But you should understand from your study of this chapter that such a conclusion is not justified. The Greeks were just beginning the development of scientific theories. Naturally they made assumptions that appear odd or wrong to us today. Their science was not "bad science," but in many ways it was a different kind of science from ours. And ours is not the last word, either. We must realize that to scientists 2,000 years from now our efforts may seem clumsy and strange.

Even today's scientific theory does not and cannot claim to account for every detail of every specific situation. Scientific concepts are general ideas which treat only selected aspects of observations. They do not cover the whole mass of raw data and raw experience that exists in the universe. Also, each period in history puts its own limits on the range of human imagination. As you learned in Unit 1, important general concepts such as force and acceleration are invented specifically to help organize observations. They are human inventions.

The history of science contains many cases in which certain factors overlooked by one researcher later turn out to be very important. But how would better systems for making predictions be developed without first trials? Theories are improved through tests and revisions, and sometimes are completely replaced by better ones.

Q14   What is a geocentric system? How does it account for the motions of the sun?

Q15   Describe the first solution to Plato's problem.

5.7 A sun-centered solution

For nearly two thousand years after Plato and Aristotle, the basic geocentric model was generally accepted, though scholars debated certain details. But a very different model, based on different assumptions, had been proposed in the third century B.C. The astronomer Aristarchus, perhaps influenced by the writings of Heracleides, who lived a century earlier, offered this new model. Aristarchus suggested that a simpler explanation of heavenly motion would place the *sun* at the center, with the earth, planets, and stars all revolving around it. A sun-centered system is called *heliocentric*.

The major writings of Aristarchus have been lost, and our knowledge of his work comes mainly from other writers. According to Archimedes, Aristarchus taught that the sun must be at least eighteen times farther from the earth than the moon. Further, Aristarchus held that the sun, being the source of light, should be at the center of the universe.

Aristarchus proposed that the celestial sphere is motionless and that the earth rotates once daily on an axis of its own. He believed that this assumption could explain all the daily motions observed in the sky. The apparent tilt of the paths of the sun, moon, and all the planets results from the tilt of the earth's own axis. The yearly changes in the sky, including retrograde motions of planets, are explained by assuming that the earth and the planets revolve around the sun. In this model, the motion previously assigned to the sun around the earth is assigned to the earth moving around the sun. Also, the earth becomes just one among several planets.

The diagram in the margin shows how such a system can explain the retrograde motions of Mars, Jupiter, and Saturn. An outer planet and the earth are assumed to be moving around the sun in circular orbits. The outer planet moves more slowly than the earth. As a result, when the earth is directly between the sun and the planet, the earth moves rapidly past the planet. To us the planet appears for a time to be moving backward in retrograde motion across the sky.

Gone are all the interlocking spheres. The heliocentric hypothesis, which also uses only uniform circular motions, has one further advantage.

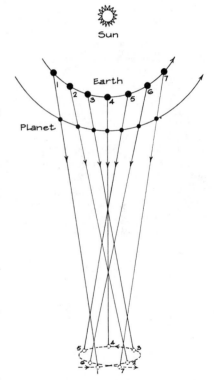

As the earth passes a planet in its orbit around the sun, the planet appears to move backwards in the sky. The arrows show the sight lines toward the planet for the different numbered positions of the earth. The lower numbered circles indicate the resulting apparent positions of the planet against the background of distant stars.

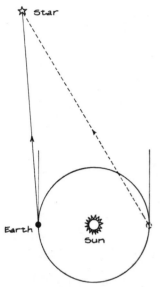

If the earth goes around the sun, then the direction in which we have to look for a star should change during the year. A shift in the relative observed positions of objects that is caused by a displacement of the observer is called a *parallax*. The greatest observed parallax of a star caused by the earth's annual motion around the sun is about 1/2400°. This is explained by the fact that the distance to this nearest star is not just hundreds of millions of miles but 25 *million* million miles.

It explains the observation that the planets are brighter during retrograde motion, since at that time the planets are nearer to the earth. Even so, the proposal by Aristarchus was neglected in his own time. It was severely criticized for three basic reasons. One reason was that the idea of a moving earth was unacceptable. It contradicted the philosophical doctrines that the earth is different from the celestial bodies and that its natural place is at the center of the universe. In fact, his contemporaries considered Aristarchus impious for even suggesting that the earth moved. Also, this new picture of the solar system contradicted common sense and everyday observations: the earth certainly *seemed* to be at rest rather than rushing through space.

Another criticism was that certain observational evidence seemed to refute Aristarchus. If the earth moved in an orbit around the sun, it would also move back and forth under the fixed stars. As shown in the sketch in the margin, the angle from the vertical at which we see any star would be different for various points in the earth's annual path. This annual shift of the fixed stars should occur if the earth moves around the sun. But it was not observed by the Greek astronomers. This awkward fact could be explained in two ways. Either (1) the earth does *not* go around the sun and so there is no shift, or (2) the earth does go around the sun but the stars are so far away that the shift is *too small to observe*. But as the Greeks realized, for the shift to be too small to detect, the stars must be enormously far away.

Today we can observe the annual shift of the stars with telescopes, so we know that Aristarchus' model is in fact useful. The shift is so small that even with telescopes it was not measured until 1838. The largest annual shift is an angle of only 1/100 of the smallest angle observable by the human eye. The shift exists, but we can sympathize with the Greeks who rejected the heliocentric theory partly because they could not observe the required shift. Only Aristarchus imagined that the stars might be as immensely distant as we now know them to be.

Finally, Aristarchus was criticized because he did not develop his system in detail, or use it to predict planetary positions. His work seems to have been purely qualitative, a general scheme of how things might be.

The geocentric and heliocentric systems offered two different ways of explaining the same observations. But the heliocentric proposal required such a drastic change in man's image of the universe that Aristarchus' hypothesis had little influence on Greek thought. Fortunately, his arguments were recorded and handed down. Eighteen centuries later, they gained new life in the thoughts of Copernicus. Ideas are not bound by space or time.

Q16 What two new assumptions were made by Aristarchus? What simplification resulted?

Q17 How can the heliocentric model proposed by Aristarchus explain retrograde motion?

Q18 What change predicted by Aristarchus' theory was not observed by the Greeks?

Q19   Why was Aristarchus considered impious? Why was his system neglected?

5.8 The geocentric system of Ptolemy

Disregarding the heliocentric model suggested by Aristarchus, the Greeks continued to develop their geocentric system. As we noted, the first solutions in terms of interlocking spheres lacked accuracy. During the 500 years after Plato and Aristotle, astronomers began to sense the need for more accurate predictions. To fit the observed data, a complex mathematical theory was required for each planet.

Several Greek astronomers made important contributions, climaxing about 150 A.D. in the geocentric theory of Claudius Ptolemy of Alexandria. Ptolemy's book on the motions of heavenly objects is a masterpiece of analysis.

Ptolemy wanted a system that would predict accurately the positions of each planet. The type of system and the motions he accepted were based on the assumptions of Aristotle. In the preface to his *Almagest,* Ptolemy defines the problem and states his assumptions as follows:

The Arabic title given to Ptolemy's book, the *Almagest,* means "the greatest."

> . . . we wish to find the evident and certain appearances from the observations of the ancients and our own, and applying the consequences of these conceptions by means of geometrical demonstrations.
>
> And so, in general, we have to state, that the heavens are spherical and move spherically; that the earth, in figure, is sensibly spherical . . .; in position, lies right in the middle of the heavens, like a geometrical center; in magnitude and distance, [the earth] has the ratio of a point with respect to the sphere of the fixed stars, having itself no local motion at all.

Ptolemy then argues that each of these assumptions is necessary and fits with all our observations. The strength of his belief is illustrated by his statement ". . . it is once for all clear from the very appearances that the earth is in the middle of the world and all weights move towards it." Notice that he supports his interpretation of astronomical observations by citing the physics of falling bodies. Later he applies this mixture of astronomy and physics to the earth itself and to its place in the scheme. In doing so, he aims to disprove Aristarchus' idea that the earth might rotate and revolve:

> Now some people, although they have nothing to oppose to these arguments, agree on something, as they think, more plausible. And it seems to them there is nothing against their supposing, for instance, the heavens immobile and the earth as

turning on the same axis [as the stars] from west to east very nearly one revolution a day. . . .

But it has escaped their notice that, indeed, as far as the appearances of the stars are concerned, nothing would perhaps keep things from being in accordance with this simpler conjecture, but that in the light of what happens around us in the air such a notion would seem altogether absurd.

Ptolemy believed that if the earth rotated it would not pull its blanket of air around with it. As a result, all clouds would fly past toward the west. All birds and other things in the air also would be carried away to the west. Even if the earth did drag the air along with it, objects in the air would still tend to be left behind by the earth and air together.

The paragraphs quoted above contain a main theme of Unit 2. Ptolemy recognized that the two systems were equally successful in *describing* motion—in the kinematics. But he preferred the geocentric theory because it fit better the *causes* of motion—the dynamics—as understood at the time. Much later, when Newton developed a completely different dynamics, the choice fell the other way.

SG 5.8

Ptolemy developed very clever and rather accurate procedures for predicting the positions of each planet on a geocentric model. He went far beyond the scheme of the earlier Greeks, constructing a model out of circles and three other geometrical devices. Each device provided for variations in the rate of angular motion as seen from the earth. In order to appreciate Ptolemy's solution, let us examine one of the very small variations he was attempting to explain.

We can divide the sun's yearly 360° path across the background of stars into four 90° parts. If the sun is at the 0 point on March 21, it will be 90° farther east on June 21, 90° farther still on September 23, another 90° farther on December 22, and back at the starting point on March 21, one whole year later. If the sun moves uniformly on a circle around the earth, the times between these dates ought to be equal. But, as you will find by consulting a calendar, they are not equal. The sun takes a few days longer to move 90° in spring or summer than it does in fall or winter. So any simple circular system based on motion with constant speed will not work for the sun.

The three devices that Ptolemy used to improve geocentric theory were the *eccentric*, the *epicycle*, and the *equant*.

Agreeing with Plato, astronomers had held previously that a celestial object must move at a uniform angular rate, and at a constant distance

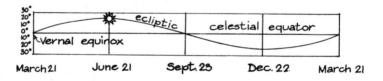

The annual path of the sun against the celestial sphere.

from the center of the earth. Ptolemy, too, believed that the earth was at
the center of the universe. But he did not insist that it stood at the
geometrical centers of all the perfect circles. He proposed that the center
C of a circle could be off-center from the earth, in an *eccentric* position.
Thus, motion that was really uniform around the center C would not
appear to be uniform when observed from the earth. An eccentric orbit of
the sun would therefore account for the seasonal variation observed in the
sun's rate of motion.

The eccentric can also account for small variations in the rate of
motion of planets. But it cannot describe such drastic changes as
retrograde motion of the planets. To account for retrograde motion,
Ptolemy used another device, the *epicycle* (see the figure at the right).
The planet is considered to be moving at a uniform rate on a small circle
called the epicycle. The center of the epicycle moves at a uniform rate on
a large circle, called the *deferent,* around the earth.

If a planet's speed on the epicycle is greater than its speed on the
large circle, the planet as seen from *above* the system appears to move
through loops. When observed from a location near the center of the
system these loops look like the retrograde motions actually observed for
planets. The photographs below show two views of the motions produced
by a simple mechanical model, an "epicycle machine." A small lamp takes
the place of the planet. The photo on the left was taken from "above," like
the diagram in the margin. The photo on the right was taken "on edge,"
almost in the plane of the motion. Thus, the loop looks much as it would
if viewed from near the center.

Epicycles can be used to describe many kinds of motion. So it was
not too difficult to produce a system that had all the main features of
observed planetary motion. One particularly interesting feature of
Ptolemy's system concerned the epicycles for the outer planets. All had the
same period: exactly one year! Moreover, the positions of the outer planets
on their epicycles always matched the position of the sun relative to the
earth. See the sketches on the opposite page for this matching of epicycles

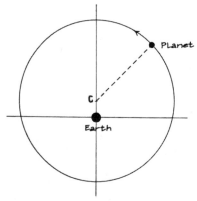

An eccentric

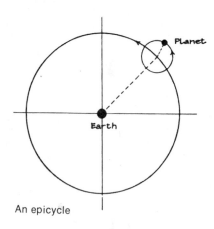

An epicycle

SG 5.9

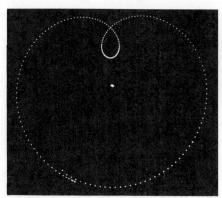

a

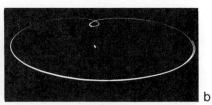

b

Retrograde motion created by a simple epicycle machine.
(a) Stroboscopic photograph of epi-
cyclic motion. The flashes were made at
equal time intervals. Note that the motion
is slowest in the loop.
(b) Loop seen from near its plane.

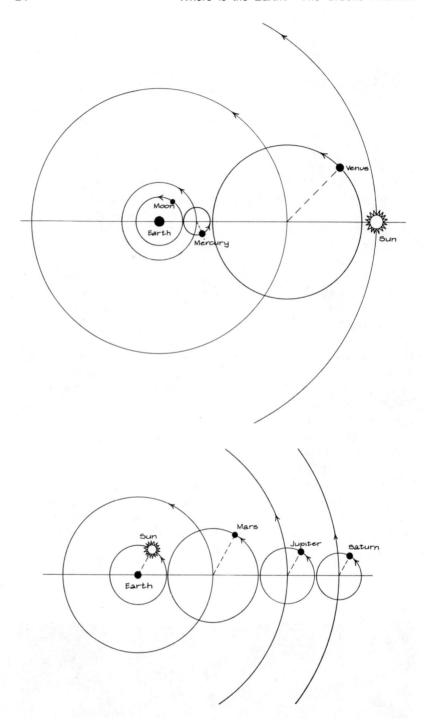

Ptolemy did not picture the planetary motions as those in an interlocking machine where each planet determined the motion of the next. Because there was no information about the distances of the planets, Ptolemy adopted an old order of distances from the earth: stars being the most remote, then Saturn, Jupiter, Mars, the sun, Venus, Mercury, and the moon. The orbits were usually shown nested inside one another so that their epicycles did not overlap.

Simplified representation of the Ptolemaic system. The scale of the upper drawing, which shows the planets between the earth and the sun, is eight times that of the lower drawing, which shows the planets that are farther than the sun. The planets' epicycles are shown along one straight line to emphasize the relative sizes of the epicycles.

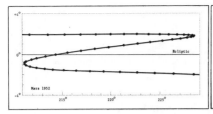
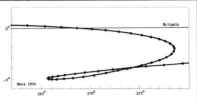
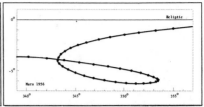

Mars plotted at four-day intervals on three consecutive oppositions. Note the different sizes and shapes of the retrograde curves.

to the relative motion of sun and earth. Fourteen centuries later, this feature became a key point of concern to Copernicus.

So far, the system of epicycles and deferents "works" well enough. It explains not only retrograde motion, but also the greater brightness of the planets when they are in retrograde motion. A planet is on the inside of its epicycle during retrograde motion. Thus it is closest to the earth, and so appears brightest. This is an unexpected bonus, since the model was not designed to explain the brightness change.

But even with combinations of eccentrics and epicycles, Ptolemy could not fit the motions of the five planets exactly. For example, as we see in the three figures above, the retrograde motion of Mars is not always of the same angular size or duration. To allow for such difficulties, Ptolemy used a third geometrical device, called the *equant*. The equant is a variation of the eccentric. As shown in the margin, the earth is again off-center from the geometric center C of the circle. But the motion along the circle is not uniform around C. Instead, it is uniform as seen from another point C'. This point is as far off-center as the earth is, but is on the other side of the center.

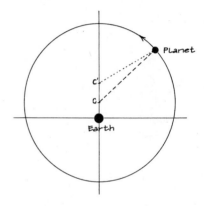

An equant. C is the center of the circle. The planet P moves at a uniform rate around the off-center point C'.

5.9 Successes and limitations of the Ptolemaic model

Ptolemy's model always used a uniform rate of angular motion around some center. To that extent, it stayed close to the assumptions of Plato. But, to fit the observations, Ptolemy was willing to displace the centers of motion from the center of the earth as much as necessary. By combining eccentrics, epicycles, and equants he described the positions of each planet separately. For each planet, Ptolemy found a combination of motions that predicted its observed positions over long periods of time. His predictions were accurate to within about two degrees (roughly four diameters of the moon)—a great improvement over earlier systems.

Ptolemy's model was quite successful, especially in its unexpected explanation of varying brightness. Such success might be taken as proof that objects in the sky actually move on epicycles and deferents around off-center points. It seems, however, that Ptolemy himself did not believe he was providing an actual physical model of the universe. He was content to give a mathematical model, one suitable for computing positions.

Of course, some difficulties remained. For example, to explain the motions of the moon, Ptolemy had to use very large epicycles. By this model, the moon would appear to grow and shrink greatly during each month, appearing at some times to have twice the diameter as at other

SG 5.10

Astronomical observations were all observations of *angles*—a small loop in the sky could be a small loop fairly near, or a larger loop much farther away.

times! Ptolemy surely knew that this was predicted by his model and that it does not happen in actual observation. But, his model was not intended to be "real." It was only a basis for predicting positions.

The Ptolemaic model was a series of mathematical devices meant to match and predict the motion of each planet separately. His geometrical analyses were like complicated equations of motion for each individual planet. But in the following centuries most scholars, including the poet Dante, accepted the model as real. They actually believed that the planets moved on transparent, invisible spheres as Eudoxus had suggested. Also, they felt that somehow the motion of all these separate spheres should be related. But in Ptolemy's original work, each planet had no necessary

SG 5.11   connection with all the others.

Ptolemy proposed his model of the planetary system in 150 A.D. Although it is now discarded, it was used for about 1,500 years. There were good reasons for this long acceptance.

It predicted fairly accurately the positions of the sun, moon, and planets.

It explained why the fixed stars do not show an annual shift when observed with the naked eye.

It agreed in most details with philosophies developed by the early Greeks, including the ideas of "natural motion" and "natural place." It had common-sense appeal to all who saw the sun, moon, planets, and stars moving around them.

It agreed with the comforting assumption that we live on an unmoving earth at the center of the universe.

Also, later, it fitted into Thomas Aquinas' widely accepted synthesis of Christian belief and Aristotelian physics.

Yet Ptolemy's system eventually was displaced by a heliocentric one.

SG 5.12   Why did this occur? What advantages did the new theory have over the old? From this historic argument about competing theories, what can we learn about the relative value of rival theories in science today? These are

SG 5.13   some of the questions to consider in the next chapter.

5.1 The Project Physics learning materials particularly appropriate for Chapter 5 include:

Experiments
Naked-Eye Astronomy
Size of the Earth
The Distance to the Moon
Height of Piton, A Mountain on the Moon
Retrograde Motion

Activities
Making Angular Measurements
Epicycles and Retrograde Motion
Celestial Sphere Model
How Long is a Sidereal Day?
Scale Model of the Solar System
Build a Sundial
Plot an Analemma
Stonehenge
Moon Crater Names
Literature

Reader Articles
The Boy Who Redeemed His Father's Name
Four Poetic Fragments About Astronomy

Film Strip
Retrograde Motion of Mars

Film Loops
Retrograde Motion—Geocentric Model

Transparencies
Stellar Motion
Celestial Sphere
Retrograde Motion
Eccentrics and Equants

In addition, the following *Reader* articles are of general interest for Unit 2:
The Black Cloud
Roll Call
A Night at the Observatory
The Garden of Epicurus
The Stars Within 22 Light-years That Could Have Habitable Planets
Scientific Study of UFO's

5.2 How could you use the shadow cast by a vertical stick on horizontal ground to find
(a) the local noon?
(b) which day was June 21st?
(c) the length of a solar year?

5.3 What is the difference between 365.24220 days and $365\frac{1}{4}$ days (a) in seconds (b) in percent?

5.4 (a) List the observations of the motions of heavenly bodies that you might make which would also have been possible in ancient Greek times.
(b) For each observation, list some reasons why the Greeks thought these motions were important.

5.5 Which of the apparent motions of the stars could be explained by a flat earth and stars fixed to a bowl that rotated around it?

5.6 Describe the motion of the moon during one month. (Use your own observations if possible.)

5.7 Mercury and Venus show retrograde motion after they have been farthest east of the sun and visible in the evening sky. Then they quickly move ahead westward toward the sun, pass it, and reappear in the morning sky. During this motion they are moving westward relative to the stars, as is shown by the plot of Mercury on page 13. Describe the rest of the cyclic motion of Mercury and Venus.

5.8 Center a protractor on point C in the top diagram on page 23 and measure the number of degrees in the four quadrants. Consider each 1° around C as one day. Make a table of the days needed for the planet to move through the four arcs as seen from the earth.

5.9 (a) How many degrees of longitude does the sun move each hour?
(b) Tell how you could roughly obtain the diameter of the earth from the following information:
i. Washington, D.C. and San Francisco have about the same latitude. How can one easily test this?
ii. A non-stop jet plane, going up wind at a ground speed of 500 mph from Washington, D.C., to San Francisco, takes 5 hours to get there.
iii. When it is just sunset in Washington, D.C., a man there turns on his TV set to watch a baseball game that is just beginning in San Francisco. The game goes into extra innings. After three hours the announcer notes that the last out occurred just as the sun set.

5.10 In Ptolemy's theory of the planetary motions there were, as in all theories, a number of assumptions. Which of the following did Ptolemy assume?
(a) the vault of stars is spherical in form
(b) the earth has no motions
(c) the earth is spherical
(d) the earth is at the center of the sphere of stars
(e) the size of the earth is extremely small compared to the distance to the stars
(f) uniform angular motion along circles (even if measured from an off-center point) is the only proper behavior for celestial objects

5.11 As far as the Greeks were concerned, and indeed as far as we are concerned, a reasonable argument can be made for either the geocentric or the heliocentric theory of the universe.
(a) In what ways were both ideas successful?
(b) In terms of Greek science, what are some advantages and disadvantages of each system?
(c) What were the major contributions of Ptolemy?

5.12 Why was astronomy the first successful science, rather than, for example, meteorology or zoology?

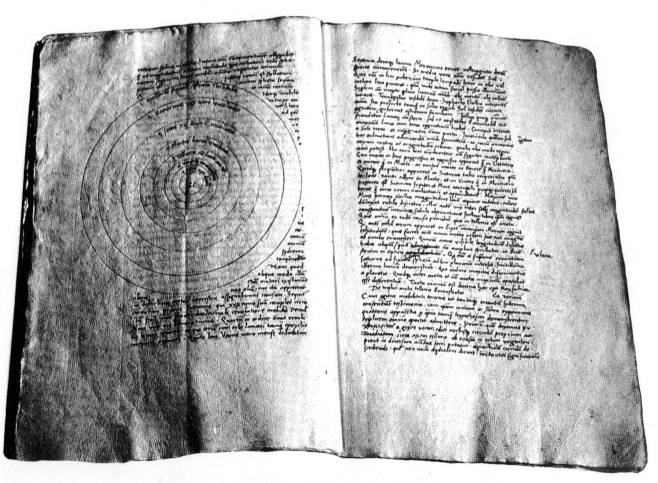

Copernicus' diagram of his heliocentric system (from his manuscript, of *De Revolutionibus*, 1543). This simplified representation omits the many small epicycles actually used in the system.

CHAPTER SIX

Does the Earth Move?—
The Work of
Copernicus and Tycho

6.1 The Copernican system

Nicolaus Copernicus (1473-1543) was a young student in Poland when America was discovered by Europeans. An outstanding astronomer and mathematician, Copernicus was also a talented and respected churchman, jurist, administrator, diplomat, physician, and economist. During his studies in Italy he read the writings of Greek and other early philosophers and astronomers. As Canon of the Cathedral of Frauenberg he was busy with civic and church affairs and also worked on calendar reform. It is said that on the day of his death in 1543, he saw the first copy of his great book, on which he had worked most of his life. It was this book which opened a whole new vision of the universe.

Copernicus titled his book *De Revolutionibus Orbium Coelestium,* or *On the Revolutions of the Heavenly Spheres.* This title suggests the early Greek notions of the spheres. Copernicus was indeed concerned with the old problem of Plato: how to construct a planetary system by combinations of the fewest possible uniform circular motions. He began his study to rid the Ptolemaic system of the equants, which seemed contrary to Plato's assumptions. In his words, taken from a short summary written about 1512,

> . . . the planetary theories of Ptolemy and most other astronomers, although consistent with the numerical data, seemed likewise to present no small difficulty. For these theories were not adequate unless certain equants were also conceived; it then appeared that a planet moved with uniform velocity neither on its deferent nor about the center of its epicycle. Hence a system of this sort seemed neither sufficiently absolute nor sufficiently pleasing to the mind.
>
> Having become aware of these defects, I often considered whether there could perhaps be found a more reasonable arrangement of circles, from which every apparent inequality would be derived and in which everything would move uniformly about its proper center.

SG 6.1

Nicolas Copernicus (1473-1543). (In Polish his name was Koppernigk, but, in keeping with the scholarly tradition of the age, he gave it the Latin form Copernicus.)

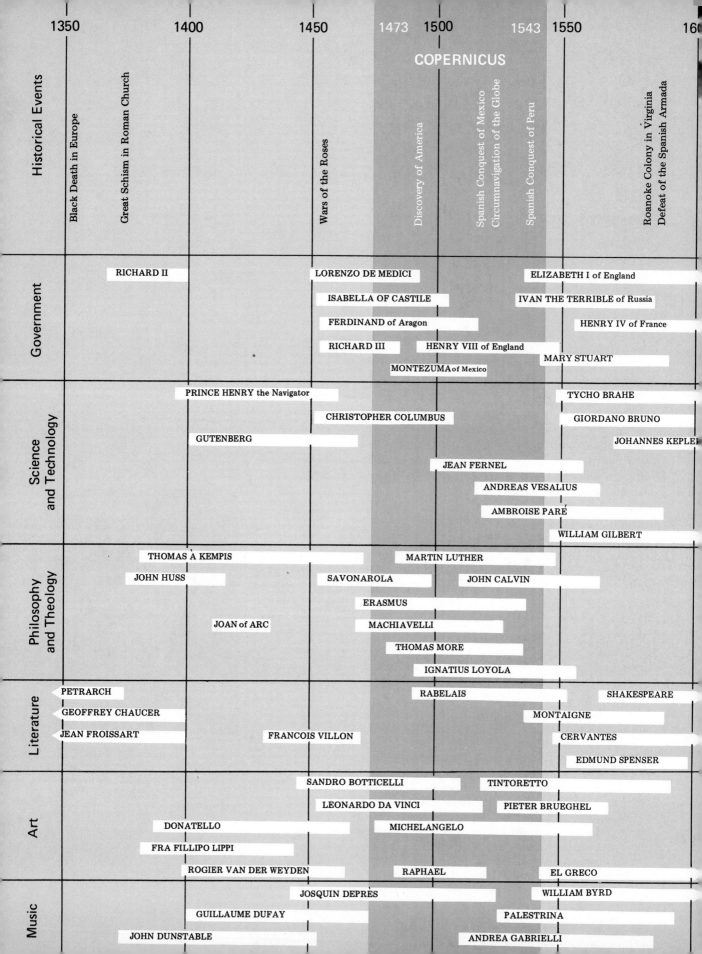

	1350	1400	1450	1473	1500	1543	1550	160

COPERNICUS

Historical Events

Black Death in Europe
Great Schism in Roman Church
Wars of the Roses
Discovery of America
Spanish Conquest of Mexico
Circumnavigation of the Globe
Spanish Conquest of Peru
Roanoke Colony in Virginia
Defeat of the Spanish Armada

Government

RICHARD II
LORENZO DE MEDICI
ELIZABETH I of England
ISABELLA OF CASTILE
IVAN THE TERRIBLE of Russia
FERDINAND of Aragon
HENRY IV of France
RICHARD III
HENRY VIII of England
MARY STUART
MONTEZUMA of Mexico

Science and Technology

PRINCE HENRY the Navigator
TYCHO BRAHE
CHRISTOPHER COLUMBUS
GIORDANO BRUNO
GUTENBERG
JOHANNES KEPLE[R]
JEAN FERNEL
ANDREAS VESALIUS
AMBROISE PARÉ
WILLIAM GILBERT

Philosophy and Theology

THOMAS À KEMPIS
MARTIN LUTHER
JOHN HUSS
SAVONAROLA
JOHN CALVIN
ERASMUS
JOAN of ARC
MACHIAVELLI
THOMAS MORE
IGNATIUS LOYOLA

Literature

PETRARCH
RABELAIS
SHAKESPEARE
GEOFFREY CHAUCER
MONTAIGNE
JEAN FROISSART
FRANCOIS VILLON
CERVANTES
EDMUND SPENSER

Art

SANDRO BOTTICELLI
TINTORETTO
LEONARDO DA VINCI
PIETER BRUEGHEL
DONATELLO
MICHELANGELO
FRA FILLIPO LIPPI
ROGIER VAN DER WEYDEN
RAPHAEL
EL GRECO

Music

JOSQUIN DEPRÈS
WILLIAM BYRD
GUILLAUME DUFAY
PALESTRINA
JOHN DUNSTABLE
ANDREA GABRIELLI

In *De Revolutionibus* he wrote:

> We must however confess that these movements [of the
> sun, moon, and planets] are circular or are composed of many
> circular movements, in that they maintain these irregularities
> in accordance with a constant law and with fixed periodic
> returns, and that could not take place, if they were not
> circular. For it is only the circle which can bring back what is
> past and over with. . . .
>
> I found first in Cicero that Nicetas thought that the Earth
> moved. And afterwards I found in Plutarch that there were
> some others of the same opinion. . . . Therefore I also . . .
> began to meditate upon the mobility of the Earth. And
> although the opinion seemed absurd, nevertheless, because I
> knew that others before me had been granted the liberty of
> constructing whatever circles they pleased in order to
> demonstrate astral phenomena, I thought that I too would be
> readily permitted to test whether or not, by the laying down
> that the Earth had some movements, demonstrations less
> shaky than those of my predecessors could be found for the
> revolutions of the celestial spheres. . . . I finally discovered by
> the help of long and numerous observations that if the
> movements of the other wandering stars are correlated with
> the circular movement of the Earth, and if the movements are
> computed in accordance with the revolution of each planet, not
> only do all their phenomena follow from that but also this
> correlation binds together so closely the order and magnitudes
> of all the planets and of their spheres or orbital circles and the
> heavens themselves that nothing can be shifted around in any
> part of them without disrupting the remaining parts and the
> universe as a whole.

In his final work, the result of nearly forty years of study, Copernicus
proposed a system of more than thirty eccentrics and epicycles. These
would, he said, "suffice to explain the entire structure of the universe and
the entire ballet of the planets." Like Ptolemy's *Almagest, De
Revolutionibus* uses long geometrical analyses and is difficult to read.
Comparison of the two books strongly suggests that Copernicus thought
he was producing an improved version of the *Almagest*. He used many of
Ptolemy's observations plus some more recent ones. Yet his system
differed from Ptolemy's in several fundamental ways. Above all, he adopted
a sun-centered system which in general matched that of Aristarchus.

Like all scientists, Copernicus made a number of assumptions in his
system. In his own words (using more modern terms in several places),
his assumptions were:

1. There is no one precise, geometrical center of all the celestial
circles or spheres.

2. The center of the earth is not the center of the universe, but
only of gravitation and of the lunar sphere.

3. All the spheres revolve about the sun . . . and therefore the
sun has a central location in the universe.

See the preface to Copernicus'
De Revolutionibus in *Reader 2.*

4. The distance from the earth to the sun is very small in comparison with the distance to the stars.

5. Whatever motion appears in the sky arises not from any motion of the sky, but from the earth's motion. The earth together with its water and air performs a complete rotation on its fixed poles in a daily motion, while the sky remains unchanged.

6. What appears to us as motions of the sun arise not from its motion but from the motion of the earth and . . . we revolve about the sun like any other planet. The earth has, then, more than one motion.

SG 6.2

7. The apparent retrograde motion of the planets arises not from their motion but from the earth's. The motions of the earth alone, therefore, are enough to explain so many apparent motions in the sky.

Compare this list with the assumptions of Ptolemy, given in Chapter 5. You will see close similarities and important differences.

Notice that Copernicus proposed that the earth rotates daily. As Aristarchus and others had realized, this rotation would explain all the daily risings and settings seen in the sky. Copernicus also proposed, as had Aristarchus, that the sun was stationary and stood at the center of the universe. The earth and other planets each moved about a different central point near the sun.

The figure at the left shows the main spheres carrying the planets around the sun (sol). Copernicus' text explains the basic features of his system:

The ideas here stated are difficult, even almost impossible, to accept; they are quite contrary to popular notions. Yet with the help of God, we will make everything as clear as day in what follows, at least for those who are not ignorant of mathematics. . . .

The first and highest of all the spheres is the sphere of the fixed stars. It encloses all the other spheres and is itself self-contained; it is immobile; it is certainly the portion of the universe with reference to which the movement and positions of all the other heavenly bodies must be considered. If some people are yet of the opinion that this sphere moves, we are of contrary mind; and after deducing the motion of the earth, we shall show why we so conclude. Saturn, first of the planets, which accomplishes its revolution in thirty years, is nearest to the first sphere. Jupiter, making its revolution in twelve years, is next. Then comes Mars, revolving once in two years. The fourth place in the series is occupied by the sphere which contains the earth and the sphere of the moon, and which performs an annual revolution. The fifth place is that of Venus, revolving in nine months. Finally, the sixth place is occupied by Mercury, revolving in eighty days. . . . In the midst of all, the sun reposes, unmoving.

Already we see an advantage in Copernicus' system that makes it "pleasing to the mind." The rates of rotation for the heavenly spheres increase progressively, from the motionless sphere of stars to speedy Mercury. The motion of each planet seems to be related to the motion of its neighbor.

SG 6.3

Q1   What reasons did Copernicus give for rejecting the use of equants?

Q2   In the following list of propositions, mark with a *P* those made by Ptolemy and with a *C* those made by Copernicus.

(a) The earth is spherical.

(b) The earth is only a point compared to the distance to the stars.

(c) The heavens rotate daily around the earth.

(d) The earth has one or more motions.

(e) Heavenly motions are circular.

(f) The observed retrograde motion of the planets results from the earth's motion around the sun.

6.2 New conclusions

A new way of looking at old observations—a new theory—can suggest quite new kinds of observations to make, or new uses for old data. Copernicus used his moving-earth model to obtain two important results which were not possible with the Ptolemaic theory. He was able to calculate (a) the period of motion of each planet around the sun, and (b) the sizes of each planet's orbit compared to the size of the earth's orbit. This, for the first time, gave a scale for the dimensions of the universe, based on observations.

To calculate the periods of the planets around the sun, Copernicus used observations recorded over many centuries. The method of calculation is similar to the "chase problem" of how often the hands of a clock pass one another. The details of this calculation are shown on page 34. In Table 6.1 below, Copernicus' results are compared with presently accepted values.

SG 6.4, 6.5

Table 6.1

PLANET	COPERNICUS' VALUE	MODERN VALUE
Mercury	0.241 y (88 d)	87.97 d
Venus	0.614 y (224 d)	224.70 d
Mars	1.88 y (687 d)	686.98 d
Jupiter	11.8 y	11.86 y
Saturn	29.5 y	29.46 y

Copernicus was also able, for the first time in history, to derive relative distances between the planets and the sun. Remember that the Ptolemaic system had no distance scale. It provided only a way of predicting the planet's angular motions and positions in the sky.

The Periods of Revolution of the Planets

The problem is to find the rate at which a planet moves around the sun by using observations made from the earth—which is itself moving around the sun. Say, for example, that a planet closer to the sun than the earth is, goes around the sun at the frequency (rate) of $1\frac{1}{4}$ cycles per year. The earth moves around the sun also, in the same direction, at the rate of 1 cycle per year. Because the earth follows along behind the planet, the planet's motion around the sun, as seen from the earth, appears to be at a rate less than $1\frac{1}{4}$ cycles per year. In fact, as the diagrams below suggest, the planet's

apparent rate of motion around the sun equals the difference between the planet's rate and the earth's rate: $1\frac{1}{4}$ cycle per·year minus 1 cycle per year, or $\frac{1}{4}$ cycle per year. In general, if an inner planet moves around the sun at frequency f_p and the earth moves around the sun with frequency f_e, then the planet's apparent rate of motion, f_{pe}, as seen from the earth, is given by $f_{pe} = f_p - f_e$.

A similar argument holds for planets farther from the sun than the earth is. (See Diagram B.) Since these "outer planets" revolve about the sun more slowly than the earth, the earth repeatedly leaves the planets behind. Consequently, for the outer planets the sign in the equation for f_{pe} is reversed: $f_{pe} = f_p + f_e$.

The apparent frequency f_{pe} represents what is actually observed. Since f_e is by definition 1 cycle per year, either equation is easily solved for the unknown actual rate f_p:

For inner planets: $f_p = 1$ cycle/yr $+ f_{pe}$
For outer planets: $f_p = 1$ cycle/yr $- f_{pe}$

Copernicus used some observations by Ptolemy and some of his own. A typical data statement in *De Revolutionibus* is "Jupiter is outrun by the earth 65 times in 71 solar years minus 5 days 45 minutes 27 seconds . . . ." In Table 6.2, Copernicus' data are rounded off to the nearest year in the first column. (They were very near to whole years to begin with.) The cycle used for the inner planets is from one position of greatest eastern displacement from the sun to the next. The cycle used for the outer planets is from one opposition to the next.

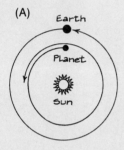

(A)

A planet that is inside the Earth's orbit and moves $1\frac{1}{4}$ revolutions around the sun in a year would, as seen from the earth, appear to have made only $\frac{1}{4}$ cycle.

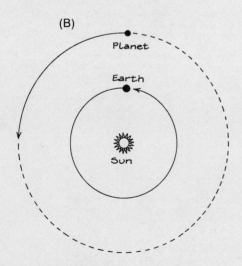

(B)

A planet that is outside the Earth's orbit and moves only $\frac{1}{4}$ revolution around the sun in a year would, as seen from the earth, appear to make about $1\frac{3}{4}$ revolution.

TABLE 6.2

	NUMBER OF YEARS OF OBSERVATION (t)	APPARENT NUMBER OF CYCLES WITH RESPECT TO SUN DURING t (n)	APPARENT FREQUENCY f_{pe} IN CYCLES PER YEAR (n/t)	FREQUENCY f_p AROUND SUN IN CYCLES PER YEAR	PERIOD AROUND SUN ($1/f_p$) IN YEARS
Mercury	46	145	3.15	4.15	0.241
Venus	8	5	0.625	1.625	0.614
Mars	79	37	0.468	0.532	1.88
Jupiter	71	65	0.915	0.085	11.8
Saturn	59	57	0.966	0.034	29.4

Ptolemy's system described the motions of the sun and five planets in terms of one-year epicycles on deferent circles. It gave only the *relative* sizes of epicycle and deferent circle, and gave them separately for each planet. Copernicus, on the other hand, described all these features of planetary motion in terms of the motion of the earth's yearly revolution *around the sun.* (The details of how this can be done are given on pages 36 and 37.) Thus, it became possible to compare the radii of the planets' orbits with the radius of the earth's orbit. Because all distances were compared to it, the average sun-earth distance is called one *astronomical unit,* and abbreviated 1 AU.

Table 6.3 below compares Copernicus' values for the orbital radii (deferent circles only, the radii of the epicycles being relatively small) with the currently accepted values for the average distances to the sun.

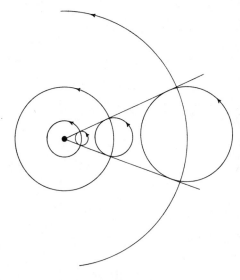

In the Ptolemaic system, only the relative size of epicycle and deferent was specified. Then size could be changed at will, so long as they kept the same proportions.

TABLE 6.3
RADII OF PLANETARY ORBITS

PLANET	COPERNICUS' VALUES	MODERN VALUE
Mercury	0.38 AU	0.39 AU
Venus	0.72	0.72
Earth	1.00	1.00
Mars	1.52	1.52
Jupiter	5.2	5.20
Saturn	9.2	9.54

Notice that Copernicus now had one system which related the size of each planet's orbit to the sizes of all the other planets' orbits. Contrast this to Ptolemy's solutions, which were completely independent for each planet. No wonder Copernicus said that "nothing can be shifted around in any part of them without disrupting the remaining parts and the universe as a whole."

SG 6.6

Q3 What new kinds of results did Copernicus obtain with a moving-earth model which were not possible with a geocentric model for the planetary system?

6.3 Arguments for the Copernican system

Copernicus knew that to many his work would seem absurd, "nay, almost contrary to ordinary human understanding," so he tried in several ways to meet the old arguments against a moving earth.

1. Copernicus argued that his assumptions agreed with religious doctrine at least as well as Ptolemy's. Copernicus' book had many sections on the faults of the Ptolemaic system (most of which had been known for centuries). Other

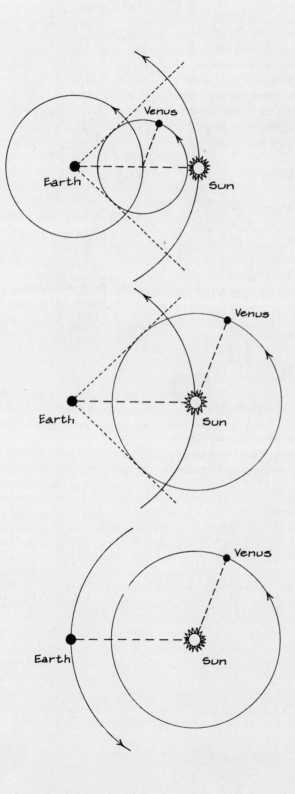

Changing Frame of Reference from the Earth to the Sun

The change of viewpoint from Ptolemy's system to Copernicus' involved what today would be called a shift in frame of reference. The apparent motion previously attributed to the deferent circles and epicycles was attributed by Copernicus to the earth's orbit and the planet's orbits around the sun.

For example, consider the motion of Venus. In Ptolemy's earth-centered system the center of Venus' epicycle was locked to the motion of the sun, as shown in the top diagram at the left. The size of Venus' deferent circle was thought to be smaller than the sun's. The epicycle was thought to be entirely between the earth and the sun. However, the observed motions to be explained by the system *required* only a certain *relative* size of epicycle and deferent. The deferent could be changed to any size, as long as the epicycle was changed proportionally.

The first step toward a sun-centered system is taken by moving the center of Venus' 1-year deferent out to the sun. Venus' epicycle is enlarged proportionally, as shown in the middle diagram at the left. Now the planet moves about the sun, while the sun moves about the earth. Tycho Brahe later proposed such a system with all visible planets moving about the moving sun.

Copernicus went further. He accounted for the relative motion of the earth and sun by considering the earth to be moving around the sun, instead of the sun moving about the earth. In the Copernican system, Venus' enlarged epicycle becomes its orbit around the sun. Meanwhile, its deferent is replaced by the earth's orbit around the sun. See the bottom diagram at the left. All three systems, Ptolemy's, Copernicus', and Tycho's, explain the same observations.

For the outer planets the argument is similar, but the roles of epicycle and deferent circle are reversed. For the outer planets on the Ptolemaic model, the epicycles instead of the deferent circles had 1-year periods and moved in parallel with the sun in its orbit. The sizes of the deferents were chosen so that the epicycle of each planet would just miss the epicycles of the planets next nearest and next farthest from the sun. (This was a beautiful example of a simplifying assumption—it filled the space with no overlap and no gaps.) This system is represented in the top diagram at the right; the planets are shown in the unlikely condition of having their epicycle centers along a single line.

The first step in shifting to a sun-centered view for these planets involves adjusting the sizes of the deferent circles, keeping the epicycles in proportion. Eventually the 1-year epicycles are the same size as the sun's 1-year orbit. See the middle diagram at the right. Next, the sun's apparent yearly motion around the earth is explained just as well by having the earth revolve around the sun. Also, the same earth orbit would explain the retrograde loops associated with the outer planets' matched 1-year epicycles. So all the matched epicycles of the outer planets and the sun's orbit are replaced by the *single* device of the earth's orbit around the sun. This shift is shown in the bottom diagram at the right. The deferent circles of the outer planets become their orbits around the sun.

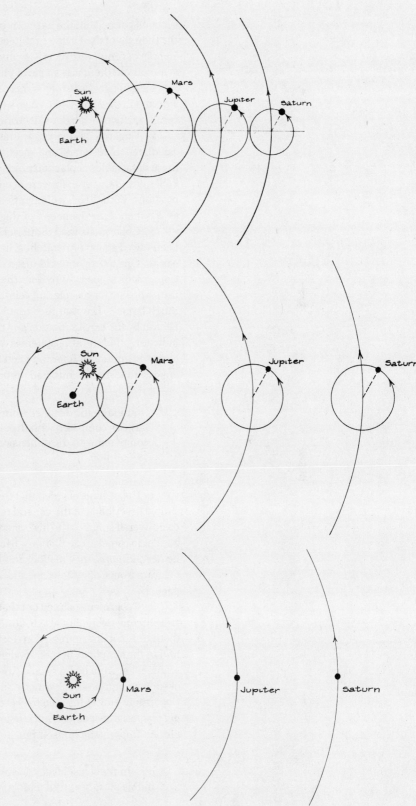

sections pointed out the harmony of his own system and how well it reflected the thought of the Divine Architect. To Copernicus, as to many scholars, complex events were merely symbols of God's thinking. To find order and symmetry in them was an act of piety, for order and symmetry were proofs of God's existence. Copernicus was a church official. He would have been stunned to think that, in Galileo's time, his theory would contribute to the conflict between religious doctrine and science.

2. Copernicus' analysis was as thorough as that of Ptolemy. He carefully calculated relative radii and speeds of the circular motions in his system. From these data, tables of planetary motion could be made. Actually, the theories of Ptolemy and Copernicus were about equally accurate in predicting planetary positions. Both theories often differed from the observed positions by as much as 2° (about four diameters of the moon).

3. Copernicus tried to answer several other objections. Most of them had been raised against Aristarchus' heliocentric system nearly nineteen centuries earlier. One argument held that a rapidly rotating earth would surely fly apart. Copernicus replied, "Why does the defender of the geocentric theory not fear the same fate for his rotating celestial sphere—so much faster because so much larger?" It was argued that birds and clouds in the sky would be left behind by the earth's rotation and revolution. He answered this objection by indicating that the atmosphere is dragged along with the earth. To the lack of observed annual shift for the fixed stars, he could only give the same kind of answer that Aristarchus had proposed:

> . . . though the distance from the sun to the earth appears very large as compared with the size of the spheres of some planets, yet compared with the dimensions of the sphere of the fixed stars, it is as nothing.

4. Copernicus claimed that the greatest advantage of his scheme was its simple description of the general motions of the planets. There certainly is a basic overall simplicity to his system as appears in his own diagram on page 28. Yet for precise calculations, because Copernicus would not use equants, he needed *more* small motions than did Ptolemy to explain the observations. A diagram from Copernicus' manuscript, showing more detail, is reproduced on page 42.

5. Copernicus pointed out that the simplicity of his system was not merely convenient, but also beautiful and "pleasing to the mind." This sort of thought is not often stressed in textbooks. But the pleasure which scientists find in the simplicity of their models is one of the most powerful experiences in science. Far from being a "cold," merely logical exercise, scientific work is full of such recognitions of harmony and beauty. Another sign of beauty that Copernicus saw in his system was the central place given to the sun, the biggest, brightest object in the heavens—the giver of light and warmth and life. As Copernicus himself put it:

> In the midst of all, the sun reposes, unmoving. Who, indeed, in this most beautiful temple would place the light-giver in any

other part than whence it can illumine all other parts? So we find
underlying this ordination an admirable symmetry in the Universe
and a clear bond of the harmony in the motion and magnitude of
the spheres, such as can be discovered in no other wise.

Look again at SG 6.2

Q4 Which of these arguments did Copernicus use in favor of his
system?
  (a) it was obvious to ordinary common sense
  (b) it was consistent with Christian beliefs
  (c) it was much more accurate in predicting planet positions
  (d) its simplicity made it beautiful
  (e) the stars showed an annual shift in position due to the earth's motion
      around the sun
Q5 What were the largest differences between observed planetary
positions and those predicted by Ptolemy? by Copernicus?
Q6 Did the Copernican system allow simple calculations of where the
planets should be seen?

6.4 Arguments against the Copernican system

Copernicus' hopes for acceptance of his theory were not quickly fulfilled.
More than a hundred years passed before the heliocentric system was
generally accepted even by astronomers. And even then, the acceptance came
on the basis of arguments quite different from those of Copernicus. In the
meantime the theory and its few defenders met powerful opposition. Most of
the criticisms were the same as those used by Ptolemy against Aristarchus.

1. Apart from its apparent simplicity, the Copernican system had no clear
scientific advantages over the geocentric theory. No known observation was
explained by one system and not by the other. Copernicus had a different
viewpoint. But he had no new types of observations, no experimental data that
could not be explained by the old theory. Furthermore, the accuracy of his
predictions of planetary positions was little better than that of Ptolemy. As
Francis Bacon wrote in the early seventeenth century: "Now it is easy to see
that both they who think the earth revolves and they who hold the old
construction are about equally and indifferently supported by the
phenomena."

Basically, the rival systems differed in their choice of a reference frame for
describing the observed motions. Copernicus himself stated the problem
clearly:

Although there are so many authorities for saying that the
Earth rests in the centre of the world that people think the
contrary supposition . . . ridiculous; . . . if, however, we consider
the thing attentively, we will see that the question has not yet been

Ptolemy too had recognized the possibility of alternative frames of reference. (Reread the quotation on p. 22 in Ch. 5.) Most of Ptolemy's followers did not share this insight.

decided and accordingly is by no means to be scorned. For every apparent change in place occurs on account of the movement either of the thing seen or of the spectator, or on account of the necessarily unequal movement of both. For no movement is perceptible relatively to things moved equally in the same directions—I mean relatively to the thing seen and the spectator. Now it is from the Earth that the celestial circuit is beheld and presented to our sight. Therefore, if some movement should belong to the Earth . . . it will appear, in the parts of the universe which are outside, as the same movement but in the opposite direction, as though the things outside were passing over. And the daily revolution . . . is such a movement.

Here Copernicus invites the reader to shift the frame of reference from the earth to a remote position overlooking the whole system with the sun at its center. As you may know from personal experience, such a shift is not easy. We can sympathize with those who preferred to hold to an earth-centered system for describing what they saw.

Physicists now generally agree that *any* system of reference may in principle be used for describing phenomena. But some systems are easier and others more complex to use or think about. Copernicus and those who followed him felt that the heliocentric system was right in some absolute sense—that the sun was really fixed in space. The same claim was made for the earth by his opponents. But the modern attitude is that the best frame of reference is the one which allows the simplest discussion of the problem being studied. We should not speak of reference systems as being right or wrong, but rather as being convenient or inconvenient. (To this day, navigators use a geocentric model for their calculations. See the page of a navigation book shown on page 41.) Yet even though different frames of reference are possible mathematically, some reference systems may involve philosophical assumptions that are unacceptable to some others.

2. The lack of an observable annual shift for the fixed stars spoke against Copernicus' model. His only possible reply was unacceptable because it meant that the stars were at an enormous distance away from the earth. Naked-eye instruments allowed positions in the sky to be measured to a precision of about 1/10°. But for an annual shift to be less than 1/10°, the stars would have to be

SG 6.8

more than 1,000 times farther from the sun than the earth is! To us this is no shock, because we live in a society that accepts the idea of enormous extensions in space and in time. Even so, such distances strain our imagination. To the opponents of Copernicus such distances were absurd. Indeed, even if an annual shift in star position had been observable, it might not have been accepted as unmistakable evidence against one and for the other theory. One can usually modify a theory more or less pleasingly to fit in a bothersome finding.

SG 6.7

The Copernican system demanded other conclusions that puzzled or threatened its critics. Copernicus determined the actual distances between the sun and the planetary orbits. Perhaps, then, the Copernican system was not just a mathematical model for predicting the positions of the planets! Perhaps Copernicus was describing a real system of planetary orbits in space (as he thought he was). But this would be difficult to accept, for the described orbits were far apart. Even the small epicycles which Copernicus still used to explain variations in planetary motions did not fill up the spaces between the planets. Then what did fill up these spaces? Because Aristotle had stated that "nature abhors a vacuum," it was agreed that something had to fill all that space. Even many of those who believed in Copernicus' system felt that space should contain something. Some of these scholars imagined various invisible fluids to fill up the emptiness. More recently, similar imaginary fluids were used in theories of chemistry and of heat, light, and electricity.

3. No definite decision between the Ptolemaic and the Copernican theories could be made on the astronomical evidence. Therefore, attention was focused on the argument concerning the central, immovable position of the earth. Despite his efforts, Copernicus could not persuade most of his readers that his heliocentric system reflected the mind of God as closely as the geocentric system. All religious faiths in Europe, including the new Protestants, opposed him. They used biblical quotations (for example, *Joshua* 10:12-13) to assert that the Divine Architect must have worked from a Ptolemaic blueprint. Indeed, Martin Luther called Copernicus "the fool who would overturn the whole science of astronomy."

Eventually, in 1616, more storm clouds were raised by the case of Galileo. The Inquisition put *De Revolutionibus* on the *Index* of forbidden books as "false and altogether opposed to Holy Scriptures." Some Jewish communities also prohibited the teaching of Copernicus's theory. It seems that humanity, believing itself central to God's plan, had to insist that the earth stood at the center of the physical universe.

The assumption that the earth was not the center of the universe was offensive enough. But worse, the Copernican system suggested that the other planets were similar to the earth. Thus, the concept of the distinctly different heavenly matter was threatened. What next? What if some rash person suggested that the sun and possibly even the stars were made of earthly materials? If other celestial bodies were similar to the earth, they might even be inhabited. And the inhabitants might be heathens, or beings as well-beloved by God as humans—possibly even more beloved! Thus, the whole Copernican scheme led to profound philosophical questions which the Ptolemaic scheme avoided.

4. The Copernican theory conflicted with the basic ideas of Aristotelian physics. This conflict is well described by H. Butterfield in *Origins of Modern Science:*

> . . . at least some of the economy of the Copernican system is
> rather an optical illusion of more recent centuries. We nowadays
> may say that it requires smaller effort to move the earth round
> upon its axis than to swing the whole universe in a twenty-four
> hour revolution about the earth; but in the Aristotelian physics it
> required something colossal to shift the heavy and sluggish earth,
> while all the skies were made of a subtle substance that was
> supposed to have no weight, and they were comparatively easy to
> turn, since turning was concordant with their nature. Above all, if
> you grant Copernicus a certain advantage in respect of

CELESTIAL OBSERVATIONS

By PHILIP KISSAM, C. E.
*Professor of Civil Engineering,
Princeton University*

I. The Principles upon which Celestial Observations are Based.

A. CONCEPTS.

1. **The Celestial Sphere.** To simplify the computations necessary for the determinations of the direction of the meridian, of latitude, and of longitude or time, certain concepts of the heavens have been generally adopted. They are the following:

  a. The earth is stationary.

  b. The heavenly bodies have been projected outward, along lines which extend from the center of the earth, to a sphere of infinite radius called the *celestial sphere.*

The celestial sphere has the following characteristics:

  a. Its center is at the center of the earth.

  b. Its equator is on the projection of the earth's equator.

  c. With respect to the earth, the celestial sphere rotates from east to west about a line which coincides with the earth's axis. Accordingly, the poles of the celestial sphere are at the prolongations of the earth's poles.

  d. The speed of rotation of the celestial sphere is 360° 59.15' per 24 hours.

  e. With the important exception of bodies in the solar system, which change position slowly, all heavenly bodies remain practically fixed in their positions on the celestial sphere, never changing more than negligible amounts in 24 hours, and accordingly are often called *fixed stars.*

Celestial navigation involves comparing the apparent position of the sun (or star) with the "actual" position as given in a table called an "ephemeris." Above is an excerpt from the introduction to the tables in the *Solar Ephemeris* for 1950. (Keuffel and Esser Co.)

que ipi d. fuerit æqualis. f quoqz sinu excentri̅
sedm distantia clm æqualem ipi . df . et g.
similiter sedm ig et r n distantias
æquales . Interea si centru̅ terræ
iam emensum fuerit utrumque
f o circumferentia sedm ar sui
epicycly, iam ipm o no describit
excentru̅ q cui centru̅ in a c
linea contingat : sed in ea que
ipi d o parallelus fuerit qualis
est L p . Quod si etia remurgant
o i et r p erunt et ipæ æquales
minores aute ipis . f et r m et
angulus d i o angulo r p l . p vij primi Euclit : et pro tanto videbi̅ (æquales)
Sohs apogeu̅ in r p linea predere
ipm a . Huic etia manifestum est
p excentrepicyclu̅ idem contingere
quoma in persistente centro q̅ descrip-
serit d epicyclu̅ circa L centru̅, centru̅ terræ
volvatur in f o circumferentia pdictis reditionibus : hoc est
plus moduro q̅ fuerit annua revolutio. Sup̅ inducet enim et q̅ anxa
alterum excentru̅ priori circa p centru̅ : accidentq̅ prorsus
eade. Cumq̅ tot modi ad eunde numeru̅ sese conferrent
quis lorum habeat haut facile dixerim : nisi quod illa nu̅-
merorum ac apparentiu̅ ppetua consonantia credere rogit
eorum esse aliquem

  Quanta sit secunda Solaris inæqualitatis differentia Cap xx
Cum igitur iam visum fuerit : quod ista secunda iæqualitas
prima ac simplic . Nam anomalia obliqtatis signiferi vel
eius similitudine sequeretur : certas habebimus eius diffe-
rentias, si no obstiterit error aliquis observatoru̅ pterorum
Habemus eni̅ ipam simplic anomalia anno Christi M D xv
sedm numeratione grad clxxo comp fere : et eius
principiu̅ facta retrorsum supputatione sexaginta fere
annis ante Christu̅ natum, et colligentur anni MDlxxv
Illui au̅ a quo principiu̅ inventa excentrotes maxima partiu̅ 4 1 7
quarumq̅ q ex centro orbis esset 10000 : nra vero, ut

        a nobis

geometrical simplicity, the sacrifice that had to be made for the sake of this was tremendous. You lost the whole cosmology associated with Aristotelianism—the whole intricately dovetailed system in which the nobility of the various elements and the hierarchical arrangement of these had been so beautifully interlocked. In fact, you had to throw overboard the very framework of existing science, and it was here that Copernicus clearly failed to discover a satisfactory alternative. He provided a neater geometry of the heavens, but it was one which made nonsense of the reasons and explanations that had previously been given to account for the movements in the sky.

In short, the sun-centered Copernican scheme was scientifically equivalent to the Ptolemaic scheme in explaining astronomical observations. But, philosophically, it seemed false, absurd, and dangerous. Most learned Europeans at that time recognized the Bible and the writings of Aristotle as their two supreme sources of authority. Both appeared to be challenged by the Copernican system. The freedom of thought that marked the Renaissance was just beginning. But the old image of the universe provided security and stability to many. Belief in a sun-centered rather than an earth-centered universe allowed a gain in simplicity. But it seemed in Copernicus' time to contradict all common sense and observation. And it required a revolution in philosophy, religion, and the physical science of the time. No wonder Copernicus had so few believers!

Conflicts between accepted beliefs and the philosophical content of new scientific theories have occurred many times, and are bound to occur again. During the last century there were at least two such conflicts. Neither is completely resolved today. In biology, the theory of evolution based on Darwin's work has caused major philosophical and religious reactions. In physics, developing theories of atoms, relativity, and quantum mechanics have challenged long-held assumptions about the nature of the world and our knowledge of reality. Units 4 and 5, and the Supplemental Unit *The Nucleus* touch upon these new theories. As the dispute between the Copernicans and the Ptolemaists illustrates, the assumptions which "common sense" defends so fiercely are often only the remains of an earlier, less complete scientific theory.

SG 6.9

Q7 Why were many people, such as Francis Bacon, undecided about the correctness of the Ptolemaic and Copernican systems?

Q8 How did the astronomical argument become involved with religious beliefs?

Q9 From a modern viewpoint, was the Ptolemaic or the Copernican system of reference more valid?

Opposite: A page from Copernicus' manuscript of *De Revolutionibus*, showing detail of some epicycles in his model.

6.5 Historical consequences

Eventually Copernicus' moving-earth model was accepted. But acceptance came very slowly. Consider, for example, a passage in the diary of John Adams, who later became the second president of the United States. Adams wrote that he attended a lecture at Harvard College in which the correctness of the Copernican viewpoint was debated—on June 19, 1753.

Soon we will study the work which gradually led to general acceptance of the heliocentric viewpoint. We will see that the detailed Copernican system of uniform circular motions with eccentrics and epicycles eventually was dropped. But this point scarcely diminishes the scientific importance of Copernicus' work. The heliocentric view opened a new approach to understanding planetary motion. This new way became dynamic, rather than just kinematic. It involved the laws relating force and motion, developed in the 150 years after Copernicus, and the application of these laws to motions in the heavens.

The Copernican model with moving earth and fixed sun opened a floodgate of new possibilities for analysis and description. According to this model the planets could be thought of as real bodies moving along actual orbits. Now Kepler and others could consider these planetary paths in quite new ways. In science, the sweep of possibilities usually cannot be foreseen by those who begin the revolution—or by their critics.

Today Copernicus is honored not so much for the details of his theory, but because he successfully challenged the prevailing world-picture. His theory became a major force in the intellectual revolution which shook humanity out of its self-centered view of the universe. As people gradually accepted the Copernican system, they also had to accept the view that the earth was only one of several planets circling the sun. Thus, it became increasingly difficult to believe that all creation centered on human beings. At the same time, the new system stimulated a new self-reliance and curiosity about the world.

SG 6.10

Acceptance of a revolutionary idea based on quite new assumptions, such as Copernicus' shift of the frame of reference, is always slow. Sometimes compromise theories are proposed as attempts to unite conflicting theories, to "split the difference." As you will see in later units, such compromises are rarely successful. But often they do stimulate new observations and concepts. In turn, these may lead to a very useful development or restatement of the original revolutionary theory.

Such a restatement of the heliocentric theory came during the 150 years after Copernicus. Many scientists provided observations and ideas. In Chapters 7 and 8 we will follow the major contributions made by Kepler, Galileo, and Isaac Newton. But first we will consider the work of Tycho Brahe, who devoted his life to improving the precision with which planetary positions were observed and to the working out of a compromise theory of planetary motion.

Q10   In terms of our historical perspective, what were the greatest contributions of Copernicus to modern planetary theory?

6.6 Tycho Brahe

Tycho Brahe was born in 1546 of a noble, but not particularly rich, Danish family. By the time he was thirteen or fourteen, he had become intensely interested in astronomy. Although he was studying law, he secretly spent his allowance on astronomical tables and books. He read the *Almagest* and *De Revolutionibus*. Soon he discovered that both Ptolemy and Copernicus had relied upon tables of planetary positions that were inaccurate. He concluded that astronomy needed new observations of the highest possible precision gathered over many years. Only then could a satisfactory theory of planetary motion be created.

Tycho's interest in studying the heavens was increased by an exciting celestial event. Although the ancients had taught that the stars were unchanging, a "new star" appeared in the constellation Cassiopeia in 1572. It soon became as bright as Venus and could be seen even during the daytime. Then over several years it faded until it was no longer visible. To Tycho these events were astonishing—changes in the starry sky! Evidently at least one assumption of the ancients was wrong. Perhaps other assumptions were wrong too.

After observing and writing about the new star, Tycho traveled through northern Europe. He met many other astronomers and collected books. Apparently he was considering moving to Germany or Switzerland where he could easily meet other astronomers. To keep the young scientist in Denmark, King Frederick II offered him an entire small island and also the income from various farms. This income would allow Tycho to build an observatory on the island and to staff and maintain it. He accepted the offer, and in a few years Uraniborg ("Castle of the Heavens") was built. It was an impressive structure with four large observatories, a library, a laboratory, shops, and living quarters for staff, students, and observers. There was even a complete printing plant. Tycho estimated that the observatory cost Frederick II more than a ton of gold. For its time, this magnificent laboratory was at least as important, complex, and expensive as some of today's great research centers. Uraniborg was a place where scientists, technicians, and students from many lands could gather to study astronomy. Here was a unity of action, a group effort under the leadership of an imaginative scientist to advance the boundaries of knowledge in one science.

In 1577 Tycho observed a bright comet, a fuzzy object whose motion seemed irregular, unlike the orderly motions of the planets. To find the distance to the comet, Tycho compared its position as observed from Denmark with is positions as observed from elsewhere in Europe. Some of these observation points lay hundreds of miles apart. Yet, at any given time, all observers reported the comet as having the same position with respect to the stars. By contrast, the moon's position in the sky was measurably different when observed from places so far apart. Therefore, Tycho concluded, the comet must be at least several times farther away than the moon.

This was an important conclusion. Up to that time comets had been believed to be some sort of local event, like clouds or lightning. Now comets had to be considered distant astronomical objects from the realm

Although there were precision sighting instruments, all observations were with the naked eye—the telescope was not to be invented for another 50 years.

Two articles on comets appear in Reader 2: "The Great Comet of 1965" and "The Boy Who Redeemed His Father's Name."

At the top left is a plan of the observatory and gardens built for Tycho Brahe at Uraniborg, Denmark.

The cross section of the observatory, above center, shows where most of the important instruments including large models of the celestial spheres were housed.

The picture at the left shows the room containing Tycho's great quadrant. On the walls are pictures of some of his instruments. He is making an observation, aided by assistants.

Above is a portrait of Tycho, painted about 1597.

The bright comet of 1965.

of eternal things beyond the moon. Stranger still, they seemed to move right through the crystalline spheres that were still generally believed to carry the planets. Tycho's book on this comet was widely read and helped to weaken old beliefs about the nature of the heavens.

SG 6.11

Q11 What event stimulated Tycho's interest in astronomy?

Q12 In what ways was Tycho's observatory like a modern research institute?

Q13 Why were Tycho's conclusions about the comet of 1577 important?

6.7 Tycho's observations

Tycho's fame results from his lifelong devotion to making unusually accurate observations of the positions of the stars, sun, moon, and planets. He did this before the telescope was invented. Over the centuries many talented observers had recorded the positions of the celestial objects. But the accuracy of Tycho's work was much greater than that of the best astronomers before him. How was Tycho Brahe able to do what no others had done before?

Singleness of purpose certainly aided Tycho. He knew that highly precise observations must be made during many years. For this he needed improved instruments that would give consistent readings. Fortunately, he had the mechanical skill to devise such instruments. He also had the funds to pay for their construction and use.

Tycho's first improvement on the astronomical instruments of the day was to make them larger. Most of the earlier instruments had been rather small, of a size that could be moved by one person. In comparison, Tycho's instruments were gigantic. For instance, one of his early devices for measuring the angular altitude of planets had a radius of about six feet. This wooden instrument, shown in the etching on page 48, was so large that it took several men to set it into position. Tycho put his instruments on heavy, firm foundations or attached them to a wall that ran exactly north-south. By fixing the instruments so solidly, Tycho increased the reliability of the readings over long periods of time.

For a more modern example of this same problem of instrumentation, you may wish to read about the development and construction of the 200-inch Hale telescope on Mt. Palomar. Also see "A Night at the Observatory" in *Reader 2*.

One of Tycho's sighting devices. Unfortunately Tycho's instruments were destroyed in 1619 during the Thirty Years War.

Throughout his career Tycho created better sighting devices, more precise scales, and stronger support systems. He made dozens of other changes in design which increased the precision of the observations.

Tycho did more than just devise better instruments for making his observations. He also determined and specified the actual limits of precision of each instrument. He realized that merely making larger and larger instruments does not always result in greater precision. In fact, the very size of the instrument can cause errors, since the parts bend under their own weight. Tycho tried to make his instruments as large and strong as he could without introducing such errors. Furthermore, in modern style, he calibrated each instrument and determined its range of error. (Nowadays many commercial instrument makers supply a measurement report with scientific instruments designed for precision work. Such reports are usually in the form of a table of small corrections that have to be applied to the direct readings.)

Apparent distortion of the setting sun. The light's path through the earth's atmosphere is bent, making the sun appear flattened and rough-edged.

Like Ptolemy and the Muslim astronomers, Tycho knew that the light coming from any celestial body was bent downward by the earth's atmosphere. He knew that this bending, or *refraction,* increased as the celestial object neared the horizon. To improve the precision of his observations, Tycho carefully determined the amount of refraction involved. Thus, each observation could be corrected for refraction effects. Such careful work was essential to the making of improved records.

Tycho worked at Uraniborg from 1576 to 1597. After the death of King Frederick II, the Danish government became less interested in helping to pay the cost of Tycho's observatory. Yet Tycho was unwilling to consider any reductions in the cost of his activities. Because he was promised support by Emperor Rudolph of Bohemia, Tycho moved his records and several instruments to Prague. There, fortunately, he hired as an assistant an able, imaginative young man named Johannes Kepler. When Tycho died in 1601, Kepler obtained all his records of observations of the motion of Mars. As Chapter 7 reports, Kepler's analysis of Tycho's data solved many of the ancient problems of planetary motion.

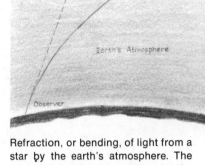

Refraction, or bending, of light from a star by the earth's atmosphere. The amount of refraction shown in the figure is greatly exaggerated over what actually occurs.

Q14   What improvements did Tycho make in astronomical instruments?

Q15   In what way did Tycho correct his observations to provide records of higher accuracy?

6.8 Tycho's compromise system

Tycho hoped that his observations would provide a basis for a new theory of planetary motion, which he had outlined in an early book. He saw the simplicity of the Copernican system, in which the planets moved around the sun. But he could not accept the idea that the earth had any motion. In Tycho's system, all the planets except the earth moved around the sun. Meanwhile, the sun moved around the stationary earth, as shown in the sketch in the margin. Thus Tycho devised a compromise model which, as he said, included the best features of both the Ptolemaic and the Copernican systems. However, he did not live to publish quantitative details of his theory.

The compromise Tychonic system was accepted by only a few people. Those who accepted the Ptolemaic model objected to having the planets moving around the sun. Those who accepted the Copernican model objected to having the earth held stationary. So the argument continued. Many scholars clung to the seemingly self-evident position that the earth was stationary. Others accepted, at least partially, the strange, exciting proposals of Copernicus that the earth might rotate and revolve around the sun. The choice depended mainly on one's philosophy. For, in fact, each of the three systems could explain the observed evidence about equally well.

All planetary theories up to that time had been developed only to

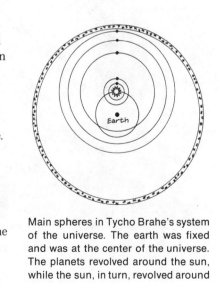

Main spheres in Tycho Brahe's system of the universe. The earth was fixed and was at the center of the universe. The planets revolved around the sun, while the sun, in turn, revolved around the fixed earth.

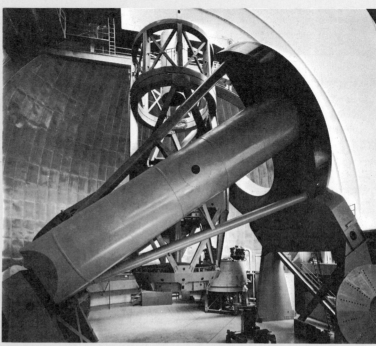

Buildings and instruments of modern observatories. Top: the 200-inch telescope and its dome on Mt. Palomar. Bottom: the complex of buildings on Mt. Wilson.

provide some system for predicting the positions of the planets fairly precisely. In the terms used in Unit 1, these would be called kinematic descriptions. The causes of the motions—what we now call dynamics—had not been considered in any detail. Aristotle had described angular motions of objects in the heavens as "natural." Everyone, including Ptolemy, Copernicus, and Tycho, agreed. Celestial objects were still considered to be completely different from earthly materials and to behave in quite different ways. *That a single theory of dynamics could describe both earthly and heavenly motions was a revolutionary idea yet to be proposed.*

As long as there was no explanation of the causes of motion, a basic problem remained unsolved. Were the orbits proposed for the planets in the various systems actual paths of real objects in space? Or were they only convenient imaginary devices for making computations? The status of the problem in the early seventeenth century was later described well by the English poet John Milton in *Paradise Lost:*

> . . . He his fabric of the Heavens
> Hath left to their disputes, perhaps to move
> His laughter at their quaint opinions wide
> Hereafter, when they come to model Heaven
> And calculate the stars, how they will wield
> The mighty frame, how build, unbuild, contrive
> To save appearances, how gird the sphere
> With centric and eccentric scribbled o'er
> Cycle and epicycle, orb in orb.

The eventual success of Newton's universal dynamics led to the belief that scientists were describing the "real world." This belief was held confidently for about two centuries. Later chapters of this text deal with recent discoveries and theories which have lessened this confidence. Today, scientists and philosophers are much less certain that the common-sense notion of "reality" is very useful in science.

Q16 In what ways did Tycho's system for planetary motions resemble the Ptolemaic and the Copernican systems?

This announces the first example of the highly successful trend of modern science toward synthesis: not two or more kinds of science, but only one. Later on: not a separate physics of energy in each branch, but one conservation law; not separate physics for optical, heat, electric, magnetic phenomena, but one (Maxwell's); not two kinds of beings—animal and human—but one (in Darwinian views); not space and time separately, but space-time; not mass and energy separately, but mass-energy, etc. Up to a point at least, the great advances of science are the results of such daring extensions of one set of ideas into new fields. The danger is the false extrapolation—that science by itself can solve all problems, including political, health, education, and "explain" all human emotions. The greater majority of and the best scientists don't think so, but many nonscientists falsely believe that all scientists do.

SG 6.12

6.1 The Project Physics learning materials particularly appropriate for Chapter 6 include the following:

Experiments
The Shape of the Earth's Orbit
Using Lenses to Make a Telescope

Activities
Frames of Reference

Reader Articles
The Boy Who Redeemed His Father's Name
The Great Comet of 1965
A Night at the Observatory

Film Loop
Retrograde Motion—Heliocentric Model

6.2 The first diagram on the next page shows numbered positions of the sun and Mars (on its epicycle) at equal time intervals in their motion around the earth, as described in the Ptolemaic system. You can easily redraw the relative positions to change from the earth's frame of reference to the sun's. Mark a sun-sized circle in the middle of a thin piece of paper; this will be a frame of reference centered on the sun. Place the circle over each successive position of the sun, and trace the corresponding numbered position of Mars and the position of the earth. (Be sure to keep the piece of paper straight.) When you have done this for all 15 positions, you will have a diagram of the motions of Mars and the earth as seen in the sun's frame of reference.

6.3 What reasons did Copernicus give for believing that the sun is fixed at or near the center of the planetary system?

6.4 Consider the short and long hands of a clock or watch. If, starting from 12:00 o'clock, you rode on the slow short hand, how many times in 12 hours would the long hand pass you? If you are not certain, slowly turn the hands of a clock or watch, and keep count. From this information, can you derive a relation by which you could conclude that the period of the long hand around the center was one hour?

6.5 The diagram at the upper right section of the next page shows the motions of Mercury and Venus east and west of the sun as seen from the earth during 1966-1967. The time scale is indicated at 10-day intervals along the central line of the sun's position.

(a) Can you explain why Mercury and Venus appear to move from farthest east to farthest west more quickly than from farthest west to farthest east?
(b) From this diagram can you find a period for Mercury's apparent position in the sky relative to the sun?
(c) Can you derive a period for Mercury's actual orbital motion around the sun?
(d) What are the major sources of uncertainty in the results you derived?
(e) Similarly, can you estimate the orbital period of Venus?

6.6 From the sequence of orbital radii from Mercury to Saturn, guess what the orbital radius would be for a new planet if one were discovered. What is the basis for your guess?

6.7 If you have had some trigonometry, try this problem: the largest observed annual shift in star position is about 1/2400 of a degree. What is the distance (in AU's) to this closest star?

6.8 How might a Ptolemaic astronomer have modified the geocentric system to account for observed stellar parallax?

6.9 Do you know of any conflicts between scientific theories and common sense today?

6.10 How did the Copernican system encourage the suspicion that there might be life on objects other than the earth? Is such a possibility seriously considered today? What important kinds of questions would such a possibility raise?

6.11 How can you explain the observed motion of Halley's comet during 1909-1910, as shown on the star chart on the next page?

6.12 To what extent do you feel that the Copernican system, with its many motions in eccentrics and epicycles, reveals real paths in space, rather than being only another way of computing planetary positions?

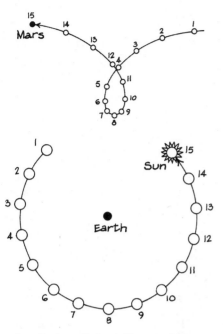

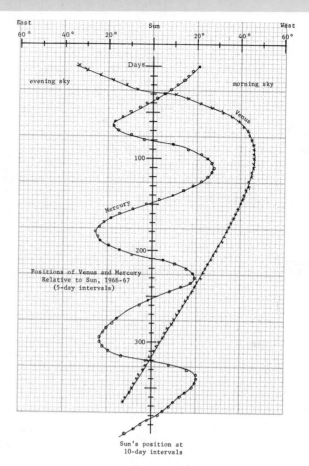

Apparent motion of Mars and Sun around the earth.

Positions of Venus and Mercury relative to Sun.

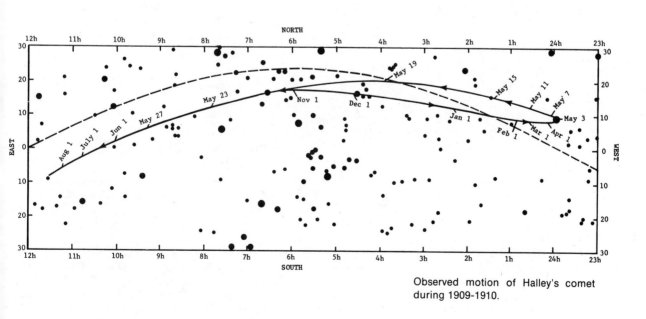

Observed motion of Halley's comet during 1909-1910.

Galileo's notes on his observations beginning "on day 7 of January 1610."

CHAPTER SEVEN

A New Universe Appears—
The Work of Kepler and Galileo

7.1 The abandonment of uniform circular motion

SG 7.1

Kepler's lifelong desire was to perfect the heliocentric theory. He viewed the harmony and simplicity of that theory with "incredible and ravishing delight." To Kepler, such patterns of geometric order and numerical relation offered clues to God's mind. He sought to unfold these patterns further through the heliocentric theory. In his first major work, he attempted to explain the spacing of the planetary orbits as calculated by Copernicus (page 35 of Chapter 6).

Kepler was searching for the reasons why there are just six visible planets (including the earth) and why they are spaced as they are. These are excellent scientific questions, but even today they are too difficult to answer. Kepler thought that the key lay in geometry. He began to wonder whether there was any relation between the six known planets and the five "regular solids." A regular solid is a polyhedron whose faces all have equal sides and angles. From the time of the Greeks, it was known that there are just five regular geometrical solids. Kepler imagined a model in which these five regular solids nested one inside the other, somewhat like a set of mixing bowls. Between the five solids would be spaces for four planetary spheres. A fifth sphere could rest inside the whole nest and a sixth sphere could lie around the outside. Kepler then sought some sequence of the five solids that, just touching the spheres, would space the spheres at the same relative distance from the center as were the planetary orbits. Kepler said:

> I took the dimensions of the planetary orbits according to the astronomy of Copernicus, who makes the sun immobile in the center, and the earth movable both around the sun and upon its own axis; and I showed that the differences of their orbits corresponded to the five regular Pythagorean figures. . . .

The five "perfect solids" taken from Kepler's *Harmonices Mundi* (Harmony of the World). The cube is a regular solid with six square faces. The dodecahedron has twelve five-sided faces. The other three regular solids have faces which are equilateral triangles: the tetrahedron has four triangular faces, the octahedron has eight triangular faces, and the icosahedron has twenty triangular faces.

For Kepler, this geometric view was related to ideas of harmony. (See "Kepler's Celestial Music" in *Reader 2.*)

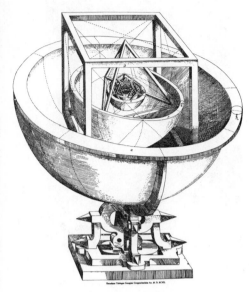

A model of Kepler's explanation of the spacing of the planetary orbits by means of the regular geometrical solids. Notice that the planetary spheres were thick enough to include the small epicycle used by Copernicus.

In keeping with Aristotelian physics, Kepler believed that force was necessary to drive the planets along their circles, not to hold them in circles.

SG 7.2

By trial and error Kepler found a way to arrange the solids so that the spheres fit within about five percent of the actual planetary distances. We now know that this arrangement was entirely accidental. But to Kepler it explained both the spacings of the planets and the fact that there were just six. Also it had the unity he expected between geometry and scientific observations. Kepler's results, published in 1597, demonstrated his imagination and mathematical ability. Furthermore, his work came to the attention of major scientists such as Galileo and Tycho. In 1600, Kepler was invited to become one of Tycho's assistants at his new observatory in Prague.

There Kepler was given the task of determining in precise detail the orbit of Mars. This unusually difficult problem had not been solved by Tycho and his other assistants. As it turned out, Kepler's study of the motion of Mars was only a starting point. From it, he went on to redirect the study of celestial motion. In the same way, Galileo used the motion of falling bodies to redirect the study of terrestrial motion.

Kepler began by trying to fit the observed motions of Mars with motions of an eccentric circle and an equant. Like Copernicus, Kepler eliminated the need for the large epicycle by putting the sun motionless at the center and having the earth moving around it (see page 31). But Kepler made an assumption which differed from that of Copernicus. Recall that Copernicus had rejected the equant as an improper type of motion, but he used small epicycles. Kepler used an equant, but refused to use even a single small epicycle. To Kepler the epicycle seemed "unphysical." He reasoned that the center of the epicycle was empty, and empty space could not exert any force on a planet. Thus, from the start, Kepler assumed that the orbits were real and that the motion resulted from physical causes—namely, the *action of forces* on the planets. Even his beloved teacher, Maestlin, advised the young man to stick to geometrical models and astronomical observation, and to avoid physical assumptions. But Kepler stubbornly stuck to his idea that the motions must be produced and explained by forces. When he finally published his results on Mars in his book *Astronomia Nova (New Astronomy)*, it was subtitled *Celestial Physics.*

For a year and a half Kepler struggled to fit Tycho's observations of Mars by various arrangements of an eccentric and an equant. When after 70 trials success finally seemed near, he made a discouraging discovery. He could represent fairly well the motion of Mars in longitude (east and west along the ecliptic). But he failed markedly with the latitude (north and south of the ecliptic). And even in longitude his very best predictions still differed by eight minutes of arc from Tycho's observed positions.

Eight minutes of arc, about a fourth of the moon's diameter, may not seem like much of a difference. Others might have been tempted to explain it away as an observational error. But Kepler knew that Tycho's instruments and observations were rarely in error by even two minutes of arc. Those eight minutes of arc meant to Kepler that his best system, using the old, accepted devices of eccentric and equant, would never work.

In his *New Astronomy,* Kepler wrote:

Since divine kindness granted us Tycho Brahe, the most diligent observer, by whose observations an error of eight minutes in the case of Mars is brought to light in this Ptolemaic calculation, it is fitting that we recognize and honor this favor of God with gratitude of mind. Let us certainly work it out, so that we finally show the true form of the celestial motions (by supporting ourselves with these proofs of the fallacy of the suppositions assumed). I myself shall prepare this way for others in the following chapters according to my small abilities. For if I thought that the eight minutes of longitude were to be ignored, I would already have corrected the hypothesis which he had made earlier in the book and which worked moderately well. But as it is, because they could not be ignored, these eight minutes alone have prepared the way for reshaping the whole of astronomy, and they are the material which is made into a great part of this work.

Kepler concluded that the orbit was not a circle and that there was no point around which the motion was uniform. Plato's idea of fitting perfect circles to the heavens had guided astronomers for twenty centuries. Now, Kepler realized, this idea must be abandoned. Kepler had in his hands the finest observations ever made, but now he had no theory by which they could be explained. He would have to start over facing two altogether new questions. First, what *is* the shape of the orbit followed by Mars? Second, how does the speed of the planet change as it moves along the orbit?

Fortunately Kepler had made a major discovery earlier which was crucial to his later work. He found that the orbits of the earth and other planets were in planes which passed through the sun. Ptolemy and Copernicus required special explanations for the motion of planets north and south of the ecliptic, but Kepler found that these motions were simply the result of the orbits lying in planes tilted to the plane of the earth's orbit.

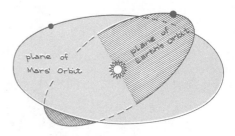

The diagram depicts a nearly edge-on view of orbital planes of earth and another planet, both intersecting at the sun.

Q1 When Kepler joined Tycho Brahe what task was he assigned?
Q2 Why did Kepler conclude that Plato's problem, to describe the motions of the planets by combinations of circular motions, could not be solved?

7.2 Kepler's law of areas

Kepler's problem was immense. To solve it would demand all of his imagination and skill.

As the basis for his study, Kepler had Tycho's observed positions of Mars and the sun on certain dates. But these observations were made from a moving earth whose orbit was not well known. Kepler realized that he must first determine more accurately the shape of the earth's orbit. This would allow him to calculate the earth's location on the dates of the various observations of Mars. Then he might be able to use the observations to determine the shape and size of the orbit of Mars. Finally, to predict positions for Mars, he would need to discover how fast Mars moved along different parts of its orbit.

As we follow this brilliant analysis here, and particularly if we repeat some of his work in the laboratory, we will see the series of problems that he solved.

To find the earth's orbit he began by considering the moments when the sun, earth, and Mars lie almost in a straight line (Figure A). After 687 days, as Copernicus had found, Mars would return to the same place in its orbit (Figure B). Of course, the earth at that time would *not* be at the same place in its own orbit as when the first observation was made. But as Figures B and C indicate, the directions to the sun and Mars, as seen from the earth against the fixed stars, would be known. The crossing point of the sight-lines to the sun and to Mars must be a point on the earth's orbit. Kepler worked with several groups of observations made 687 days apart (one Mars "year"). In the end, he determined fairly accurately the shape of the earth's orbit.

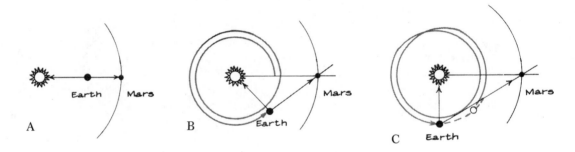

The orbit Kepler found for the earth appeared to be almost a circle, with the sun a bit off center. Knowing now the shape of the earth's path, and knowing also the recorded apparent position of the sun as seen from the earth for each date of the year, he could locate the position of the earth on its orbit, and its speed along the orbit. Now he had the orbit and the timetable for the earth's motion. You may have had the opportunity to make a similar plot in the experiment "The Shape of the Earth's Orbit."

Kepler's plot of the earth's motion revealed that the earth moves fastest when nearest the sun. Kepler wondered why this occurred. He thought that the sun might exert some force that drove the planets along their orbits. This concern with the physical cause of planetary motion marked the change in attitude toward motion in the heavens.

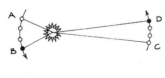

The drawings at the left represent (with great exaggeration) the earth's motion for two parts of its orbit. The different positions on the orbit are separated by equal time intervals. Between points A and B there is a relatively large distance, so the planet is moving rapidly. Between points C and D it moves more slowly. Kepler noticed, however, that the two *areas* swept over by a line from the sun to the planet are equal. It is believed that he actually calculated such areas only for the nearest and farthest positions of two planets, Earth and Mars. Yet the beautiful simplicity of the relation led him to conclude that it was generally true for all parts of orbits. In its general form the Law of Areas states: *The line from the sun to the moving planet sweeps over areas that are proportional to the time intervals.* Later, when Kepler found the exact shape of orbits, his law of areas became a powerful tool for predicting positions. In the next section we will use both laws and see in detail how they work.

You may be surprised that the first rule we find for the motions of the planets deals with the areas swept over by the line from the sun to the planet. We had been considering circles, eccentric circles, epicycles, and equants. Now we come upon a quite unexpected property: the area swept over per unit time is the first property of the orbital motion to remain constant. (As we will see in Chapter 8, this major law of nature applies to all orbits in the solar system and also to double stars.) Besides being new and different, the law of areas drew attention to the central role of the sun. Thus, it strengthened Kepler's faith in the still widely neglected Copernican idea of a heliocentric system.

As you will see, Kepler's other labors would have been of little use without this basic discovery. However, the rule does not give any hint why such regularity exists. It merely describes the relative rates at which the earth and Mars (and, Kepler thought, any other planet) move at any point of their orbits. Kepler could not fit the rule to Mars by assuming a circular orbit, so he set out to find what shape Mars' orbit was.

Q3 What observations did Kepler use to plot the earth's orbit?

Q4 State Kepler's law of areas.

Q5 Where in its orbit does a planet move the fastest?

7.3 Kepler's law of elliptical orbits

Kepler knew the orbit and timetable of the earth. Now he could reverse his analysis and find the shape of Mars' orbit. Again he used observations separated by one Martian year. Because this interval is somewhat less than two earth years, the earth is at different positions in its orbit at the two times. Therefore, the two directions from the earth to Mars differ. Where they cross is a point on the orbit of Mars. From such pairs of observations Kepler fixed many points on the orbit of Mars. The diagrams below illustrate how two such points might be plotted. By

SG 7.4

Another way to express this relationship for the nearest and farthest positions would be to say the speeds were inversely proportional to the distance; but this rule does *not* generalize to any other points on the orbit. (A modification of the rule that *does* hold is explained on pages 64 and 65.)

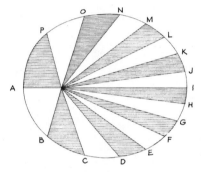

Kepler's Law of Areas. A planet moves along its orbit at a rate such that the line from the sun to the planet sweeps over areas which are proportional to the time intervals. The time taken to cover AB is the same as that for BC, CD, etc.

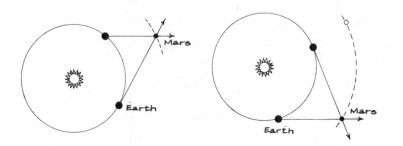

In this experiment the orbit of Mars is plotted from measurements made on pairs of sky photographs taken one Martian year apart.

SG 7.5

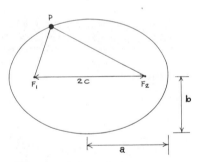

An ellipse showing the semimajor axis *a,* the semiminor axis *b,* and the two foci F_1 and F_2. The shape of an ellipse is described by its eccentricity *e,* where $e = c/a$.

SG 7.6

SG 7.7

In the Orbit of Mercury Experiment, you can plot the shape of Mercury's very eccentric orbit from observational data. See also SG 7.8.

SG 7.9

drawing a curve through such points, he obtained fairly accurate values for the size and shape of Mars' orbit. Kepler saw at once that the orbit of Mars was not a circle around the sun. You will find the same result from the experiment, "The Orbit of Mars." But what sort of path was this? How could it be described most simply? As Kepler said, "The conclusion is quite simply that the planet's path is not a circle—it curves inward on both sides and outward again at opposite ends. Such a curve is called an oval." But what kind of oval?

Many different closed curves can be called ovals. Kepler thought for a time that the orbit was egg-shaped. But this shape did not agree with his ideas of physical interaction between the sun and the planet. He concluded that there must be some better way to describe the orbit. For many months, Kepler struggled with the question. Finally he realized that the orbit was a simple curve which had been studied in detail by the Greeks two thousand years before. The curve is called an *ellipse*. It is the shape you see when you view a circle at a slant.

Ellipses can differ greatly in shape. They have many interesting properties. For example, you can draw an ellipse by looping a piece of string around two thumb tacks pinned to a drawing board at points F_1 and F_2 as shown at the left. Pull the loop taut with a pencil point (P) and run the pencil around the loop. You will have drawn an ellipse. (If the two thumb tacks had been together, on the same point, what curve would you have drawn? What results do you get as you separate the two tacks more and more?)

Each of the points F_1 and F_2 is called a *focus* of the ellipse. The greater the distance between F_1 and F_2, the flatter, or more *eccentric* the ellipse becomes. As the distance between F_1 and F_2 shrinks to zero, the ellipse becomes more nearly circular. A measure of the eccentricity of the ellipse is the ratio of the distance F_1F_2 to the long axis. If the distance between F_1 and F_2 is $2c$ and the length of the long axis is $2a$, then the eccentricity *e* is defined by the equation $e = c/a$.

The eccentricities are given for each of the ellipses shown in the margin of the next page. You can see that a circle is the special case of an ellipse with $e = 0$. Also note that the greatest possible eccentricity for

Table 7.1 The Eccentricities of Planetary Orbits

PLANET	ORBITAL ECCENTRICITY	NOTES
Mercury	0.206	Too few observations for Kepler to study
Venus	0.007	Nearly circular orbit
Earth	0.017	Small eccentricity
Mars	0.093	Largest eccentricity among planets Kepler could study
Jupiter	0.048	Slow moving in the sky
Saturn	0.056	Slow moving in the sky
Uranus	0.047	Not discovered until 1781
Neptune	0.009	Not discovered until 1846
Pluto	0.249	Not discovered until 1930

an ellipse is $e = 1.0$.

Kepler's discovery that the orbit of Mars is an ellipse was remarkable enough in itself. But he also found that the sun is at one focus of the orbit. (The other focus is empty.) Kepler stated these results in his *Law of Elliptical Orbits: The planets move in orbits which are ellipses and have the sun at one focus.*

As Table 7.1 shows, Mars has the largest orbital eccentricity of any planet that Kepler could have studied. (The other planets for which there were enough data at the time were Venus, Earth, Jupiter, and Saturn.) Had he studied any planet other than Mars, he might never have noticed that the orbit was an ellipse! Even for Mars, the difference between the elliptical orbit and an off-center circle is quite small. No wonder Kepler later wrote that "Mars alone enables us to penetrate the secrets of astronomy which otherwise would remain forever hidden from us."

Like Kepler, we believe that our observations represent some aspects of reality more stable than the changing emotions of human beings. Like Plato and all scientists after him, we assume that nature is basically orderly and consistent. Therefore, it must be understandable in a simple way. This faith has led to great theoretical and technical gains. Kepler's work illustrates a basic scientific attitude: we regard wide varieties of phenomena as better understood when they can be summarized by simple law, preferably expressed in mathematical form.

After Kepler's initial joy at discovering the law of elliptical paths, he may have asked himself a question. Why are the planetary orbits elliptical rather than in some other geometrical shape? While we might understand Plato's desire for uniform circular motions, nature's insistence on the ellipse is surprising.

In fact, there was no satisfactory answer to this question for almost 80 years. At last, Newton showed that elliptical orbits were necessary results of a more general law of nature. Let us accept Kepler's laws as rules that contain the observed facts about the motions of the planets. As *empirical laws,* they each summarize the data obtained by observing the motion of any planet. The law of orbits describes the paths of planets as ellipses around the sun. It gives us all the possible positions each planet can have

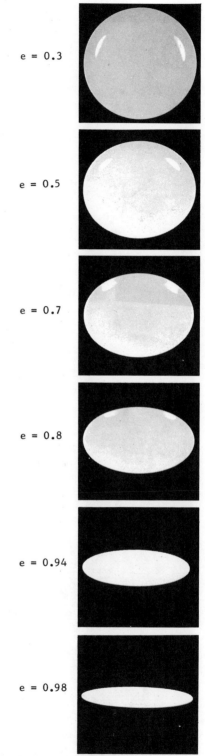

$e = 0.3$

$e = 0.5$

$e = 0.7$

$e = 0.8$

$e = 0.94$

$e = 0.98$

Ellipses of different eccentricities. (The pictures were made by photographing a saucer at different angles.)

Empirical means based on observation, but not on theory.

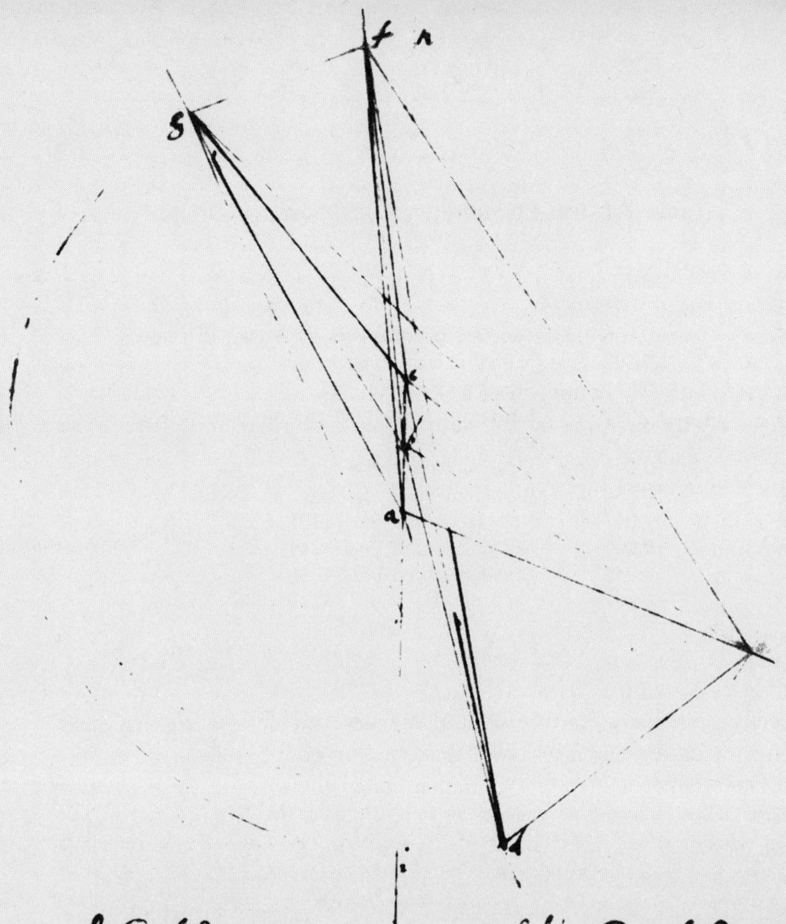

B Centrum orbitæ ♂ A corpus solis. C centrum æq
libationis Martis GCH E ♁ orbita Martis. HAb
Circa apogæi. F Sitg Martis ꝰ 87. in nob ♍
                G Sitg Martin ꝰ 91 in 20 ♏
                D Sitg Martis ꝰ 93 in 17 ♌
                E Sitg Martis ꝰ 95 in 18 ♊

F. 147. 26. 0.
G. 238. 36. 24   FAG. 91.10.24   FGG. 94.59.4.
    91. 10. 24   GAD. 75. 29. 51 GCD. 64. 8. 36
                      CAE. 65. 9. 42   DCE. 57. 16. 12
G   238. 36. 24   EAF. 128 10. 3. ECF. 143. 76. 8
D   314. 6. 15   360. 0. 0.
    75. 29. 51

C   314. 6. 15
E   3. 19. 15. 57½   Summa CGA, ADC . 11. 21. 15
       65. 9. 42   Summa CFA, AEC. - 15. 26. 4.
                      Summa CGA, AEC. 19. 14. 45.
E. 19. 15. 57   Summa CFA, ADC. 7. 32. 35.
G   238. 36. 24
    147. 26. 0.
    128. 10. 3   Excessus CGA ♁ ADC: — 7. 53. 30.
                      Excessus CFA ♁ AEC — 3. 48. 40.

GCD 64. 8. 36
DCE 57. 16. 12
?CE 121. 44. 48

CAD. ??. ?. 51
CAE. 65. 7. 64
GAE. 140. 39. 33
    39. 14. 45

FGG. 94. 59. 4.
GCD. 64. 8. 36
FCD. 159. 7. 40

FAG. 91. 10. 24
GAD. 75. 29. 51
FAD. 166. 15
    ? 32. 35

DAE 65. 9. 42
DCE. 57. 16. 12
    7. 53. 30.

GAE 91. 10. 24
GCE. 94. 59. 4
    7. 48. 40.

hæc racenus certa et data sint. Iam
oportet Apogæum H hic ordinare, ut ex
ius quatuor lineæ FB, GB, DB, EB, sicut
æq tales, ædod erit indicium, illas quidem
te in indicio civerium. Positis lineis tg
indicino gato est ut necessariis: donim
hato tam non æridita et æ alio qualiq Cæfar

if we know the orbit's size and eccentricity. However, it does not tell us
when the planet will be at any particular position on its ellipse or how
rapidly it will be moving then. The law of areas, on the other hand, does
not specify the shape of the orbit. But it does describe how the angular
speed changes as the distance from the sun changes. Clearly these two
laws complement each other. Using them together, we can determine both
the position and angular speed of a planet at any time, past or future. To
do so, we need only to know the values for the size and eccentricity of the
orbit, and to know the position of the planet at any one time on its orbit.
We can also find the earth's position for the same instant. Thus, we can
calculate the position of the planet as it would have been or will be seen
from the earth.

The elegance and simplicity of Kepler's two laws are impressive.
Surely Ptolemy and Copernicus would have been amazed to see the
problem of planetary motions solved in such short statements. But we
must remember that these laws were distilled from Copernicus' idea of a
moving earth and the great labors that went into Tycho's fine
observations, as well as the imagination and devotion of Kepler.

Q6 What was special about Mars' orbit that made Kepler's study of it
so fortunate?

Q7 If the average distance and eccentricity of a planet's orbit are
known, which of the following can be predicted from the law of areas
alone? From the law of elliptical orbits alone? Which require both?
(a) All possible positions in the orbit,
(b) speed at any point in an orbit,
(c) position at any given time.

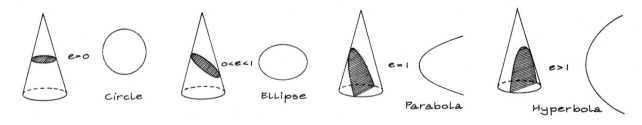

Conic Sections are figures produced
by cutting a cone with a plane—the
eccentricity of a figure is related to
the angle of the cut. In addition to
circles and ellipses, parabolas and
hyperbolas are conic sections, with
eccentricities greater than ellipses.
Newton eventually showed that all of
these shapes are possible paths for a
body moving under the influence of
the sun.

Opposite: A page from Kepler's notebooks.

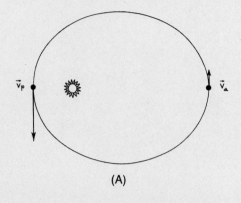

(A)

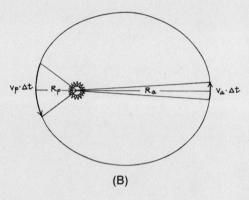

(B)

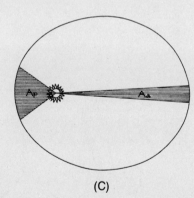

(C)

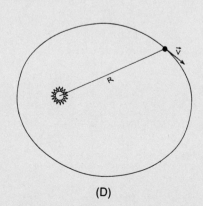

(D)

A General Equation for Orbital Speed

Figure A represents the elliptical orbit of a planet, with the sun at one focus. By a short analysis we can find the ratio of the speeds at the position nearest to the sun (perihelion) and farthest from the sun (aphelion).

Figure B shows a small part of the planet's path around perihelion, during a time interval Δt. If Δt is very short, then the average speed along the path during Δt will very nearly equal the speed the planet has just at perihelion. This speed is called the *instantaneous* speed at perihelion, v_p. The path length will be $v_p \times \Delta t$.

Also, if Δt is very short, the section of orbit is almost straight. Hence, it can be considered the base of a long, thin triangle of altitude R_p, the shaded part in Figure C. The area of any triangle is $\frac{1}{2}$ *base* $\times$ *altitude,* so the area A_p of this triangle is $\frac{1}{2}(v_p \times \Delta t)R_p$.

Similarly, the area A_a of a triangle swept over during Δt at aphelion is $\frac{1}{2}(v_a \times \Delta t)R_a$. By Kepler's law of areas, equal areas are swept over in equal times, so $A_a = A_p$. Then

$$\tfrac{1}{2}v_a \times \Delta t \times R_a = \tfrac{1}{2}v_p \times \Delta t \times R_p$$

and, dividing both sides by $\frac{1}{2}\Delta t$,

$$v_aR_a = v_pR_p$$

We can rearrange the equation to the form

Insert
$$\frac{v_a}{v_p} = \frac{R_p}{R_a}$$

This shows that the speeds at aphelion and perihelion are inversely proportional to the distances from the sun. In other words, the larger the distance, the smaller the speed.

Finding the relation between the speeds and distances at these two points was easy, because at these points the velocity is perpendicular to the line drawn to the sun. When the planet is at some position other than

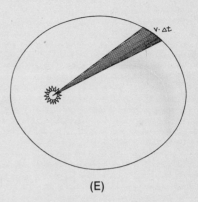

(E)

perihelion or aphelion, the velocity vector is not perpendicular. See Figure D. However, we can approximate the area swept over (Figure E) by a triangle of altitude R (Figure F). Notice that it includes a tiny corner of extra area, but also leaves out a tiny corner. For a very short time interval Δt, the triangle will be very thin and the difference between the two tiny corners will essentially disappear. As shown in Figure G, the base of the triangle is not given by $v \times \Delta t$. Rather, it is given by $v_\perp \times \Delta t$, where $v_\perp$ is the portion, or *component*, of v that points perpendicular to the sun-planet line.

Thus, the area swept out during Δt can be expressed as

$$\tfrac{1}{2} v_\perp \times \Delta t \times R$$

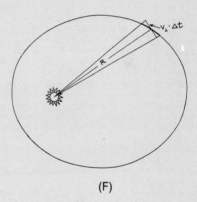

(F)

This same equation will hold for any part of the orbit over a short time interval Δt. By Kepler's law of areas, the areas swept over during equal time intervals are also equal, so we can write

$$\tfrac{1}{2} v_\perp \times \Delta t \times R = \tfrac{1}{2} v'_\perp \times \Delta t \times R' = \tfrac{1}{2} v''_\perp \times \Delta t \times R'' \text{ etc.}$$

or, dividing through by $\tfrac{1}{2} \Delta t$,

$$v_\perp R = v'_\perp R' = v''_\perp R'' \text{ etc.}$$

Therefore, we can express Kepler's law of areas as

$$v_\perp R = constant$$

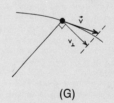

(G)

If we know the eccentricity of the orbit and the speed and distance at any one point, we can use this equation to calculate the speed at any other point in the orbit. (See SG 7.10.) This relation is derived from the law of areas. Later, we will see that this law holds true for the motion of any body that experiences a force directed toward one focus of the ellipse—a so-called "central force." So the relation $v_\perp R = constant$ applies to double stars and to atoms as well as to the solar system.

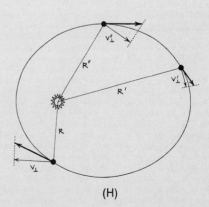

(H)

7.4 Kepler's law of periods

Kepler published his first two laws in 1609 in his book *Astronomia Nova*. But he was still dissatisfied. He had not yet found any relation among the motions of the different planets. Each planet seemed to have its own elliptical orbit and speed. But there appeared to be no overall pattern relating all planets to one another. Kepler had begun his career by trying to explain the number of planets and their spacing. He was convinced that the observed orbits and speeds could not be accidental. There *must* be some regularity linking all the motions in the solar system. His conviction was so strong that he spent years examining possible combinations of factors by trial and error. Surely one combination would reveal a third law, relating all the planetary orbits. His long, stubborn search illustrates a belief that has run through the whole history of science: that despite apparent difficulties in getting a quick solution, underneath it all nature's laws are rationally understandable. This belief is still a source of inspiration in science, keeping up one's spirit in periods of seemingly fruitless labor. For Kepler it made endurable a life of poverty, illness, and other personal misfortunes. Finally, in 1619, he could write triumphantly in his *Harmony of the World:*

> . . . after I had by unceasing toil through a long period of time, using the observations of Brahe, discovered the true relation . . .[It] overcame by storm the shadows of my mind, with such fullness of agreement between my seventeen years' labor on the observations of Brahe and this present study of mine that I at first believed that I was dreaming . . . .

Kepler's law of periods, also called the "harmonic law," relates the periods of the planets to their average distances from the sun. The period is the time taken to go once completely around the orbit. The law states that *the squares of the periods of the planets are proportional to the cubes of their average distances from the sun*. Calling the period T and the average distance R_{av}, this law can be expressed as

$$T^2 \propto R_{av}{}^3 \text{ or } T^2 = kR_{av}{}^3 \text{ or } \frac{T^2}{R_{av}{}^3} = k$$

As Einstein later put it: "The Lord is subtle, but He is not malicious."

For the earth, T is one year. The average distance R_{av} of the earth from the sun is one astronomical unit, 1AU. So one way to express the value of the constant k is $k = 1$ year^2/AU^3.

Verification of Kepler's Law of Periods

PLANET	Using Copernicus' Values			Using Modern Values		
	PERIOD T, (YEARS)	AVERAGE DISTANCE R_{av}(AU)	$\frac{T^2}{R_{av}{}^3}$	PERIOD T, (YEARS)	AVERAGE DISTANCE R_{av}(AU)	$\frac{T^2}{R_{av}{}^3}$
Mercury	0.241	0.38	1.06	0.241	0.387	1.00
Venus	0.614	0.72	1.01	0.615	0.723	1.00
Mars	1.881	1.52	1.01	1.881	1.523	1.00
Jupiter	11.8	5.2	0.99	11.862	5.20	1.00
Saturn	29.5	9.2	1.12	29.458	9.54	1.00

where k is a constant. This relation applies to all the planets (see the table on page 66) and even to comets in orbit around the sun.

We can use it to find the period of any planet if we know its average distance from the sun, and *vice versa*.

Kepler's three laws are so simple that their great power may be overlooked. And combined with his discovery that each planet moves in a plane passing through the sun, their value is greater still. They let us derive the past and future history of each planet if we know six quantities about that planet. Two of these quantities are the size (long axis, a) and eccentricity (e) of the orbit. Three others are angles that relate the plane of the orbit to that of the earth's orbit. The sixth quantity needed is where in its orbit the planet was on any *one* date. These quantities are explained more fully as used in the Activities and Experiments listed in the *Handbook* for Chapters 7 and 8.

In this manner the past and future positions of each planet and each comet can be found. Kepler's system was vastly simpler and more precise than the multitude of geometrical devices in the planetary theories of Ptolemy, Copernicus, and Tycho. With different assumptions and procedures Kepler had at last solved the problem which had occupied so many great scientists over the centuries. Although he abandoned the geometrical *devices* of Copernicus, Kepler did depend on the Copernican *viewpoint* of a sun-centered universe. None of the earth-centered models could have led to Kepler's three laws.

In 1627, after many troubles with his publishers and Tycho's heirs, Kepler published a set of astronomical tables. These tables combined Tycho's observations and the three laws in a way that permitted accurate calculations of planetary positions for any time, past or future. These tables remained useful for a century, until telescopic observations of greater precision replaced Tycho's data.

Kepler's scientific interest went beyond the planetary problem. Like Tycho, who was fascinated by the new star of 1572, Kepler observed and wrote about new stars that appeared in 1600 and 1604. His observations and comments added to the impact of Tycho's earlier statement that changes did occur in the starry sky.

As soon as Kepler learned of the development of the telescope, he spent most of a year studying how the images were formed. He published his findings in a book titled *Dioptrice* (1611), which became the standard work on optics for many years. Kepler wrote other important books on mathematical and astronomical problems. One was a popular and widely read description of the Copernican system as modified by his own discoveries. This added to the growing interest in and acceptance of the sun-centered system.

SG 7.11–7.14

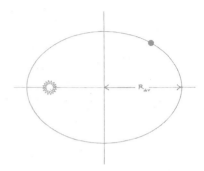

The value of R_{av} for an ellipse is just half the major axis.

The tables, named for Tycho's and Kepler's patron, Emperor Rudolph II, were called the *Rudolphine Tables.* They were also important for a quite different reason. In them Kepler pioneered in the use of logarithms for making rapid calculations and included a long section, practically a textbook, on the nature and use of logarithms (first described in 1614 by Napier in Scotland). His tables spread the use of this computational aid, widely needed for nearly three centuries, until modern computing machines came into use.

Q8 State Kepler's law of periods.

7.5 The new concept of physical law

One general feature of Kepler's life-long work greatly affected the development of all the physical sciences. When Kepler began his studies, he still accepted Plato's assumptions about the importance of geometric models. He also agreed with Aristotle's emphasis on "natural place" to explain motion. But later he came to concentrate on algebraic laws describing how planets moved. His successful statement of empirical laws in mathematical form helped to establish the *equation* as a normal form of stating physical laws.

More than anyone before him, Kepler expected a theory to agree with precise and quantitative observation. From Tycho's observations he learned to respect the power of precise measurement. Models and theories can be modified by human inventiveness. But good data endure regardless of changes in assumptions or viewpoints.

Going beyond observation and mathematical description, Kepler attempted to explain motion in the heavens in terms of physical forces. In Kepler's system the planets no longer moved by some divine nature or influence, or in "natural" circular motion caused by their spherical shapes. Rather, Kepler looked for physical laws, based on observed phenomena and describing the whole universe in a detailed quantitative manner. In an early letter to Herwart (1605), he expressed his guiding thought:

> I am much occupied with the investigation of the physical causes. My aim in this is to show that the celestial machine is to be likened not to a divine organism but rather to a clockwork . . . insofar as nearly all the manifold movements are carried out by means of a single; quite simple magnetic force, as in the case of a clockwork, all motions are caused by a simple weight. Moreover, I show how this physical conception is to be presented through calculation and geometry.

Kepler's description of the celestial machine as a clockwork driven by a single force was like a look into the future of scientific thought. Kepler had read William Gilbert's work on magnetism, published a few years earlier. Now he could imagine magnetic forces from the sun driving the planets along their orbits. This was a reasonable and promising hypothesis. As Newton later showed (Chapter 8), the basic idea that a single kind of force controls the motions of all the planets was correct. But the force is not magnetism, and does not keep the planets moving forward, but rather bends their paths into closed orbits.

Even though Kepler did not understand correctly the nature of the forces responsible for celestial motion, his work illustrates an enormous change in outlook that had begun more than two centuries earlier. Kepler still shared the ancient idea that each planet had a "soul." But he refused to base his explanation of planetary motion on this idea. Instead, he began to search for physical causes. Copernicus and Tycho were willing to settle for geometrical models by which planetary positions could be predicted. Kepler was one of the first to seek dynamic *causes* for the motions. This new desire for physical explanations marks the beginning of a chief characteristic of modern physical science.

Kepler's statement of empirical laws reminds us of Galileo's suggestion, made at about the same time. Galileo said that science should deal first with the *how* of motion in free fall, and then with the *why*. A half century later Newton used the concept of *gravitational force* to tie together Kepler's three planetary laws with laws of terrestrial mechanics. This magnificent synthesis will be the subject of Chapter 8.

Q9 In what ways did Kepler's work exemplify a "new" concept of physical law?

7.6 Galileo and Kepler

One of the scientists with whom Kepler corresponded about scientific developments was Galileo. Kepler's main contributions to planetary theory were his empirical laws based on Tycho's observations. Galileo contributed to both theory and observation. As we reported in Chapters 2 and 3, Galileo based his theory of motion on observations of bodies moving on the earth's surface. His work in the new science of mechanics contradicted Aristotelian assumptions about physics and the nature of the heavens. Galileo's books and speeches triggered wide discussion about the differences or similarities of earth and heaven. Interest extended far outside of scientific circles. The poet John Milton wrote, some years after his visit to Galileo in 1638

> . . . What if earth
> Be but the shadow of Heaven, and things therein
> Each to the other like, more than on earth is thought?

(*Paradise Lost*, Book V, line 574, published 1667.)

Galileo challenged the ancient interpretations of experience. As we stated earlier, he focused attention on new concepts: time and distance, velocity and acceleration, forces and matter. In contrast, the Aristotelians spoke of essences, final causes, and fixed geometric models. In Galileo's study of falling bodies he insisted on fitting the concepts to the observed facts. By seeking results that could be expressed in algebraic form, he paralleled the new style being used by Kepler.

The sharp break between Galileo and most other scientists of the time arose from the kind of questions he asked. To his opponents, many of Galileo's problems seemed trivial. His procedures for studying the world also seemed peculiar. What was important about watching pendulums swing or rolling balls down inclines, when deep philosophical problems needed solving?

Although Kepler and Galileo lived at the same time, their lives were quite different. Kepler lived in near poverty and was driven from city to city by the religious wars of the time. Few people, other than a handful of friends and correspondents, knew of or cared about his studies and results. He wrote long, complex books which demanded expert knowledge from his readers.

Galileo, on the other hand, wrote his essays and books in Italian. His language and style appealed to many readers who did not know scholarly Latin. Galileo was a master at publicizing his work. He wanted as many people as possible to know of his studies and to accept the Copernican theory. He wrote not only to small groups of scholars, but to the nobles and for civic and religious leaders. His arguments included humorous attacks on individuals or ideas. In return, his efforts to inform and persuade on such a "dangerous" topic as cosmological theory stirred up ridicule and even violence. Those who have a truly new point of view often must face such a reaction.

In recent times, similar receptions were initially given to such artists as the painter Picasso, and the sculptor Giacometti, and the composers Stravinski and Schönberg. The same has often been true in most fields, whether literature or mathematics, economics or politics. But while great creative novelty is often attacked at the start, it does not follow that, conversely, everything that is attacked must be creative.

Q10 Which of the following would you associate more with Galileo's work than with that of his predecessors: qualities and essences, popular language, concise mathematical expression, final causes?

7.7 The telescopic evidence

Like Kepler, Galileo was surrounded by scholars who believed the heavens were eternal and could not change. So he took special interest in the sudden appearance in 1604 of a new star, one of those observed by Kepler. Where there had been nothing visible in the sky, there was now a brilliant star. Like Tycho and Kepler, Galileo realized that such events conflicted with the old idea that the stars could not change. This new star awakened in Galileo an interest in astronomy which lasted all his life.

Four or five years later, Galileo learned that a Dutchman "had constructed a spy glass by means of which visible objects, though very distant from the eye of the observer, were distinctly seen as if nearby." Galileo (as he tells it) quickly worked out some of the optical principles involved. He then set to work to grind the lenses and build such an instrument himself. His first telescope made objects appear three times closer than when seen with the naked eye. Reporting on his third telescope in his book *The Starry Messenger:*

Two of Galileo's telescopes, displayed at the Museum of Science in Florence.

> Finally, sparing neither labor nor expense, I succeeded in constructing for myself so excellent an instrument that objects seen by means of it appeared nearly one thousand times larger and over thirty times closer than when regarded with our natural vision.

Galileo meant that the *area* of the object was nearly 1000 times greater. The area is proportional to the *square* of the magnification (or "power") as we define it now.

What would you do if you were handed "so excellent an instrument"? Like the men of Galileo's time, you probably would put it to practical uses. "It would be superfluous," Galileo agreed,

to enumerate the number and importance of the advantages of
such an instrument at sea as well as on land. But forsaking
terrestrial observations, I turned to celestial ones, and first I
saw the moon from as near at hand as if it were scarcely two
terrestrial radii away. After that I observed often with
wondering delight both the planets and the fixed stars . . . .

In a few short weeks in 1609 and 1610, Galileo used his telescope to
make several major discoveries. First, he pointed his telescope at the
moon. What he saw convinced him that

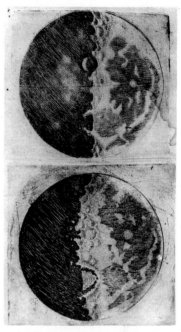

   . . . the surface of the moon is not smooth, uniform, and
precisely spherical as a great number of philosophers believe it
(and other heavenly bodies) to be, but is uneven, rough, and
full of cavities and prominences, being not unlike the face of
the earth, relieved by chains of mountains, and deep valleys.

Galileo did not stop with that simple observation, so contrary to the
Aristotelian idea of heavenly perfection. He supported his conclusions with
several kinds of evidence, including careful measurement. For instance, he
worked out a method for determining the height of mountains on the
moon from the length of their shadows. (His value of about four miles for
the height of some lunar mountains is not far from modern results. For
example, try the experiment, *The Height of Piton, a Mountain on the
Moon,* in the *Handbook.*)

Two of Galileo's early drawings of the
moon (from Galileo's *Siderius Nun-
cius*).

Next he looked at the stars. To the naked eye the Milky Way had
seemed to be a continuous blotchy band of light. But through the
telescope it was seen to consist of thousands of faint stars. Wherever
Galileo pointed his telescope in the sky, he saw many more stars than
appeared to the unaided eye. This observation clashed with the old
argument that the stars were created to help humans to see at night. By
this argument, there should not be stars invisible to the naked eye. But
Galileo found thousands.

Galileo soon made another discovery which, in his opinion, ". . .
deserves to be considered the most important of all—the disclosure of four
Planets never seen from the creation of the world up to our time." He is
referring to his discovery of four of the satellites which orbit about Jupiter.
Here before his eyes was a miniature solar system with its own center of
revolution. Today, as to Galileo so long ago, it is a sharp thrill to see the
moons of Jupiter through a telescope for the first time. The sight
strikingly contradicts the Aristotelian notion that the earth is the center of
the universe and the chief center of revolution.

The manner in which Galileo discovered Jupiter's "planets" is a
tribute to his ability as an observer. On each clear night during this period
he was discovering dozens if not hundreds of new stars never before seen
by man. On the evening of January 7, 1610, he was looking in the vicinity
of Jupiter. He noticed ". . . that beside the planet there were three

Telescopic photograph of Jupiter and its four bright satellites. This is approximately what Galileo saw and what you see through the simple telescope described in the *Handbook*.

As of 1970, 12 satellites of Jupiter have been observed.

These sketches of Galileo's are from the first edition of *The Starry Messenger*.

starlets, small indeed, but very bright. Though I believe them to be among the hosts of fixed stars, they aroused my curiosity somewhat by appearing to lie in an exact straight line. . . ." (The first page of the notebook in which he recorded his observations is reproduced on page 54.) When he looked again on the following night, the "starlets" had changed position with reference to Jupiter. Each clear evening for weeks he observed and recorded their positions in drawings. Within days he had concluded that there were four "starlets" and that they were indeed satellites of Jupiter. He continued observing until he could estimate their periods of revolution around Jupiter.

Of all of Galileo's discoveries, that of the satellites of Jupiter caused the most stir. His book, *The Starry Messenger,* was an immediate success. Copies sold as fast as they could be printed. For Galileo the result was a great demand for telescopes and great fame.

Galileo continued to use his telescope with remarkable results. By projecting an image of the sun on a screen, he observed sunspots. This seemed to indicate that the sun, like the moon, was not perfect in the Aristotelian sense: it was disfigured rather than even and smooth. Galileo also noticed that the sunspots moved across the face of the sun in a regular pattern. He concluded that the sun rotated with a period of about 27 days.

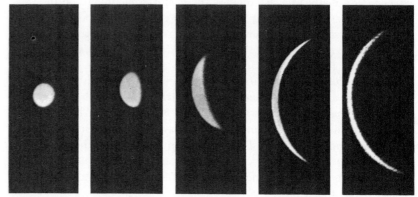

Photographs of Venus at various phases with a constant magnification.

He also found that Venus showed all phases, just as the moon does. (See photos above.) Therefore, Venus could not stay always between the earth and the sun, as Ptolemaic astronomers assumed. Rather it must move completely around the sun as Copernicus and Tycho had believed. Saturn seemed to carry bulges around its equator, as indicated in the drawings on the next page. But Galileo's telescopes were not strong enough to show that these were rings. (He called them "ears.") With his telescopes, Galileo collected an impressive array of new information about the heavens. And all of it seemed to contradict the basic assumptions of the Ptolemaic world scheme.

Q11 Could Galileo's observations of all phases of Venus support the heliocentric theory, the Tychonic system, or Ptolemy's system?

Q12 In what way did telescopic observation of the moon and sun weaken the earth-centered view of the universe?

Q13 What significance did observations of Jupiter have in weakening the Ptolemaic view of the world?

7.8 Galileo focuses the controversy

Galileo's observations supported his belief in the heliocentric Copernican system. But they were not the *cause* of his belief. His great work, *Dialogue Concerning the Two Chief World Systems* (1632), was based more on assumptions that seemed self-evident to him than on observations. He recognized, as Ptolemy and Copernicus had, that the observed motions of planets do not prove either the heliocentric or the geocentric hypothesis right and the other one wrong. With proper adjustments of the systems, said Galileo, "The same phenomena would result from either hypothesis." But he accepted the earth's motion as real because the heliocentric system seemed simpler and more pleasing. The support for the heliocentric view provided by the "observed facts" was of course necessary, but the "facts" by themselves are not sufficient. Elsewhere in this course you will find other cases like this. Scientists quite often accept or reject an idea because of some strong belief or feeling that, at the time, cannot be proved decisively by experiment.

In the *Dialogue Concerning the Two Chief World Systems,* Galileo presents his arguments in a systematic and lively way. Like his later book, *Discourses Concerning Two New Sciences,* mentioned in Chapter 2, it is in the form of a discussion between three learned men. Salviati, the voice of Galileo, wins most of the arguments. His opponent is Simplicio, an Aristotelian who defends the Ptolemaic system. The third member, Sagredo, represents the objective and intelligent citizen not yet committed to either system. However, Sagredo usually accepts Galileo's arguments in the end.

In *Two Chief World Systems,* Galileo's arguments for the Copernican system are mostly those given by Copernicus. Oddly enough, Galileo makes no use of Kepler's laws. But Galileo's observations did provide new evidence for Kepler's laws. In studying Jupiter's four moons, Galileo found that the larger the orbit of the satellite, the longer was its period of revolution. Copernicus had noted that the periods of the planets increased with their average distances from the sun. Kepler's law of periods had stated this relation in detailed quantitative form. Now Jupiter's satellite system showed a similar pattern, reinforcing the challenge to the old assumptions of Plato, Aristotle, and Ptolemy.

Two Chief World Systems relies upon Copernican arguments, Galilean observations, and attacks on basic assumptions of the geocentric model. In

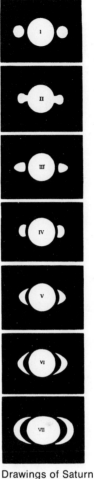

Drawings of Saturn made in the seventeenth century.

response, Simplicio desperately tries to dismiss all of Galileo's arguments with a typical counter argument:

> . . . with respect to the power of the Mover, which is infinite, it is just as easy to move the universe as the earth, or for that matter a straw.

But to this Galileo makes a very interesting reply. Notice how he quotes Aristotle against the Aristotelians:

> . . . what I have been saying was with regard not to the Mover, but only the movables . . . Giving our attention, then, to the movable bodies, and not questioning that it is a shorter and readier operation to move the earth than the universe, and paying attention to the many other simplifications and conveniences that follow from merely this one, it is much more probable that the diurnal motion belongs to the earth alone than to the rest of the universe excepting the earth. This is supported by a very true maxim of Aristotle's which teaches that . . . 'it is pointless to use many to accomplish what may be done with fewer.'

Galileo thought his telescopic discoveries would soon demolish the assumptions that prevented wide acceptance of the Copernican theory. But people cannot believe what they are not ready to believe. The Aristotelians firmly believed that the heliocentric theory was obviously false and contrary to observation and common sense. The evidences provided by the telescope could be distorted; after all, glass lenses change the path of light rays. And even if telescopes seemed to work on earth, nobody could be sure they worked when pointed at the vastly distant stars.

Most Aristotelians really could not even consider the Copernican system as a possible theory. To do so would involve questioning too many of their own basic assumptions, as we saw in Chapter 6. It is nearly humanly impossible to give up all of one's common-sense ideas and find new bases for one's religious and moral doctrines. The Aristotelians would have to admit that the earth is not at the center of creation. Then perhaps the universe was not created especially for mankind. No wonder Galileo's arguments stirred up a storm of opposition!

Galileo's observations intrigued many, but were unacceptable to Aristotelian scholars. Most of these critics had reasons one can respect. But a few were driven to positions that must have seemed silly even then. For example, the Florentine astronomer Francesco Sizzi argued in 1611 that there could not possibly be any satellites around Jupiter:

> There are seven windows in the head, two nostrils, two ears, two eyes and a mouth; so in the heavens there are two favorable stars, two unpropitious, two luminaries, and Mercury alone undecided and indifferent. From which and many other similar phenomena of nature such as the seven metals, etc.,

which it were tedious to enumerate, we gather that the number of planets is necessarily seven [including the sun and moon but excluding the earth] . . . . Besides, the Jews and other ancient nations, as well as modern Europeans, have adopted the division of the week into seven days, and have named them from the seven planets; now if we increase the number of planets, this whole system falls to the ground. . . . Moreover, the satellites are invisible to the naked eye and therefore can have no influence on the earth, and therefore would be useless, and therefore do not exist.

A year after his discoveries, Galileo wrote to Kepler:

> You are the first and almost the only person who, even after a but cursory investigation, has . . . given entire credit to my statements. . . . What do you say of the leading philosophers here to whom I have offered a thousand times of my own accord to show my studies, but who with the lazy obstinacy of a serpent who has eaten his fill have never consented to look at the planets, or moon, or telescope?

Q14 Did Galileo's telescopic observations cause him to believe in the Copernican viewpoint?

Q15 What reasons did Galileo's opponents give for ignoring telescopic observations?

Some of the arguments that were brought forward against the new discoveries were so silly that it is hard for the modern mind to take them seriously. . . . One of his [Galileo's] opponents, who admitted that the surface of the moon looked rugged, maintained that it was actually quite smooth and spherical as Aristotle had said, reconciling the two ideas by saying that the moon was covered with a smooth transparent material through which mountains and craters inside it could be discerned. Galileo, sarcastically applauding the ingenuity of this contribution, offered to accept it gladly—provided that his opponent would do him the equal courtesy of allowing him then to assert that the moon was even more rugged than he had thought before, its surface being covered with mountains and craters of this invisible substance ten times as high as any he had seen. [Quoted from *Discoveries and Opinions of Galileo*, translated by Stillman Drake.]

SG 7.16

7.9 Science and freedom

The political and personal tragedy that struck Galileo is described at length in many books. Here we will mention only some of the major events. Galileo was warned in 1616 by the highest officials of the Roman Catholic Church to cease teaching the Copernican theory as true. It could be taught only as just one of several possible methods for computing the planetary motions. The Inquisitors held that the theory was contrary to Holy Scripture. At the same time, Copernicus' book was placed on the *Index of Forbidden Books* "until corrected." As we saw before, Copernicus had used Aristotelian doctrine whenever possible to support his theory. But Galileo had reached a new point of view: he urged that the heliocentric system be accepted on its merits alone. Galileo himself was a devoutly religious man. But he deliberately ruled out questions of religious faith from scientific discussions. This was a fundamental break with the past.

Cardinal Barberini, once a close friend of Galileo, was elected in 1623 to be Pope Urban VIII. Galileo talked with him about the decree against Copernican ideas. As a result of the discussion, Galileo considered it safe to write again on the topic. In 1632, having made some required changes, Galileo obtained consent to publish *Two Chief World Systems*. This book presented very persuasively the Ptolemaic and Copernican viewpoints and their relative merits. After its publication, his opponents argued that Galileo had tried to get around the warning of 1616. Furthermore, Galileo sometimes spoke and acted without tact. This, and the Inquisition's need to demonstrate its power over suspected heretics, combined to mark him for punishment.

Among the many factors in this complex story, we must repeat that Galileo considered himself religiously faithful. In letters of 1613 and 1615 Galileo wrote that God's mind contains all the natural laws. Consequently, the occasional glimpses of these laws that scientists might gain are direct revelations of God, just as true as those in the Bible: "From the Divine Word, the Sacred Scripture and Nature did both alike proceed. . . . Nor does God less admirably discover himself to us in Nature's action than in the Scripture's sacred dictions." These opinions are held by many people today, whether scientists or not. Few people think of them as conflicting with religion. But in Galileo's time such ideas were widely regarded as symptoms of pantheism. This was one of the religious "crimes" or heresies for which Galileo's contemporary, Giordano Bruno, was burned at the stake. The Inquisition was alarmed by Galileo's seeming denial of the Bible as a certain source of knowledge about natural science. In reply, arrogant as Galileo often was, he quoted Cardinal Baronius: "The Holy Spirit intended to teach us how to go to heaven, not how the heavens go."

Though he was old and sick, Galileo was called to Rome and confined for a few months. The records of his trial are still partly secret. But we know that he was tried, threatened with torture, and forced to make a formal confession for holding and teaching forbidden ideas. He was also forced to deny the Copernican theory. In return for his confessions and denial, he was sentenced only to perpetual house arrest. Galileo's friends in Italy did not dare to defend him publicly. His book was placed on the *Index*. It remained there, along with that of Copernicus and one of Kepler's, until 1835. Thus, Galileo was used as a warning to all people that demands for spiritual conformity also required intellectual conformity.

But without intellectual freedom, science cannot flourish for long. Italy had given the world many outstanding scholars. But for two centuries after Galileo, Italy produced hardly a single great scientist, while elsewhere in Europe many appeared. Today scientists are acutely aware of this famous part of the story of the development of planetary theories. Teachers and scientists in our time have had to face strong enemies of open-minded inquiry and of unrestricted teaching. Today, as in Galileo's time, men and women who create or publicize new thoughts must be ready to stand up for them. For there still are people who fear and wish to stamp out the open discussion of new ideas and new evidence.

Plato knew that a government that wishes to control its people totally is threatened by new ideas. To prevent the spread of such ideas, Plato recommended the now well-known treatment: re-education, prison, or death. Not long ago, Soviet geneticists were required to discard well-established theories. They did so not on the basis of new scientific evidence, but because party "philosophers" accused them of conflicts with political doctrines. Similarly, the theory of relativity was banned from textbooks in Nazi Germany because Einstein's Jewish background was

Pantheism refers to the idea that God is no more (and no less) than the forces and laws of nature.

According to a well-known, but probably apocryphal story, at the end of these proceedings Galileo muttered, *"E pur se muove* — but it does move."

said to make his work worthless. Another example of intolerance was the prejudice that led to the "Monkey Trial" held in 1925 in Tennessee. There, the teaching of Darwin's theory of biological evolution was attacked because it conflicted with certain types of biblical interpretation.

On two points, one must be cautious not to romanticize the lessons of this episode. While a Galileo sometimes still may be neglected or ridiculed, not everyone who feels neglected or ridiculed is for that reason a Galileo. He may in fact be just wrong. Secondly, it has turned out that, at least for a time, science in some form can continue to live in the most hostile surroundings. When politicians decide what may be thought and what may not, science will suffer like everything else. But it will not necessarily be extinguished. Scientists can take comfort from the judgment of history. Less than fifty years after Galileo's trial, Newton's great book, the *Principia,* appeared. Newton brilliantly united the work of Copernicus, Kepler, and Galileo with his own new statement of the principles of mechanics. Without Kepler and Galileo, there probably could have been no Newton. As it was, the work of these three, and of many others working in the same spirit, marked the triumphant beginning of modern science. Thus, the hard-won new laws of science and new views of humanity's place in the universe were established. What followed has been termed by historians The Age of Enlightenment.

Over 200 years after his confinement in Rome, opinions had changed so that Galileo was honored as in the fresco "Galileo presenting his telescope to the Venetian Senate" by Luigi Sabatelli (1772-1850).

Q16 Which of the following appears to have contributed to Galileo's being tried by the Inquisition?
  (a) He did not believe in God.
  (b) He was arrogant.
  (c) He separated religious and scientific questions.
  (d) He wrote in Italian.

SG 7.17

Palomar Observatory houses the 200-inch Hale reflecting telescope. It is located on Palomar Mountain in southern California.

7.1 The Project Physics learning materials particularly appropriate for Chapter 7 include the following:

Experiments
  The Orbit of Mars
  Inclination of Mars Orbit
  The Orbit of Mercury

Activities
  Three-dimensional Model of Two Orbits
  Demonstrating Satellite Orbits
  Galileo
  Conic-Section Models
  Challenging Problems: Finding Earth-Sun
    Distance
  Measuring Irregular Areas

Reader Articles
  Kepler
  Kepler on Mars
  Kepler's Celestial Music
  The Starry Messenger
  Galileo

Film Loop
  Jupiter Satellite Orbit

Transparency
  Orbit Parameters

7.2 How large was an error of 8 minutes of arc in degrees? How far right or left do you think a dot over an i on this page would have to be before you would notice it was off-center? What angle would this shift be as seen from a reading distance of 10 inches?

7.3 Summarize the steps Kepler used to determine the orbit of the earth.

7.4 For the orbit positions nearest and furthest from the sun, a planet's speeds are inversely proportional to the distances from the sun. What is the percentage change between the earth's slowest speed in July when it is 1.02 AU from the sun, and its greatest speed in January when it is 0.98 AU from the sun?

7.5 Summarize the steps Kepler used to determine the orbit of Mars.

7.6 In any ellipse the sum of the distances from the two foci to a point on the curve equals the length of the major axis, or $(F_1P + F_2P) = 2a$. This property of ellipses allows us to draw them by using a loop of string around two tacks at the foci. What should the length of the string be?

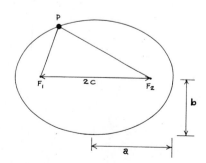

7.7 In describing orbits around the sun, the point nearest the sun is called the *perihelion point* and the point farthest from the sun is called the *aphelion point*. The distances of these two points from the sun are called the *perihelion distance* and the *aphelion distance* respectively. The terms perihelion and aphelion come from the Greek, in which *helios* is the sun, *peri* means near, and *apo* means away from.
(a) List some other words in which the prefixes *peri* and *apo* or *ap* have similar meanings.
(b) In describing earth satellite orbits, the terms *apogee* and *perigee* are often used. What do they mean?
(c) What would such points for satellites orbiting the moon be called?

7.8 For the planet Mercury the perihelion distance (closest approach to the sun) has been found to be about 45.8×10^6 kilometers, and the aphelion distance (greatest distance from the sun) is about 70.0×10^6 kilometers. What is the eccentricity of the orbit of Mercury?

7.9 The eccentricity of Pluto's orbit is 0.254. What will be the ratio of the minimum orbital speed to the maximum orbital speed of Pluto?

7.10 The rule $v_\perp R = $ const. makes it easy to find $v_\perp$ for any point on an orbit if the speed and distance at any other point are known. Make a sketch to show how you would find v once you know $v_\perp$.

7.11 Halley's comet has a period of 76 years, and its orbit has an eccentricity of .97.
(a) What is its average distance from the sun?
(b) What is its greatest distance from the sun?
(c) What is its least distance from the sun?
(d) How does its greatest speed compare with its least speed?

7.12 The mean distance of the planet Pluto from the sun is 39.6 AU. What is the orbital period of Pluto?

7.13 Three new major planets have been discovered since Kepler's time. Their orbital periods and mean distances from the sun are given in the table below. Determine whether Kepler's law of periods holds for these planets also.

	Discovery Date	Orbital Period	Average Distance From Sun	Eccentricity of Orbit
Uranus	1781	84.013 yr	19.19 AU	0.047
Neptune	1846	164.783	30.07	0.009
Pluto	1930	248.420	39.52	0.249

7.14 Considering the data available to him, do you think Kepler was justified in concluding that the ratio T^2/R_{av}^3 is a constant?

7.15 The chart on p. 79 is reproduced from the January, 1969, issue of *Sky and Telescope*.
(a) Make a sketch of how Jupiter and its satellites appeared at one week intervals, beginning with day "0."

JUPITER'S SATELLITES

The four curving lines represent Jupiter's four bright (Galilean) satellites: I, Io; II, Europa; III, Ganymede; IV, Callisto. The location of the planet's disk is indicated by the pairs of vertical lines. If a moon is invisible because it is behind the disk (that is, occulted by Jupiter), the curve is broken.

For successive dates, the horizontal lines mark 0^h Universal time, or 7 p.m. Eastern standard time (or 4 p.m. Pacific standard time) on the preceding date. Along the vertical scale, 1/16 inch is almost seven hours. In this chart, west is to the left, as in an inverting telescope for a Northern Hemisphere observer. At the bottom, "d" is the point of disappearance of a satellite in the shadow of Jupiter; "r" is the point of reappearance. From the *American Ephemeris and Nautical Almanac.*

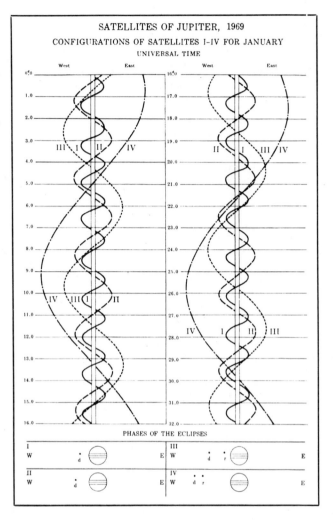

SATELLITES OF JUPITER, 1969
CONFIGURATIONS OF SATELLITES I–IV FOR JANUARY
UNIVERSAL TIME

PHASES OF THE ECLIPSES

(b) Make measurements of the chart to find the R_{av} and T for each satellite. (For this problem, R_{av} can be to any convenient scale, such as cm on the diagram.)

(c) Does Kepler's law of periods $T^2/R_{av}^3 =$ constant hold for Jupiter's satellites?

7.16 Below are two passages from Galileo's "Letters on Sunspots." On the basis of these quotations, comment on Galileo's characteristics as an observer and as a scientist.

(May 4th, 1612)

I have resolved not to put anything around Saturn except what I have already observed and revealed – that is, two small stars which touch it, one to the east and one to the west, in which no alteration has ever yet been seen to take place and in which none is to be expected in the future, barring some very strange event remote from every other motion known to or even imagined by us. But as to the supposition of Apelles that Saturn sometimes is oblong and sometimes accompanied by two stars on its flanks. Your Excellency may rest assured that this results either from the imperfection of the telescope or the eye of the observer, for the shape of Saturn is thus: oOo , as shown by perfect vision and perfect instruments, but appears thus: ⬦, where perfection is lacking, the shape and distinction of the three stars being imperfectly seen. I, who have observed it a thousand times at different periods with an excellent instrument, can assure you that no change whatever is to be seen in it. And reason, based upon our experiences of all other stellar motions, renders us certain that none ever will be seen, for if these stars had any motion similar to those of other stars, they would long since have been separated from or conjoined with the body of Saturn, even if that movement were a thousand times slower than that of any other star which goes wandering through the heavens.

(December 1, 1612)

About three years ago I wrote that to my great surprise I had discovered Saturn to be three-bodied; that is, it was an aggregate of three stars arranged in a straight line parallel to the ecliptic, the central star being much larger than the others. I believed them to be mutually motionless, for when I first saw them they seemed almost to touch, and they remained so for almost two years without the least change. It was reasonable to believe them to be fixed with respect to each other, since a single second of arc (a movement incomparably smaller than any other in even the largest orbs) would have become sensible in that time, either by separating or by completely uniting these stars. Hence I stopped observing Saturn for more than two years. But in the past few days I returned to it and found it to be solitary, without its customary supporting stars, and as perfectly round and sharply bounded as Jupiter. Now what can be said of this strange metamorphosis? That the two lesser stars have been consumed in the manner of the sunspots? Has Saturn devoured his children? Or was it indeed an illusion and a fraud with which the lenses of my telescope deceived me for so long—and not only me, but many others who have observed it with me? Perhaps the day has arrived when languishing hope may be revived in those who, led by the most profound reflections, once plumbed the fallacies of all my new observations and found them to be incapable of existing!

I need not say anything definite upon so strange an event; it is too recent, too unparalleled, and I am restrained by my own inadequacy and the fear of error. But for once I shall risk a little temerity; may this be pardoned by Your Excellency since I confess it to be rash, and

protest that I mean not to register here as a prediction. but only as a probable conclusion. I say, then, that I believe that after the winter solstice of 1614 they may once more be observed.

(*Discoveries and Opinions of Galileo,* translated by Stillman Drake, Doubleday, 1957, pp. 101-102, 143-144.)

7.17 What are the current procedures by which the public is informed of new scientific theories? Do you think they are adequate? To what extent do news media emphasize clashes of points of view? Bring in some examples from news magazines.

7.18 Recently the Roman Catholic Church decided to reconsider its condemnation of Galileo. The article reproduced opposite, which appeared in *The New York Times,* July 1968, quotes passages from an Austrian Cardinal's view of the question.

(a) In the quoted remarks Cardinal Konig lists three forms of knowledge: "divine revelations," "philosophical constructions," and "spontaneously naive views of reality." Under which of these do you think he would classify Galileo's claims? Would Galileo agree?

(b) What seems to be the basis for the reconsideration? Is it doubt about the *conclusions* of the trial, or about the *appropriateness* of trying scientific ideas at all? Is it being reconsidered because of a change in Church philosophy, or because Galileo turned out to be right?

To Rehabilitate Galileo

The following are excerpts from a speech entitled "Religion and Natural Sciences" by Franz Cardinal König of Vienna at a meeting of Nobel Prize winners in Germany last week.

Neither the Christian churches nor modern science have managed to date to control that component of human nature which mirrors visibly a like phenomenon in the animal kingdom: aggressiveness. I hold that the neutralization of this instinct, which now is creating more dangers than ever before, ought to be a prime goal of objective cooperation between theologians and scientists. This work should try to bridge the incongruity between man's complete and perfected power of destruction and his psychic condition which remains unbridled and prey to atavism.

Removing Barriers

To enable such cooperation it is first of all necessary to remove the barriers of the past. Perhaps the biggest obstacle, blocking for centuries cooperation between religion and science, was the trial of Galileo.

For the church after the second Vatican Council, turning as it is to the world as an advocate of legitimate rights and the freedom of the human mind, the time appears to have come to terminate as thoroughly as possible the era of unpleasantness and distrust which began with Galileo's censure in 1633. For over 300 years the scientific world has rightly regarded as a painful, unhealing wound the church's unjust verdict on one of those men who prepared the path for modern science. Galileo's judgment is felt all the more painful today since all intelligent people inside and outside the church have come to the conclusion that the scientist Galileo was right and that his work particularly gave modern mechanics and physics a first, firm basis. His insights enabled the human mind to develop a new understanding of nature and universe, thus replacing concepts and notions inherited from antiquity.

An open and honest clarification of the Galileo case appears all the more necessary today if the church's claim to speak for truth, justice and freedom is not to suffer in credibility and if those people are not to lose faith in the church who in past and present have defended freedom and the right to independent thought against various forms of totalitariansim and the so-called *raison d'état*.

I am in a position to announce before this meeting that competent authorities have already initiated steps to bring the Galileo case a clear and open solution.

The Catholic Church is undoubtedly ready today to subject the judgment in the Galileo trial to a revision. Clarification of the questions which at Galileo's time were still clouded allow the church today to resume the case with full confidence in itself and without prejudice. Faithful minds have struggled for truth under pain and gradually found the right way through experience and discussions conducted with passion.

The church has learned to treat science with frankness and respect. It now knows that harmony is possible between modern man's scientific thinking and religion. The seeming contradiction between the Copernican system or, more precisely, the initial mechanics of modern physics and the Biblical story of creation has gradually disappeared. Theology now differentiates more sharply between essentially divine revelations, philosophical constructions and spontaneously naive views of reality.

What used to be insurmountable obstacles for Galileo's contemporaries have stopped long ago to irritate today's educated faithful. From their perspective Galileo no longer appears as a mere founder of a new science but also as a prominent proponent of religious thinking. In this field, too, Galileo was in many respects a model pioneer.

Trial and Error

In Galileo's wake and in the spirit of his endeavors the Catholic church has through trial and error come to recognize the possibility of harmonious cooperation between free research and free thinking on the one hand and absolute loyalty to God's word on the other. Today's task is to draw the consequences from this recognition. Without fixing borders, God has opened his creation—the universe—to man's inquiring mind.

The church has no reason whatsoever to shun a revision of the disputed Galileo verdict. To the contrary, the case provides the church with an opportunity to explain its claim to infallibility in its realm and to define its limits. However, it will also be a chance to prove that the church values justice higher than prestige.

Excerpt from The New York Times, July 1968.

Isaac Newton (1642-1727)

CHAPTER EIGHT

The Unity of Earth and Sky—
The Work of Newton

8.1 Newton and seventeenth-century science

Forty-five years passed between the death of Galileo in 1642 and the publication of Newton's *Principia* in 1687. In those years major changes occurred in the social organization of scientific studies. The new philosophy of experimental science, applied with enthusiasm and imagination, produced a wealth of new results. Scholars began to work together and organize scientific societies in Italy, France, and England. One of the most famous, the Royal Society of London for Improving Natural Knowledge, was founded in 1662. Through these societies scientific experimenters exchanged information, debated new ideas, argued against opponents of the new experimental activities, and published technical papers. Each society sought public support for its work and published studies in widely read scientific journals. Through the societies, scientific activities became well-defined, strong, and international.

This development was part of the general cultural, political, and economic change occurring in the 16th and 17th centuries. (See the time chart on page 84.) Craftsmen and people of wealth and leisure became involved in scientific studies. Some sought to improve technological methods and products. Others found the study of nature through experiment a new and exciting hobby. But the availability of money and time, the growing interest in science, and the creation of organizations are not enough to explain the growing success of scientific studies. This rapid growth also depended upon able scientists, well-formulated problems, and good experimental and mathematical tools.

Some of the important scientists who lived between 1600 and 1750 are shown in the time chart for the Age of Newton. The list includes amateurs as well as university professors.

SG8.1

The forms "1500's" and "16th century" are used interchangeably in referring to the time period roughly between 1500 and 1600.

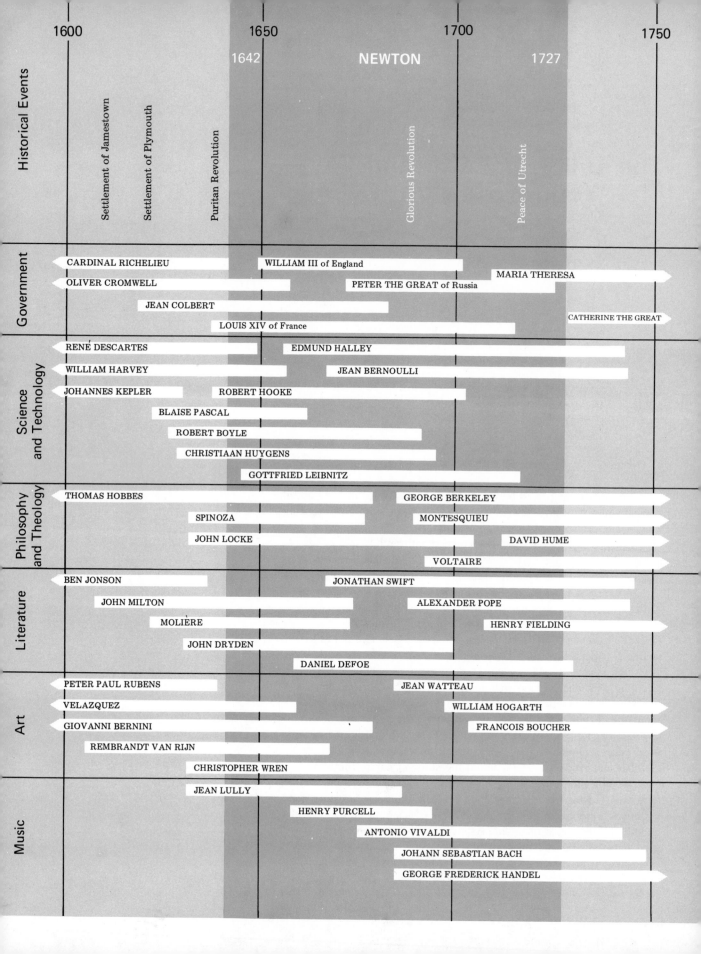

Many well-formulated problems appear in the writings of Galileo and Kepler. Their studies showed how useful mathematics could be when combined with experimental observation. Furthermore, their works raised exciting new questions. For example, what forces act on the planets and cause the paths actually observed? Why do objects fall as they do near the earth's surface?

Good experimental and mathematical tools were being created. With mathematics being applied to physics, studies in each field stimulated development in the other. Similarly, the instrument-maker and the scientist aided each other.

Another factor of great importance was the rapid build-up of scientific knowledge itself. From the time of Galileo, scientists had reported repeatable experiments in books and journals. Theories could now be tested, modified, and applied. Each study built on those done previously.

Newton, who lived in this new scientific age, is the central person in this chapter. However, in science as in any other field, many workers made useful contributions. The structure of science depends not only upon recognized geniuses, but also upon many lesser-known scientists. As Lord Rutherford, one of the founders of modern atomic theory, said:

It is not in the nature of things for any one man to make a sudden violent discovery; science goes step by step, and every man depends upon the work of his predecessors. . . . Scientists

Newton entered Trinity College, Cambridge University, in 1661 at the age of eighteen. He was doing experiments and teaching while still a student. This early engraving shows the quiet student wearing a wig and heavy academic robes.

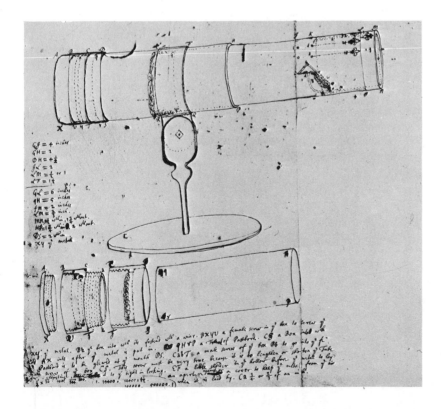

This drawing of the reflecting telescope he invented was done by Newton while he was still a student.

are not dependent on the ideas of a single man, but on the combined wisdom of thousands. . . .

To tell the story properly, we should trace fully each scientist's debt to others who worked previously and in the same age. We should also trace each scientist's influence upon future scientists. But within the space available, we can only briefly hint at these relationships.

Isaac Newton was born on Christmas Day, 1642, in the small English village of Woolsthorpe in Lincolnshire. He was a quiet farm boy. But, like young Galileo, he loved to build mechanical gadgets and seemed to have a liking for mathematics. With financial help from an uncle he went to Trinity College of Cambridge University in 1661. There he enrolled in the study of mathematics and was a successful student. In 1665 the Black Plague swept through England. The college was closed, and Newton went home to Woolsthorpe. There, by the time he was twenty-four, he had made spectacular discoveries. In mathematics, he found the binomial theorem and differential calculus. In optics he worked out a theory of colors. In mechanics, he already had formulated a clear concept of the first two laws of motion and the law of gravitational attraction. He also had discovered the equation for centripetal acceleration. However, he did not announce this equation until many years after Huygens' equivalent statement.

This must have been the time of the famous and disputed fall of the apple. One version of the apple story appears in a biography of Newton written by his friend, William Stukeley. In it we read that on a particular occasion Stukeley was having tea with Newton. They were sitting under some apple trees in a garden, and Newton recalled that:

> he was just in the same situation, as when formerly, the notion of gravitation came into his mind. It was occasion'd by the fall of an apple, as he sat in a contemplative mood. Why should that apple always descend perpendicularly to the ground, thought he to himself. Why should it not go sideways or upwards, but constantly to the earth's centre?

The main emphasis in this story probably should be placed on the "contemplative mood" and not on the apple. We have seen this pattern before: a great puzzle (here, that of the forces acting on planets) begins to be solved when a clear-thinking person contemplates a familiar event (the fall of an object on earth). Where others had seen no relationship, Newton did. Referring to the plague years, Newton once wrote:

> I began to think of gravity extending to the orb of the moon, and . . . from Kepler's rule [third law, law of periods] . . . I deduced that the forces which keep the Planets in their

orbs must be reciprocally as the squares of their distances from the centers about which they revolve: and thereby compared the force requisite to keep the moon in her orb with the force of gravity at the surface of the earth, and found them to answer pretty nearly. All this was in the two plague years of 1665 and 1666, for in those days [at age 21 or 22] I was in the prime of my age for invention, and minded mathematics and philosophy more than at any time since.

Soon after Newton's return to Cambridge, he was chosen to follow his former teacher as professor of mathematics. He taught at the university and contributed papers to the Royal Society. At first, his contributions were mainly on optics. His *Theory of Light and Colors,* finally published in 1672, fired a long and bitter controversy with certain other scientists. Newton, a private and complex man, resolved never to publish anything more.

In 1684 Newton's devoted friend Halley, a noted astronomer, came to ask his advice. Halley was involved in a controversy with Christopher Wren and Robert Hooke about the force needed to cause a body to move along an ellipse in accord with Kepler's laws. This was one of the most debated and interesting scientific problems of the time. Halley was pleasantly surprised to learn that Newton had already solved this problem ("and much other matter"). Halley then persuaded his friend to publish these important studies. To encourage Newton, Halley became responsible for all the costs of publication. Less than two years later, Newton had the *Principia* ready for the printer. Publication of the *Principia* in 1687 quickly established Newton as one of the greatest thinkers in history.

Several years afterward, Newton appears to have had a nervous breakdown. He recovered, but from then until his death, thirty-five years later, he made no major scientific discoveries. He rounded out earlier studies on heat and optics and turned more and more to writing on theology. During those years he received many honors. In 1699 he was appointed Master of the Mint, partly because of his great knowledge of the chemistry of metals. There he helped to re-establish the value of British coins, in which lead and copper had been introduced in place of silver and gold. In 1689 and 1701 he represented Cambridge University in Parliament, and he was knighted in 1705 by Queen Anne. He was president of the Royal Society from 1703 until his death in 1727. He was buried in Westminster Abbey.

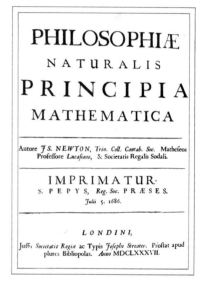

Title page of Newton's *Principia mathematica.* Because the Royal Society sponsored the book, the title page includes the name of the Society's president, Samuel Pepys, famous for his diary, which describes life during the seventeenth century.

8.2 Newton's *Principia*

The original preface to Newton's *Principia,* parts of which we have already studied, gives an outline of the book:

Since the ancients (as we are told by Pappus) esteemed the science of mechanics of greatest importance in the investigation of natural things, and the moderns, rejecting substantial forms and occult qualities, have endeavored to subject the phenomena of nature to the laws of mathematics, I have in this treatise cultivated mathematics as far as it relates to philosophy [we would say 'physical science'] . . . for the whole burden of philosophy seems to consist in this—from the phenomena of motions to investigate [induce] the forces of nature, and then from these forces to demonstrate [deduce] the other phenomena, and to this end the general propositions in the first and second Books are directed. In the third Book I give an example of this in the explication of the system of the World; for by the propositions mathematically demonstrated in the former Books, in the third I derive from the celestial phenomena the forces of gravity with which bodies tend to the sun and the several planets. Then from these forces, by other propositions which are also mathematical, I deduce the motions of the planets, the comets, the moon, and the sea [tides] . . . .

The work begins with definitions—mass, momentum, inertia, force. Next come the three laws of motion and the principles of addition for forces and velocities (discussed in Unit 1). Newton also included an equally important and remarkable passage on "Rules of Reasoning in Philosophy." The four rules, or assumptions, reflect his profound faith in the uniformity of all nature. Newton intended the rules to guide scientists in making hypotheses. He also wanted to make clear to the reader his own philosophical assumptions. These rules had their roots in ancient Greece, and are still useful. The first has been called a Principle of Parsimony, the second and third, Principles of Unity. The fourth expresses a faith needed for us to use the process of logic.

In a brief form, and using some modern language, Newton's four Rules of Reasoning are:

These rules are stated by Newton at the beginning of Book III of the *Principia*.

1. "Nature does nothing . . . in vain, and more is in vain when less will serve." Nature is essentially simple. Therefore we ought not to introduce more hypotheses than are needed to explain observed facts. This fundamental faith of all scientists had been also expressed in Galileo's "Nature . . . does not that by many things, which may be done by few." Galileo in turn was reflecting an opinion of Aristotle. Thus, the belief in simplicity has a long history.
2. "Therefore to the same natural effects we must, as far as possible, assign the same causes. As to respiration in a man and in a beast; the descent of stones in Europe and in America; . . . the reflection of light in the earth, and in the planets."
3. Properties common to all bodies within reach of our experiments are assumed (until proved otherwise) to apply to all bodies in general.

For example, all physical objects known to experimenters had always been found to have mass. So by this rule Newton proposed that *every* object has mass—even those beyond our reach in the celestial region.

4. In "experimental philosophy," hypotheses or generalizations based on experience should be accepted as "accurately or very nearly true, notwithstanding any contrary hypotheses that may be imagined." We must accept such hypotheses until we have additional evidence by which they may be made more accurate or revised.

Notice that Newton's assumption denies the distinction between terrestrial and celestial matter.

You should restate these rules in your own words before going on to the next section. (A good topic for an essay would be whether Newton's rules of reasoning are applicable outside of science.)

The *Principia* is an extraordinary document. Its three main sections contain a wealth of mathematical and physical discoveries. But overshadowing everything else is the theory of universal gravitation, with the proofs and arguments leading to it. Newton uses a form of argument patterned after that of Euclid. You encountered this type of proofs in studying geometry. But the style of detailed mathematical steps used in the *Principia* is unfamiliar today. Therefore, many of the steps Newton used in his proofs will be more understandable when restated in modern terms as will be done in what follows.

The central idea of universal gravitation can be simply stated: *every object in the universe attracts every other object*. Moreover, the amount of attraction depends in a simple way on the masses of the objects and the distance between them.

This was Newton's great synthesis, boldly combining terrestrial laws of force and motion with astronomical laws of motion. Gravitation is a *universal* force. It applies to the earth and apples, to the sun and planets, and to all other bodies (such as comets) moving in the solar system. Heaven and earth were united in one grand system dominated by the Law of Universal Gravitation. The general astonishment and awe were reflected in the words of the English poet Alexander Pope:

Nature and Nature's laws lay hid in night:
God said, Let Newton be! and all was light.

The *Principia,* written in Latin, was filled with long geometrical arguments and was difficult to read. Happily, several gifted writers wrote summaries that allowed a wide circle of readers to learn of Newton's arguments and conclusions. One of the most popular of these books was published in 1736 by the French philosopher and reformer Voltaire.

Readers of these books must have been excited and perhaps puzzled by the new approach and assumptions. For two thousand years, from the time of the ancient Greeks until well after Copernicus, the ideas of natural place and natural motion had been used to explain the general position and movements of the planets. From the time of the Greeks, scholars had widely believed that the planets' orbits were their "natural motion." However, to Newton the natural motion of a body was at a uniform rate along a straight line. Motion in a curve showed that a net force was continuously accelerating the planets away from their natural straight-line motion. Yet the force acting on the planets was entirely natural, and acted between all bodies in heaven and on earth. Furthermore, it was the same force that caused bodies on the earth to fall. What a reversal of the old assumptions about what was "natural"!

8.3 The inverse-square law of planetary force

Newton believed that the natural straight-line path of a planet was forced into a curve by the influence of the sun. He demonstrated that Kepler's law of areas could be true if, and only if, forces exerted on the planets were always directed toward a single point. (Details of his argument for this "central" force are given on the special pages entitled "Motion under a central force.") He showed also that the single point was the location of the sun. The law of areas is obeyed no matter what *magnitude* the force has, as long as the force is always directed to the same point. But Newton still had to show that a central gravitational force would cause the exact relationship observed between orbital radius and period. How great was the gravitational force, and how did it differ for different planets?

The combination of Kepler's laws with Newton's laws provide a fine example of the power of logical reasoning. Recall these laws:

Newton's Laws

1. A body continues in a state of rest, or of uniform motion in a straight line, unless acted upon by a net force. (Law of Inertia.)

2. The net force acting on an object is directly proportional to and in the same direction as the acceleration.

3. To every action there is an equal and opposite reaction.

Kepler's Laws

1. The planets move in orbits which are ellipses and have the sun at one focus.

2. The line from the sun to a planet sweeps over areas which are proportional to the time intervals.

3. The squares of the periods of the planets are proportional to the cubes of their mean distances from the sun.

$$T^2 = k \cdot R^3{}_{av}$$

According to Newton's first law, a change in motion, either in direction or in magnitude (speed), requires the action of a net force. But according to Kepler, the planets move in orbits which are ellipses, that is, curved orbits. Therefore, a net force must be acting to change their motion. Notice that this conclusion does not specify the type or direction of the net force.

Combining Newton's second law with the first two laws of Kepler clarifies the direction of the force. According to Newton's second law, the net force is exerted in the direction of the observed acceleration. But what is the direction of the force acting on the planets? Newton employed the geometrical analysis described on pages 94-95, "Motion under a central force."

His analysis indicated that a body moving under a central force will, when viewed from the center of the force, move according to Kepler's law of areas. But Kepler's law of areas relates to the distance of the planets from the sun. Therefore, Newton could conclude that the sun at one focus of each ellipse was the source of the central force acting on the planets.

Newton then found that motion in an elliptical path would occur only when the central force was an inverse-square force, $F \propto 1/R^2$. Thus only an inverse-square force exerted by the sun would result in the observed elliptical orbits described by Kepler. Newton then clinched the argument by showing that such a force law would also result in Kepler's third law, the Law of Periods, $T^2 = kR^3_{av}$.

From this analysis Newton concluded that one general Law of Universal Gravitation applied to all bodies moving in the solar system. This is the central argument of Newton's great synthesis.

Let us consider the motions of the six known planets in terms of their centripetal acceleration toward the sun. By Newton's proof, mentioned above, this acceleration decreases inversely as the square of the planets' average distances from the sun. The proof for circular orbits is very short. The expression for centripetal acceleration a_c of a body moving uniformly in a circular path, in terms of the radius R and the period T, is

$$a_c = \frac{4\pi^2 R}{T^2}$$

(We derived this expression in Chapter 4.) Kepler's law of periods stated a definite relation between the orbital periods of the planets and their average distances from the sun:

$$\frac{T^2}{R_{av}^3} = \text{constant}$$

If we use the symbol k for the constant, we can write

$$T^2 = kR_{av}^3$$

For circular orbits, R_{av} is just R. Substituting kR^3 for T^2 in the centripetal force equation gives

$$a_c = \frac{4\pi^2 R}{kR^3} = \frac{4\pi^2}{kR^2}$$

Since $4\pi^2/k$ is a constant, we can write simply

$$a_c \propto \frac{1}{R^2}$$

This conclusion follows necessarily from Kepler's law of periods and the definition of acceleration. If Newton's second law $F \propto a$ holds for planets as well as for bodies on earth, then there must be a centripetal force F_c acting on a planet. Furthermore, this force must decrease in proportion to the square of the distance of the planet from the sun

$$F_c \propto \frac{1}{R^2}$$

Newton showed that the same result holds for all ellipses. Indeed, it holds for any object moving in an orbit around a center of force. (The possible orbital shapes are circle, ellipse, parabola, or hyperbola—all conic sections.) Any such object is being acted upon by a centripetal force that varies inversely with the square of the distance from the center of force.

In Newton's time, four of Jupiter's satellites and four of Saturn's satellites had been observed.

SG 8.2

Newton had still more evidence from telescopic observations of Jupiter's satellites and Saturn's satellites. The satellites of each planet obeyed Kepler's law of areas around the planet as a center. For Jupiter's satellites, Kepler's law of periods $T^2/R^3 = constant$ held. But the *value* of the constant was different from that for the planets around the sun. The law held also for Saturn's satellites, but with still a different constant. Therefore, Jupiter's satellites were acted on by a central force directed toward Jupiter and decreasing with the square of the distance from Jupiter. The same held true for Saturn's satellites and Saturn. These observed interactions of astronomical bodies supported Newton's proposed "$1/R^2$" central attractive force.

Q1 What can be proved from the fact that the planets sweep out equal areas with respect to the sun in equal times?

Q2 With what relationship can $T^2/R_{av}^3 = constant$ be combined to prove that the gravitational attraction varies as $1/R^2$?

Q3 What simplifying assumption was made in the derivation given in this section?

Q4 Did Newton limit his own derivation by the same assumption?

8.4 Law of universal gravitation

Subject to further evidence, we will now accept the idea that a central force is holding the planets in their orbits. Furthermore, the strength of this central force changes inversely with the square of the distance from the sun. This strongly suggests that the sun is the source of the force— but it does not necessarily require this conclusion. Newton's results so far describe the force in mathematical terms but do not provide any mechanism for its transmission.

The French philosopher Descartes (1596-1650) had proposed that all space was filled with a thin, invisible fluid. This fluid carried the planets around the sun in a huge whirlpool-like motion. This was an interesting idea, and it was widely accepted at the time. However, Newton proved by a precise argument that this mechanism could not explain the details of planetary motion summarized in Kepler's laws.

SG 8.3

Kepler had made a different suggestion some years earlier. He proposed that some magnetic force reached out from the sun to keep the planets moving. He was the first to regard the sun as the controlling mechanical agent behind planetary motion. But Kepler's magnetic model was inadequate. And so the problem remained: was the sun actually the source of the force? If so, on what properties of the sun or planets did the amount of the force depend?

As you read in Section 8.1, Newton had begun to think about planetary force while living at home during the Black Plague. There an idea came to him, perhaps when he saw an apple fall, and perhaps not. Newton's idea was that the planetary force was the same kind of force that caused objects near the earth's surface to fall. He first tested this idea on the earth's attraction for the moon. The data available to him fixed the distance between the center of the earth and the center of the moon at nearly sixty times the radius of the earth. Newton believed that the attractive force varies as $1/R^2$. Therefore, the gravitational acceleration the earth exerts on the moon should be only $1/(60)^2$, $(1/3600)$ of that exerted upon objects at the earth's surface. Observations of falling bodies had long established gravitational acceleration at the earth's surface as about 9.80 meters per second per second. Therefore, the moon *should* fall at 1/3600 of that acceleration value: (9.80/3600) meters per second per second, or 2.72×10^{-3} m/sec². Does it?

To us, who have heard about gravity from our early school years, this may not seem to have been a particularly clever idea. But in Newton's time, after centuries of believing celestial events to be completely different from earthly events, it was the mental leap of a genius. Newton had already assumed the planets to be subject to the earth's laws of motion when he derived a $1/R^2$ force law using the formula for a_c. But it was a still greater step to guess that the force on planets was not some special celestial force, but nothing other than familiar old weight of everyday objects.

Newton started from the knowledge that the orbital period of the moon was very nearly $27\frac{1}{3}$ days. The centripetal acceleration a_c of a body moving uniformly with period T in a circle of radius R is $a_c = 4\pi^2 R/T^2$. (We developed this equation in Section 4.6, Unit 1.) When we insert values for the known quantities R and T (in meters and seconds) and do the arithmetic, we find that the *observed* acceleration is:

$$a_c = 2.74 \times 10^{-3} \text{m/sec}^2$$

This is in very good agreement with the value of 2.72×10^{-3} m/sec² we predicted above. From the values available to Newton, which were close to these, he concluded that he had

. . . compared the force requisite to keep the moon in her orbit with the force of gravity at the surface of the earth, and found them to answer pretty nearly.

Therefore, the force by which the moon is retained in its orbit becomes, at the very surface of the earth, equal to the force of gravity which we observe in heavy bodies there. And, therefore, (by Rules of Reasoning 1 and 2) the force by which the moon is retained in its orbit is that very same force which we commonly call gravity . . . .

Motion under a central force

How will a moving body respond to a central force? In order to follow Newton's analysis, we shall need to remember that the area of a triangle equals ½ *base × altitude*. Any of the three sides can be chosen as the base, and the altitude is the perpendicular distance to the opposite corner.

Suppose that a body was initially passing some point P, already moving at uniform speed v along the straight line through PQ. (See Figure A below.) If it goes on with no force acting, then in

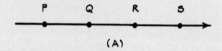

(A)

equal intervals of time Δt it will continue to move equal distances, PQ, QR, RS, etc.

How will its motion appear to an observer at some point O? Consider the triangles OPQ and OQR in Figure B below.

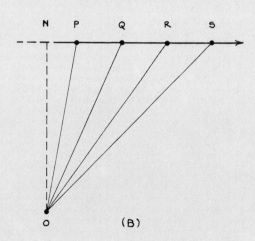

(B)

The triangles have equal bases, PQ = QR = RS, and also equal altitudes, ON, for all three. Therefore the triangles OPQ and OQR have equal areas. And therefore the line drawn from an observer at point O to the body moving at a uniform speed in a straight line PQR will sweep over equal areas in equal times.

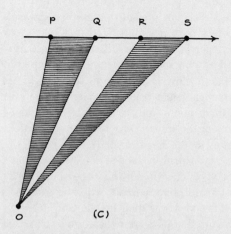

(C)

So, strange as it may seem at first, Kepler's law of areas applies even to a body on which the net force has the value *zero*, and which therefore is moving uniformly along a straight line.

Now, suppose that the object discussed in Figure A, while passing through point Q, is briefly exposed to a force, such as a blow. If this force is directed toward point O, how will the object's motion change? (Refer to Figure D below.)

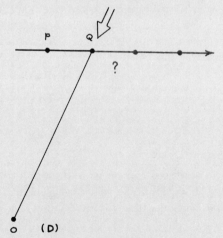

(D)

First, consider what happens if a body initially at rest at point Q were exposed to the same blow. The body would be accelerated during the blow toward O. It would then continue to move toward O at constant speed, and after some definite time interval Δt, it will have moved a definite distance to a new point Q'. (See Figure E on the next page.)

(E)

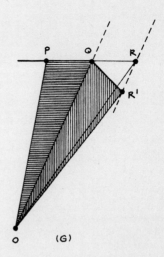

(G)

Now, consider the effect of the blow on the object that was initially moving toward point R. The resultant motion is the combination of these two components, and the object moves to point R'. (See Figure F below.)

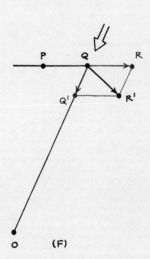

(F)

Earlier we found that the areas of the triangles OPQ and OQR were equal. Is the area of the triangle OQR' the same? Both triangles OQR and OQR' have a common base, OQ. Also, the altitudes of both triangles are the perpendicular distance from line OQ to line RR'. (See Figure G.) Therefore, the areas of triangles OQR and OQR' are equal.

If now another blow directed toward O were given at point R', the body would move to some

point S", as indicated in Figure H below. By a similar analysis you can find that the areas of triangles OR'S" and OR'S' are equal. Their areas also equal the area of triangle OPQ.

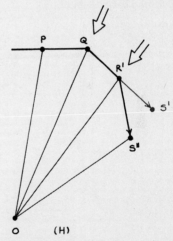

(H)

In this geometrical argument we have always applied the force toward the same point, O. A force always directed toward a single point is called a *central* force. (Notice that the proof has nothing to do with the *magnitude* of the force, or how it changes with distance from O.) Also, we have applied the force at equal intervals Δt. If each time interval Δt were made vanishingly small, the force would appear to be applied continuously. And the argument would still hold. We then have an important conclusion: *If a body is acted upon by any central force, it will move in accordance with Kepler's law of areas.*

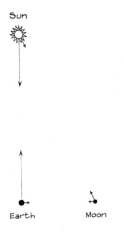

The sun, moon, and earth each pull on the other. The forces are in matched pairs, in agreement with Newton's third law of motion. As the moon moves through space, the gravitational attraction of the earth causes the moon to "fall" toward the earth. The continuous combination of its straight line inertial motion and its "fall" produce the curved orbit.

This was really a triumph. The same gravity that brings apples down from trees also holds the moon in its orbit. This assertion is the first portion of what is known as the Law of Universal Gravitation. It claims that *every object in the universe attracts every other object with a gravitational force*. If this is so, there must be gravitational forces not only between a rock and the earth, but also between the earth and the moon, between Jupiter and its satellites—and between the sun and each of the planets.

But Newton did not stop at saying that a gravitational force exists between the planets and the sun. He further claimed that the force is exactly the right size to explain *completely* the motion of every planet. No other mechanism is needed—no whirlpools of invisible fluids, no magnetic forces. Gravitation, and gravitation alone, underlies the dynamics of the heavens.

This concept is so commonplace to us that we are in danger of passing it by without really understanding what Newton was claiming. First, he proposed a truly universal physical law. Following his Rules of Reasoning, he extended to the whole universe what he found true for its observable parts. He excluded no object in the universe from the effect of gravity.

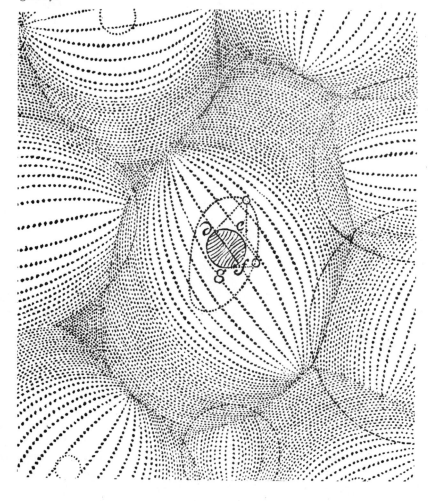

A drawing by which Descartes (1596-1650) illustrated his theory of space being filled with whirlpools of matter that drive the planets along their orbits.

The idea that terrestrial laws and forces were the same as those that regulated the whole universe had stunning impact. Less than a century before, it would have been dangerous even to suggest such a thing. But Kepler and Galileo had laid the foundation for combining the physics of the heavens and earth. Newton carried this work to its conclusion. Today, his extension of the mechanics of terrestrial objects to the motion of celestial bodies is called the *Newtonian synthesis*.

Newton's claim that a planet's orbit is determined by the gravitational attraction between it and the sun had another effect. It moved science away from geometrical explanations and towards physical ones. Most philosophers and scientists before Newton had been occupied mainly with the question "What are the motions?" Newton asked instead, "What force explains the motions?" In both the Ptolemaic and Copernican systems the planets moved about *points* in space rather than about *objects*. And they moved as they did because of their "nature" or geometrical shape, not because forces acted on them. Newton, on the other hand, spoke not of points, but of things, of objects, of physical bodies. Unless the gravitational attraction to the sun deflected them continuously from straight-line paths, the planets would fly out into the darkness of deep space. Thus it was the physical sun that was important, not the point at which the sun happened to be located.

Newton's synthesis centered on the idea of gravitational force. But calling it a force of gravity, Newton knew that he was not explaining *why* it existed. When you hold a stone above the surface of the earth and release it, it accelerates to the ground. Our laws of motion tell us that there must be a force acting on the stone to accelerate it. We know the *direction* of the force. And we can find the *magnitude* of the force by multiplying the mass of the stone by the acceleration. We can give it a name: weight, or gravitational attraction to the earth. But why such an interaction between bodies exists remains a puzzle. It is still an important problem in physics today.

Q5 What idea came to Newton while he was thinking about falling objects and the moon's acceleration?

Q6 Kepler, too, believed that the sun exerted forces on the planets. How did his view differ from Newton's?

Q7 The central idea of Chapter 8 is the "Newtonian synthesis." What did Newton bring together?

8.5 Newton and hypotheses

Newton's claim that there is a mutual force (gravitational interaction) between a planet and the sun raised a new question. How can a planet and the sun act upon each other at enormous distances without any visible connections between them? On earth you can exert a force on an object by pushing it or pulling it. We are not surprised to see a cloud or a balloon drifting across the sky, even though nothing seems to be touching it. Air is invisible, but we know that it is actually a material substance which we can feel when it moves. Falling objects and iron objects being attracted to a magnet are harder to explain, but the distances are small. However, the earth is over 90 million miles, and Saturn more than 800 million miles, from the sun. How could there possibly be any physical contact between such distant objects? How can we account for such "action at a distance"?

In Newton's time and for a long time afterward, scholars advanced suggestions for solving this problem. Most involved imagining space to be filled with some invisible substance (an "ether") that transmitted force. Newton himself privately guessed that such an ether was involved. But he could find no way to test this belief. Therefore, at least in public, he refused to speculate on possible mechanisms. As he said in a famous passage which he added in the second edition of the *Principia* (1713):

> . . . Hitherto I have not been able to discover the cause of those properties of gravity from phenomena, and I frame no hypotheses; for whatever is not deduced from the phenomena is to be called an hypothesis; and hypotheses, whether metaphysical or physical, whether of occult qualities or mechanical, have no place in experimental philosophy . . . . And to us it is enough that gravity does really exist, and act according to the laws which we have explained, and abundantly serves to account for all the motions of the celestial bodies, and of our sea.

We quote Newton at length because one particular phrase is often misquoted and misinterpreted. The original Latin reads: *hypotheses non fingo*. This means "I frame no hypotheses" or "I do not feign hypotheses." The sense is, "I do not make *false* hypotheses." We know that Newton in fact made many hypotheses in his publications. Also, his letters to friends contain many speculations which he did not publish. So his stern denial of "framing" hypotheses must be properly interpreted. The fact is that there are two main kinds of hypotheses or assumptions: (1) The most common hypothesis is a proposal of some hidden mechanism to explain observations. For example, we might observe the moving hands of a watch. Then we might propose or imagine some arrangement of gears and springs that causes the motion. This would be a *hypothesis that is directly or indirectly testable, at least in principle, by reference to phenomena*. Our hypothesis about the watch, for example, can be tested by opening the watch or by making an x-ray photograph of it. In this context, consider an invisible fluid that transmitted gravitational force, the so-called "ether." Newton and others thought that certain direct tests might establish the presence of this substance. Many experimenters tried to "catch" the ether. A common approach involved pumping the air from a bottle. Then tests were made to see if any wind, pressure, or friction due to the ether remained to affect objects in the bottle. Nothing of this sort worked (nor has it since). So Newton wisely avoided making public any hypothesis for which he could not also propose a test.

(2) A quite different type of assumption is often made in published scientific work. It involves a hypothesis which everyone knows is not directly testable, but which still is necessary *just to get started on one's work*. An example is such a statement as "nature is simple" or any other of Newton's Four Rules of Reasoning. Acceptance of either the heliocentric system or the geocentric system is another example. In choosing the heliocentric system, Copernicus, Kepler, and Galileo made the hypothesis that the sun is at the center of the universe. They knew that this hypothesis was not directly testable, and that either system seemed to explain "the phenomena" equally well. Yet they adopted the point of view that seemed to them simpler, more convincing, and more "pleasing to the mind." It was this kind of hypothesis that Newton used without apology in his published work. Every scientist's work involves both kinds of hypothesis. The popular image of the scientist is of a person who uses only deliberate, logical, objective thoughts, and immediately tests them by definitive experiments. But, in fact, the working scientist feels quite free to entertain any guess, imaginative speculation, or hunch—provable or not—that might be helpful. (Sometimes these hunches are dignified by the phrase "working hypotheses." Without them there would be little progress!) Like Newton, however, most scientists today do not like to *publish* something that is still only an unproven hunch.

Q8   Did Newton explain the gravitational attraction of all bodies?

Q9   What was the popular type of explanation for "action at a distance"? Why didn't Newton use this type of explanation?

Q10   What are two main types of hypotheses used in science?

8.6   The magnitude of planetary force

The general statement that gravitational forces exist universally must now be turned into a quantitative law. An expression is needed for both the *magnitude* and *direction* of the forces any two objects exert on each other. It was not enough for Newton to assert that a mutual gravitational attraction exists between the sun and, say, Jupiter. To be convincing, he had to specify what quantitative factors determine the magnitudes of those mutual forces. He had to show how they could be measured, either directly or indirectly.

The first problem was defining precisely the distance R. Should it, for example, be taken as the distance between the surface of the earth and the surface of the moon? For many astronomical problems, the sizes of

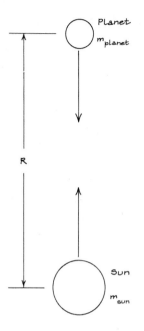

The gravitational force on a planet owing to the sun's pull is equal and opposite to the gravitational force on the sun owing to the planet.

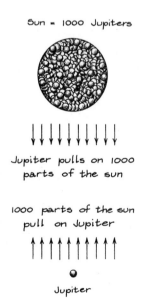

Sun = 1000 Jupiters

Jupiter pulls on 1000 parts of the sun

1000 parts of the sun pull on Jupiter

Jupiter

the interacting bodies are extremely small compared to the distances between them. In such cases the distance between the surfaces is practically the same as the distance between the centers. (For the earth and the moon, the distance between centers is only about 2% greater than the distance between surfaces.) Yet, some historians believe, Newton's uncertainty about a proper answer to this problem led him to drop the study for many years.

Eventually Newton solved the problem. The gravitational force exerted *by* a spherical body was the same as if all its mass were concentrated at its center. The gravitational force exerted *on* a spherical body by another body is the same as would be exerted on it if all its mass were concentrated at its center. Therefore, the distance R in the Law of Gravitation is the distance between centers.

This was a very important discovery. It allows us to consider the gravitational attraction between spherical bodies as though their masses were concentrated at single points. Thus, in thought, we can replace the objects by *mass-points*.

Newton's third law states that action equals reaction. If this is universally true, the amount of force the sun exerts on a planet must exactly equal the amount of force the planet exerts on the sun. For such a very large mass and such a relatively small mass, this may seem contrary to common sense. But the equality is easy to prove. First, let us assume only that Newton's third law holds between small chunks of matter. For example, we readily understand that a 1-kg chunk of Jupiter pulls *on* a 1-kg chunk of the sun as much as it is pulled *by* it. Now consider the total attraction between Jupiter and the sun, whose mass is about 1,000 times greater than Jupiter's. As the figure in the left margin indicates, we can consider the sun as a globe containing 1,000 Jupiters. Let us define one unit of force as the force that two Jupiter-sized masses exert on each other when separated by the distance of Jupiter from the sun. Then Jupiter pulls on the *sun* (a globe of 1,000 Jupiters) with a total force of 1,000 units. Each of the 1,000 parts of the sun also pulls on the planet Jupiter with one unit. Therefore, the total pull of the sun on *Jupiter* is also 1,000 units. Each part of the massive sun not only pulls *on* the planet, but is also pulled upon *by* the planet. The more mass there is to *attract,* the more there is to *be attracted.* (But although the mutual attractive forces are equal in magnitude, the resulting *accelerations* are not. Jupiter pulls on the sun as hard as the sun pulls on Jupiter. But the sun *responds* to the pull with only 1/1000 of the acceleration, because its *inertia* is 1,000 times Jupiter's.)

In Section 3.8 of Unit 1, we explained why bodies of different mass fall with the same acceleration near the earth's surface. We saw that the greater the inertia of a body, the more strongly it is acted upon by gravity. More precisely: near the earth's surface, the gravitational force on a body is directly proportional to its mass. Like Newton, let us extend this earthly effect to all gravitation. We then can assume that the gravitational force exerted on a planet by the *sun* is proportional to the mass of the planet. Similarly, the gravitational force exerted on the sun by the *planet* is proportional to the mass of the sun. We have just seen that the forces the sun and planet exert on each other are equal in magnitude. It follows that

the magnitude of the gravitational force is proportional to the mass of the
sun *and* to the mass of the planet. That is, the gravitational attraction
between two bodies is proportional to the *product* of their masses. If the   SG 8.4
mass of either body is tripled, the force is tripled. If the masses of both
bodies are tripled, the force is increased by a factor of 9. Using the symbol
F_{grav} for the magnitude of the forces, we can write $F_{grav} \propto m_{planet} \, m_{sun}$.

Our conclusion is that the amount of attraction between the sun and
a planet is proportional to the product of their masses. Earlier we   SG 8.5
concluded that the attraction also depends on the square of the distance
between the centers of the bodies. Combining these two proportionalities
gives us *one* force law, which now includes mass and distance:

$$F_{grav} \propto \frac{m_{planet} m_{sun}}{R^2}$$

Such a proportionality can be written as an equation by introducing a
constant. (The constant allows for the units of measurement used.) Using
G for the proportionality constant, we can write the law of planetary forces
as:

$$F = G \frac{m_{planet} m_{sun}}{R^2}$$

This equation asserts that the force between the sun and any planet
depends *only* upon three factors. These factors are the masses of the sun
and planet and the distance between them. The equation seems
unbelievably simple when we remember how complex the observed
planetary motions seemed. Yet every one of Kepler's empirical Laws of   SG 8.6
Planetary Motion agrees with this relation. In fact, we can even *derive*
Kepler's empirical laws from this force law and Newton's second law of
motion. More important still, the force allows us to calculate details of
planetary motion not obtainable with Kepler's laws alone.

Newton's proposal that this simple equation describes completely the
forces between the sun and planets was not the final step. He saw
nothing to limit this mutual force to the sun and planets, or to the earth
and apples. Rather, he insisted that an identical relation should apply
universally. This relation would hold true for *any two bodies* separated by
a distance that is large compared to their dimensions. It would apply
equally to two atoms or two stars. In short, Newton proposed a *general
Law of Universal Gravitation:*

$$F_{grav} = G \frac{m_1 m_2}{R^2}$$

where m_1 and m_2 are the masses of the bodies and R is the distance
between their centers. The numerical constant G is called the *constant of
universal gravitation*. Newton assumed it to be the same for all
gravitational interaction, whether between two grains of sand, two
members of a solar system, or two stars in different parts of the sky. As
you will see, the successes made possible by this simple relationship have
been very great. In fact, we have come to assume that this equation
applies everywhere and at all times, past, present, and future.

Even before we gather more supporting evidence, the sweeping
majesty of Newton's theory commands our wonder and admiration. It also
leads to the question of how such a bold universal theory can be proved.
There is no complete proof, of course, for that would mean examining
every interaction between all bodies in the universe! But the greater the
variety of single tests we make, the greater will be our belief in the
correctness of the theory.

SG 8.7

SG 8.8

Q11   According to Newton's law of action and reaction, the earth
should experience a force and accelerate toward a falling stone.
  (a) How does the force on the earth compare with the force on the
      stone?
  (b) How does the earth's acceleration compare with the stone's
      acceleration?

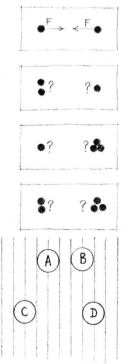

Q12   The top diagram at the right
represents two bodies of equal
mass which exert gravitational forces of
magnitude F on one another. What is the
magnitude of the gravitational attractions in
each of the other cases?

Q13   A, B, C, and D are bodies with
equal masses. How do the forces of
attraction that A and B exert on each other
compare with the forces that C and D exert
on each other?
  (a) $F_{AB} = 3 \times F_{CD}$
  (c) $F_{AB} = 4 \times F_{CD}$
  (b) $F_{AB} = 9 \times F_{CD}$
  (d) $F_{AB} = 16 \times F_{CD}$

This photograph, of the surface of the moon, shows some latter-day evidence that the laws of mechanics for heavenly bodies are at least, similar to those applying on earth: the trails of two huge boulders that rolled about 1000 ft down a lunar slope.

8.7 Planetary motion and the gravitational constant

Suppose that a planet of mass m_p is moving along an orbit of radius R and period T. According to Newton's mechanics, there is a continual centripetal acceleration $a_c = 4\pi^2 R/T^2$. Therefore, there must be a continual force $F_c = m_p a_c = 4\pi^2 R m_p/T^2$. If we identify gravity as the central force, then

$$F_{\text{grav}} = F_c$$

or
$$G\frac{m_p m_{\text{sun}}}{R^2} = \frac{4\pi^2 R m_p}{T^2}$$

By simplifying this equation and rearranging some terms, we can get an expression for G:

$$G = \frac{4\pi^2}{m_{\text{sun}}}\left(\frac{R^3}{T^2}\right)$$

We know from Kepler that for the planets' motion around the sun, the ratio R^3/T^2 is a constant; $4\pi^2$ is a constant also. If we assume that the mass of the sun is constant, then all factors on the right of the equation for G are constant. So G must be a constant for the gravitational effect of the sun on the planets. By similar reasoning, the value of G must be a constant for the effect of Jupiter on its moons. And it must be constant for Saturn and its moons, for earth and its moon, and for an apple falling to the earth. But is it the same value of G for all these cases?

It is impossible to *prove* that G is the same for the gravitational interaction of *all* bodies. But if we *assume* that G is a universal constant, we can get some remarkable new information—the relative masses of the sun and the planets!

We begin by again equating the centripetal force on the planets with the gravitational attraction to the sun. But this time we solve the equation for m_{sun}:

$$F_{grav} = F_c$$
$$\frac{Gm_p m_{sun}}{R^2} = \frac{4\pi^2 R m_p}{T^2}$$
$$m_{sun} = \frac{4\pi^2 R^3}{GT^2}$$

If we write k_{sun} for the constant ratio T^2/R^3, we have

$$m_{sun} = \frac{4\pi^2}{Gk_{sun}}$$

By similar derivation,

$$m_{Jupiter} = \frac{4\pi^2}{Gk_{Jupiter}} \qquad m_{Saturn} = \frac{4\pi^2}{Gk_{Saturn}} \qquad m_{earth} = \frac{4\pi^2}{Gk_{earth}}$$

Here $k_{Jupiter}$, k_{Saturn}, and k_{earth} are the known values of the constant ratios T^2/R^3 for the satellites of Jupiter, Saturn, and the earth.

To compare Jupiter's mass to the mass of the sun, we simply divide the formula for $m_{Jupiter}$ by the formula for m_{sun}:

$$\frac{m_{Jupiter}}{m_{sun}} = \frac{\dfrac{4\pi^2}{Gk_{Jupiter}}}{\dfrac{4\pi^2}{Gk_{sun}}} \qquad \text{or} \qquad \frac{m_{Jupiter}}{m_{sun}} = \frac{k_{sun}}{k_{Jupiter}}$$

SG 8.9

Masses Compared to Earth

Earth	1
Saturn	95
Jupiter	318
Sun	333,000

Similarly, we can compare the masses of any two planets if we know the values of T^2/R^3 for them both. That is, both must have satellites whose motion has been carefully observed.

These comparisons are based on the *assumptions* that G is a universal constant. Calculations based on this assumption have led to *consistent* results for a wide variety of astronomical data. One example is the successful orbiting and landing of a space vehicle on the moon. Results consistent with this assumption also appeared in difficult calculations of the small disturbing effects that the planets have on each other. There is still no way of proving G is the same everywhere and always. But it is a reasonable working assumption until evidence to the contrary appears.

If the numerical value of G were known, the *actual* masses of the earth, Jupiter, Saturn, and the sun could be calculated. G is defined by the equation $F_{grav} = Gm_1 m_2/R^2$. To find the value of G we must know values for all the other variables. That is, we must measure the force F_{grav} between two measured masses m_1 and m_2, separated by a measured distance R. Newton knew this. But in his time there were no instruments sensitive enough to measure the very tiny force expected between masses small enough for experimental use.

Q14   What information can be used to compare the masses of two planets?

Q15   What additional information is necessary for calculation of the actual masses?

8.8 The value of G and the actual masses of the planets

The masses of small solid objects can be found easily enough from their weights. And measuring the distance between solid objects of spherical shape presents no problem. But how can one measure the tiny mutual gravitational force between relatively small objects in a laboratory? (Remember that each object is also experiencing separately a huge gravitational force toward the tremendously massive earth.)

This serious technical problem was eventually solved by the English scientist, Henry Cavendish (1731-1810). For measuring gravitational forces, he employed a torsion balance. In this device, the gravitational attraction between two pairs of lead spheres twisted a wire holding up one of the pairs. The twist of the wire could be measured against the twist produced by small known forces. A typical experiment might involve a 100-kg sphere and a 1-kg sphere at a center-to-center distance of 0.1 m. The resulting force would be about one-millionth of a newton! As the calculations in the margin show, these data lead to a value for G of about 10^{-10}(N·m²/kg²). This experiment has been steadily improved, and the accepted value of G is now:

Calculation of G from approximate experimental values:

$$F_{grav} = G\frac{Mm}{R^2}$$

so
$$G = \frac{F_{grav}\ R^2}{Mm}$$
$$= \frac{(10^{-6}\ \text{N})\,(0.1\ \text{m})^2}{(100\ \text{kg})\,(1\ \text{kg})}$$
$$= \frac{10^{-6} \times 10^{-2}}{10^2}\ \text{N·m}^2/\text{kg}^2$$
$$= 10^{-10}\ \text{N·m}^2/\text{kg}^2$$

$$G = 6.67 \times 10^{-11}\ \text{N·m}^2/\text{kg}^2$$

Evidently gravitation is a weak force which becomes important only when at least one of the masses is very great. The gravitational force on a 1-kg mass at the surface of the earth is 9.8 newtons. We know this because, if released, a 1-kg mass falls with an acceleration of 9.8 m/sec². Substituting 9.8 newtons for F_{grav} and the radius of the earth for R, you can calculate the mass of the earth! (See SG 8.11.)

Let us assume that the same value for G applies to all gravitational interaction. Now we can calculate the masses of the planets from the known values of T^2/R^3 for their satellites. Since Newton's time, satellites have been discovered around all of the outer planets except Pluto. The values of these planets' masses, calculated from $m = 4\pi^2/G \times R^3/T^2$, are given in the table in the margin. Venus and Mercury have no satellites. Their masses are found by analyzing the slight disturbing effects each has on other planets. Modern values for the actual masses of the planets are listed in the margin. Notice that the planets taken together make up not much more than 1/1000 of the mass of the solar system. By

N·m²/kg² can be expressed as m³/kg · sec²

SG 8.10–8.13

Actual Masses (in units of 10^{24} kg)

Sun	1,980,000
Mercury	.328
Venus	4.83
Earth	5.98
Mars	.637
Jupiter	1,900
Saturn	567
Uranus	88.0
Neptune	103.
Pluto	1.1

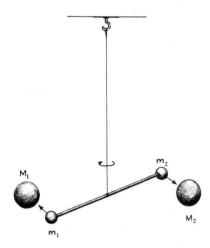

Schematic diagram of the device used by Cavendish for determining the value of the gravitational constant G. Large lead balls of masses M_1 and M_2 were brought close to small lead balls of masses m_1 and m_2. The mutual gravitational attraction between M_1 and m_1 and between M_2 and m_2, caused the vertical wire to be twisted by a measurable amount.

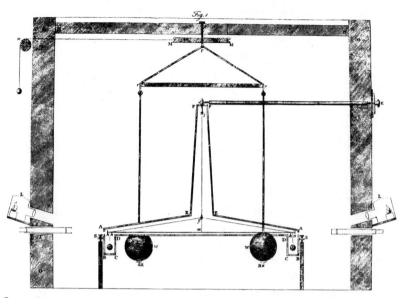

Cavendish's original drawing of his apparatus for determining the value of G. To prevent disturbance from air currents, he inclosed it in a sealed case. He observed the deflection of the balance rod from outside with telescopes.

far, most of the mass is in the sun. For this reason, the sun dominates the motion of the planets, acting almost like an infinitely massive, fixed object.

In light of Newton's third law, we should modify this picture a little. For every pull the sun exerts on a planet, the sun itself experiences an equally strong pull in the opposite direction. Of course, the very much greater mass of the sun keeps its acceleration to a correspondingly smaller value. But some slight acceleration does exist. Hence, the sun cannot really be fixed in space even within the solar system, if we accept Newtonian dynamics. Rather, it moves a little about the point that forms the common center of mass of the sun and each moving planet. This is true for every one of the nine planets. And since the planets rarely move all in one line, the sun's motion is actually a combination of nine small ellipses. Such motion might be important in a solar system in which the planets were very heavy compared to their sun. But in our solar system, it is not large enough to be of interest for most purposes.

SG 8.14 – 8.17

Q16 Which of the quantities in the equation $F_{grav} = Gm_1m_2/R^2$ did Cavendish *measure*?

Q17 Knowing a value for G, what other information can be used to find the mass of the earth?

Q18 Knowing a value for G, what other information can be used to find the mass of Saturn?

Q19 The mass of the sun is about 1,000 times the mass of Jupiter. How does the sun's acceleration due to Jupiter's attraction compare with Jupiter's acceleration due to the sun's attraction?

8.9 Further successes

Newton did not stop with the fairly direct demonstrations we have described so far. In the *Principia* he showed that his law of universal gravitation could explain other complicated gravitational interactions. Among these were the tides of the sea and the peculiar drift of comets across the sky.

The tides: Knowledge of the tides had been vital to navigators, tradesmen, and explorers through the ages. But the *cause* of the tides had remained a mystery despite the studies of such scientists as Galileo. Newton, however, by applying the law of gravitation, was able to explain the main features of the ocean tides. He found them to result from the attraction of the moon and the sun upon the waters of the earth. Each day two high tides normally occur. Also, twice each month, the moon, sun, and earth are in line with each other. At these times the tides are significantly higher than average.

Two questions about tidal phenomena demand special attention. First, why do high tides occur on both sides of the earth, including the side away from the moon? Second, why does high tide occur at a given location some hours after the moon was highest in the sky?

Newton knew that the gravitational attractions of the moon and sun accelerate the whole solid earth. These forces also accelerate the fluid water at the earth's surface. Newton realized that the tides result from the *difference* in acceleration of the earth and its waters. The moon's distance from the earth's center is 60 earth radii. On the side of the earth nearer the moon, the distance of the water from the moon is only 59 radii. On the side of the earth away from the moon, the water is 61 earth radii from the moon. The accelerations are shown in the figure at the left. On the side nearer the moon, the acceleration of the water toward the moon is greater than the acceleration of the earth as a whole. The net effect is that the water is accelerated away from the earth. On the side of the earth away from the moon, the acceleration of the water toward the moon is less than that of the earth as a whole. The net result is that the earth is accelerated away from the water there.

Perhaps you have watched the tides change at the seashore or examined tide tables. If so, you know that high tide occurs some hours *after* the moon is highest in the sky. To explain this, even qualitatively, we must remember that on the whole the oceans are not very deep. The ocean waters moving in from more distant parts of the oceans in response to the moon's attraction are slowed by friction with the ocean floors, especially in shallow water. Thus, the time of high tide is delayed. In any particular place, the amount of delay and the height of the tides depends greatly upon how easily the waters can flow. No general theory can account for all the particular details of the tides. Most local predictions in the tide tables are based on empirical rules using the tidal patterns recorded in the past.

Since there are tides in the seas, you may wonder if the atmosphere and the earth itself undergo tides. They do. The earth is not completely rigid, but bends somewhat like steel. The tide in the earth is about a foot high. The atmospheric tides are generally masked by other weather

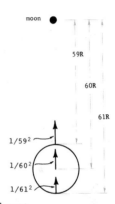

Tidal Forces.
The earth-moon distance indicated in the figure is greatly reduced because of the space limitations.

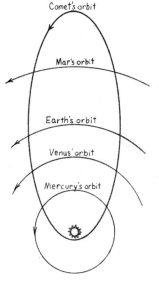

Schematic diagram of the orbit of a comet projected onto the ecliptic plane; comet orbits are tilted at all angles.

SG 8.18

SG 8.19

changes. However, at altitudes of about a hundred miles, satellites have recorded considerable rises and falls in the thin atmosphere.

Comets: From earliest history through the Middle Ages, comets have been interpreted as omens of disaster. But Halley and Newton showed them to be only shiny, cloudy masses moving around the sun according to Kepler's laws, just as planets do. They found that most comets are visible only when closer to the sun than the distance of Jupiter. Several very bright comets have orbits that take them well inside the orbit of Mercury. Such comets pass within a few million miles of the sun, as the figure at the left indicates. Many orbits have eccentricities near 1.0 and are almost parabolas; these comets have periods of thousands or even millions of years. Some other faint comets have periods of only five to ten years.

Unlike the planets, all of whose orbits lie nearly in a single plane, the planes of comet orbits tilt at all angles. Yet, like all members of the solar system, they obey all the laws of dynamics, including the law of universal gravitation.

Edmund Halley applied Newton's concepts of celestial motion to the motion of bright comets. Among the comets he studied were those seen in 1531, 1607, and 1682. Halley found the reported orbits for these comets to be very nearly the same. He suspected that they might be *one* comet, moving in a closed orbit with a period of about seventy-five years. He predicted that the comet would return in about 1757—which it did, although Halley did not live to see it. Halley's comet appeared in 1833 and 1909 and is due to be near the sun and very bright in 1985.

With the period of this bright comet known, its dates of appearance could be traced back in history. Ancient Indian, Chinese, and Japanese documents record all expected appearances except one since 240 B.C. Almost no European records of this great comet exist. This is a sad comment upon the level of culture in Europe during the so-called Dark Ages. One of the few European records is the famous Bayeux tapestry, embroidered with seventy-two scenes of the Norman Conquest of England in 1066. One scene shows the comet overhead while King Harold of England and his court cower below. A major triumph of Newtonian science was its explanation of comets. Now they were seen to be regular members of the solar system, instead of unpredictable, fearful events.

The scope of the principle of universal gravitation: Newton applied his law of universal gravitation to many other problems which we cannot consider in detail here. For example, he investigated the causes of the somewhat irregular motion of the moon. He showed that these motions are explained by the gravitational forces acting on the moon. As the moon moves around the earth, the moon's distance from the sun changes continually. This changes the resultant force of the earth and the sun on the orbiting moon. Newton also showed that other changes in the moon's motion occur because the earth is not a perfect sphere. (The earth's diameter at the equator is twenty-seven miles greater than the diameter through the poles.) Newton commented on the problem of the moon's motion that "the calculation of this motion is difficult." Even so, he

MIRANT STELLA

HAROLD

A scene from the Bayeux tapestry, which was embroidered about 1070. The bright comet of 1066 can be seen at the top of the figure. This comet was later identified as being Halley's comet. At the right, Harold, pretender to the throne of England, is warned that the comet is an ill omen. Later that year at the Battle of Hastings, Harold was defeated by William the Conqueror.

obtained predicted values reasonably close to the observed values available at that time. He even predicted some details of the motion which had not been noticed before.

Newton investigated the variations of gravity at different latitudes on the spinning and bulging earth. He noted differences in the rates at which pendulums swing at different latitudes. From these data, he derived an approximate shape for the earth.

In short, Newton created a whole new quantitative approach to the study of astronomical motion. Because some of his predicted variations had not been observed, improved instruments were built. These improved on the old observations which had been fitted together under the grand theory. Many new theoretical problems also clamored for attention. For example, what were the predicted and observed influences among the planets themselves upon their motions? Although the planets are small compared to the sun and are very far apart, their interactions are observable. As precise data accumulated, the Newtonian theory permitted calculations about the past and future of the planetary system. For past or future intervals beyond some hundreds of millions of years, such extrapolations become too uncertain. But for shorter intervals, Newtonian theory tells us that the planetary system has been and will be about as it is now.

Newton's greatness went beyond the scope and genius of his work in mechanics. It went beyond the originality and elegance of his proofs. It had another dimension: the astonishing detail in which he developed the full meaning of each of his ideas. Sure of his principle of universal gravitation, he applied it successfully to a vast range of terrestrial and celestial problems. As a result, the theory became more and more widely accepted. Newton's theory has been the chief tool for solving all of the new problems concerning motion in the solar system. For example, the motion of every artificial satellite and space probe is calculated according to Newton's law of universal gravitation. We can well agree with the reply given to ground control as Apollo 8 returned from the first trip to the moon. Ground control: "Who's driving up there?" Crew of Apollo 8: "I think Isaac Newton is doing most of the driving right now."

Beyond the solar system: We have seen how Newton's laws explain motions and other physical events on the earth and in the solar system. But now we turn to a new and even broader question. Do Newton's laws also apply at greater distances, for example among the stars?

Over the years following publication of the *Principia,* several sets of observations provided an answer to this important question. One observer was William Herschel, a British musician turned amateur astronomer. In the late 1700's, with the help of his sister, Caroline, Herschel made a remarkable series of observations. Using his homemade high quality telescopes, Herschel hoped to measure the parallax of stars due to the earth's motion around the sun. Occasionally he noticed that one star seemed quite close to another. Of course, this might mean only that two stars happened to lie in the same line of sight. But Herschel suspected that some of these pairs were actually double stars held together by their mutual gravitational attractions. He continued to observe the directions and distances from one star to the other in such pairs. In some cases one star moved during a few years through a small arc of a curved path around the other. (The figure shows the motion of one of the two stars in a system.) Other astronomers gathered more information about these double stars, far removed from the sun and planets. Eventually, it was clear that they move around each other according to Kepler's laws. Therefore, their motions also agree with Newton's law of universal gravitation. Using the same equation as we used for planets (see page 103), astronomers have calculated the masses of these stars. They range from about 0.1 to 50 times the sun's mass.

A theory can never be completely proven. But theories become increasingly acceptable as they are found useful over a wider and wider range of problems. No theory has stood this test better than Newton's theory of universal gravitation as applied to the planetary system. It took nearly a century for physicists and astronomers to comprehend, verify, and

Tiny variations from a $1/R^2$ centripetal acceleration of satellites in orbit around the moon have led to a mapping of "mascons" on the moon—usually dense concentrations of mass under the surface.

The motion over many years for one of the two components of a binary star system. Each circle indicates the average of observations made over an entire year.

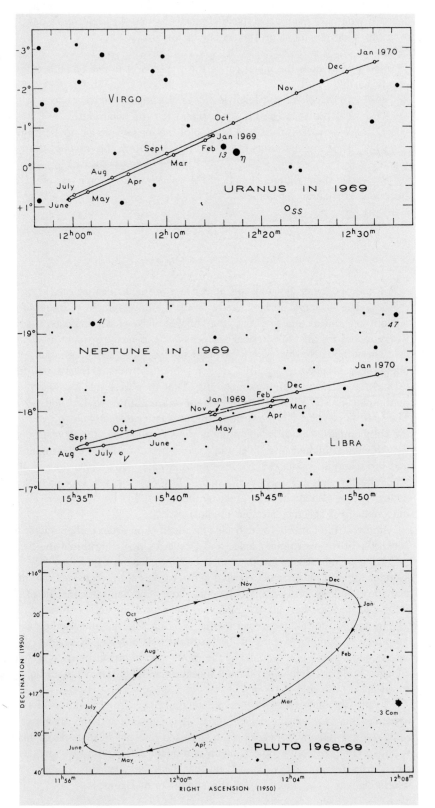

Paths of the outer three planets during 1969 (Diagrams reproduced from *Sky and Telescope* magazine.)

The planet Uranus was discovered in 1781 with a reflecting telescope. Disturbances in Uranus' orbit observed over many years led astronomers to seek another planet beyond Uranus: Neptune was observed in 1846 just where it was expected to be from analysis of Uranus' orbit disturbance (by Newtonian mechanics). A detailed account of the Neptune story appears in the Project Physics Supplementary Unit, *Discoveries in Physics*. Disturbances observed in Neptune's orbit over many years led astronomers to seek still another planet. Again the predictions from Newtonian mechanics were successful, and Pluto (too faint to be seen by eye even in the best telescopes) was discovered in 1930 with a long time-exposure photograph.

extend Newton's work on planetary motion. As late as the 19th century, most of what had been accomplished in mechanics since Newton's day was but a development or application of his work.

Q20 Why does the moon cause the water level to rise on *both* sides of the earth?
Q21 In which of the following does the moon produce tides?
(a) the seas (b) the atmosphere (c) the solid earth
Q22 Why is the precise calculation of the moon's motion so difficult?
Q23 How are the orbits of comets different from the orbits of the planets?
Q24 Do these differences affect the validity of Newton's law of universal gravitation for comets?

8.10 Some effects and limitations of Newton's work

Today we honor Newton and his system of mechanics for many reasons. The *Principia* formed the basis for the development of much of our physics and technology. Also, the success of Newton's approach made it the model for all the physical sciences for the next two centuries.

Throughout Newton's work, we find his basic belief that celestial phenomena can be explained by applying quantitative earthly laws. He felt that his laws had real physical meaning. That they were not just mathematical conveniences behind which unknowable laws lay hidden. The natural physical laws governing the universe *could* be known. And the simple mathematical forms of the laws were evidence of their reality.

Newton combined the skills and approaches of both the experimental and the theoretical scientist. He invented pieces of equipment, such as the first reflecting telescope. He performed skillful experiments, especially in optics. Yet he also applied his great mathematical and logical powers to the creation of specific, testable predictions.

Many of the concepts which Newton used came from earlier scientists and those of his own time. Galileo and Descartes had contributed the first steps to a proper idea of inertia, which became Newton's First Law of Motion. Kepler's planetary laws were central in Newton's consideration of planetary motions. Huygens, Hooke, and others clarified the concepts of force and acceleration, ideas which had been evolving for centuries.

In addition to his own experiments, Newton selected and used data from a large number of sources. Tycho Brahe was only one of several astronomers whose observations of the motion of the moon he used. When Newton could not complete his own measurements, he knew whom he could ask.

Lastly, we must recall how completely and how fruitfully he used and expanded his own specific contributions. A good example is his theory of universal gravitation. In developing it, he used his laws of motion and his various mathematical inventions again and again. Yet Newton was modest about his achievements. He once said that if he had seen further than others "it was by standing upon the shoulders of Giants."

We recognize today that Newton's mechanics holds true only within a well-defined region of our science. For example, the forces within each galaxy appear to be Newtonian. But this may not be true for forces acting between one galaxy and another. At the other end of the scale are atoms and subatomic particles. Entirely non-Newtonian concepts had to be developed to explain the observed motions of these particles.

Even within the solar system, there are several small differences between the predictions and the observations. The most famous involves the angular motion of the axis of Mercury's orbit. This motion is greater than the value predicted from Newton's laws by about 1/80° per century. What causes this error? For a while, it was thought that gravitational force might not vary inversely *exactly* with the square of the distance. Perhaps, for example, the law was $F_{grav} = 1/R^{2.000001}$.

Such difficulties should not be hastily assigned to some minor imperfection. The law of gravitation applies with unquestionable accuracy to all other planetary motions. But it may be that the basic assumptions in the theory make it too limited, as with the Ptolemaic system of epicycles. Many studies have shown that there is no way to modify the details of Newtonian mechanics to explain certain observations. Instead, these observations can be accounted for only by constructing *new* theories based on some very different assumptions. The predictions from these theories are almost identical to those from Newton's laws for phenomena familiar to us. But they also are accurate in some extreme cases where the Newtonian predictions begin to show inaccuracies. Thus, Newtonian science is linked at one end with *relativity theory,* which is important for bodies with very great mass or moving at very high speeds. At the other end Newtonian science approaches *quantum mechanics,* which is important for particles of extremely small mass and size—atoms, molecules, and nuclear particles. For a vast range of problems between these extremes, Newtonian theory gives accurate results and is far simpler to use. Moreover, it was in Newtonian mechanics that relativity theory and quantum mechanics had their roots.

Newtonian mechanics refers to the science of the motion of bodies, based on Newton's work. It includes his laws of motion and of gravitation as applied to a range of bodies from microscopic size to stars, and incorporates developments of mechanics for over two centuries after Newton's own work.

SG 8.20 – 8.22

How to find the mass of a double star

To demonstrate the power of Newton's laws as well as the kind of problem that interests some modern astronomers, let us study a double star system. You can even derive its mass from your own observations.

An interesting double star of short period is the system called Krüger 60. The finding chart locates it less than one degree south of the variable star Delta Cephei in the northern sky.

The series of photographs (Figure A), spaced in proportion to their dates, show the double star on the right. Another star, which just happens to be in the line of sight, appears on the left. The photographs show the revolution of the double-star system, which has a period of about 45 years. As you can see, the stars were farthest apart, about 3.4 seconds of arc, in the mid-1940's. The chart of their relative positions (Figure B) shows that they were closest together at 1.4 seconds of arc around 1971. The circle marks the center of mass of the two-star system. If you measure the direction and distance from one star to the other at five-year intervals, you can plot the motion of one star relative to the other on graph paper. Would you expect this to be an ellipse? Should Kepler's law of areas apply? Does it? Have you assumed that the orbital plane is perpendicular to the line of sight?

The sequence of pictures shows also another motion. The center of mass of Krüger 60 is drifting away from the star at the left. If you extended the lines back to earlier dates, you would find that in the 1860's Krüger 60 passed only 4 seconds of arc from the reference star.

The drift of the whole system Krüger 60 relative to the reference star shows that the stars do move relative to each other. Most stars are at too great a distance for this motion, called *proper motion,* to be detected from the earth. Krüger 60 is, however, relatively nearby, only about 13 light-years away. (A light year is the distance light travels in one

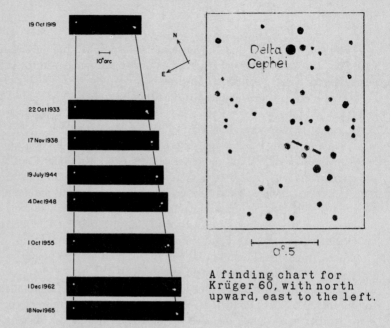

Figure A   The orbital and linear motions of the visual binary, Krüger 60, are both shown in this chart, made up of photographs taken at Leander McCormick Observatory (1919 and 1933) and at Sproul Observatory (1938 to 1965).

A finding chart for Krüger 60, with north upward, east to the left.

year at the rate of 3.0×10^8 meters per second.) The distance to Krüger 60 is then: 13 years $\times 3.0 \times 10^8$ m/sec $\times 3.2 \times 10^7$ sec/year $= 13 \times 10^{16}$ m or 8.7×10^5 AU
(One year contains about 3.2×10^7 seconds. One AU is 1.5×10^{11} meters.)

From the photographs and the scale, we can derive the change in distance of Krüger 60 from the reference star between 1919 and 1965. From the photographs our measurements give the distances as 55 seconds of arc in 1919, and 99 seconds of arc in 1965.* Thus the proper motion was 44 seconds in 46 years, very nearly 1.0 second of arc per year. This angle is about $1/2.1 \times 10^5$ of the distance to the star. Then in one year the star moves 13×10^{16}m$/2.1 \times 10^5$, or 6.7×10^{11}m/year. In one second the

*Adapted from a paper by James F. Wanner of the Sproul Observatory, Swarthmore College, in *Sky and Telescope,* January 1967.

component of the star's velocity vector across the sky is 1.9×10^4m. That is, its velocity perpendicular to the line of sight is 19 km/sec. Probably the star also has a component of motion *along* the line of sight, called *radial velocity*. But this must be found from another type of observation.

The masses of the two stars of Krüger 60 can be found from the photographs shown in Figure B and the application of an equation similar to the one on page 104 for the mass of Jupiter to the mass of the sun ratio. When we developed this equation we assumed that the mass of one body of each pair (sun-planet, or planet-satellite) was much smaller than the mass of the other. In the equation, the mass is actually the sum of the two. So for the double star we must write $(m_1 + m_2)$. Then we have

$$\frac{(m_1 + m_2)\ \text{pair}}{m_{\text{sun}}} = \left[\frac{T_{\text{earth}}}{T_{\text{pair}}}\right]^2 \left[\frac{R_{\text{pair}}}{R_{\text{earth}}}\right]^3$$

The arithmetic is much simpler if we take the periods in years and the distances in astronomical units (AU), which are both unity for the earth. The period of Krüger 60 is about 45 years. The average distance between the two stars can be found in seconds of arc from the diagram (Figure B). The average separation is

$$\frac{\text{max} + \text{min}}{2} = \frac{3.4\ \text{sec} + 1.4\ \text{sec}}{2} = 2.4\ \text{sec}$$

Earlier we found that the distance from the sun to the pair is about 8.7×10^5 AU. Then the average angular separation of 2.4 seconds is

$$\frac{2.4 \times 8.7 \times 10^5\ \text{A.U.}}{2.1 \times 10^5} = 10\ \text{AU}$$

We see that the stars are separated by about the same distance as Saturn is from the sun.

Now, substituting the numbers into the above equation we have

$$\frac{(m_1 + m_2)\ \text{pair}}{m_{\text{sun}}} = \left[\frac{1}{45}\right]^2 \left[\frac{10}{1}\right]^3 = \frac{1000}{2020} = 0.50$$

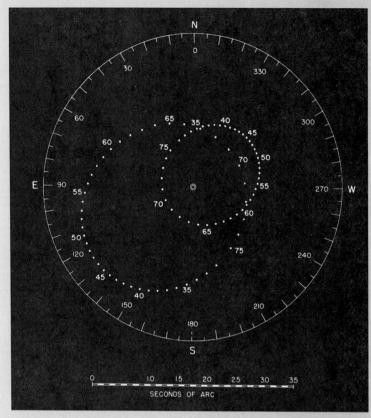

Thus, the two stars together have about half the mass of the sun.

We can even find the mass of each star separately. In the diagram of motions relative to the center of mass, we see that one star has a smaller motion. Therefore, it must be more massive. For the positions of 1970 (or those observed a cycle earlier in 1925), the less massive star is 1.7 times farther than the other from the center of mass. So the masses of the two stars are in the ratio 1.7 : 1. Of the total mass of the pair, the less massive star has

$$\frac{1}{1 + 1.7} \times 0.5 = 0.18\ \text{mass of the sun}$$

The other star, therefore, has 0.32 the mass of the sun. The more massive star is more than four times brighter than the smaller star. Both stars are "red dwarfs", less massive and considerably cooler than the sun.

Figure B   Krüger 60's components trace elliptical orbits, indicated by dots, around their center of mass, marked by a cross. For the years 1932 to 1975, each dot is plotted on September 1st. The outer circle is calibrated in degrees, so the position angle of the companion may be read directly, through the next decade.

EPILOGUE In this unit we started at the beginning of recorded history and followed human attempts to explain the cyclic motions observed in the heavens. We saw the long, gradual change from an earth-centered view to the modern one in which the earth is just another planet moving around the sun. We examined some of the difficulties encountered in making this change of viewpoint. We also tried to put into perspective Newton's synthesis of earthly and heavenly motions. From time to time we suggested that there was an interaction of these new world views with the general culture. We stressed that all scientists are products of their times. They are limited in the degree to which they can abandon the teachings on which they were raised. But gradually, through the work of many scientists over the centuries, a new way of looking at heavenly motions arose. This in turn opened new possibilities for even further new ideas, and the end is not in sight.

In addition, we took a look at how theories are made and tested. We discussed the place of assumption and experiment, of mechanical models and mathematical description. In later parts of the course, we will come back to this discussion in more recent context. We will find that attitudes developed toward theory-making during the seventeenth-century scientific revolution remain immensely helpful today.

In our study we have referred to scientists in Greece, Egypt, Poland, Denmark, Austria, Italy, England, and other countries. Each, as Newton said of himself, stood on the shoulders of those who came earlier. And for each major success there are many lesser advances or, indeed, failures. We see science as a cumulative intellectual activity not restricted by national boundaries or by time. It is not constantly and unfailingly successful, but grows as a forest grows. New growth replaces and draws nourishment from the old, sometimes with unexpected changes in the different parts. Science is not a cold, calculated pursuit. It may involve passionate controversy, religious convictions, judgments of what beauty is, and sometimes wild private speculation.

It is also clear that the Newtonian synthesis did not put an end to the study of science by solving all problems. In many ways it opened whole new lines of investigation, both theoretical and observational. In fact, much of our present science and also our technology had their effective beginnings with the work of Newton. New models, new mathematical tools, and a new self-confidence encouraged those who followed to attack the new problems. A never-ending series of questions, answers, and more questions was well-launched. The modern view of science is that it is a continuing exploration of ever more interesting fields.

One problem remaining after Newton's work was the study of objects interacting not by gravitational forces, but by friction and collision. This study led, as the next unit shows, to the concepts of momentum and energy. It brought about a much broader view of the connection between different parts of science—physics, chemistry, and biology. Eventually, this line of study produced other statements as grand as Newton's law of universal gravitation. Among them were the conservation laws on which much of modern science and technology are based. An important part of

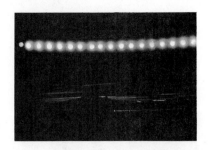

these laws describes how systems work which consist of many interacting bodies. That account will be the main subject of Unit 3.

Newton's influence was not limited to science alone. The century following his death in 1727 was a period of further understanding and application of his discoveries and methods. His influence was felt especially in philosophy and literature, but also in many other fields outside science. Let us round out our view of Newton by considering some of these effects.

The 1700's are often called the Age of Reason or Century of Enlightenment. During these years the Newtonian cosmology became firmly established in European science and philosophy. We can scarcely exaggerate the impact of Newton's achievements. He had shown that observation, reasoning, and use of mechanical models and mathematical laws could uncover the workings of the physical universe. Therefore, it was argued, the same method would open up not only nature but also society and the human mind. As the French writer Fontenelle (1657-1757) expressed it:

> "The geometric spirit is not so bound up with geometry that it cannot be disentangled and carried into other fields. A work of morals, or politics, of criticism, perhaps even of eloquence, will be finer, other things being equal, if it is written by the hand of a geometer."

The English philosopher John Locke (1632-1704) was greatly influenced by Newton's work. In turn, he reinforced Newton's influence on others. Locke argued that the goal of philosophy should be to solve problems, including those that affect our daily life. It could best do this through observation and reasoning. "Reason must be our best judge and guide in all things," he said. Locke thought that the concept of "natural law" could be used in religion as well as in physics. This notion of a religion "based on reason" appealed to many Europeans who remembered the bitter religious wars of the 1600's.

Locke advanced the theory that the mind of a new-born child contains no "innate ideas." Rather, it is like a blank piece of paper on which anything may be written. Thus, it was futile to search within oneself for a God-given sense of what is true or morally right. Instead, one must look at nature and society to discover any "natural laws" that may exist. Conversely, if one wants to improve the quality of human intelligence, one must improve human society.

Locke's view also implied an "atomistic" structure of society. Each person was seen as separate from other individuals in the sense that no "organic" relation exists between people. Previous political theories had pictured society as an organism in which each person has a prescribed place, function, and obligation. Later theories, following Locke, asserted that government should have no function except to protect the freedom and property of individuals.

The engraving of the French Academy by Sebastian LeClerc (1698) reflects the activity of learned societies at that time. The picture does not depict an actual scene, of course, but in allegory shows the excitement of communication that grew in an informal atmosphere. The dress is symbolic of the Greek heritage of the sciences. Although all the sciences are represented, the artist has put anatomy, botany, and zoology, symbolized by skeletons and dried leaves, toward the edges, along with alchemy and theology. Mathematics and the physical sciences, including astronomy, occupy the center stage.

"Reason" was the motto of the eighteenth-century philosophers. However, their theories about improving religion and society were not necessarily perfectly reasonable. For example, they believed strongly in the doctrine of equal rights for all men. Yet no strictly mathematical or scientific proof for it supported this belief. Newtonian physics, religious toleration, and republican government were all advanced by the same movement. But this does not mean there was really a logical connection among these concepts. Nor were many eighteenth-century thinkers in any field or nation much bothered by other gaps in logic and feeling. For example, they believed that "all men are created equal." Yet they did little to remove the chains of black slaves, the ghetto walls imprisoning Jews, or the laws that denied rights to women.

Still, compared with the previous century, the dominant theme of the 1700's was *moderation,* the "happy medium." The emphasis was on toleration of different opinions, restraint of excess, and balance of opposing forces. Even reason was not allowed to question religious faith too strongly. Atheism, which some philosophers thought would logically result from unlimited rationality, was still regarded with horror by most Europeans.

The Constitution of the United States of America is one of the most enduring achievements of this period. Its system of "checks and balances" was designed specifically to prevent any one group from getting too much power. It attempts to establish in politics a state of equilibrium of opposing trends. This equilibrium, some thought, resembled the balance between the sun's gravitational pull and the tendency of a planet to fly off in a straight line. If the gravitational attraction upon the planet increased without a corresponding increase in planetary speed, the planet would fall into the sun. If the planet's speed increased without a corresponding increase in gravitational attraction, it would escape from the solar system.

Political philosophers, some of whom used Newtonian physics as a model, hoped to create a similar balance in government. They aimed to devise a system which would avoid the extremes of dictatorship and anarchy. According to James Wilson (1742-1798), who played a major role in writing the American Constitution:

> In government, the perfection of the whole depends on the balance of the parts, and the balance of the parts consists in the independent exercise of their separate powers, and, when their powers are separately exercised, then in their mutual influence and operation on one another. Each part acts and is acted upon, supports and is supported, regulates and is regulated by the rest. It might be supposed, that these powers, thus mutually checked and controlled, would remain in a state of inaction. But there is a necessity for movement in human affairs; and these powers are forced to move, though still to move in concert. They move, indeed, in a line of direction somewhat different from that, which each acting by itself would have taken; but, at the same time, in a line partaking of the natural directions of the whole—the true line of public liberty and happiness.

Both Newton's life and his writings seemed to support the idea of political democracy. A former farm boy had penetrated to the outermost reaches of the human imagination. What he had found there meant, first of all, that only one set of laws governed heaven and earth. This smashed the old beliefs about "natural place" and extended a new democracy throughout the universe. Newton had shown that all matter, whether the sun or an ordinary stone, was created equal. That is to say, all matter had the same standing before "the Laws of Nature and of Nature's God." (This phrase was used at the beginning of the Declaration of Independence to justify the desire of the people in the colonies to throw off their inferior political system and to become an independent people.) All political thought at this time was heavily influenced by Newtonian ideas. The *Principia* seemed to offer a parallel to theories about democracy. It seemed logical that all men, like all natural objects, are created equal before nature's creator. Some of these important trends are discussed in articles in *Reader 2.*

In literature, too, many welcomed the new scientific viewpoint. It supplied many new ideas, convenient figures of speech, parallels, and concepts which writers used in poems and essays. Newton's discovery that white light is composed of colors was referred to in many poems of the 1700's. (See Unit 4.) Samuel Johnson advocated that words drawn from the vocabulary of the natural sciences be used in literary works. He defined many such words in his *Dictionary* and illustrated their application in his "Rambler" essays.

Other writers distrusted the new cosmology. In his long poem *The Rape of the Lock,* Alexander Pope exaggerated the new scientific vocabulary for comic effect. Jonathan Swift, sending Gulliver on his travels to Laputa, described an academy of scientists and mathematicians. Their experiments and theories were as absurd as those of the Royal Society must have seemed to the non-scientists of the 1700's.

The first really powerful reaction against Newtonian cosmology was the Romantic movement. Romanticism was started in Germany about 1780 by young writers inspired by Johann Wolfgang von Goethe. The most familiar examples of Romanticism in English literature are the poems and novels of Blake, Coleridge, Wordsworth, Shelley, Byron, and Scott. The Romantics scorned the mathematical view of nature, and emphasized the importance of quality rather than quantity. They preferred to study an individual person or experience, rather than make abstractions. They praised emotion and feeling at the expense of reason and calculation. In particular, they protested the theory that nature is in any way like a clockwork. They refused to accept a universe of inert matter set into motion by a God who never again appears. Reflecting this attitude, the historian and philosopher of science E. A. Burtt wrote:

This is, of course, a distortion of what scientists themselves believe —one of the wrong images of science discussed in "The Seven Images of Science" in *Reader 3.*

. . . the great Newton's authority was squarely behind that view of the cosmos which saw in man a puny, irrelevant spectator (so far as being wholly imprisoned in a dark room can be called such) of the vast mathematical system whose regular motions according to mechanical principles constituted the world of nature. The gloriously romantic universe of Dante and Milton, that set no bounds to the imagination of man as it played over space and time, had now been swept away. Space was identified with the realm of geometry, time with the continuity of number. The world that people had thought themselves living in—a world rich with color and sound, redolent with fragrance, filled with gladness, love and beauty, speaking everywhere of purposive harmony and creative ideals—was crowded now into minute corners in the brains of scattered organic beings. The really important world outside was a world hard, cold, colorless, silent, and dead; a world of quantity, a world of mathematically computable motions in mechanical regularity. The world of qualities as immediately perceived by man became just a curious and quite minor effect of that infinite machine beyond.

The Romantics believed that any whole thing, whether a single human being or the entire universe, is filled with a unique spirit. This spirit cannot be explained by reason; it can only be *felt.* The Romantics insisted that phenomena cannot be meaningfully analyzed and reduced to their separate parts by mechanical explanations.

Many Continental leaders of the Romantic movement agreed with the German philosopher Friedrich Schelling (1775-1854). Schelling proposed a new way of doing scientific research, a new type of science called *Naturphilosophie,* or "Nature Philosophy." (This term is not to be confused with the older "natural philosophy," meaning mainly physics.) Nature philosophy does not analyze phenomena into separate parts or factors which can be measured quantitatively in the laboratory. At least, that is not its primary purpose. Instead, the goal is to understand each phenomenon as a whole, and to find non-mathematical basic principles that are supposed to govern all phenomena. The Romantic philosophers in Germany regarded Goethe as their greatest scientist as well as their greatest poet. They pointed in particular to his theory of color, which flatly contradicted Newton's theory of light. Goethe held that white light does not consist of a mixture of colors, and that it is useless to "reduce" a beam of white light by passing it through a prism to study its separate spectral colors. Rather, he charged, the colors of the spectrum are artificially produced by the prism, acting on and changing the light which is itself pure.

In the judgment of all modern scientists, Newton was right and Goethe wrong. This does not mean that Nature Philosophy was without any value. It encouraged speculation about ideas so general that they could not be easily tested by experiment. At the time, it was condemned by most scientists for just this reason. But today most historians of science agree that Nature Philosophy eventually played an important role in making possible certain scientific discoveries. Among these was the general principle of conservation of energy, which is described in Chapter 10. This principle asserted that all the "forces of nature"—the phenomena of heat, gravity, electricity, magnetism, and so forth—are forms of one underlying "force" (which we now call energy). This idea agreed well with the viewpoint of Nature Philosophy. But it also could eventually be put in a scientifically acceptable form.

Some modern artists, some intellectuals, and most members of the "counterculture" movements express a dislike for science. Their reasoning is similar to that of the Romantics. It is based on the mistaken notion that scientists claim to be able to find a mechanical explanation for *everything,* including human thoughts and emotions. If everything were explained by Newtonian science, then everything would also be *determined,* as the motions of machine parts are determined. Most modern scientists today do not believe that such an explanation is possible. But some scientists in the past argued strongly that it *was* possible. For example, the French mathematical physicist Laplace (1749-1827) said:

We ought then to regard the present state of the universe as the effect of its previous state and as the cause of the one which is to follow. Given for one instant a mind which could comprehend all the forces by which nature is animated and the respective situation of the beings who compose it—a mind sufficiently vast to submit these data to analysis—it would embrace in the same formula the movements of the greatest bodies of the universe and those of the lightest atom; for it, nothing would be uncertain and the future, as the past, would be present to its eyes.

Even the Roman philosopher Lucretius (100-55 B.C.), who supported the atomic theory in his poem *On the Nature of Things,* did not go this far. To preserve some trace of "free will" in the universe, Lucretius suggested that atoms might swerve randomly in their paths. This was not enough for the Romantics and also for some scientists. For example, Erasmus Darwin, a scientist and grandfather of evolutionist Charles Darwin, asked:

> Dull atheist, could a giddy dance
>   Of atoms lawless hurl'd
> Construct so wonderful, so wise,
>   So harmonised a world?

SG 8.23, 8.24

The Nature Philosophers thought they could discredit the Newtonian scientists by forcing them to answer this question. To say "yes," they argued, would be absurd, and to say "no" would be disloyal to Newtonian beliefs. But the Newtonians succeeded quite well without committing themselves to any definite answer to Erasmus Darwin's question. They went on to discover immensely powerful and valuable laws of nature, discussed in the next units.

8.1 The Project Physics learning materials particularly appropriate for Chapter 8 include:

Experiment
Stepwise Approximation to an Orbit
Model of the orbit of Halley's comet
Activities
Other comet orbits
Forces on a pendulum
Haiku
Trial of Copernicus
Discovery of Neptune and Pluto
Reader Articles
Newton and the *Principia*
The Laws of Motion and Proposition I
Universal Gravitation
An Appreciation of the Earth
The Great Comet of 1965
Gravity Experiments
Space the Unconquerable
The Life Story of a Galaxy
Expansion of the Universe
Negative Mass
The Dyson Sphere
Flim Loops
Jupiter Satellite Orbit
Program Orbit I
Program Orbit II
Central forces—iterated blows
Kepler's Laws
Unusual Orbits
Transparency
Motion under central force

8.2 In the table below are the periods and distances from Jupiter of the four large satellites, as measured by telescopic observations. Does Kepler's law of periods apply to the Jupiter system?

SATELLITE	PERIOD	DISTANCE FROM JUPITER'S CENTER (in terms of Jupiter's radius, r)
I	1.77 days	6.04 r
II	3.55	9.62
III	7.15	15.3
IV	16.7	27.0

8.3 Give some reasons why Descartes' theory of planetary motion might have been "a useful idea."

8.4 On p. 101 it was claimed that the dependence of the gravitational force on the masses of both interacting bodies could be expressed as $m_{sun} \, m_{planet}$.

(a) Using a diagram similar to that for Q 13 on p. 102, show that this is correct.
(b) To test alternatives to using the product, consider the possibilities that the force could depend upon the masses in either of two ways:
(1) total force depends on $(m_{sun} + m_{planet})$, or
(2) total force depends on (m_{sun}/m_{planet}).
What would these relationships imply would happen to the force if either mass were reduced to zero? Would there still be a force even though there were only one mass left? Could you speak of a gravitational force when there was no body to be accelerated?

8.5 Use the values for the mass and size of the moon to show that the "surface gravity" (acceleration due to gravity near the moon's surface) is only about $\frac{1}{8}$ of what it is near the earth's. (Mass of moon = 7.34 × 10²² kg; radius of moon = 1.74 × 10⁶ m.)

8.6 The mathematics of calculus is necessary to find the exact force exerted by a spherical body, but it is not difficult to prove that the *direction* of the net force is toward the center. Newton's argument involved symmetry and considering tiny pieces of the whole body. Develop such an argument.

8.7 Use the equation for centripetal force and the equation for gravitational force to derive an expression for the period of a satellite orbiting around a planet in terms of the radius of the orbit and mass of the planet.

8.8 The sun's mass is about 27,000,000 times greater than the moon's mass; the sun is about 400 times further from the earth than the moon is. How does the gravitational force exerted on the earth by the sun compare with that exerted by the moon?

8.9 By Newton's time, telescopic observations of Jupiter led to values for the orbital periods and radii of Jupiter's four large satellites. For example, the one named Callisto was found to have a period of 16.7 days and the radius of its orbit was calculated as 1/80 AU.

(a) From these data calculate the value of $k_{Jupiter}$. (First convert days to years.)
(b) Show that Jupiter's mass is about 1/1000 the mass of the sun.
(c) How was it possible to have a value for the orbital radius of a satellite of Jupiter?

8.10 What orbit radius must an earth satellite be given to keep it always above the same place on the earth—that is, in order to have a 24-hour period? (Hint: See SG 8.7)

8.11 Calculate the mass of the earth from the fact that a 1kg object at the earth's surface is attracted to the earth with a force of 9.8 newtons. The distance from the earth's center to its surface is 6.4 × 10⁶ meters. How many times greater is this than the greatest masses which you have had some experience in accelerating (for example, cars)?

8.12 The mass of the earth can be calculated also from the distance and period of the moon. Show that the value obtained in this way agrees with the value calculated from measurements at the earth's surface.

8.13 Cavendish's value for *G* made it possible to calculate the mass of the earth, and therefore its average density. The "density" of water is 1000 kg per cubic meter. That is, for any sample of water, dividing the mass of the sample by its volume gives 1000 kg/m³.

(a) What is the earth's average density?
(b) The densest kind of rock known has a density of about 5000 kg/m³. Most rock we find has a density of about 3000 kg/m³.

What do you conclude from this about the structure of the earth?

8.14 The manned Apollo 8 capsule (1968) was put into a nearly circular orbit 112 km above the moon's surface. The period of the orbit was 120.5 minutes. From these data calculate the mass of the moon. (The radius of the moon is 1740 km. Don't forget to use a consistent set of units.)

8.15 Why do you suppose there is no reliable value for the mass of Pluto?

8.16 Mars has two satellites. Phobos and Deimos —Fear and Panic. A science-fiction story was once written in which the natives of Mars showed great respect for a groove in the ground. The groove turned out to be the path of Mars' closest moon, "Bottomos."

  (a) If such an orbit were possible, what would the period be?
  (b) What speed would it need to have in order to go into such an orbit?
  (c) What difficulties do you see for such an orbit?

8.17 Using the values given in the table on p. 105 make a table of relative masses compared to the mass of the earth.

8.18 The period of Halley's comet is about 75 years. What is its average distance from the sun? The eccentricity of its orbit is 0.967. How far from the sun does it go? How close?

8.19 Accepting the validity of $F_{grav} = Gm_1m_2/R^2$, and recognizing that G is a universal constant, we are able to derive, and therefore to understand better, many particulars that previously seemed separate. For example, we can conclude:

  (a) That a_g for a body of any mass m_0 should be constant at a particular place on earth.
  (b) That a_g might be different at places on earth at different distances from the earth's center.
  (c) That at the earth's surface the weight of a body be related to its mass.
  (d) That the ratio R^3/T^2 is a constant for all the satellites of a body.
  (e) That tides occur about six hours apart.

Describe briefly how each of these conclusions can be derived from the equation.

8.20 The making of theories to account for observations is a major purpose of scientific study. Therefore some reflection upon the theories encountered thus far in this course will be useful. Comment in a paragraph or more, with examples from Units 1 and 2, on some of the statements below. Look at all the statements and select at least six, in any order you wish.

  (1) A good theory should summarize and not conflict with a body of tested observations.

  (For example, Kepler's unwillingness to explain away the difference of eight minutes of arc between his predictions and Tycho's observations.)
  (2) There is nothing more practical than a good theory.
  (3) A good theory should permit predictions of new observations which sooner or later can be made.
  (4) A good new theory should give almost the same predictions as older theories for the range of phenomena where they worked well.
  (5) Every theory involves assumptions. Some involve also esthetic preferences of the scientist.
  (6) A new theory relates some previously unrelated observations.
  (7) Theories often involve abstract concepts derived from observation.
  (8) Empirical laws or "rules" organize many observations and reveal how changes in one quantity vary with changes in another but such laws provide no explanation of the causes or mechanisms.
  (9) A theory never fits all data exactly.
  (10) Predictions from theories may lead to the observation of new effects.
  (11) Theories that later had to be discarded may have been useful because they encouraged new observations.
  (12) Theories that permit quantitative predictions are preferred to qualitative theories.
  (13) An "unwritten text" lies behind the statement of every law of nature.
  (14) Communication between scientists is an essential part of the way science grows.
  (15) Some theories seem initially so strange that they are rejected completely or accepted only very slowly.
  (16) Models are often used in the making of a theory or in describing a theory to people.
  (17) The power of theories comes from their generality.

8.21 What happened to Plato's problem? Was it solved?

8.22 Why do we believe today in a heliocentric system? Is it the same as either Copernicus' or Kepler's? What is the experimental evidence? Is the geocentric system disproved?

8.23 Is Newton's work only of historical interest, or is it useful today? Explain.

8.24 What were some of the major consequences of Newton's work on scientists' view of the world?

PROJECT PHYSICS

3

The Triumph of Mechanics

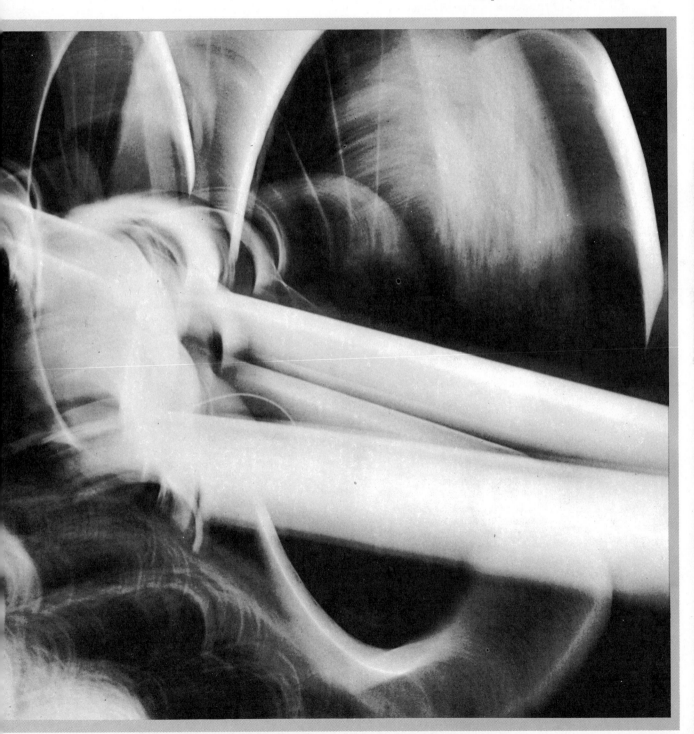

Experiments

3-1 Collisions in One Dimension I
3-2 Collisions in One Dimension II
3-3 Collisions in Two Dimensions I
3-4 Collisons in Two Dimensions II
3-5 Conservation of Energy I
3-6 Conservation of Energy II
3-7 Measuring the Speed of a Bullet
3-8 Energy Analysis of a Pendulum Swing
3-9 Least Energy
3-10 Temperature and Thermometers
3-11 Calorimetry
3-12 Ice Calorimetry
3-13 Monte Carlo Experiment on Molecular
Collisions
3-14 Behavior of Gases
3-15 Wave Properties
3-16 Waves in a Ripple Tank
3-17 Measuring Wavelength
3-18 Sound
3-19 Ultrasound

Activities

Is Mass Conserved?
Exchange of Momentum Devices
Student Horsepower
Steam-powered Boat
Problems of Scientific and Technological
Growth
Predicting the Range of an Arrow
Drinking Duck
Mechanical Equivalent of Heat
A Diver in a Bottle
Rockets
How to Weigh a Car with a Tire Pressure
Gauge
Perpetual Motion Machines?
Standing Waves on a Drum and Violin
Moire Patterns
Music and Speech Activities
Measurement of the Speed of Sound
Mechanical Wave Machines
Resource Letter

Film Loops

L18 One-Dimensional Collisions I
L19 One-Dimensional Collisions II
L20 Inelastic One-Dimensional Collisions
L21 Two-Dimensional Collisions I
L22 Two-Dimensional Collisions II
L23 Inelastic Two-Dimensional Collisions
L24 Scattering of a Cluster of Objects
L25 Explosion of a Cluster of Objects
L26 Finding the Speed of a Rifle Bullet I
L27 Finding the Speed of a Rifle Bullet II
L28 Recoil
L29 Colliding Freight Cars
L30 Dynamics of a Billiard Ball
L31 A Method of Measuring Enegy—Nails
Driven into Wood
L32 Gravitational Potential Energy
L33 Kinetic Energy
L34 Conservation of Energy—Pole Vault
L35 Conversation of Energy—Aircraft
Take-off
L36 Reversibility of Time

L37 Superposition
L38 Standing Waves on a String
L39 Standing Waves in a Gas
L40 Vibrations of a Wire
L41 Vibrations of a Rubber Hose
L42 Vibrations of a Drum
L43 Vibrations of a Metal Plate

Programmed Instruction Booklets

The Kinetic-Molecular Theory of Gases
Waves 1 The Superposition Principle
Waves 2 Periodic Waves

Reader Articles

1 *Silence, Please*
by Arthur C. Clarke
2 *The Steam Engine Comes of Age*
by R. J. Forbes and E. J. Dijksterhuis
3 *The Great Conservation Principles*
by Richard P. Feynman
4 *The Barometer Story*
by Alexander Calandra
5 *The Great Molecular Theory of Gases*
by Eric M. Rogers
6 *Entropy and the Second Law of
Thermodynamics*
by Kenneth W. Ford
7 *The Law of Disorder*
by George Gamow
8 *The Law*
by Robert M. Coates
9 *The Arrow of Time*
by Jacob Bronowski
10 *James Clerk Maxwell*
by James R. Newman
11 *Frontiers of Physics Today: Acoustics*
by Leo L. Beranek
12 *Randomness and the Twentieth Century*
by Alfred M. Bork
13 *Waves*
by Richard Stevenson and R. B. Moore
14 *What is a Wave?*
by Albert Einstein and Leopold Infeld
15 *Musical Instruments and Scales*
by Harvey E. White
16 *Founding a Family of Fiddles*
by Carleen M. Hutchins
17 *The Seven Images of Science*
by Gerald Holton
18 *Scientific Cranks*
by Martin Gardner
19 *Physics and the Vertical Jump*
by Elmer L. Offenbacher

Transparencies

T19 One-Dimensional Collisions
T20 Equal Mass Two-Dimensional Collisions
T21 Unequal Mass Two-Dimensional
Collisions
T22 Inelastic Two-Dimensional Collisions
T23 Slow Collisions
T24 The Watt Engine
T25 Superposition
T26 Square Wave Analysis
T27 Standing Waves
T28 Two-Slit Interference
T29 Interference Pattern Analysis

Contents TEXT, UNIT 3

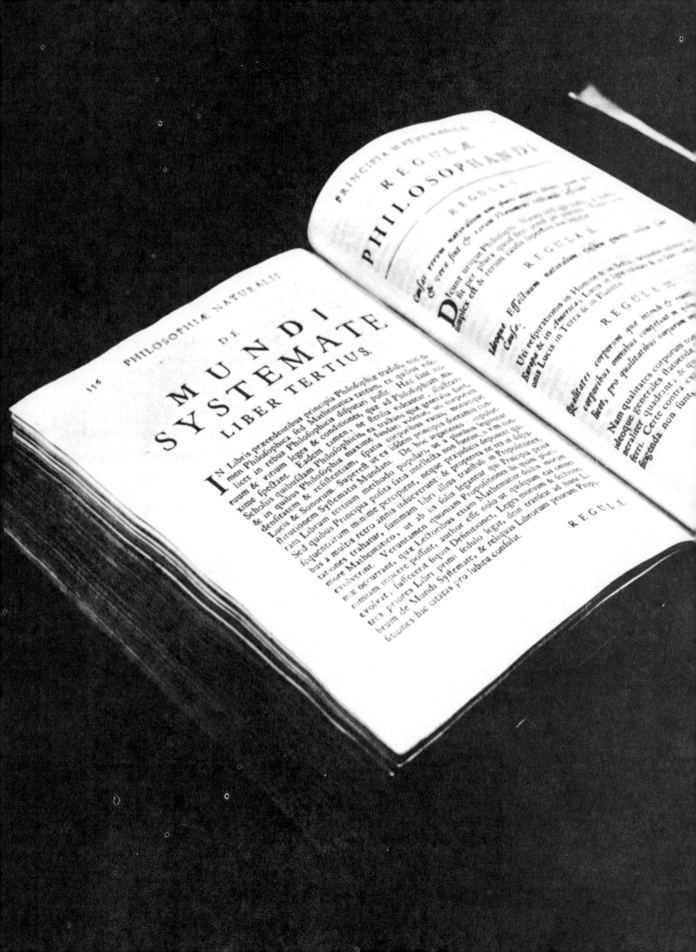

The Triumph of Mechanics

PROLOGUE   The success of Isaac Newton in uniting the studies of astronomy and of terrestrial motion is one of the glories of the human mind. It was a turning point in the development of science and humanity. Never before had a scientific theory been so successful in finding simple order in observable events. Never before had the possibilities for using one's rational faculties for solving any kind of problem seemed so promising. So it is not surprising that after his death in 1727 Newton was looked upon almost as a god, especially in England. Many poems like this one appeared:

> Newton the unparalled'd, whose Name
> No Time will wear out of the Book of Fame,
> Celestial Science has promoted more,
> Than all the Sages that have shone before.
> Nature compell'd his piercing Mind obeys,
> And gladly shows him all her secret Ways;
> 'Gainst Mathematics she has no defence,
> And yields t' experimental Consequence;
> His tow'ring Genius, from its certain Cause
> Ev'ry Appearance *a priori* draws
> And shews th' Almighty Architect's unalter'd Laws.

(From J. T. Desagulier, *The Newtonian System of the World, the Best Model of Government, an Allegorical Poem.*)

Newton's success in mechanics altered profoundly the way in which scientists viewed the universe. Physicists after Newton explained the motion of the planets around the sun by treating the solar system as a huge machine. Its "parts" were held together by gravitational forces rather than by nuts and bolts. But the motions of these parts relative to each other, according to Newton's theory, were determined once and for all after the system had first been put together.

We call this model of the solar system the *Newtonian world-machine.* As is true for any model, certain things are left out. The mathematical equations which govern the motions of the model cover only the main properties of the

Beginning of Book 3, "The Systems of the World," in the 1713 edition of Newton's *Principia.*

real solar system. The masses, positions and velocities of the parts of the system, and the gravitational forces among them are well described. But the Newtonian model neglects the internal structure and chemical composition of the planets, heat, light, and electric and magnetic forces. Nevertheless, it serves splendidly to deal with observed motions. Moreover, it turned out that Newton's approach to science and many of his concepts became useful later in the study of those aspects he had to leave aside.

The idea of a world machine does not trace back only to Newton's work. In his *Principles of Philosophy* (1644), Rene Descartes, the most influential French philosopher of the seventeenth century, had written:

> I do not recognize any difference between the machines that artisans make and the different bodies that nature alone composes, unless it be that the effects of the machines depend only upon the adjustment of certain tubes or springs, or other instruments, that, having necessarily some proportion with the hands of those who make them, are always so large that their shapes and motions can be seen, while the tubes and springs that cause the effects of natural bodies are ordinarily too small to be perceived by our senses. And it is certain that all the laws of Mechanics belong to Physics, so that all the things that are artificial, are at the same time natural.

Robert Boyle (1627-1691), a British scientist, is known particularly for his studies of the properties of air. (See Chapter 11.) Boyle, a pious man, expressed the "mechanistic" viewpoint even in his religious writings. He argued that a God who could design a universe that ran by itself like a machine was more wonderful than a God who simply created several different kinds of matter and gave each a natural tendency to behave as it does. Boyle also thought it was insulting to God to believe that the world machine would be so badly designed as to require any further divine adjustment once it had been created. He suggested that an engineer's skill in designing "an elaborate engine" is more deserving of praise if the engine never needs supervision or repair. "Just so," he continued,

> . . . it more sets off the wisdom of God in the fabric of the universe, that he can make so vast a machine perform all those many things, which he designed it should, by the meer contrivance of brute matter managed by certain laws of local motion, and upheld by his ordinary and general concourse, than if he employed from time to time an intelligent overseer, such as nature is fancied to be, to regulate, assist, and controul the motions of the parts. . . .

Boyle and many other scientists in the seventeenth and eighteenth centuries tended to think of God as a supreme engineer and physicist. God had set down the laws of matter and motion. Human scientists could best glorify the Creator by discovering and proclaiming these laws.

Our main concern in this unit is with physics as it developed after Newton. In mechanics, Newton's theory was extended to cover a wide range of

"The Ancient of Days" by William Blake, an English poet who had little sympathy with the Newtonian style of "natural philosophy."

phenomena, and new concepts were introduced. The conservation laws to be discussed in Chapters 9 and 10 became increasingly important. These powerful principles offered a new way of thinking about mechanics. They opened up new areas to the study of physics—for example, heat and wave motion.

Newtonian mechanics treated directly only a small range of experiences. It dealt with the motion of simple bodies, or those largely isolated from others as are planets, projectiles, or sliding discs. Do the same laws work when applied to complex phenomena? Do real solids, liquids, and gases behave like machines or mechanical systems? Can their behavior be explained by using the same ideas about matter and motion that Newton used to explain the solar system?

At first, it might seem unlikely that everything can be reduced to matter and motion, the principles of mechanics. What about temperature, colors, sounds, odors, hardness, and so forth? Newton himself believed that the mechanical view would essentially show how to investigate these and all other properties. In the preface to the *Principia* he wrote:

> I wish we could derive the rest of the phenomena of Nature by the same kind of reasoning from mechanical principles, for I am induced by many reasons to suspect that they may all depend upon certain forces by which the particles of bodies, by some causes hitherto unknown, are mutually impelled towards one another, and cohere according to regular figures, or are repelled and recede from one another. These forces being unknown, philosophers have hitherto attempted the search of Nature in vain; but I hope the principles here laid down will afford some light either to this or some truer method of Philosophy.

Scientists after Newton strove to understand nature in many different areas, "by the same kind of reasoning from mechanical principles." We will see in this unit how wide was the success of Newtonian mechanics—but you will see also some evidence of limits to its applicability.

Ironically, Newton himself explicitly rejected the deterministic aspects of the "World-Machine" which his followers had popularized.

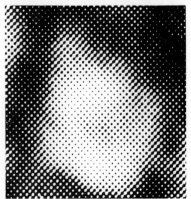

A small area from the center of the picture has been enlarged to show what the picture is "really" like. Is the picture only a collection of dots? Knowing the underlying structure doesn't spoil our other reactions to the picture, but rather gives us another dimension of understanding it.

CHAPTER NINE

Conservation of Mass and Momentum

9.1 Conservation of mass

The idea that despite ever-present, obvious change all around us the total amount of material in the universe does not change is really very old. The Roman poet Lucretius restated (in the first century B.C.) a belief held in Greece as early as the fifth century B.C.:

> . . . and no force can change the sum of things; for there is no thing outside, either into which any kind of matter can emerge out of the universe or out of which a new supply can arise and burst into the universe and change all the nature of things and alter their motions. [*On the Nature of Things*]

SG 9.1

Just twenty-four years before Newton's birth, the English philosopher Francis Bacon included the following among his basic principles of modern science in *Novum Organum* (1620):

> There is nothing more true in nature than the twin propositions that "nothing is produced from nothing" and "nothing is reduced to nothing" . . . the sum total of matter remains unchanged, without increase or diminution.

This view agrees with everyday observation to some extent. While the form in which matter exists may change, in much of our ordinary experience matter appears somehow indestructible. For example, we may see a large boulder crushed to pebbles, and not feel that the amount of matter in the universe has diminished or increased. But what if an object is burned to ashes or dissolved in acid? Does the amount of matter remain unchanged even in such chemical reactions? Or what of large-scale changes such as the forming of rain clouds or of seasonal variations?

In some open-air chemical reactions, the mass of objects seems to decrease, while in others it seems to increase.

Note the closed flask shown in his portrait on p. 7.

SG 9.2

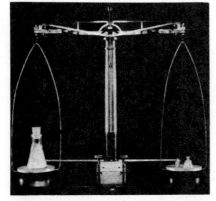

Conservation of mass was demonstrated in experiments on chemical reactions in closed flasks.

The meaning of the phrase "closed system" will be discussed in more detail in Sec. 9.5.

To test whether the total quantity of matter actually remains constant, we must know how to measure that quantity. Clearly it cannot simply be measured by its volume. For example, we might put water in a container, mark the water level, and then freeze the water. If so, we find that the volume of the ice is larger than the volume of the water we started with. This is true even if we carefully seal the container so that no water can possibly come in from the outside. Similarly, suppose we compress some gas in a closed container. The volume of the gas decreases even though no gas escapes from the container.

Following Newton, we regard the *mass* of an object as the proper measure of the amount of matter it contains. In all our examples in Units 1 and 2, we assumed that the mass of a given object does not change. But a burnt match has a smaller mass than an unburnt one; and an iron nail increases in mass as it rusts. Scientists had long assumed that something escapes from the match into the atmosphere, and that something is added from the surroundings to the iron of the nail. Therefore nothing is really "lost" or "created" in these changes. But not until the end of the eighteenth century was sound experimental evidence for this assumption provided. The French chemist Antoine Lavoisier produced this evidence.

Lavoisier caused chemical reactions to occur in *closed* flasks. He carefully weighed the flasks and their contents before and after the reaction. For example, he burned iron in a closed flask. The mass of the iron oxide produced equalled the sum of the masses of the iron and oxygen used in the reaction. With experimental evidence like this at hand, he could announce with confidence in *Traité Élémentaire de Chimie* (1789):

> We may lay it down as an incontestable axiom that in all the operations of art and nature, nothing is created; an equal quantity of matter exists both before and after the experiment, . . . and nothing takes place beyond changes and modifications in the combinations of these elements. Upon this principle, the whole art of performing chemical experiments depends.

Lavoisier knew that if he put some material in a well-sealed bottle and measured its mass, he could return at any later time and find the same mass. It would not matter what had happened to the material inside the bottle. It might change from solid to liquid or liquid to gas, change color or consistency, or even undergo violent chemical reactions. But at least one thing would remain unchanged—the *total* mass of all the different materials in the bottle.

In the years after Lavoisier's pioneering work, a vast number of similar experiments were performed with ever increasing accuracy. The result was always the same. As far as we now can measure with sensitive balances (having a precision of better than 0.000001%), mass is *conserved*—that is, it remains constant—in chemical reactions.

To sum up: despite changes in location, shape, chemical composition and so forth, *the mass of any closed system remains constant*. This is the statement of what we will call the *law of conservation of mass*. This law is basic to both physics and chemistry.

TRAITE
ÉLÉMENTAIRE
DE CHIMIE,

PRÉSENTÉ DANS UN ORDRE NOUVEAU

ET D'APRÈS LES DÉCOUVERTES MODERNES;

Avec Figures:

Par M. LAVOISIER, de l'Académie des
Sciences, de la Société Royale de Médecine, des
Sociétés d'Agriculture de Paris & d'Orléans, de
la Société Royale de Londres, de l'Institut de
Bologne, de la Société Helvétique de Basle, de
celles de Philadelphie, Harlem, Manchester,
Padoue, &c.

TOME PREMIER.

A PARIS,

Chez CUCHET, Libraire, rue & hôtel Serpente.

M. DCC. LXXXIX.

Sous le Privilège de l'Académie des Sciences & de la
Société Royale de Médecine.

Antoine Laurent Lavoisier (1743-1794) is known as the "father of modern chemistry" because he showed the decisive importance of quantitative measurements, confirmed the principle of conservation of mass in chemical reactions, and helped develop the present system of nomenclature for the chemical elements. He also showed that organic processes such as digestion and respiration are similar to burning.

To earn money for his scientific research, Lavoisier invested in a private company which collected taxes for the French government. Because the tax collectors were allowed to keep any extra tax which they could collect from the public, they became one of the most hated groups in France. Lavoisier was not directly engaged in tax collecting, but he had married the daughter of an important executive of the company, and his association with the company was one of the reasons why Lavoisier was guillotined during the French Revolution.

Also shown in the elegant portrait by David is Madame Lavoisier. She had been only fourteen at the time of her marriage. Intelligent as well as beautiful, she assisted her husband by taking data, translating scientific works from English into French, and making illustrations. About ten years after her husband's execution, she married another scientist, Count Rumford, who is remembered for his experiments which cast doubt on the caloric theory of heat.

Obviously, one must know whether a given system is closed or not before applying this law to it. For example, it is perhaps surprising that the earth itself is not exactly a closed system within which all mass would be conserved. Rather, the earth, including its atmosphere gains and loses matter constantly. The most important addition occurs in the form of dust particles. These particles are detected by their impacts on satellites that are outside most of the atmosphere. Also, they create light and ionization when they pass through the atmosphere and are slowed down by it. The number of such particles is larger for those particles which are of smaller size. The great majority are very thin particles on the order of 10^{-4} cm diameter. Such small particles cannot be individually detected from the ground when they enter the atmosphere. They are far too small to appear as meteorites, which result when particles at least several millimeters in diameter vaporize. The total estimated inflow of mass of all these particles, large and small, is about 10^5 g/sec over the whole surface of the earth. (Note: the mass of the earth is about 6×10^{27} g.) This gain is not balanced by any loss of dust or larger particles, not counting an occasional spacecraft and its debris. The earth also collects some of the hot gas evaporating from the sun, but this amount is comparatively small.

The earth does lose mass by evaporation of molecules from the top of the atmosphere. The rate of this evaporation depends on how many molecules are near enough to the top of the atmosphere to escape without colliding with other molecules. Also, such molecules must have velocities high enough to escape the earth's gravitational pull. The velocities of the molecules are determined by the temperature of the upper atmosphere. Therefore the rate of evaporation depends greatly on this temperature. At present the rate is probably less than 5×10^3 g/sec over the whole earth. This loss is very small compared with the addition of dust. (No water molecules are likely to be lost directly by atmospheric "evaporation;" they would first have to be dissociated into hydrogen and oxygen molecules.)

SG 9.3–9.7

Q1 *True or false:* Mass is conserved in a closed system only if there is no chemical reaction in the system.

Q2 If 50 cm³ of alcohol is mixed with 50 cm³ of water, the mixture amounts to only 98 cm³. An instrument pack on the moon weighs much less than on earth. Are these examples of contradictions with the law of conservation of mass?

Q3 Which one of the following statements is true?
(a) Lavoisier was the first person to believe that the amount of material stuff in the universe did not change.
(b) Mass is measurably increased when heat enters a system.
(c) A closed system was used to establish the law of conservation of mass experimentally.

9.2 Collisions

Looking at moving things in the world around us easily leads to the conclusion that everything set in motion eventually stops. Every clock, every machine eventually runs down. It appears that the amount of motion in the universe must be decreasing. The universe, like any machine, must be running down.

Many philosophers of the 1600's could not accept the idea of a universe that was running down. The concept clashed with their idea of the perfection of God, who surely would not construct such an imperfect mechanism. Some definition of "motion" was needed which would permit one to make the statement that "the quantity of motion in the universe is constant."

Is there such a constant factor in motion that keeps the world machine going? To answer these questions most directly, we can do some simple laboratory experiments. We will use a pair of identical carts with nearly frictionless wheels, or better, two dry-ice discs or two air-track gliders. In the first experiment, a lump of putty is attached so that the carts will stick together when they collide. The carts are each given a push so that they approach each other with equal speeds and collide head-on. As you will see when you do the experiment, both carts stop in the collision: their motion ceases. But is there anything related to their motions which does not change?

Yes, there is. If we add the velocity $\vec{v}_A$ of one cart to the velocity $\vec{v}_B$ of the other cart, we find that the *vector sum* does not change. The vector sum of the velocities of these oppositely moving carts is zero *before* the collision. It is also zero for the carts at rest *after* the collision.

We might wonder whether this finding holds for all collisions. In other words, is there a "law of conservation of velocity"? The example above was a very special circumstance. Carts with equal masses approach each other with equal speeds. Suppose we make the mass of one of the carts twice the mass of the other cart. (We can conveniently double the mass of one cart by putting another cart on top of it.) Now let the carts approach each other with equal speeds and collide, as before. This time the carts do *not* come to rest. There is some motion remaining. Both objects move together in the direction of the initial velocity of the more massive object. Our guess that the vector sum of the velocities might be conserved in all collisions is wrong.

Another example of a collision will confirm this conclusion. This time let the first cart have twice the mass of the second, but only half the speed. When the carts collide head-on and stick together, they stop. The vector sum of the velocities is equal to zero *after* the collision. But it was not equal to zero *before* the collision. Again, there is no conservation of velocity.

We have been trying to show that the "quantity of motion" is always the same before and after the collision. But our results indicate that the proper definition of "quantity of motion" may involve the *mass* of a body

Note that in Units 1 and 2 we dealt mostly with phenomena in which this fact did not have to be faced.

In symbols, $\Delta \Sigma_i \ \vec{v}_i = \Delta \Sigma_f \ \vec{v}_f = \mathbf{0}$ in *this* particular case.

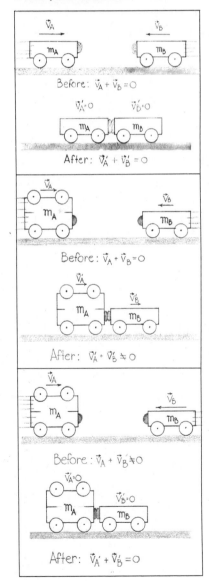

Before: $\vec{v}_A + \vec{v}_B = 0$

$\vec{v}_A' = 0 \qquad \vec{v}_B' = 0$

After: $\vec{v}_A' + \vec{v}_B' = 0$

Before: $\vec{v}_A + \vec{v}_B = 0$

After: $\vec{v}_A' + \vec{v}_B' \neq 0$

Before: $\vec{v}_A + \vec{v}_B \neq 0$

$\vec{v}_A' = 0 \qquad \vec{v}_B' = 0$

After: $\vec{v}_A' + \vec{v}_B' = 0$

as well as its speed. Descartes had suggested that the proper measure of a body's quantity of motion was the product of its mass and its speed. Speed does not involve direction and is considered always to have a positive value. The examples above, however, show that this product (a scalar and always positive) is not a conserved quantity. In the first and third collisions, for example, the products of mass and speed are zero for the stopped carts *after* the collision. But they obviously are not equal to zero *before* the collision.

But if we make one very important change in Descartes' definition, we do obtain a conserved quantity. Instead of defining "quantity of motion" as the product of mass and *speed, mv*, we can define it (as Newton did) as the product of the mass and *velocity, $m\vec{v}$*. In this way we include the idea of the *direction* of motion as well as the speed. On the next page the quantities $m\vec{v}$ are analyzed for the three collisions we have considered. In all three head-on collisions, the motion of both carts before and after collision is described by the equation:

In general symbols,
$\Delta\Sigma\ m_i\vec{v}_i = 0$.

$$\underbrace{m_A\vec{v}_A + m_B\vec{v}_B}_{\substack{\text{before} \\ \text{collision}}} = \underbrace{m_A\vec{v}_A{}' + m_B\vec{v}_B{}'}_{\substack{\text{after} \\ \text{collision}}}$$

Where m_A and m_B represents the masses of the carts, $\vec{v}_A$ and $\vec{v}_B$ represent their velocities before the collision and $\vec{v}_A{}'$ and $\vec{v}_B{}'$ represent their velocities after the collision.

In Unit 1, initial and final velocities were represented as $\vec{v}_i$ and $\vec{v}_f$. Here they are represented by $\vec{v}$ and $\vec{v}$ because we now need to add subscripts such as *A* and *B*.

In words: *the vector sum of the quantities mass × velocity is constant, or conserved, in all these collisions.* This is a very important and useful equation, leading directly to a powerful law.

SG 9.8, 9.9

Q4 Descartes defined the quantity of motion of an object as the product of its mass and its speed. Is his quantity of motion conserved as he believed it was? If not, how would you modify his definition so the quantity of motion would be conserved?

Q5 Two carts collide head-on and stick together. In which of the following cases will the carts be at rest immediately after the collision?

	Cart A		Cart B	
	mass	speed before	mass	speed before
(a)	2 kg	3 m/sec	2 kg	3 m/sec
(b)	2	2	3	3
(c)	2	3	3	2
(d)	2	3	1	6

9.3 Conservation of momentum

Since the momentum of a system is the vector sum of the momentum of its parts, it is sometimes called the "total momentum" of the system. We will assume that "total" is understood.

The product of mass and velocity often plays an interesting role in mechanics. It therefore has been given a special name. Instead of being called "quantity of motion," as in Newton's time, it is now called *momentum*. The total momentum of a system of objects (for example, the two carts) is the vector sum of the momenta of all objects in the system.

Analyses of Three Collisions

In Section 9.2 we discuss three examples of collisions between two carts. In each case the carts approached each other head-on, collided, and stuck together. We will show here that in each collision the motion of the carts before and after the collision is described by the *general* equation

$$m_A\vec{v}_A + m_B\vec{v}_B = m_A\vec{v}_A' + m_B\vec{v}_B'$$

where m_A and m_B represent the masses of the carts, $\vec{v}_A$ and $\vec{v}_B$ their velocities before collision, and $\vec{v}_A'$ and $\vec{v}_B'$ their velocities after the collision.

Example 1: Two carts with equal masses move with equal speeds—but in opposite directions—before the collision. The speed of the stuck-together carts after the collision is zero. Before collision, the product of mass and velocity has the same magnitude for each cart, but opposite direction. So their vector sum is obviously zero. After collision, each velocity is zero, so the product of mass and velocity is also zero.

This simple case could be described in a few sentences. More complicated cases are much easier to handle by using an equation and substituting values in the equation. To show how this works, we will go back to the simple case above, even though it will seem like a lot of trouble for such an obvious result. We substitute specific values into the general equation given in the first paragraph above for two colliding bodies. In this specific case $m_A = m_B$, $\vec{v}_B = -\vec{v}_A$, and $\vec{v}_A' = \vec{v}_B' = 0$. Just before collision, the vector sum of the separate momenta is given by $m_A\vec{v}_A + m_B\vec{v}_B$, which in this case is equal to $m_A\vec{v}_A + m_A(-\vec{v}_A)$ or $m_A\vec{v}_A - m_A\vec{v}_A$ which equals zero.

After the collision, the vector sum of the momenta is given by $m_A\vec{v}_A' + m_B\vec{v}_B'$. Since both velocities after collision is zero, then

$$m_A(0) + m_B(0) = 0$$

Thus, before the collision, the vector sum of the products of mass and velocity is zero, and the same is true for the vector sum after the collision. The general equation is therefore "obeyed" in this case.

Example 2: The carts move with equal speeds toward each other before the collision. The mass of one cart is twice that of the other. After the collision, the velocity of the stuck-together carts is found to be $\frac{1}{3}$ the original velocity of the more massive cart. In symbols: $m_A = 2m_B$, $\vec{v}_B = -\vec{v}_A$, and $\vec{v}_A' = \vec{v}_B' = \frac{1}{3}\vec{v}_A$. Before the collision:

$$\begin{aligned}
m_A\vec{v}_A = m_B\vec{v}_B &= (2m_B)\vec{v}_A + m_B(-\vec{v}_A) \\
&= 2m_B\vec{v}_A - m_B\vec{v}_A \\
&= m_B\vec{v}_A
\end{aligned}$$

After the collision:

$$\begin{aligned}
m_A\vec{v}_A + m_B\vec{v}_B &= (2m_B)\tfrac{1}{3}\vec{v}_A + m_B\tfrac{1}{3}\vec{v}_A \\
&= \tfrac{2}{3}m_B\vec{v}_A + \tfrac{1}{3}m_B\vec{v}_A \\
&= m_B\vec{v}_A
\end{aligned}$$

Again, the sum of $m\vec{v}$'s is the same before and after the collision. Therefore, the general equation describes the collision correctly.

Example 3: Two carts approach each other; the mass of one cart is twice that of the other. Before the collision, the speed of the less massive cart is twice that of the more massive cart. The speed of the stuck-together carts after the collision is found to be zero. In symbols: $m_A = 2m_B$, $\vec{v}_B = -2\vec{v}_A$ and $\vec{v}_A' = \vec{v}_B' = 0$. Before the collision:

$$\begin{aligned}
m_A\vec{v}_A + m_B\vec{v}_B &= (2m_B)\vec{v}_A + m_B(-2\,\vec{v}_A) \\
&= 2m_B\vec{v}_A - 2m_B\vec{v}_A \\
&= 0
\end{aligned}$$

After the collision:

$$m_A(0) + m_B(0) = 0$$

Again, the principle holds. Indeed, *it holds for all collisions of this kind* on which no external pushes or pulls are exerted, regardless of their masses and their initial velocities.

In these examples all motion has been along a straight line. However, the principle is most useful for collisions that are not directly head-on and where the bodies go off at different angles. An example of such a collision is on page 23.

SG 9.10, 9.11

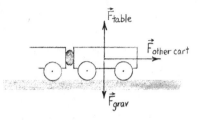

Forces on cart *B* during collision.

Consider each of the collisions that we examined. The momentum of the system as a whole—the vector sum of the individual parts—is the same before and after collision. Moreover, the total momentum doesn't change *during* the collision, as the results of a typical experiment on page 10 show. Thus, we can summarize the results of the experiments briefly: *the momentum of the system is conserved.*

We arrived at this rule (or law, or principle) by observing the special case of collisions between two carts that stuck together after colliding. But in fact this *law of conservation of momentum* is a completely general, universal law. The momentum of *any* system is conserved *if one condition is met:* that no net force is acting on the system.

To see just what this condition means, let us examine the forces acting on one of the carts. Each cart experiences three main forces. There is of course a downward pull $\vec{F}_{grav}$ exerted by the earth and an upward push $\vec{F}_{table}$ exerted by the table. During the collision, there is also a push $\vec{F}_{from\ other\ cart}$ exerted by the other cart. The first two forces evidently cancel, since the cart is not accelerating up or down. Thus the net force on each cart is just the force exerted on it by the other cart as they collide. (To simplify, we assume that frictional forces exerted by the table and the air are small enough to neglect. That was the reason for using dry-ice disks, air-track gliders, or carts with "frictionless" wheels. This assumption makes it easier to discuss the law of conservation of momentum. But we will see that the law holds whether friction exists or not.)

The two carts form a *system* of bodies, each cart being a part of the system. The force exerted by one cart on the other cart is a force exerted by one part of the system on another part. But it is *not* a force on the system as a whole. The outside forces acting on the carts (by the earth and by the table) exactly cancel. Thus, there is no *net* outside force. We can say that the system is "isolated." This condition must be met in order for the momentum of a system to stay constant, to be conserved.

If the net force on a system of bodies is zero, the momentum of the system will not change. This is the *law of conservation of momentum* for systems of bodies that are moving with linear velocity $\vec{v}$.

So far we have considered only cases in which two bodies collide directly and stick together. But the remarkable thing about the law of conservation of momentum is how universally it applies. For example:

(a) It holds true no matter what *kind* of forces the bodies exert on each other. They may be gravitational forces, electric or magnetic forces, tension in strings, compression in springs, attraction or repulsion. The sum of the $m\vec{v}$'s before is equal to the sum of $m\vec{v}$'s after any interaction.

(b) It doesn't matter whether the bodies stick together or scrape against each other or bounce apart. They don't even have to touch. When two strong magnets repel or when an alpha particle is repelled by a nucleus, conservation of momentum still holds.

(c) The law is not restricted to systems of only two objects; there can be any number of objects in the system. In those cases, the basic conservation equation is made more general simply by adding a term for each object to both sides of the equation.

In general, for *n* objects the law can be written

$$\sum_{j=1}^{n} (m_j\vec{v})_{before} = \sum_{j=1}^{n} (m_j v_j)_{after}$$

Example of the Use of the Conservation of Momentum

Here is an example that illustrates how one can use the law of conservation of momentum.

(a) A space capsule at rest in space, far from the sun or planets, has a mass of 1,000 kg. A meteorite with a mass of 0.1 kg moves towards it with a speed of 1,000 m/sec. How fast does the capsule (with the meteorite stuck in it) move after being hit?

m_A mass of the meteorite = 0.1 kg
m_B mass of the capsule = 1,000 kg
$\vec{v}_A$ initial velocity of meteorite = 1,000 m/sec
$\vec{v}_B$ initial velocity of capsule = 0
$\left.\begin{array}{l} \vec{v}_A' \text{ final velocity of meteorite} \\ \vec{v}_B' \text{ final velocity of capsule} \end{array}\right\} = ?$

The law of conservation of momentum states that

$$m_A\vec{v}_A + m_B\vec{v}_B = m_A\vec{v}_A' + m_B\vec{v}_B'$$

Inserting the values given,

(0.1 kg) (1000 m/sec) + (1000 kg) (0) =
$\qquad$ (0.1 kg)$\vec{v}_A'$ + (1000 kg)$\vec{v}_B'$
100 kg·m/sec = (0.1 kg)$\vec{v}_A'$ + (1000 kg)$\vec{v}_A'$

Since the meteorite sticks to the capsule, $\vec{v}_B' = \vec{v}_A'$ so we can write

100 kg·m/sec = (0.1 kg)$\vec{v}_A'$ + (1000 kg)$\vec{v}_A'$
100 kg·m/sec = (1000.1 kg)$\vec{v}_A'$

Therefore

$$\vec{v}_A' = \frac{100\ \text{kg·m/sec}}{1000.1\ \text{kg}}$$
$$= 0.1\ \text{m/sec}$$

(in the original direction of the motion of the meteorite). Thus, the capsule (with the stuck meteorite) moves on with a speed of 0.1 m/sec.

Another approach to the solution is to handle the symbols first, and substitute in the values only as a final step. Substituting $\vec{v}_A'$ for $\vec{v}_B'$ and letting $\vec{v}_B' = 0$ would leave the equation $m_A\vec{v}_A =$ $m_A\vec{v}_A' + m_B\vec{v}_A' = (m_A + m_B)\vec{v}_A'$. Solving for v_A'

$$\vec{v}_A' = \frac{m_A\vec{v}_A}{(m_A + m_B)}$$

This equation holds true for any projectile hitting (and staying with) a body initially at rest that moves on in a straight line after collision.

(b) An identical capsule at rest nearby is hit by a meteorite of the same mass as the other.

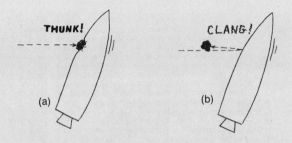

(a) THUNK! (b) CLANG!

But this meteorite, hitting another part of the capsule, does not penetrate. Instead it bounces straight back with almost no change of speed. (Some support for the reasonableness of this claim is given in SG 9.24.) How fast does the capsule move on after being hit? Since all these motions are along a straight line, we can drop the vector notation from the symbols and indicate the reversal in direction of the meteorite with a minus sign.

The same symbols are appropriate as in (a):

m_A = 0.1 kg $\qquad$ v_B = 0
m_B = 1000 kg $\qquad$ v_A' = −1000 m/sec
v_A = 1000 m/sec $\qquad$ v_B' = ?

The law of conservation of momentum stated that $m_A\vec{v}_A + m_B\vec{v}_B = m_A\vec{v}_A' + m_B\vec{v}_B'$. Here

(0.1 kg) (1000 m/sec) + (1000 kg) (0) =
$\qquad$ (0.1 kg) (−1000 m/sec) + (1000 kg)v_B'
100 kg·m/sec = −100 kg·m/sec + (1000 kg)v_B'

$$v_B' = \frac{200\ \text{kg·m/sec}}{1000\ \text{kg}} = 0.2\ \text{m/sec}$$

Thus, the struck capsule moves on with about twice the speed of the capsule in (a). (A general symbolic approach can be taken to this solution, too. But the result is valid only for the special case of a projectile rebounding perfectly elastically from a body of much greater mass.)

There is a general lesson here. It follows from the law of conservation of momentum that a struck object is given less momentum if it *absorbs* the projectile than if it *reflects* it. (A goalie who catches the soccer ball is pushed back less than one who lets the ball bounce off his chest.) Some thought will help you to understand this idea: an interaction that merely stops the projectile is not as great as an interaction that first stops it and then propels it back again.

SG 9.12 – 9.15

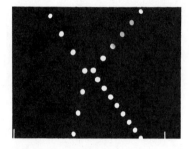

One of the stroboscopic photographs that appears in the *Handbook*.

(d) The size of the system is not important. The law applies to a galaxy as well as to an atom.

(e) The angle of the collision does not matter. All of our examples so far have involved collisions between two bodies moving along the same straight line. They were "one-dimensional collisions." But if two bodies make a glancing collision rather than a head-on collision, each will move off at an angle to the line of approach. The law of conservation of momentum applies to such two-dimensional collisions also. (Remember that momentum is a vector quantity.) The law of conservation of momentum also applies in *three* dimensions. The vector sum of the momenta is still the same before and after the collision.

On page 13 is a worked-out example that will help you become familiar with the law of conservation of momentum. At the end of the chapter is a special page on the analysis of a two-dimensional collision. There are also stroboscopic photographs in the Project Physics *Handbook* and film loops of colliding bodies and exploding objects. These include collisions and explosions in two dimensions. The more of them you analyze, the more convinced you will be that the law of conservation of momentum applies to *any* isolated system.

The worked-out example of page 13 displays a characteristic feature of physics. Again and again, physics problems are solved by applying the expression of a *general* law to a specific situation. Both the beginning student and the veteran research physicist find it helpful, but also somewhat mysterious, that one can *do* this. It seems strange that a few general laws enable one to solve an almost infinite number of specific individual problems. Everyday life seems different. There you usually cannot calculate answers from general laws. Rather, you have to make quick decisions, some based on rational analysis, others based on "intuition." But the use of general laws to solve scientific problems becomes, with practice, quite natural also.

Q6 Which of the following has the least momentum? Which has the greatest momentum?
 (a) a pitched baseball
 (b) a jet plane in flight
 (c) a jet plane taxiing toward the terminal

Q7 A girl on ice skates is at rest on a horizontal sheet of smooth ice. As a result of catching a rubber ball moving horizontally toward her, she moves at 2 cm/sec. Give a rough estimate of what her speed would have been

(a) if the rubber ball were thrown twice as fast
(b) if the rubber ball had twice the mass
(c) if the girl had twice the mass
(d) if the rubber ball were not caught by the girl, but bounced off and went straight back with no change of speed.

9.4 Momentum and Newton's laws of motion

In Section 9.2 we developed the concept of momentum and the law of conservation of momentum by considering experiments with colliding carts. The law was an "empirical" law. That is, we arrived at it as a summary of experimental results, not from theory. The law was discovered—perhaps "invented" or "induced" are better terms—as a generalization from experiment.

SG 9.16

We can show, however, that the law of conservation of momentum follows directly from Newton's laws of motion. It takes only a little algebra. We will first put Newton's second law into a somewhat different form than we used before.

Newton's second law expresses a relation between the net force $\vec{F}_{net}$ acting on a body, the mass m of the body, and its acceleration a. We wrote this as $\vec{F}_{net} = m\vec{a}$. But we can also write this law in terms of *change of momentum* of the body. Recalling that acceleration is the rate-of-change of velocity, $\vec{a} = \Delta\vec{v}/\Delta t$, we can write:

or

$$\vec{F}_{net} = m\frac{\Delta\vec{v}}{\Delta t}$$
$$\vec{F}_{net}\Delta t = m\,\Delta\vec{v}$$

If m is a constant,
$\Delta(m\vec{v}) = m\vec{v}'' - m\vec{v}'$
$\qquad = m(\vec{v}'' - \vec{v}')$
$\qquad = m\,\Delta\vec{v}$

If the mass of the body is constant, the change in its momentum, $\Delta(m\vec{v})$, is the same as its mass times its change in velocity, $m(\Delta\vec{v})$. So then we can write:

$\vec{F}\Delta t$ is called the "impulse."

$$\vec{F}_{net}\,\Delta t = \Delta(m\vec{v})$$

SG 9.17–9.20

That is, *the product of the net force on a body and the time interval during which this force acts equals the change in momentum of the body.*

This statement of Newton's second law is more nearly what Newton used in the *Principia*. Together with Newton's third law, it enables us to derive the law of conservation of momentum for the cases we have studied. The details of the derivation are given on page 16. Thus Newton's laws and the law of conservation of momentum are not separate, independent laws of nature.

In Newton's second law, "change of motion" meant change of momentum—see Definition II at the beginning of the *Principia*.

Deriving Conservation of Momentum from Newton's Laws

Suppose two bodies with masses m_A and m_B exert forces on each other (by gravitation or by mutual friction, etc.). $\vec{F}_{AB}$ is the force exerted on a body A by body B, and $\vec{F}_{BA}$ is the force exerted on body B by body A. No other unbalanced force acts on either body; they form an isolated system. By Newton's third law, the forces $\vec{F}_{AB}$ and $\vec{F}_{BA}$ are at every instant equal in magnitude and opposite in direction. Each body acts on the other for exactly the same time Δt. Newton's second law, applied to each of the bodies, says

$$\vec{F}_{AB}\,\Delta t = \Delta(m_A \vec{v}_A)$$
and
$$\vec{F}_{BA}\,\Delta t = \Delta(m_B \vec{v}_B)$$

By Newton's third law

$$\vec{F}_{AB}\,\Delta t = -\vec{F}_{BA}\Delta t$$
therefore
$$\Delta(m_A \vec{v}_A) = -\Delta(m_B \vec{v}_B)$$

Suppose that each of the masses m_A and m_B are constant. Let $\vec{v}_A$ and $\vec{v}_B$ stand for the velocities of the two bodies at some instant and let $\vec{v}_A{}'$ and $\vec{v}_B{}'$ stand for their velocities at some later instant. Then we can write the last equation as

$$m_A \vec{v}_A{}' - m_A \vec{v}_A = -(m_B \vec{v}_B{}' - m_B \vec{v}_B)$$

A little rearrangement of terms leads to

$$m_A \vec{v}_A{}' - m_A \vec{v}_A = -m_B \vec{v}_B{}' + m_B \vec{v}_B$$
and
$$m_A \vec{v}_A{}' + m_B v_B{}' = m_A \vec{v}_A + m_B \vec{v}_B$$

You will recognize this as our original expression of the law of conservation of momentum.

Here we are dealing with a system consisting of two bodies. But this method works equally well for a system consisting of any number of bodies. For example, SG 9.21 shows you how to derive the law of conservation of momentum for a system of three bodies.

Globular clusters of stars like this one contain tens of thousands of suns held together by gravitational attraction.

In all examples we considered each body to have constant mass. But a change of momentum can arise from a change of mass as well as from (or in addition to) a change of velocity. For example, as a rocket spews out exhaust gases, its mass decreases. The mass of a train of coal cars increases as it moves under a hopper which drops coal into the cars. In Unit 5 you will find that *any* body's mass increases as it moves faster and faster. (However, this effect is great enough to notice only at extremely high speeds.) The equation $F_{net} = ma$ is a form of Newton's second law that works in special cases where the mass is constant. But this form is not appropriate for situations where mass changes. Nor do the forms of the law of conservation of momentum that are based on $F_{net} = ma$ work in such cases. But other forms of the law can be derived for systems where mass is not constant. See, for example, the first pages of the article "Space Travel" in *Reader 5*.

SG 9.21 – 9.24

In one form or another, the law of conservation of momentum can be derived from Newton's second and third laws. Nevertheless, the law of conservation of momentum is often the preferred tool because it enables us to solve many problems which would be difficult to solve using Newton's laws directly. For example, suppose a cannon that is free to move fires a shell horizontally. Although it was initially at rest, the cannon is forced to move while firing the shell; it *recoils*. The expanding gases in the cannon barrel push the cannon backward just as hard as they push the shell forward. Suppose we had a continuous record of the magnitude of the force. We could then apply Newton's second law separately to the cannon and to the shell to find their respective accelerations. After a few more steps (involving calculus) we could find the speed of the shell and the recoil speed of the cannon. But in practice it is very difficult to get a continuous record of the magnitude of the force. For one thing, the force almost certainly decreases as the shell moves toward the end of the barrel. So it would be very difficult to use Newton's laws to find the final speeds.

However, we can use the law of conservation of momentum even if we know nothing about the force. The law of conservation of momentum is a law of the kind that says "before = after." Thus, it works in cases where we do not have enough information to apply Newton's laws during the whole interval between "before" and "after." In the case of the cannon and shell the momentum of the system (cannon plus shell) is zero initially. Therefore, by the law of conservation of momentum, the momentum will also be zero after the shell is fired. If we know the masses and the speed of one, after firing we can calculate the speed of the other. (The film loop titled "Recoil" provides just such an event for you to analyze.) On the other hand, if both speeds can be measured afterwards, then the ratio of the masses can be calculated. In the Supplemental Unit entitled *The Nucleus* you will see how just such an approach was used to find the mass of the neutron when it was originally discovered.

SG 9.25

SG 9.26
SG 9.27

Q8 Since the law of conservation of momentum can be derived from Newton's laws, what good is it?

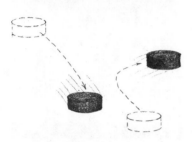

SG 9.28 – 9.33

9.5 Isolated systems

There are important similarities between the conservation law of mass and that of momentum. We test both laws by observing systems that are in some sense isolated from the rest of the universe. When testing or using the law of conservation of *mass,* we arrange an isolated system such as a sealed flask. Matter can neither enter or leave this system. When testing or using the law of conservation of *momentum,* we arrange another kind of isolated system. Such a system is closed in the sense that each body in it experiences no net force from outside the system.

Consider for example two dry-ice pucks colliding on a smooth horizontal table. The very low friction pucks form a very nearly closed or isolated system. We need not include in it the table and the earth, for their individual effects on each puck cancel. Each puck experiences a downward gravitational force exerted by the earth. But the table exerts an equally strong upward push.

Even in this artificial example, the system is not entirely closed. There is always a little friction with the outside world. The layer of gas under the puck and air currents, for example, exert friction. All outside forces are not *completely* balanced, and so the two pucks do not form a truly isolated system. Whenever this is unacceptable, one can expand or extend the system so that it *includes* the bodies that are responsible for the external forces. The result is a new system on which the unbalanced forces are small enough to ignore.

For example, picture two cars skidding toward a collision on an icy road. The frictional forces exerted by the road on each car may be several hundred pounds. These forces are very small compared to the immense force (many tons) exerted by each car on the other when they collide. Thus, for many purposes, we can forget about the action of the road. For such purposes, the two skidding cars *during the collision* are nearly enough an isolated system. However, if friction with the road (or the table on which the pucks move) is too great to ignore, the law of conservation of momentum still holds, but we must apply it to a larger system, one which includes the road or table. In the case of the skidding cars or the pucks, the table or road is attached to the earth. So we would have to include the entire earth in a "closed system."

Q9 Define what is meant by "closed" or "isolated" system for the purpose of the law of conservation of mass; for the purpose of the law of conservation of momentum.

Q10 Explain whether or not each of the following can be considered as an isolated system.

(a) a baseball thrown horizontally

(b) an artificial earth satellite
(c) the earth and the moon

9.6 Elastic collisions

In 1666, members of the recently-formed Royal Society of London witnessed a demonstration. Two hardwood balls of equal size were suspended at the ends of two strings to form two pendula. One ball was released from rest at a certain height. It swung down and struck the other, which had been hanging at rest.

After impact, the first ball stopped at the point of impact while the second ball swung from this point to the same height as that from which the first ball had been released. When the second ball returned and struck the first, it now was the second ball which stopped at the point of impact as the first swung up to almost the same height from which it had started. This motion repeated itself for several swings.

This demonstration aroused great interest among members of the Society. In the next few years, it also caused heated and often confusing arguments. Why did the balls rise each time to nearly the same height after each collision? Why was the motion "transferred" from one ball to the other when they collided? Why didn't the first ball bounce back from the point of collision, or continue moving forward after the second ball moved away from the collision point?

Our law of momentum conservation explains what is observed. But it would also allow quite different results. It says only that the momentum of ball A just before it strikes ball B is equal to the total momentum of A and B just after collision. It does not say how A and B share the momentum. The actual result is just one of infinitely many different outcomes that would all agree with conservation of momentum. For example, suppose (though it is never observed to happen) that ball A bounced back with ten times its initial speed. Momentum would still be conserved *if* ball B went ahead at eleven times A's initial speed.

In 1668 three men reported to the Royal Society on the whole matter of impact. The three men were the mathematician John Wallis, the architect and scientist Christopher Wren, and the physicist Christian Huygens. Wallis and Wren offered partial answers for some of the features of collisions; Huygens analyzed the problem in complete detail.

Huygens explained that in such collisions *another conservation law* also holds, in addition to the law of conservation of momentum. Not only was the vector sum of $m\vec{v}$'s conserved, but so was the ordinary arithmetic sum of mv^2's! In modern algebraic form, the relationship he discovered can be expressed as

In general symbols, $\Delta\Sigma_j \frac{1}{2}m_j v_j^2 = 0$.

$$\tfrac{1}{2}m_A v_A{}^2 \;+\; \tfrac{1}{2}m_B v_B{}^2 \;=\; \tfrac{1}{2}m_A v_A{}'^2 \;+\; \tfrac{1}{2}m_B v_B{}'^2$$

Compare this equation with the conservation of momentum equation on page 10.

SG 9.34 – 9.37

Christiaan Huygens (1629-1695) was a Dutch physicist. He devised an improved telescope with which he discovered a satellite of Saturn and saw Saturn's rings clearly. He was the first to obtain the expression for centripetal acceleration (v^2/R), he worked out a wave theory of light, and he invented a pendulum-controlled clock. His scientific contributions were major, and his reputation would undoubtedly have been greater were he not overshadowed by his contemporary, Newton.

Huygens, and others after him for about a century, did not use the factor $\frac{1}{2}$. The quantity mv^2 was called *vis viva*, Latin for "living force." Seventeenth- and eighteenth-century scientists were greatly interested in distinguishing and naming various "forces." They used the word loosely; it meant sometimes a push or a pull (as in the colloquial modern use of the word force), sometimes what we now call "momentum," and sometimes what we now call "energy." The term *vis viva* is no longer used.

The scalar quantity $\frac{1}{2}mv^2$ has come to be called *kinetic energy*. (The reason for the $\frac{1}{2}$, which doesn't really affect the rule here, will become clear in the next chapter.) The equation stated above, then, is the mathematical expression of the conservation of kinetic energy. This relationship holds for the collision of two "perfectly hard" objects similar to those observed at the Royal Society meeting. There, ball A stopped and ball B went on at A's initial speed. A little algebra will show that this is the *only* result that agrees with *both* conservation of momentum and conservation of kinetic energy. (See SG 9.33.)

But is the conservation of kinetic energy as general as the law of conservation of momentum? Is the total kinetic energy present conserved in *any* interaction occurring in *any* isolated system?

It is easy to see that it is not. Consider the first example of Section 9.2. Two carts of equal mass (and with putty between the bumping surfaces) approach each other with equal speeds. They meet, stick together, and stop. The kinetic energy of the system after the collision is 0, since the speeds of both carts are zero. Before the collision the kinetic energy of the system was $\frac{1}{2}m_A v_A^2 + \frac{1}{2}m_B v_B^2$. But both $\frac{1}{2}m_A v_A^2$ and $\frac{1}{2}m_B v_B^2$ are always positive numbers. Their sum cannot possibly equal zero (unless both v_A and v_B are zero, in which case there would be no collision—and not much of a problem). Kinetic energy is *not* conserved in this collision in which the bodies stick together. In fact, *no* collision in which the bodies stick together will show conservation of kinetic energy. It applies only to the collision of "perfectly hard" bodies that bounce back from each other.

The law of conservation of kinetic energy, then, is *not* as general as the law of conservation of momentum. If two bodies collide, the kinetic energy may or may not be conserved, depending on the type of collision. It *is* conserved if the colliding bodies do not crumple or smash or dent or stick together or heat up or change physically in some other way. We call bodies that rebound without any such change "perfectly elastic." We describe collisions between them as "perfectly elastic collisions." In perfectly elastic collisions, *both* momentum and kinetic energy are conserved.

Most collisions that we witness, are not perfectly elastic and kinetic energy is not conserved. Thus, the sum of the $\frac{1}{2}mv^2$'s after the collision is *less* than before the collision. Depending on how much kinetic energy is "lost," such collisions might be called "partially elastic," or "perfectly inelastic." The loss of kinetic energy is greatest in perfectly inelastic collisions, when the colliding bodies remain together.

Collisions between steel ball-bearings, glass marbles, hardwood balls, billiard balls, or some rubber balls (silicone rubber) are almost perfectly elastic, if the colliding bodies are not damaged in the collision. The total kinetic energy after the collision might be as much as, say, 96% of this value before the collision. Examples of true perfectly elastic collisions are found only in collisions between atoms or sub-atomic particles.

SG 9.38-9.40

Q11 Which phrases correctly complete the statement? Kinetic energy is conserved

(a) in all collisions

(b) whenever momentum is conserved

(c) in some collisions

(d) when the colliding objects are not too hard

Q12 Kinetic energy is never negative because

(a) scalar quantities are always positve

(b) it is impossible to draw vectors with negative length

(c) speed is always greater than zero

(d) it is proportional to the square of the speed

9.7 Leibniz and the conservation law

Rene Descartes believed that the total quantity of motion in the universe did not change. He wrote in his *Principles of Philosophy:*

> It is wholly rational to assume that God, since in the creation of matter He imparted different motions to its parts, and preserves all matter in the same way and conditions in which he created it, so He similarly preserves in it the same quantity of motion.

Descartes proposed to define the quantity of motion of an object as the product of its mass and its speed. But as we saw in Section 1.1 this product is a conserved quantity only in very special cases.

Gottfried Wilhelm Leibniz was aware of the error in Descartes' ideas on motion. In a letter in 1680 he wrote:

> M. Descartes' physics has a great defect; it is that his rules of motion or laws of nature, which are to serve as the basis, are for the most part false. This is demonstrated. And his great principle, that the same quantity of motion is conserved in the world, is an error.

Leibniz, however was as sure as Descartes had been that *something* involving motion was conserved. Leibniz called this something he identified as "force" the quantity mv^2 (which he called *vis viva*). We notice that this is just twice the quantity we now call kinetic energy. (Of course, whatever applies to mv^2 applies equally to $\frac{1}{2}mv^2$.)

As Huygens had pointed out, the quantity $(\frac{1}{2})mv^2$ is conserved only in perfectly elastic collisions. In other collisions the total quantity of $(\frac{1}{2})mv^2$ after collision is always *less* than before the collision. Still, Leibniz was convinced that $(\frac{1}{2})mv^2$ is *always* conserved. In order to save his conservation law, he invented an explanation for the apparent loss of *vis viva*. He maintained that the *vis viva* is *not* lost or destroyed. Rather, it is merely "dissipated among the small parts" of which the colliding bodies are made. This was pure speculation and Leibniz offered no supporting evidence. Nonetheless, his explanation anticipated modern ideas about the connection between energy and the motion of molecules. We will study some of these ideas in Chapter 11.

Descartes (1596-1650) was the most important French scientist of the seventeenth century. In addition to his early contribution to the idea of momentum conservation, he is remembered by scientists as the inventor of coordinate systems and the graphical representation of algebraic equations. His system of philosophy, which used the deductive structure of geometry as its model, is still influential.

Leibniz (1646-1716), a contemporary of Newton, was a German philosopher and diplomat, an advisor to Louis XIV of France and Peter the Great of Russia. Independently of Newton he invented the method of mathematical analysis called calculus. A long public dispute resulted between the two great men concerning charges of plagiarism of ideas.

Leibnitz extended conservation ideas to phenomena other than collisions. For example, when a stone is thrown straight upward, its quantity of $(\frac{1}{2})mv^2$ decreases as it rises, even without any collision. At the top of the trajectory, $(\frac{1}{2})mv^2$ is zero for an instant. Then it reappears as the stone falls. Leibniz wondered whether something applied or given to a stone at the start is somehow *stored* as the stone rises, instead of being lost. His idea would mean that $(\frac{1}{2})mv^2$ is just one part of a more general, and really conserved quantity. In Chapter 10, this idea will lead us directly to the most powerful of all laws of science—the law of conservation of energy.

Q13 According to Leibniz, Descartes' principle of conservation of mv was

    (a) correct, but trivial.

    (b) another way of expressing the conservation of *vis viva*.

    (c) incorrect.

    (d) correct only in elastic collisions.

Q14 How did Leibniz explain the apparent disappearance of the quantity $(\frac{1}{2})mv^2$

    (a) during the upward motion of a thrown object?

    (b) when the object strikes the ground?

A Collision in Two Dimensions

The stroboscopic photograph shows a collision between two wooden discs on a "frictionless horizontal table" photographed from straight above the table. The discs are riding on tiny plastic spheres which make their motion nearly frictionless. Body B (marked **x**) is at rest before the collision. After the collision it moves to the left and Body A (marked −) moves to the right. The mass of Body B is known to be twice the mass of Body A: $m_B = 2m_A$. We will analyze the photograph to see whether momentum was conserved. (Note: The size reduction factor of the photograph and the [constant] stroboscopic flash rate are not given here. So long as all velocities for this test are measured in the same units, it does not matter what those units are.)

In this analysis we will measure in centimeters the distance the discs moved on the photograph. We will use the time between flashes as the unit of time. Before the collision, Body A (coming from the lower part of the photograph) traveled 36.7 mm in the time between flashes: $\vec{v}_A = 36.7$ speed-units. Similarly we find that $\vec{v}_A' = 17.2$ speed-units, and $\vec{v}_B' = 11.0$ speed-units.

The total momentum before the collision is just $m_A\vec{v}_A'$. It is represented by an arrow 36.7 momentum-units long, drawn at right.

The vector diagram shows the momenta $m_A\vec{v}_A'$ and $m_B\vec{v}_B'$ after the collision; $m_A\vec{v}_A'$ is represented by an arrow 17.2 momentum-units long. Since $m_B = 2m_A$, the $m_B\vec{v}_B'$ arrow is 22.0 momentum-units long.

The dotted line represents the vector sum of $m_A\vec{v}_A'$ and $m_B\vec{v}_B'$; that is, the total momentum after the collision. Measurement shows it to be 34.0 momentum-units long. Thus, our measured values of the total momentum before and after the collision differ by 2.7 momentum-units. This is a difference of about −7%. We can also verify that the *direction* of the total is the same before and after the collision to within a small uncertainty.

Have we now demonstrated that momentum was conserved in the collision? Is the 7% difference likely to be due entirely to measurement inaccuracies? Or is there reason to expect that the total momentum of the two discs after the collision is really a bit less than before the collision?

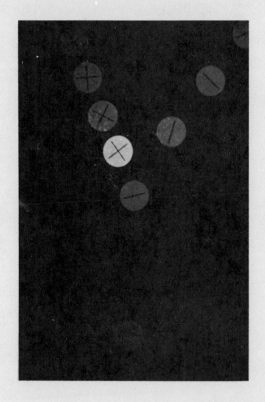

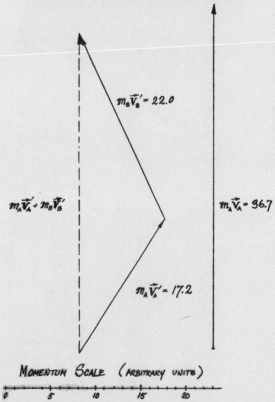

$m_B\vec{v}_B' = 22.0$

$m_A\vec{v}_A' + m_B\vec{v}_B'$

$m_A\vec{v}_A = 36.7$

$m_A\vec{v}_A' = 17.2$

MOMENTUM SCALE (ARBITRARY UNITS)

0   5   10   15   20

9.1 The Project Physics learning materials particularly appropriate for Chapter 9 include:

Experiments
Collisions in One Dimension
Collisions in Two Dimensions

Film Loops
One-dimensional Collisions I
One-dimensional Collisions II
Inelastic One-dimensional Collisions
Two-dimensional Collisions I
Two-dimensional Collisions II
Inelastic Two-dimensional Collisions
Scattering of a Cluster of Objects
Explosion of a Cluster of Objects

Transparencies
One-dimensional Collisions
Equal Mass Two-dimensional Collisions
Unequal Mass Two-dimensional Collisions
Inelastic Two-dimensional Collisions

In addition, the *Reader 3* articles "The Seven Images of Science" and "Scientific Cranks" are of general interest in the course.

9.2 Certainly Lavoisier did not investigate every possible interaction. What justification did he have for claiming mass was conserved "in all the operations of art and nature"?

9.3 It is estimated that every year at least 2000 tons of meteoric dust fall on to the earth. The dust is mostly debris that was moving in orbits around the sun.
(a) Is the earth (whose mass is about 6×10^{21} tons) reasonably considered to be a closed system with respect to the law of conservation of mass?
(b) How large would the system, including the earth, have to be in order to be completely closed?

9.4 Would you expect that in your lifetime, when more accurate balances are built, you will see experiments which show that the law of conservation of mass does not entirely hold for chemical reactions in closed systems?

9.5 Dayton C. Miller, a renowned experimenter at Case Institute of Technology, was able to show that two objects placed side by side on an equal-arm pan balance did not exactly balance two otherwise identical objects placed one on top of the other. (The reason is that the pull of gravity decreases with distance from the center of the earth.) Does this experiment contradict the law of conservation of mass?

9.6 A children's toy known as a Snake consists of a tiny pill of mercuric thiocyanate. When the pill is ignited, a large, serpent-like foam curls out almost from nothingness. Devise and describe an experiment by which you would test the law of conservation of mass for this demonstration.

9.7 Consider the following chemical reaction, which was studied by Landolt in his tests of the law of conservation of mass. In a closed container, a solution of 19.4 g of potassium chromate in 100.0 g of water is mixed with a solution of 33.1 g of lead nitrate in 100.0 g of water. A bright yellow solid precipitate forms and settles to the bottom of the container. When removed from the liquid, this solid is found to have a mass of 32.3 g and is found to have properties different from either of the reactants.
(a) What is the mass of the remaining liquid? (Assume the combined mass of all substances in the system is conserved.)
(b) If the remaining liquid (after removal of the yellow precipitate) is then heated to 95°C, the water it contains will evaporate, leaving a white solid. What is the mass of this solid? (Assume that the water does not react with anything, either in (a) or in (b).)

9.8 If a stationary cart is struck head-on by a cart with twice the mass, and the two carts stick together, they will move together with a speed $\frac{2}{3}$ as great as the moving cart had before collision. Show that this is consistent with the conservation of momentum equation.

9.9 A freight car of mass 10^5 kg travels at 2.0 m/sec and collides with a motionless freight car of mass 1.5×10^5 kg on a horizontal track. The two cars lock, and roll together after impact. Find the velocity of the two cars after collision. HINTS:
The general equation for conservation of momentum for a two-body system is:

$$m_A \vec{v}_A + m_B \vec{v}_B = m_A \vec{v}_A' + m_B \vec{v}_B'$$

(a) What quantities does the problem give for the equation?
(b) Rearrange terms to get an expression for $\vec{v}_A'$.
(c) Find the value of $\vec{v}_A'$. (Note $\vec{v}_A' = \vec{v}_B'$.)

9.10 You have been given a precise technical definition for the word *momentum*. Look it up in a large dictionary and record its various uses. Can you find anything similar to our definition in these more general meanings? How many of the uses seem to be consistent with the technical definition here given?

9.11 Benjamin Franklin, in correspondence with his friend James Bowdoin (founder and first president of the American Academy of Arts and Sciences), objected to the corpuscular theory of light by saying that a particle traveling with such immense speed (3×10^8 m/sec) would have the impact of a 10-kg ball fired from a cannon at 100 m/sec. What mass did Franklin assign to the "light particle"?

9.12 If powerful magnets are placed on top of each of two carts, and the magnets are so arranged that like poles face each other when one cart is pushed toward the other, the carts bounce away from each other without actually making contact.
(a) In what sense can this be called a collision?
(b) Will the law of conservation of momentum apply?
(c) Describe an arrangement for testing your answer to (b).

9.13 From the equation

$$m_A \vec{v}_A + m_B \vec{v}_B = m_A \vec{v}_A{}' + m_B \vec{v}_B{}'$$

show that the change in momentum of object A is equal and opposite to the change of momentum of object B. Using the symbol $\Delta \vec{p}$ for change of momentum, rewrite the law of conservation of momentum for two bodies. What might it be for 3 bodies? for n bodies?

9.14 A person fires a fast ball vertically. Clearly, the momentum of the ball is not conserved; it first loses momentum as it rises, then gains it as it falls. How large is the "closed system" within which the ball's momentum, *together* with that of other bodies (tell which), *is* conserved. What happens to the rest of the system as the ball rises? as it falls?

9.15 If everyone in the world were to stand together in one field and jump up with an initial speed of 1 m/sec,
    (a) For how long would they be off the ground?
    (b) How high would they go?
    (c) What would be the earth's speed downward?
    (d) How far would it move?
    (e) How big would the field have to be?

9.16 Did Newton arrive at the law of conservation of momentum in the *Principia*? If a copy of the *Principia* is available, read Corollary III and Definition II (just before and just after the three laws).

9.17 If mass remains constant, then $\Delta(mv) = m(\Delta v)$. Verify this relation by substituting some numerical values, for example for the case where m is 3 units and v changes from 4 units to 6 units.

9.18 (a) Why can ocean liners or planes not turn corners sharply?
    (b) In the light of your knowledge of the relationship between momentum and force, comment on reports about un-identified flying objects (UFO) turning sharp corners in full flight.

9.19 A girl on skis (mass of 60 kg including skis) reaches the bottom of a hill going 20 m/sec. What is her momentum? She strikes a snowdrift and stops within 3 seconds. What force does the snow exert on the girl? How far does she penetrate the drift? What happened to her momentum?

9.20 During sports, the forces exerted on parts of the body and on the ball, etc., can be astonishingly large. To illustrate this, consider the forces in hitting a golf ball. Assume the ball's mass is .046 kg. From the strobe photo on p. 27 of Unit 1, in which the time interval between strobe flashes was 0.01 sec, estimate:
    (a) the speed of the ball after impact
    (b) the magnitude of the ball's momentum after impact
    (c) how long the impact lasted
    (d) the average force exerted on the ball during impact.

9.21 The *Text* derives the law of conservation of momentum for two bodies from Newton's third and second laws. Is the principle of the conservation of mass essential to this derivation? If so, where does it enter?

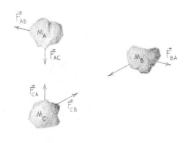

9.22 Consider an isolated system of three bodies, A, B, and C. The forces acting among the bodies can be indicated by subscript: for example, the force exerted on body A by body B can be given the symbol $\vec{F}_{AB}$. By Newton's third law of motion, $\vec{F}_{BA} = -\vec{F}_{AB}$. Since the system is isolated, the only force on each body is the sum of the forces exerted on it by the other two; for example, $\vec{F}_A = \vec{F}_{AB} + \vec{F}_{AC}$. Using these principles, show that the total momentum change of the system will be zero.

9.23 In Chapter 4, SG 4.24 was about putting an Apollo capsule into an orbit around the moon.
    The question was: "Given the speed v_0 necessary for orbit and the present speed v, how long should the rocket engine with thrust F fire to give the capsule of mass m the right speed?" There you solved the problem by considering the acceleration.
    (a) Answer the question more directly by considering change in momentum.
    (b) What would be the total momentum of all the exhaust from the rocket?
    (c) If the "exhaust velocity" were v_e, about what mass of fuel would be required?

9.24 (a) Show that when two bodies collide their changes in velocity are inversely proportional to their masses. That is, if m_A and m_B are the masses and $\Delta \vec{v}_A$ and $\Delta \vec{v}_B$ the velocity changes, show that numerically,

$$\frac{\Delta v_A}{\Delta v_B} = \frac{m_B}{m_A}$$

    (b) Show how it follows from conservation of momentum that if a light particle (like a B.B. pellet) bounces off a massive object (like a bowling ball), the velocity of the light particle is changed much more than the velocity of the massive object.
    (c) For a head-on elastic collision between a body of mass m_A moving with velocity v_A and a body of mass m_B at rest, combining the equations for conservation of momentum and conservation of kinetic energy leads to the relationship $v_A{}' = v_A(m_A - m_B)/(m_A + m_B)$. Show that if body B has a much greater mass than body A, then $v_A{}'$ is almost exactly the same as v_A—that is, body A bounces back with virtually no loss in speed.

9.25 The equation $m_A\vec{v}_A + m_B\vec{v}_B = m_A\vec{v}_A{}' + m_B\vec{v}_B{}'$ is a general equation applicable to countless separate situations. For example, consider a 10-kg shell fired from a 1000-kg cannon. If the shell is given a speed of 1000 m/sec, what would be the recoil speed of the cannon? (Assume the cannon is on an almost frictionless mount.) Hint: your answer could include the following steps:
(a) If A refers to the cannon and B to the shell, what are $\vec{v}_A$ and $\vec{v}_B$ (before firing)?
(b) What is the total momentum before firing?
(c) What is the total momentum after firing?
(d) Compare the magnitudes of the momenta of the cannon and of the shell after firing.
(e) Compare the ratios of the speeds and of the masses of the shell and cannon after firing.

9.26 The engines of the first stage of the Apollo/Saturn rocket develop an average thrust of 35 million newtons for 150 seconds. (The entire rocket weighs 28 million newtons near the earth's surface.)
(a) How much momentum will be given to the rocket during that interval?
(b) The final speed of the vehicle is 6100 miles/hour. What would one have to know to compute its mass?

9.27 Newton's second law can be written $\vec{F}\Delta t = \Delta(m\vec{v})$. Use the second law to explain the following:
(a) It is safer to jump into a fire net or a load of hay than onto the hard ground.
(b) When jumping down from some height, you should bend your knees as you come to rest, instead of keeping your legs stiff.
(c) Hammer heads are generally made of steel rather than rubber.
(d) Some cars have plastic bumpers which, temporarily deformed under impact, slowly return to their original shape. Others are designed to have a somewhat pointed front-end bumper.

9.28 A student in a physics class, having learned about elastic collisions and conservation laws, decides that he can make a self-propelled car. He proposes to fix a pendulum on a cart, using a "super-ball" as a pendulum bob. He fixes a block to the cart so that when the ball reaches the bottom of the arc, it strikes the block and rebounds elastically. It is supposed to give the cart a series of bumps that propel it along.
(a) Will his scheme work? (Assume the "super-ball" is perfectly elastic.) Give reasons for your answer.
(b) What would happen if the cart had an initial velocity in the forward direction?
(c) What would happen if the cart had an initial velocity in the backward direction?

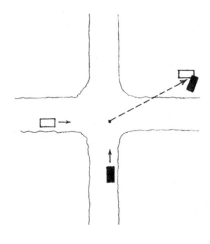

9.29 A police report of an accident describes two vehicles colliding (inelastically) at an icy intersection of country roads. The cars slid to a stop in a field as shown in the diagram. Suppose the masses of the cars are approximately the same.
(a) How did the speeds of the two cars compare just before collision?
(b) What information would you need in order to calculate the actual speeds of the automobiles?
(c) What simplifying assumptions have you made in answering (b)?

9.30 Two pucks on a frictionless horizontal surface are joined by a spring.
(a) Can they be considered an isolated system?
(b) How do gravitational forces exerted by the earth affect your answer?
(c) What about forces exerted by the pucks *on* the earth?
(d) How big would the system have to be in order to be considered completely isolated?

9.31 A hunter fires a gun horizontally at a target fixed to a hillside. Describe the changes of momentum to the hunter, the bullet, the target and the earth. Is momentum conserved
(a) when the gun is fired?
(b) when the bullet hits?
(c) during the bullet's flight?

9.32 A billiard ball moving 0.8 m/sec collides with the cushion along the side of the table. The collision is head-on and can here be regarded as perfectly elastic. What is the momentum of the ball
(a) before impact?
(b) after impact?
(Pool sharks will recognize that it depends upon the spin or "English" that the ball has, but to make the problem simpler, neglect this condition.
(c) What is the change in momentum of the ball
(d) Is momentum conserved?

9.33 Discuss conservation of momentum for the system shown in this sketch from *Le Petit Prince*. What happens
  (a) if he leaps in the air?
  (b) if he runs around?

Le petit prince sur l'astéroïde B 612.

9.34 When one ball collides with a stationary ball of the same mass, the first ball stops and the second goes on with the speed the first ball had. The claim is made on p. 20 that this result is the only possible result that will be consistent with conservation of both momentum and kinetic energy. (That is, if $m_A = m_B$ and $v_B = 0$, then the result must be $v_A' = 0$ and $v_B' = v_A$.) Combine the equations that express the two conservation laws and show that this is actually the case. (Hint:

rewrite the equations with m for m_A and m_B' and $v_B = 0$; solve the simplified momentum equation for v_A'; substitute in the simplified kinetic energy equation; solve for v_B'.)

9.35 Fill in the blanks for the following motions:

Object	m (kg)	v m/sec	mv kg·m/sec	$\frac{1}{2}mv^2$ kg·m²/sec²
baseball	0.14	30.0	—	—
hockey puck	—	50.0	8.55	—
superball	0.050	1.5	—	—
light car	1460	—	—	1.79×10^6
mosquito	—	—	2.0×10^5	4.0×10^{-6}
football player	—	—	—	—

9.36 Two balls, one of which has three times the mass of the other, collide head-on, each moving with the same speed. The more massive ball stops, the other rebounds with twice its original speed. Show that both momentum and kinetic energy are conserved.

9.37 If both momentum and kinetic energy are conserved, say that a ball of mass m moving at speed v strikes, elastically, head-on, a second ball of mass $3m$ which is at rest. Using the principle of conservation of momentum and kinetic energy, find the speeds of the two balls after collision.

9.38 Devise a way of giving a numerical estimate just how far from "perfectly elastic" a collision is—for example, the collision between a ball and the ground from which it bounces.

9.39 Apply the law of conservation of momentum to discuss qualitatively a man swimming; a ship changing course; a man walking; a rocket taking off; a rifle being fired; a propeller plane in straight line motion, and while circling; a jet plane ascending; an apple dropping to earth; a comet being captured by the sun; a spaceship leaving earth; an atomic nucleus emitting a small particle.

9.40 Describe the changes of kinetic energy involved in pole vaulting from the start of the vaulter's run to his landing.

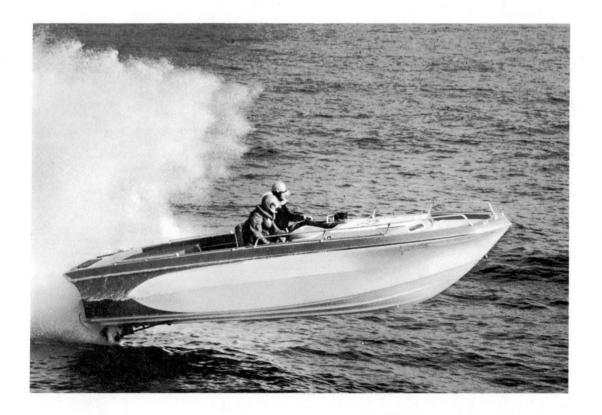

CHAPTER TEN

Energy

10.1 Work and kinetic energy

In everyday language we say that pitching, catching, and running on the baseball field is "playing," while sitting at a desk, reading, writing, and thinking is "working." But, in the language of physics, studying involves very little work, while playing baseball involves a great deal of work. The term "doing work" means something very definite in physics. It means "exerting a force on an object while the object moves in the direction of the force." When you throw a baseball, you exert a large force on it while it moves forward for about one meter. In doing so, you do a large amount of work. By contrast, in writing or in turning the pages of a book you exert only a small force over a short distance. This does not require much work, as the term work is understood in physics.

Suppose you are employed in a factory to lift boxes from the floor straight upward to a conveyor belt at waist height. Here the language of common usage and the physics both agree that you are doing work. If you lift two boxes at once you do twice as much work as you do if you lift one box. And if the conveyor belt were twice as high above the floor, you would do twice as much work to lift a box to it. The work you do depends on both the *magnitude* of the force you must exert on the box and the *distance* through which the box moves in the direction of the force.

With this example in mind, we can define work in a way that allows us to give a numerical value to the concept. The work W done on an object by a force $\vec{F}$ is defined as the product of the magnitude F of the force and the distance d that the object moves *in the direction of $\vec{F}$* while the force is being exerted:

$$W = Fd$$

To lift a box weighing 100 newtons upward through 0.8 meters requires you to apply an upward force of 100 newtons. The work you do on the box is 100 newtons × 0.8 meters = 80 newton-meters.

SG 10.1

Note that work you do on a box does not depend on how *fast* you do your job.

The way d is defined here, the $W = Fd$ is correct. It does not, however, explicit tell how to compute W if the motion is not in exactly the same direction as the force. The definition of d implies that it would be the component of the displacement along the direction of F; and this is entirely correct.

From our definition of work it follows that no work is done if there is no displacement. No matter how hard you push on a wall, no work is done if the wall does not move. Also, no work is done if the only motion is perpendicular to the direction of the force. For example, suppose you are carrying a book bag. You must pull up against the downward pull of gravity to keep the bag at a constant height. But as long as you are standing still you do no work on the bag. Even if you walk along with it steadily in a horizontal line, the only work you do is in moving it forward against the small resisting force of the air.

Work is a useful concept in itself. But the concept is most useful in understanding the concept of *energy*. There are a great many forms of energy. A few of them will be discussed in this chapter. We will define them, in the sense of describing how they can be measured and how they can be expressed algebraically. We will also discuss how energy changes from one form to another. The *general* concept of energy is very difficult to define. But to define some *particular* forms of energy is easy enough. The concept of work helps greatly in making such definitions.

The chief importance of the concept of work is that work represents an amount of energy transformed from one form to another. For example, when you throw a ball you do work on it. You also transform chemical energy, which your body obtains from food and oxygen, into energy of motion of the ball. When you lift a stone (doing work on it), you transform chemical energy into gravitational potential energy. If you release the stone, the earth pulls it downward (does work on it); gravitational potential energy is transformed into energy of motion. When the stone strikes the ground, it compresses the ground below it (does work on it); energy of motion is transformed into heat. These are some of the forms energy takes; and work is a measure of how much energy is transferred.

The form of energy we have been calling "energy of motion" is perhaps the simplest to deal with. We can use the definition of work $W = Fd$, together with Newton's laws of motion, to get an expression of this form of energy. Remember that a moving body has many attributes which are related by separate ideas. For example, we have studied speed v (Chapter 1), velocity $\vec{v}$ (Chapter 3), momentum $m\vec{v}$ (Chapter 9). We also saw how the seventeenth century thinkers groped for a clear idea of some *conserved* quantity in all motion. Now let us imagine that we exert a constant net force F on an object of mass m. This force accelerates the object over a distance d from rest to a speed v. Using Newton's second law of motion, we can show in a few steps of algebra that

$$Fd = \tfrac{1}{2}mv^2$$

The details of this derivation are given on the first half of page 32, "Doing Work on a Sled."

We recognize Fd as the expression for the work done on the object by whatever exerted the force F. The work done on the object equals the amount of energy transformed from some form into energy of motion of

Note that work is a scalar quantity. A more general definition of work will be given in Sec. 10.4.

The equation $W = Fd$ implies that work is always a positive quantity. However, by convention, when the force on a body and its displacement are in opposite directions, the work is negative. This implies that the body's energy would be decreased. The sign convention follows naturally from the more rigorous definition of mechanical work as $W = Fl\cos\theta$ where θ is the angle between $\vec{F}$ and $\vec{l}$.

SG 10.2

the object. So $\frac{1}{2}mv^2$ is the expression for the energy of motion of the object. The energy of motion of an object at any instant is given by the quantity $\frac{1}{2}mv^2$ at that instant, and is called *kinetic energy*. We will use the symbol *KE* to represent kinetic energy. By definition then,

$$KE = \tfrac{1}{2}mv^2$$

Now it is clearer why we wrote $\frac{1}{2}mv^2$ instead of just mv^2 in Chapter 9. If one is conserved, so must be the other—and conservation was all that we were concerned with there. But $\frac{1}{2}mv^2$ also relates directly to the concept of work, and so provides a more useful expression for energy of motion.

The equation $Fd = \frac{1}{2}mv^2$ was obtained by considering the case of an object initially at rest. In other words, the object had an initial kinetic energy of zero. But the relation also holds for an object already in motion when the net force is applied. In that case the work done on the object still equals the change in its kinetic energy:

$$Fd = \Delta(KE)$$

The quantity $\Delta(KE)$ is by definition equal to $(\frac{1}{2}mv^2)_{\text{final}} - (\frac{1}{2}mv^2)_{\text{initial}}$. The proof of this general equation appears on the second half of page 32.

Work is defined as the product of a force and a distance. Therefore, its units in the mks system are *newtons* × *meters* or newton·meters. A newton·meter is also called a *joule* (abbreviated *J*). The joule is the unit of work or of energy.

> The Greek word *kinetos* means "moving."

> The speed of an object must be measured relative to some reference frame, so kinetic energy is a relative quantity also. See SG 10.3.

> SG 10.3–10.8

> The name of the unit of energy and work commemorates J. P. Joule, a nineteenth-century English physicist, famous for his experiments showing that heat is a form of energy (see Sec. 10.7). There is no general agreement today whether the name should be pronounced like "jool" or like "jowl." The majority of physicists favor the former.

Q1   If a force F is exerted on an object while the object moves a distance d in the direction of the force, the work done on the object is (a) F (b) Fd (c) F/d (d) $\frac{1}{2}Fd^2$

Q2   The kinetic energy of a body of mass m moving at a speed v is (a) $\frac{1}{2}mv$ (b) $\frac{1}{2}mv^2$ (c) mv^2 (d) $2mv^2$ (e) m^2v^2

10.2 Potential energy

As we have seen in the previous section, doing work on an object can increase its kinetic energy. But work can be done on an object *without* increasing its kinetic energy. For example, you might lift a book straight up at a small, constant speed, so that its kinetic energy stays the same. But you are still doing work on the book. And by doing work you are using your body's store of chemical energy. Into what form of energy is it being transformed?

The answer, as Leibniz suggested, is that there is "energy" associated with height above the earth. This energy is called *gravitational potential energy*. Lifting the book higher and higher increases the gravitational potential energy. You can see clear evidence of this effect when you drop the book. The gravitational potential energy is transformed rapidly into kinetic energy of fall. In general terms, suppose a force $\vec{F}$ is used to displace an object upwards a distance d, without changing its *KE*. Then

Doing Work on a Sled

Suppose a loaded sled of mass m is initially at rest on low-friction ice. You, wearing spiked shoes, exert a constant horizontal force F on the sled. The weight of the sled is balancced by the upward push exerted by the ice, so F is the net force on the sled. You keep pushing, running faster and faster as the sled accelerates, until the sled has moved a total distance d.

Since the net force F is constant, the acceleration of the sled is constant. Two equations that apply to motion starting from rest with constant acceleration are

$$v = at$$
and
$$d = \tfrac{1}{2}at^2$$

where a is the acceleration of the body, t is the time interval during which it accelerates

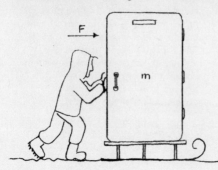

(that is, the time interval during which a net force acts on the body), v is the final speed of the body and d is the distance it moves in the time interval t.

According to the first equation $t = v/a$. If we substitute this expression for t into the second equation, we obtain

$$d = \tfrac{1}{2}at^2 = \tfrac{1}{2}a\frac{v^2}{a^2} = \tfrac{1}{2}\frac{v^2}{a}$$

The work done on the sled is $W=Fd$. From Newton's second law, $F=ma$, so

$$W = Fd$$
$$= ma \times \tfrac{1}{2}\frac{v^2}{a}$$

The acceleration cancels out, giving

$$W = \tfrac{1}{2}mv^2$$

So the work done in this case can be found from just the mass of the body and its final speed. With more advanced mathematics, it can be shown that the result is the same whether the force is constant or not.

More generally, we can show that the change in kinetic energy of a body already moving is equal to the work done on the body. By the definition of average speed,

$$d = v_{av}t$$

If we consider a uniformly accelerated body whose speed changes from v_0 to v, the average speed during t is $\tfrac{1}{2}(v + v_0)$. Thus

$$d = \frac{v + v_0}{2} \times t$$

By the definition of acceleration, $a = \Delta v/t$;

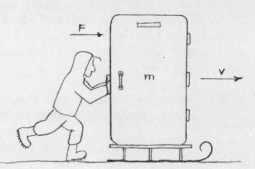

therefore $t = \Delta v/a = (v - v_0)/a$
Substituting $(v - v_0)/a$ for t gives

$$d = \frac{v + v_0}{2} \times \frac{v - v_0}{a}$$
$$= \frac{(v + v_0)(v - v_0)}{2a}$$
$$= \frac{v^2 - v_0^2}{2a}$$

The work W done is $W=Fd$, or, since $F=ma$,

$$W = ma \times d$$
$$= ma \times \frac{v^2 - v_0^2}{2a}$$
$$= \frac{m}{2}(v^2 - v_0^2)$$
$$= \tfrac{1}{2}mv^2 - \tfrac{1}{2}mv_0^2$$

the increase in gravitational potential energy, $\Delta(PE)_{\text{grav}}$, is

$$\Delta(PE)_{\text{grav}} = Fd$$

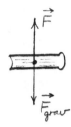

To lift the book at constant speed, you must exert an upward force $\vec{F}$ equal in magnitude to the weight F_{grav} of the book. The work you do in lifting the book through distance d is Fd, which is numerically equal to $F_{\text{grav}}d$. See SG 10.9 and 10.10.

Potential energy can be thought of as *stored* energy. As the book falls, its gravitational potential energy decreases while its kinetic energy increases correspondingly. When the book reaches its original height, all of the gravitational potential energy stored during the lift will have been transformed into kinetic energy.

Many useful applications follow from this idea of potential or stored energy. For example, the steam hammer used by construction crews is driven up by high-pressure steam ("pumping in" energy). When the hammer drops, the gravitational potential energy is converted to kinetic energy. Another example is the proposal to use extra available energy from electric power plants during low demand periods to pump water into a high reservoir. When there is a large demand for electricity later, the water is allowed to run down and drive the electric generators.

There are forms of potential energy other than gravitational. For example, if you stretch a rubber band or a spring, you increase its *elastic potential energy*. When you release the rubber band, it can deliver the stored energy to a projectile in the form of kinetic energy. Some of the work done in blowing up an elastic balloon is also stored as potential energy.

Other forms of potential energy are associated with other kinds of forces. In an atom, the negatively charged electrons are attracted by the positively charged nucleus. If an externally applied force pulls an electron *away* from the nucleus, the *electric potential energy* increases. If the electron is pulled back and moves *toward* the nucleus, the potential energy decreases as the electron's kinetic energy increases.

If two magnets are pushed together with north poles facing, the *magnetic potential energy* increases. When released, the magnets will move apart, gaining kinetic energy as they lose potential energy.

Where is the potential energy located in all these cases? It might seem at first that it "belongs" to the body that has been moved. But this is not the most useful way of thinking about it. For without the other object—the earth, the nucleus, the other magnet—the work would not increase any potential form of energy. Rather, it would increase only the kinetic energy of the object on which work was done. The potential energy belongs not to *one* body, but to the whole system of interacting bodies! This is evident in the fact that the potential energy is available to any one or to all of these interacting bodies. For example, you could give either magnet all the kinetic energy, just by releasing it and holding the other in place. Or suppose you could fix the book somehow to a hook that would hold it at one point in space. The earth would then "fall" up toward the book. Eventually the earth would gain just as much kinetic energy at the expense of stored potential energy as the book would if it were free to fall.

The increase in gravitational potential energy "belongs" to the earth-book *system,* not to the book alone. The work is done by an "outside"

A set mouse-trap contains elastic potential energy.

SG 10.11

SG 10.12

SG 10.13

agent (you), increasing the total energy of the earth-book system. When the book falls, it is responding to forces exerted by one part of the system on another. The *total energy* of the system does not change—it just is converted from *PE* to *KE*. This is discussed in more detail in the next section.

> The work you have done on the earth-book system is equal to the energy you have given up from your store of chemical energy.

Q3 If a stone of mass m falls a vertical distance d, pulled by its weight $F_{grav} = ma_g$, the decrease in gravitational potential energy is (a) md (b) ma_g (c) $ma_g d$ (d) $\frac{1}{2}md^2$ (e) d.

Q4 When you compress a coil spring you do work on it. The elastic potential energy (a) disappears (b) breaks the spring (c) increases (d) decreases.

Q5 Two electrically charged objects repel one another. To increase the electric potential energy, you must

    (a) make the objects move faster

    (b) move one object in a circle around the other object

    (c) attach a rubber band to the objects

    (d) pull the objects farther apart

    (e) push the objects closer together.

10.3 Conservation of mechanical energy

In Section 10.1 we stated that the amount of work done on an object *equals* the amount of energy transformed from one form to another. For example, the chemical energy of a muscle is transformed into the kinetic energy of a thrown ball. Our statement implied that the *amount* of energy involved does not change—only its *form* changes. This is particularly obvious in motions where no "outside" force is applied to a mechanical system.

While a stone falls freely, for example, the gravitational potential energy of the stone-earth system is continually transformed into kinetic energy. Neglecting air friction, the *decrease* in gravitational potential energy is, for any portion of the path, equal to the *increase* in kinetic energy. Or consider a stone thrown upward. Between any two points in its path, the *increase* in gravitational potential energy equals the *decrease* in kinetic energy. For a stone falling or rising (without external forces such as friction),

$$\Delta(PE)_{grav} = -\Delta(KE)$$

> The equations in this section are true only if friction is negligible. We shall extend the range later to include friction, which can cause the conversion of mechanical energy into heat energy.

This relationship can be rewritten as

$$\Delta(KE) + \Delta(PE)_{grav} = 0$$

or still more concisely as

$$\Delta(KE + PE_{grav}) = 0$$

If $(KE + PE_{grav})$ represents the *total mechanical energy* of the system, then the *change* in the system's total mechanical energy is *zero*. In other words, the total mechanical energy, $\Delta(KE + PE_{grav})$ remains constant; it is *conserved*.

SG 10.14

A similar statement can be made for a vibrating guitar string. While the string is being pulled away from its unstretched position, the string-guitar system gains elastic potential energy. When the string is released, the elastic potential energy decreases while the kinetic energy of the string increases. The string coasts through its unstretched position and becomes stretched in the other direction. Its kinetic energy then decreases as the elastic potential energy increases. As it vibrates, there is a repeated transformation of elastic potential energy into kinetic energy and back again. The string loses some mechanical energy—for example, sound waves radiate away. Otherwise, the decrease in elastic potential energy over any part of the string's motion would be accompanied by an equal increase in kinetic energy, and *vice versa*:

$$\Delta(PE)_{elastic} = -\Delta(KE)$$

Up to here we have always considered only *changes* in PE. There is some subtlety in defining an actual value of PE. See SG 10.15.

In such an ideal case, the total mechanical energy $(KE + PE_{elastic})$ remains constant; it is conserved.

We have seen that the potential energy of a system can be transformed into the kinetic energy of some part of the system, and *vice versa*. Potential energy also can be transformed into another form of potential energy without change in the *total energy (KE + PE)*. We can write this rule in several equivalent ways:

$$\Delta KE = -\Delta PE$$

or

$$\Delta KE > \Delta PE = 0$$

or

$$\Delta(KE + PE) = 0$$

or

$$KE + PE = \text{constant}$$

These equations are different ways of expressing the *law of conservation of mechanical energy* when there is no "external" force. But suppose that an amount of work W is done on part of the system by some external force. Then the energy of the system is increased by an amount equal to W. Consider, for example, a suitcase-earth system. You must do work on the suitcase to pull it away from the earth up to the second floor. This work increases the total mechanical energy of the earth + suitcase system. If you yourself are included in the system, then your internal chemical energy decreases in proportion to the work you do. Therefore, the *total* energy of the lifter + suitcase + earth system does not change.

The law of conservation of energy can be derived from Newton's laws of motion. Therefore, it tells us nothing that we could not, in principle, compute directly from Newton's laws of motion. However, there are situations where there is simply not enough information about the forces involved to apply Newton's laws. It is in these cases that the law of conservation of mechanical energy demonstrates its usefulness. Before long you will see how the law came to be very useful in understanding a huge variety of natural phenomena.

A perfectly elastic collision is a good example of a situation where we often cannot apply Newton's laws of motion. In such collisions we do not know and cannot easily measure the force that one object exerts on the other. We do know that during the actual collision, the objects distort one another. (See the photograph of the golf ball in the margin.) The distortions are produced against elastic forces. Thus, some of the combined kinetic energy of the objects is transformed into elastic potential energy as they distort one another. Then elastic potential energy is transformed back into kinetic energy as the objects separate. In an ideal case, both the objects and their surroundings are exactly the same after colliding as they were before. They have the same shape, same temperature, etc. In such a case, all of the elastic potential energy is converted back into kinetic energy.

This is useful but incomplete knowledge. The law of conservation of mechanical energy gives only the *total* kinetic energy of the objects after the collision. It does not give the kinetic energy of each object separately. (If enough information were available, we could apply Newton's laws to get more detailed results: namely, the speed of *each* object.) You may recall that the law of conservation of momentum also left us with useful but incomplete knowledge. We can use it to find the *total* momentum, but not the *individual* momentum vectors, of elastic objects in collision. In Chapter 9 we saw how conservation of momentum and conservation of mechanical energy together limit the possible outcomes of perfectly elastic collisions. For two colliding objects, these two restrictions are enough to give an exact solution for the two velocities after collision. For more complicated systems, conservation of energy remains important. We usually are not interested in the detailed motion of each of every part of a complex system. We are not likely to care, for example, about the motion of every molecule in a rocket exhaust. Rather, we probably want to know only about the overall thrust and temperature. The principle of conservation of energy applies to total, defined systems, and such systems usually interest us most.

During its contact with a golf club, a golf ball is distorted, as is shown in the high-speed photograph. As the ball moves away from the club, the ball recovers its normal spherical shape, and elastic potential energy is transformed into kinetic energy.

Q6 As a stone falls frictionlessly
(a) its kinetic energy is conserved
(b) its gravitational potential energy is conserved
(c) its kinetic energy changes into gravitational potential energy
(d) no work is done on the stone
(e) there is no change in the total energy

Q7 In what position is the elastic potential energy of the vibrating guitar string greatest? At which position is its kinetic energy greatest?

Q8 If a guitarist gives the same amount of elastic potential energy to a bass string and to a treble string, which one will gain more speed when released? (The mass of a meter of bass string is greater than that of a meter of treble string.)

Q9 How would you compute the potential energy stored in the system shown in the margin made up of the top boulder and the earth?

10.4 Forces that do no work

In Section 10.1 we defined the *work* done on an object. It is the product of the magnitude of the force $\vec{F}$ applied to the object and the magnitude of the distance $\vec{d}$ in the direction of $\vec{F}$ through which the object moves while the force is being applied. In all our examples so far, the object moved in the same direction as that of the force vector.

But usually the direction of motion and the direction of the force are *not* the same. For example, suppose you carry a book at constant speed and horizontally, so that its kinetic energy does not change. Since there is no change in the book's energy, you are doing no work on the book (by our definition of work). You do apply a force on the book, and the book does move through a distance. But here the applied force and the distance are at right angles. You exert a vertical force on the book—upwards to balance its weight. But the book moves horizontally. Here, an applied force $\vec{F}$ is exerted on an object while the object moves at right angles to the direction of the force. Therefore $\vec{F}$ has no component in the direction of $\vec{d}$, and so the force *does no work*. This statement agrees entirely with the idea of work as *energy being transformed from one form to another*. Since the book's speed is constant, its kinetic energy is constant. And since its distance from the earth is constant, its gravitational potential energy is constant. So there is no transfer of mechanical energy.

A similar reasoning, but not so obvious, applies to a satellite in a circular orbit. The speed and the distance from the earth are both constant. Therefore, the kinetic energy and the gravitational potential energy are both constant, and there is no energy transformation. For a circular orbit the centripetal force vector is perpendicular to the tangential direction of motion at any instant. So no work is being done. To put an artificial satellite into a circular orbit requires work. But once it is in orbit, the *KE* and *PE* stay constant and no further work is done on the satellite.

When the orbit is eccentric, the force vector is usually not perpendicular to the direction of motion. In such cases energy is continually transformed between kinetic and gravitational potential forms. The total energy of the system remains constant, of course.

Situations where the net force is exactly perpendicular to the motion are as rare as situations where the force and motion are in exactly the same direction. What about the more usual case, involving some angle between the force and the motion?

In general, the work done on an object depends on how far the body moves *in the direction of the force.* As stated before, the equation $W = Fd$ properly defines work only if d is the distance moved in the direction of the force. Consider the example of a child sliding down a playground

SG 10.16

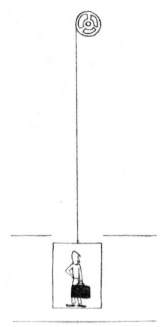

slide. The gravitational force $\vec{F}_{\text{grav}}$ is directed *down*. So only the distance *down* determines the amount of work done by $\vec{F}_{\text{grav}}$. It does not matter how long the slide is, or what its shape is. Change in gravitational potential energy depends *only* on change in height—near the earth's surface, at least. For example, consider raising a suitcase from the first floor to the second floor. The same increase in PE_{grav} of the suitcase-earth system occurs regardless of the path by which the suitcase is raised. Also, each path requires the same amount of work.

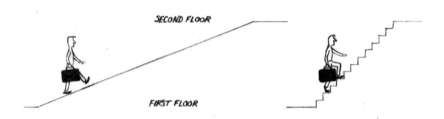

More generally, change in PE_{grav} depends only on change of position. The details of the path followed in making the change make no difference at all. The same is true for changes in elastic potential energy and electric potential energy. The changes depend only on the initial and final positions, and not on the path taken between these positions.

An interesting conclusion follows from the fact that change in PE_{grav} depends only on change in height. For the example of the child on the slide, the gravitational potential energy decreases as his altitude decreases. If frictional forces are vanishingly small, all the work goes into transforming PE_{grav} into KE. Therefore, the increases in KE depend only on the decrease in altitude. In other words, the child's speed when he reaches the ground will be the same whether he slides down or jumps off the top. A similar principle holds for satellites in orbit and for electrons in TV tubes: in the absence of friction, the change in kinetic energy depends only on the initial and final positions, and not on the path taken between them. This principle gives great simplicity to some physical laws, as we will see when we consider gravitational and electric fields in Chapter 14.

> If frictional forces also have to be overcome, additional work will be needed, and that additional work may depend on the path chosen— for example, whether it is long or short.

SG 10.17

Q10 How much work is done on a satellite during each revolution if its mass is m, its period is T, its speed is v, and its orbit is a circle of radius R?

Q11 Two skiers were together at the top of a hill. While one skier skied down the slope and went off the jump, the other rode the ski-lift down. Compare their changes in gravitational potential energy.

Q12 A third skier went directly down a straight slope. How would his speed at the bottom compare with that of the skier who went off the jump?

Q13 No work is done when
(a) a heavy box is pushed at constant speed along a rough horizontal floor
(b) a nail is hammered into a board
(c) there is no component of force parallel to the direction of motion
(d) there is no component of force perpendicular to the direction of motion.

10.5 Heat energy and the steam engine

So far we have assumed that our equations for work and energy hold only if friction is absent or very small. Why? Suppose that frictional forces *do* affect a suitcase or other object as it is being lifted. The object must do work against these forces as it moves. (This work in fact serves to warm up the stairs, the air, etc.). Consequently, that much less work is available to increase *PE* or *KE* or both. How can we modify our expression of the law of conservation of mechanical energy to include these effects?

Suppose that a book on a table has been given a shove and is sliding across the table top. If the surface is rough, it will exert a fairly large frictional force and the book will stop quickly. Its kinetic energy will rapidly disappear. But no corresponding increase in potential energy will occur, since there is no change in height. It appears that, in this example, mechanical energy is not conserved.

However, close examination of the book and the tabletop show that they are warmer than before. The disappearance of kinetic energy of the book is accompanied by the appearance of *heat*. This suggests—but by no means proves—that the kinetic energy of the book was transformed into heat. If so, then heat must be one form of energy. This section deals with how the idea of heat as a form of energy gained acceptance during the nineteenth century. You will see how theory was aided by practical knowledge of the relation of heat and work. This knowledge was gained in developing, for very practical reasons, the steam engine.

Until about 200 years ago, most work was done by people or animals. Work was obtained from wind and water also, but these were generally unreliable as sources of energy. For one thing, they were not always available when and where they were needed. In the eighteenth century, miners began to dig deeper and deeper in search of greater coal supply. But water tended to seep in and flood these deeper mines. The need arose for an economical method for pumping water out of mines. The steam engine was developed initially to meet this very practical need.

The steam engine is a device for converting the energy of some kind of fuel into heat energy. For example, the chemical energy of coal or oil, or the nuclear energy of uranium is converted to heat. The heat energy in turn is converted into mechanical energy. This mechanical energy can be

used directly to do work, as in a steam locomotive, or can be transformed into electrical energy. In typical twentieth-century industrial societies, most of the energy used in factories and homes comes from electrical energy. Falling water is used to generate electricity in some parts of the country. But steam engines still generate most of the electrical energy used in the United States today. There are other heat engines, too—internal combustion engines and turbines for example. But the steam engine remains a good model for the basic operation of this whole family of engines.

The generation and transmission of electrical energy, and its conversion into mechanical energy, will be discussed in Chapter 15. Here we will focus on the central and historic link in the chain of energy conversion, the steam engine.

Since ancient times it had been known that heat could be used to produce steam, which could then do mechanical work. The "aeolipile," invented by Heron of Alexandria about 100 A.D., worked on the principle of Newton's third law. (See margin.) The rotating lawn sprinkler works the same way except that the driving force is water pressure instead of steam pressure.

Heron's aeolipile was a toy, meant to entertain rather than to do any useful work. Perhaps the most "useful" application of steam to do work in the ancient world was another of Heron's inventions. This steam-driven device astonished worshippers in a temple by causing a door to open when a fire was built on the altar. Not until late in the eighteenth century, however, were commercially successful steam engines invented.

Today we would say that a steam engine uses a supply of heat energy to do mechanical work. That is, it converts heat energy into mechanical energy. But many inventors in the eighteenth and nineteenth centuries did not think of heat in this way. They regarded heat as a thin, invisible substance that could be used over and over again to do work without being used up itself. But they did not need to learn all the presently known laws of physics in order to become successful engineers. In fact, the sequence of events was just the opposite. Steam engines were developed first by inventors who knew relatively little about science. Their main interest lay in making money, or in improving the effectiveness and safety of mining. Later, scientists with both a practical knowledge of *what* would work and a curiosity about *how* it worked made new discoveries in physics.

The first commercially successful steam engine was invented by Thomas Savery (1650-1715), an English military engineer. Follow the explanation of it one sentence at a time, referring to the diagram on page 41. In the Savery engine the water in the mine shaft is connected by a pipe and a valve **D** to a chamber called the cylinder. With valve **D** closed and valve **B** open, high-pressure steam from the boiler is admitted to the cylinder through valve **A.** This forces the water out of the cylinder and up the pipe. The water empties at the top and runs off at ground level. Valve **A** and valve **B** are closed. Valve **D** is opened, allowing an open connection between the cylinder and the water in the mine shaft.

When valve **C** is opened, cold water pours over the cylinder. The

A model of Heron's aeolipile. Steam produced in the boiler escapes through the nozzles on the sphere, causing it to rotate.

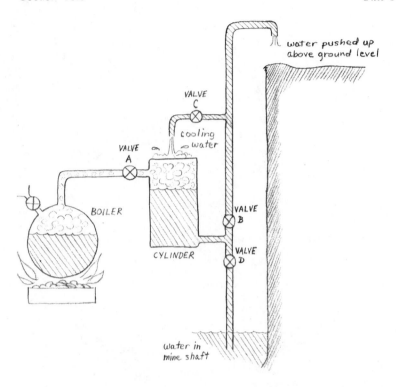

VALVE
C

cooling
water

VALVE
A

BOILER

VALVE
B

CYLINDER

VALVE
D

water pushed up
above ground level

water in
mine shaft

Schematic diagram of Savery engine.

steam left in the cylinder cools and condenses to water. Since water
occupies a much smaller volume than the same mass of steam, a partial
vacuum forms in the cylinder. This vacuum allows the air pressure in the
mine to force water from the mine shaft up the pipe into the cylinder.

The same process, started by closing valve **D** and opening valves **A**
and **B,** is repeated over and over. The engine is in effect a pump. It
moves water from the mine shaft to the cylinder, then from the cylinder to
the ground above.

However, the Savery engine's use of high-pressure steam produced a
serious risk of boiler or cylinder explosions. This defect was remedied by
Thomas Newcomen (1663-1729), another Englishman. Newcomen
invented an engine that used steam at lower pressure. His engine was
superior in other ways also. For example, it could raise loads other than
water.

The Newcomen engine features a rocking beam. This beam connects
to the load on one side and to a piston in a cylinder on the other side.
When valve **A** is open, the cylinder is filled with steam at normal
atmospheric pressure. The beam is balanced so that the weight of the load
raises the piston to the upper end of the cylinder. While the piston is
coming toward this position, valve **A** is still open and valve **B** is still
closed.

But when the piston reaches its highest position, valve **A** is closed
and valve **C** is opened. Cooling water flows over the cylinder and the
steam condenses, making a partial vacuum in the cylinder. This allows the
pressure of the atmosphere to push the piston down. As the piston reaches
the bottom of the cylinder, valve **C** is closed and valve **B** is opened briefly.

In the words of Erasmus Darwin,
the engine
Bade with cold streams, the
  quick expansion stop,
  And sunk the immense of va-
  pour to a drop
Press'd by the ponderous air
  the Piston falls
Resistless, sliding through
  its iron walls:
Quick moves the balanced
  beam, of giant-birth
Wields his large limbs, and
  nodding shakes the earth.

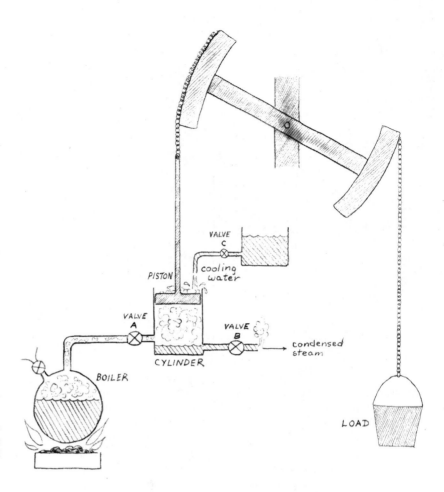

Schematic diagram of Newcomen engine. In the original Newcomen engine the load was water being lifted from a mine shaft.

The cooled and condensed steam runs off. The valve **A** is opened, and the cycle begins all over again.

Originally someone had to open and close the valves by hand at the proper times in the cycle. But later models did this automatically. The automatic method used the rhythm and some of the energy of the moving parts of the engine itself to control the sequence of operation. This idea, of using part of the output of the process to regulate the process itself, is called *feedback*. It is an essential part of the design of many modern mechanical and electronic systems. (See the article "Systems, Feedback, Cybernetics" in Unit 3 *Reader*.

SG 10.18

The Newcomen engine was widely used in Britain and other European countries throughout the eighteenth century. By modern standards it was not a very good engine. It burned a large amount of coal but did only a small amount of work at a slow, jerky rate. But the great demand for machines to pump water from mines produced a good market even for Newcomen's uneconomical engine.

Q14 When a book slides to a stop on the horizontal rough surface of a table

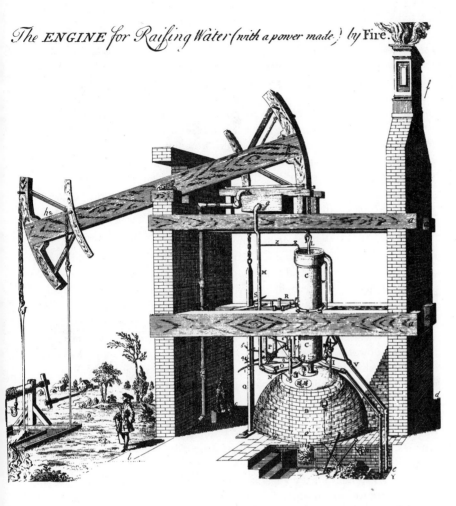

The ENGINE for Raising Water (with a power made) by Fire.

At the left, a contemporary engraving of a working Newcomen steam engine. In July, 1698 Savery was granted a patent for "A new invention for raising of water and occasioning motion to all sorts of mill work by the impellent force of fire, which will be of great use and advantage for drayning mines, serving townes with water, and for the working of all sorts of mills where they have not the benefitt of water nor constant windes." The patent was good for 35 years and prevented Newcomen from making much money from his superior engine during this period.

   (a) the kinetic energy of the book is transformed into potential energy.

   (b) heat is transformed into mechanical energy.

   (c) the kinetic energy of the book is transformed into heat energy.

   (d) the momentum of the book itself is conserved.

Q15   True or false: The invention of the steam engine depended strongly on theoretical developments in the physics of heat.

Q16   In Savery's steam engine, the ＿＿＿＿＿＿ energy of coal was changed (by burning) into ＿＿＿＿＿＿ energy which in turn was converted into the ＿＿＿＿＿＿ energy of the pump.

10.6 James Watt and the Industrial Revolution

A greatly improved steam engine originated in the work of a Scotsman, James Watt. Watt's father was a carpenter who had a successful business selling equipment to ship owners. Watt was in poor health much of his life and gained most of his early education at home. In

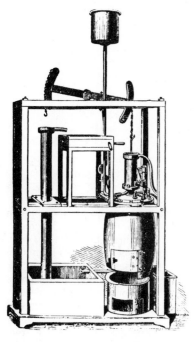

The actual model of the Newcomen engine that inspired Watt to conceive of the separation of condenser and piston.

his father's attic workshop, he developed considerable skill in using tools. He wanted to become an instrument-maker and went to London to learn the trade. Upon his return to Scotland in 1757, he obtained a position as instrument maker at the University of Glasgow.

In the winter of 1763-1764, Watt was asked to repair a model of Newcomen's engine that was used for demonstration lectures at the university. As it turned out, this assignment had immense worldwide consequences. In acquainting himself with the model, Watt was impressed by how much steam was required to run the engine. He undertook a series of experiments on the behavior of steam and found that a major problem was the temperature of the cylinder walls. Newcomen's engine wasted most of its heat in warming up the walls of its cylinders. The walls were then cooled again every time cold water was injected to condense the steam.

Early in 1765, Watt remedied this wasteful defect by devising a modified type of steam engine. In retrospect, it sounds like a simple idea. The steam in its cylinder, after pushing the piston up, was admitted to a *separate* container to be condensed. With this system, the cylinder could be kept hot all the time and the condenser could be kept cool all the time.

The diagram opposite represents Watt's engine. With valve **A** open and valve **B** closed, steam under pressure enters the cylinder and pushes the piston upward. When the piston nears the top of the cylinder, valve **A** is closed to shut off the steam supply. Then valve **B** is opened, so that steam leaves the cylinder and enters the condenser. The condenser is kept cool by water flowing over it, so the steam condenses. As steam leaves the cylinder, the pressure there decreases. Atmospheric pressure (helped by the inertia of the flywheel) pushes the piston down. When the piston reaches the bottom of the cylinder, valve **B** is closed and valve **A** is opened, starting the cycle again.

Watt's invention of the separate condenser might seem only a small step in the development of steam engines. But in fact it was a decisive one. Not having to reheat the cylinder again and again allowed huge fuel

Watt in his workshop contemplating a model of a Newcomen engine. (A romanticized engraving from a nineteenth-century volume on technology.)

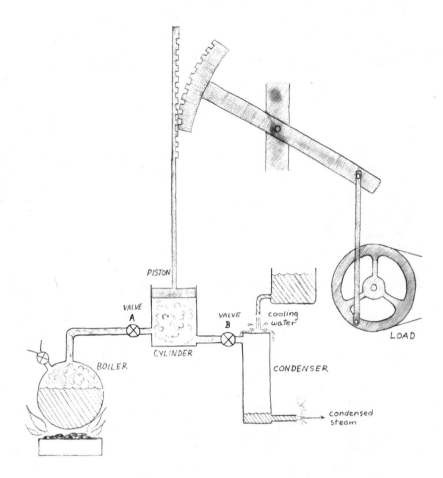

Schematic diagram of Watt engine.

savings. Watt's engine could do more than twice as much work as
Newcomen's with the same amount of fuel. This improvement enabled
Watt to make a fortune by selling or renting his engines to mine owners.

The fee that Watt charged for the use of his engines depended on
their *power*. Power is defined as the *rate* of doing work (or the rate at
which energy is transformed from one form to another). The mks unit of
power is the joule-per-second, which is now fittingly called one *watt:*

$$1 \cdot \text{watt} = 1 \text{ joule/sec}$$

James Watt expressed the power of his engines in different units.

One "foot-pound" is defined as the work done when a force of one
pound is exerted on an object while the object moves a distance of one
foot. (In mks units, this corresponds roughly to a force of 4 newtons while
the object moves $\frac{1}{3}$ meter. Thus, 1 foot-pound is approximately $\frac{4}{3}$ newton-
meters.) Watt found that a strong workhorse, working steadily, could lift a
150-pound weight at the rate of almost four feet per second. In other
words, it could do about 550 foot-pounds of work per second. Watt used
this as a definition of a convenient unit for expressing the power of his
engines: the *horsepower*. To this day the "horsepower" unit is used in

Matthew Boulton (Watt's business
partner) proclaimed to Boswell (the
biographer of Samuel Johnson):
"I sell here, Sir, what all the world
desires to have: POWER!"

engineering—although it is now defined as precisely 746 watts.

Typical power ratings (in horsepower)

SG 10.19–10.26

Man turning a crank	0.06 h.p.
Overshot waterwheel	3
Turret windmill	10
Savery steam engine (1702)	1
Newcomen engine (1732)	12
Smeaton's Long Benton engine (1772)	40
Watt engine (of 1778)	14
Cornish engine for London waterworks (1837)	135
Electric power station engines (1900)	1000
Nuclear power station turbine (1970)	300,000

[Adapted from R. J. Forbes, in C. Singer et al, *History of Technology.*]

A steam locomotive from the early part of the 20th century.

Watt's invention, so superior to Newcomen's engine, stimulated the development of engines that could do many other jobs. Steam drove machines in factories, railway locomotives, steamboats, and so forth. Watt's engine gave an enormous stimulus to the growth of industry in Europe and America. It thereby helped transform the economic and social structure of Western civilization.

The widespread development of engines and machines revolutionized mass production of consumer goods, construction, and transportation. The average standard of living in Western Europe and the United States rose sharply. Nowadays it is difficult for most people in the industrially "developed" countries to imagine what life was like before the Industrial Revolution. But not all the effects of industrialization have been beneficial. The nineteenth-century factory system provided an opportunity for some greedy and cruel employers to treat workers almost like slaves. These employers made huge profits, while keeping employees and their families on the edge of starvation. This situation, which was especially serious in England early in the nineteenth century, led to demands for reform. New laws eventually eliminated the worst excesses.

More and more people left the farms—voluntarily or forced by poverty and new land laws—to work in factories. Conflict grew intense between the working class, made up of employees, and the middle class, made up of employers and professional men. At the same time, some artists and intellectuals began to attack the new tendencies of their society. They saw this society becoming increasingly dominated by commerce, machinery, and an emphasis on material goods. In some cases they confused research science itself with its technical applications (as is still done today). In some cases scientists were accused of explaining away all the awesome mysteries of nature. They denounced both science and technology, while often refusing to learn anything about them. In a poem by William Blake we find the questions:

> And did the Countenance Divine
>   Shine forth upon our clouded hills?
> And was Jerusalem builded here
>   Among these dark Satanic mills?

Elsewhere, Blake advised his readers "To cast off Bacon, Locke, and
Newton." John Keats was complaining about science when he included in
a poem the line: "Do not all charms fly/At the mere touch of cold
philosophy?" These attitudes are part of an old tradition, going back to the
ancient Greek opponents of Democritus' atomism. We saw that Galilean
and Newtonian physics also was attacked for distorting values. The same
type of accusation can still be heard today.

Steam engines are no longer widely used as direct sources of power in
industry and transportation. But steam is indirectly still the major source
of power. The steam turbine, invented by the English engineer Charles
Parsons in 1884, has now largely replaced older kinds of steam engines.
At present, steam turbines drive the electric generators in most electric-

Richard Trevithick's railroad at Euston Square, London, 1809.

A nineteenth-century French steam cultivator.

TREVITHICKS,
PORTABLE STEAM ENGINE.

Catch me who can.

Mechanical Power Subduing
Animal Speed.

The "Charlotte Dundas," the first practical steamboat, built by William Symington, an engineer who had patented his own improved steam engine. It was tried out on the Forth and Clyde Canal in 1801.

power stations. These steam-run generators supply most of the power for the machinery of modern civilization. Even in nuclear power stations, the nuclear energy is generally used to produce steam, which then drives turbines and electric generators.

The basic principle of the Parsons turbine is simpler than that of the Newcomen and Watt engines. A jet of high-pressure steam strikes the blades of a rotor, driving the rotor around at high speed. A description of the type of steam turbine used in modern power stations shows the change of scale since Heron's toy:

> The boiler at this station [in Brooklyn, New York] is as tall as a 14-story building. It weighs about 3,000 tons, more than a U.S. Navy destroyer. It heats steam to a temperature of 1,050° F and to a pressure of 1,500 pounds per square inch. It generates more than 1,300,000 pounds of steam an hour. This steam runs a turbine to make 150,000 kilowatts of electricity, enough to supply all the homes in a city the size of Houston, Texas. The boiler burns 60 tons (about one carload) of coal an hour.
>
> The 14-story boiler does not rest on the ground. It hangs—all 3,000 tons of it—from a steel framework. Some boilers are even bigger—as tall as the Statue of Liberty—and will make over 3,000,000 pounds of steam in one hour. This steam spins a turbine that will make 450,000 kilowatts of electricity—all of the residential needs for a city of over 4,000,000 people!

Below, a 200 thousand kilowatt turbine being assembled. Notice the thousands of blades on the rotor.

Q17 The purpose of the separate condenser in Watt's steam engine is to

(a) save the water so it can be used again

(b) save fuel by not having to cool and reheat the cylinder

(c) keep the steam pressure as low as possible

(d) make the engine more compact

Q18 The history of the steam engine suggests that the social and economic effects of technology are

(a) always beneficial to everyone

(b) mostly undesirable

(c) unimportant one way or another

(d) very different for different levels of society

Q19 What is horsepower?

10.7 The experiments of Joule

In the steam engine a certain amount of heat does a certain amount of work. What happens to the heat in doing the work?

Early in the nineteenth century, most scientists and engineers thought that the amount of heat remained constant; and that heat could do work as it passed from a region at one temperature to a region at a lower temperature. For example, early steam engines condensed steam at high

James Prescott Joule (1818-1889) Joule was the son of a wealthy Manchester brewer. He is said to have become first interested in his arduous experiments by the desire to develop more efficient engines for the family brewery.

temperatures to water at low temperature. Heat was considered to be a substance called "caloric." The total amount of caloric in the universe was thought to be conserved.

According to the caloric theory, heat could do work in much the same way that water can do work. Water falling from a high level to a low level can do work, with the total amount of water used remaining the same. The caloric explanation seemed reasonable. And most scientists accepted it, even though no one measured the amount of heat before and after it did work.

A few scientists, however, disagreed. Some favored the view that heat is a form of energy. One who held this view was the English physicist James Prescott Joule. During the 1840's Joule conducted a long series of experiments designed to show that heat is a form of energy. He hoped to demonstrate in a variety of different experiments that the same decrease in mechanical energy always produced the same amount of heat. This, Joule reasoned, would mean that heat is a form of energy.

For one of his early experiments he constructed a simple electric generator, which was driven by a falling weight. The electric current that was generated heated a wire. The wire was immersed in a container of water which it heated. From the distance that the weight descended he calculated the work done (the decrease in gravitational potential energy). The product of the mass of the water and its temperature rise gave him a measure of the amount of heat produced. In another experiment he compressed gas in a bottle immersed in water, measuring the amount of work done to compress the gas. He then measured the amount of heat given to the water as the gas got hotter on compression.

But his most famous experiments involved an apparatus in which slowly descending weights turned a paddle-wheel in a container of water. Owing to the friction between the wheel and the liquid, work was done on the liquid, raising its temperature.

Joule repeated this experiment many times, constantly improving the apparatus and refining his analysis of the data. He learned to take very great care to insulate the container so that heat was not lost to the room. He measured the temperature rise with a precision of a small fraction of a degree. And he allowed for the small amount of kinetic energy the descending weights had when they reached the floor.

Joule published his results in 1849. He reported:

> 1st. That the quantity of heat produced by the friction of bodies, whether solid or liquid, is always proportional to the quantity of [energy] expended. And 2nd. That the quantity of heat capable of increasing the temperature of a pound of water . . . by 1° Fahr. requires for its evolution the expenditure of a mechanical energy represented by the fall of 772 lb through the distance of one foot.

The first statement is the evidence that heat is a form of energy, contrary to the caloric theory. The second statement gives the numerical magnitude of the ratio he had found. This ratio related a unit of mechanical energy (the foot-pound) and a unit of heat (the heat required

The idea of heat as a conserved substance is consistent with many phenomena. An experiment showing this is "Calorimetry" in the *Handbook*.

Joule used the word "force" instead of "energy." The current scientific vocabulary was still being formed.

to raise the temperature of one pound of water by one degree on the Fahrenheit scale).

In the mks system, the unit of heat is the kilocalorie and the unit of mechanical energy is the joule. Joule's results are equivalent to the statement that 1 kilocalorie equals 4,150 joules. Joule's paddle-wheel experiment and other basically similar ones have since been performed with great accuracy. The currently accepted value for the "mechanical equivalent of heat" is

$$1 \text{ kilocalorie} = 4{,}184 \text{ joules}$$

We might, therefore, consider heat to be a form of energy. We will consider the nature of the "internal" energy associated with temperature further in Chapter 11.

Joule's finding a value for the "mechanical equivalent of heat" made it possible to describe engines in a new way. The concept of *efficiency* applies to an engine or any device that transforms energy from one form to another. Efficiency is defined as the percentage of the input energy that appears as useful output. Since energy is conserved, the greatest possible efficiency is 100%—when *all* of the input energy appears as useful output. Obviously, efficiency must be considered as seriously as power output in designing engines. However, there are theoretical limits on efficiency. Thus, even a perfectly designed machine could never do work at 100% efficiency. We will hear more about this in Chapter 11.

This unit is called a *British Thermal Unit* (BTU).

SG 10.27, 10.28

A kilocalorie is what some dictionaries call "large calorie." It is the amount of heat required to raise the temperature of 1 kilogram of water by 1° Celsius ("centigrade"). This unit is identical to the "Calorie" (with a capital C) used to express the energy content of foods in dietetics.

The efficiency of a steam engine is roughly 15–20%; for an automobile it is about 22%; and for a diesel engine it is as high as 40%.

In Sec. 10.10 we mention some qualifications that must be placed on the simple idea of heat as a form of energy.

Q20 According to the caloric theory of heat, caloric
(a) can do work when it passes between two objects at the same temperature
(b) is another name for temperature
(c) is produced by steam engines
(d) is a substance that is conserved

Q21 The kilocalorie is
(a) a unit of temperature
(b) a unit of energy
(c) 1 kilogram of water at 1°C
(d) one pound of water at 1°F

Q22 In Joule's paddle-wheel experiment, was all the change of gravitational potential energy used to heat the water?

10.8 Energy in biological systems

All living things need a supply of energy to maintain life and to carry on their normal activities. Human beings are no exception; like all animals, we depend on food to supply us with energy.

Most human beings are omnivores; that is, they eat both animal and plant materials. Some animals are herbivores, eating only plants, while others are carnivores, eating only animal flesh. But all animals, even carnivores, ultimately obtain their food energy from plant material. The animal eaten by the lion has previously dined on plant material, or on another animal which had eaten plants.

Green plants obtain energy from sunlight. Some of that energy is used by the plant to perform the functions of life. Much of the energy is used to make carbohydrates out of water (H_2O) and carbon dioxide (CO_2). The energy used to synthesize carbohydrates is not lost; it is stored in the carbohydrate molecules as chemical energy.

The process by which plants synthesize carbohydrates is called photosynthesis. It is still not completely understood and research in this field is lively. We know that the synthesis takes place in many small steps, and many of the steps are well understood. It is conceivable that we may learn how to photosynthesize carbohydrates without plants thus producing food economically for the rapidly increasing world population. The overall process of producing carbohydrates (the sugar glucose, for example) by photosynthesis can be represented as follows:

carbon dioxide + water + energy ⟶ glucose + oxygen

The energy stored in the glucose molecules is used by the animal that eats the plant. This energy maintains the body temperature, keeps its heart, lungs, and other organs operating, and enables various chemical reactions to occur in the body. The animal also uses it to do work on external objects. The process by which the energy stored in sugar molecules is made available to the cell is very complex. It takes place mostly in tiny bodies called mitochondria, which are found in all cells. Each mitochondrion contains enzymes which, in a series of about ten steps, split glucose molecules into simpler molecules. In another sequence of reactions these molecules are oxidized (combined with oxygen), thereby releasing most of the stored energy and forming carbon dioxide and water.

glucose + oxygen ⟶ carbon dioxide + water + energy

Proteins and fats are used to build and restore tissue and enzymes, and to pad delicate organs. They also can be used to provide energy. Both proteins and fats can enter into chemical reactions which produce the same molecules as the split carbohydrates. From that point, the energy-releasing process is the same as in the case of carbohydrates.

The released energy is used to change a molecule called adenosine diphosphate (ADP) into adenosin triphosphate (ATP). In short, chemical energy originally stored in glucose molecules in plants is eventually stored as chemical energy in ATP molecules in animals. The ATP molecules pass out of the mitochondrion into the body of the cell. Wherever energy is needed in the cell, it can be supplied by an ATP molecule. As it releases its stored energy, the ATP changes back to ADP. Later, back in a mitochondrion, the ADP is reconverted to energy-rich ATP.

The overall process in the mitochondrion involves breaking glucose, in the presence of oxygen, into carbon dioxide and water. The energy released is transferred to ATP and stored there until needed by the animal's body.

Carbohydrates are molecules made of carbon, hydrogen, and oxygen. A simple example is the sugar glucose, the chemical formula for which is $C_6H_{12}O_6$.

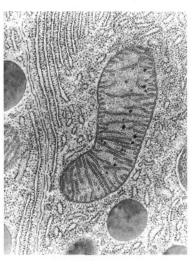

Electron micrograph of an energy-converting mitochondrion in a bat cell (200,000 times actual size).

The chemical and physical operations of the living body are in some ways like those in an engine. Just as a steam engine uses chemical energy stored in coal or oil, the body uses chemical energy stored in food. In both cases the fuel is oxidized to release its stored energy. The oxidation is vigorous in the steam engine, and gentle, in small steps, in the body. In both the steam engine and the body, some of the input energy is used to do work; the rest is used up internally and eventually "lost" as heat to the surroundings.

Some foods supply more energy per unit mass than others. The energy stored in food is usually measured in kilocalories. (1 kilocalorie = 10^3 calories). However it could just as well be measured in joules or foot-pounds or British Thermal Units. The table in the margin gives the energy content of some foods. (The "calorie" or "large calorie" used by dieticians, is identical to what we have defined as the kilocalorie.)

Much of the energy you obtain from food keeps your body's internal "machinery" running and keeps your body warm. Even when asleep your body uses about one kilocalorie every minute. This amount of energy is needed just to keep alive.

To do work, you need more energy. Yet only a fraction of this energy can be used to do work; the rest is wasted as heat. Like any engine, the body of humans or other animals is not 100% efficient. Its efficiency when it does work varies with the job and the physical condition and skill of the worker. But efficiency probably never exceeds 25%, and usually is less. Studies of this sort are carried out in *bioenergetics,* one of the many fascinating and useful fields where physics and biology overlap.

The table in the margin gives the results of experiments done in the United States of the rate at which a healthy young person of average build and metabolism uses energy in various activities. The estimates were made by measuring the amount of carbon dioxide exhaled. Thus, they show the total amount of food energy used, including the amount necessary just to keep the body functioning.

According to this table, if the subject did nothing but sleep for eight hours a day and lie quietly the rest of the time, he would still need at least 1,700 kilocalories of energy each day. There are countries where large numbers of working people exist on less than 1,700 kilocalories a day. The U.N. Yearbook of National Accounts Statistics for 1964 shows that in India the average food intake was about 1,600 kilocalories per day. The United States average was 3,100 kilocalories per day. About half the population of Southeast Asia is at or below the starvation line. Vast numbers of people elsewhere in the world, including some parts of the United States, are also close to that line. It is estimated that if the available food were equally distributed among all the earth's inhabitants, each would have about 2,400 kilocalories a day on the average. This is only a little more than the minimum required by a working person.

It is now estimated that at the current rate of increase, the population of the world may double in 30 years. Thus by the year 2000 it would be 7 billion or more. Furthermore, the *rate* at which the population is increasing is itself increasing! Meanwhile, the production of food supply per person has not increased markedly on a global scale. For example, in

---

Approximate Energy Content of Various Foods (In Calories per kilogram)

Butter	7000
Chocolate (sweetened)	5000
Beef (hamburger)	4000
Bread	2600
Milk (whole)	700
Apples (raw)	500
Lettuce	150

Adapted from U.S. Department of Agriculture, Agriculture Handbook No. 8, June 1950.

The chemical energy stored in food can be determined by burning the food in a closed container immersed in water and measuring the temperature rise of water.

Approximate Rates of Using Energy During Various Activities (In Calories per hour)

Sleeping	70
Lying down (awake)	80
Sitting still	100
Standing	120
Typewriting rapidly	140
Walking (3 mph)	220
Digging a ditch	400
Running fast	600
Rowing in a race	1200

Adapted from a handbook of the U.S. Department of Agriculture.

SG 10.29-10.31

SG 10.32

The physics of energy transformations in biological processes is one example of a lively interdisciplinary field, namely biophysics (where physics, biology, chemistry, and nutrition all enter). Another connection to physics is provided by the problem of inadequate world food supply; here, too, many physicists, with others, are presently trying to provide solutions through work using their special competence.

the last ten years the increase in crop yield per acre in the poorer countries has averaged less than one percent per year, far less than the increase in population. The problem of supplying food energy for the world's hungry is one of the most difficult problems facing humanity today.

In this problem of life-and-death importance, what are the roles science and technology can play? Obviously, better agricultural practice should help, both by opening up new land for farming and by increasing production per acre on existing land. The application of fertilizers can increase crop yields, and factories that make fertilizers are not too difficult to build. But right here we meet a general law on the use of applications of science through technology: Before applying technology, study all the consequences that may be expected; otherwise you may create two new problems for every old one that you wish to "fix."

In any particular country, the questions to ask include these: How will fertilizers interact with the plant being grown and with the soil? Will some of the fertilizer run off and spoil rivers and lakes and the fishing industry in that locality? How much water will be required? What variety of the desired plant is the best to use within the local ecological framework? How will the ordinary farmer be able to learn the new techniques? How will he be able to pay for using them?

Upon study of this sort it may turn out that in addition to fertilizer, a country may need just as urgently a better system of bank loans to small farmers, and better agricultural education to help the farmer. Such training has played key roles in the rapid rise of productivity in the richer countries. Japan, for example, produces 7,000 college graduate agriculturalists each year. All of Latin America produces only 1,100 per year. In Japan there is one farm advisor for each 600 farms. Compare this with perhaps one advisor for 10,000 farms in Colombia, and one advisor per 100,000 farms in Indonesia.

But for long-run solutions, the problem of increasing food production in the poorer countries goes far beyond changing agricultural practices. Virtually all facets of the economies and cultures of the affected countries are involved. Important factors range from international economic aid and internal food pricing policies to urbanization, industrial growth, public health, and family planning practice.

Where, in all this, can the research scientist's contribution come in to help? It is usually true that one of the causes of some of the worse social problems is ignorance, including the absence of specific scientific knowledge. For example, knowledge of how food plants can grow efficiently in the tropics is lamentably sparse. Better ways of removing salt from sea water or brackish ground water are needed to allow irrigating fields with water from these plentiful sources. But before this will be economically possible, more basic knowledge will be needed on just how the molecules in liquids are structured, and how molecules move through membranes of the sort usable in de-salting equipment. Answers to such questions, and many like them, can only come through research in "pure" science, from trained research workers having access to adequate research facilities.

"The Repast of the Lion"
by Henri Rousseau
The Metropolitan Museum of Art

Q23 Animals obtain the energy they need from food, but plants
(a) obtain energy from sunlight
(b) obtain energy from water and carbon dioxide
(c) obtain energy from seeds
(d) do not need a supply of energy

Q24 The human body has an efficiency of about 20%. This means
that
(a) only one-fifth of the food you eat is digested
(b) four-fifths of the energy you obtain from food is destroyed
(c) one-fifth of the energy you obtain from food is used to run the
    "machinery" of the body
(d) you should spend 80% of each day lying quietly without working
(e) only one-fifth of the energy you obtain from food can be used to
    enable your body to do work on external objects

Q25 Explain this statement: "The repast of the lion is sunlight."

10.9 Arriving at a general law

In Section 10.3 we introduced the law of conservation of *mechanical* energy. This law applies only in situations where no mechanical energy is transformed into heat energy or *vice versa*. But early in the nineteenth century, developments in science, engineering and philosophy suggested new ideas about energy. It appeared that all forms of energy (including heat) could be transformed into one another with no loss. Therefore the total amount of energy in the universe must be constant.

Volta's invention of the electric battery in 1800 showed that chemical reactions could produce electricity. It was soon found that electric currents could produce heat and light. In 1820, Hans Christian Oersted, a Danish physicist, discovered that an electric current produces magnetic effects. And in 1831, Michael Faraday, the great English scientist, discovered electromagnetic induction: the effect that when a magnet moves near a coil or a wire, an electric current is produced in the coil or wire. To some thinkers, these discoveries suggested that all the phenomena of nature were somehow united. Perhaps all natural events resulted from the same basic "force." This idea, though vague and imprecise, later bore fruit in the form of the law of conservation of energy. All natural events involve a transformation of energy from one form to another. But the total *quantity* of energy does not change during the transformation.

The invention and use of steam engines helped to establish the law of conservation of energy by showing how to measure energy changes. Almost from the beginning, steam engines were rated according to a quantity termed their "duty." This term referred to how heavy a load an engine could lift using a given supply of fuel. In other words, the test was how much *work* an engine could do for the price of a ton of coal. This very practical approach is typical of the engineering tradition in which the steam engine was developed.

The concept of work began to develop about this time as a measure of the amount of energy transformed from one form to another. (The actual words "work" and "energy" were not used until later.) This made possible quantitative statements about the transformation of energy. For example, Joule used the work done by descending weights as a measure of the amount of gravitational potential energy transformed into heat energy.

In 1843, Joule had stated that whenever a certain amount of mechanical energy seemed to disappear, a definite amount of heat always appeared. To him, this was an indication of the conservation of what we now call energy. Joule said that he was

> . . . satisfied that the grand agents of nature are by the Creator's fiat *indestructible;* and that, wherever mechanical [energy] is expended, an exact equivalent of heat is *always* obtained.

Having said this, Joule got back to his work in the laboratory. He was basically a practical man who had little time to speculate about a deeper philosophical meaning of his findings. But others, though using speculative arguments, were also concluding that the total amount of

Joule began his long series of experiments by investigating the "duty" of electric motors. In this case duty was measured by the work the motor could do when a certain amount of zinc was used up in the battery that ran the motor. Joule's interest was to see whether motors could be made economically competitive with steam engines.

energy in the universe is constant.

A year before Joule's remark, for example, Julius Robert Mayer, a German physician, had proposed a general law of conservation of energy. Unlike Joule, Mayer had done no quantitative experiments. But he had observed body processes involving heat and respiration. And he had used other scientists' published data on the thermal properties of air to calculate the mechanical equivalent of heat. (Mayer obtained about the same value that Joule did.)

Mayer had been influenced strongly by the German philosophical school now known as *Naturphilosophie* or "nature-philosophy." This movement flourished in Germany during the late eighteenth and early nineteenth centuries. (See also the Epilogue to Unit 2.) Its most influential leaders were Johann Wolfgang von Goethe and Friedrich von Schelling. Neither of these men is known today as a scientist. Goethe is generally considered Germany's greatest poet and dramatist, while Schelling is remembered as a minor philosopher. But both men had great influence on the generation of German scientists educated at the beginning of the nineteenth century. The nature-philosophers were closely associated with the Romantic movement in literature, art, and music. The Romantics protested against the idea of the universe as a great machine. This idea, which had arisen after Newton's success in the seventeenth century, seemed morally empty and artistically worthless to them. The nature-philosophers also detested the mechanical world view. They refused to believe that the richness of natural phenomena—including human intellect, emotions, and hopes—could be understood as the result of the motions of particles.

At first glance, nature-philosophy would seem to have little to do with the law of conservation of energy. That law is practical and quantitative, whereas nature-philosophers tended to be speculative and qualitative. But nature-philosophy did insist on the value of searching for the underlying reality of nature. And this attitude did influence the discovery of the law of conservation of energy. Also, the nature-philosophers believed that the various phenomena of nature—gravity, electricity, magnetism, etc.—are not really separate from one another. Rather, they are simply different forms of one basic "force." This philosophy encouraged scientists to look for connections between different "forces" (or, in modern terms, between different forms of energy). It is perhaps ironic that in this way, it stimulated the experiments and theories that led to the law of conservation of energy.

The nature-philosophers claimed that nature could be understood as it "really" is only by direct observation. But no complicated "artificial" apparatus must be used—only feelings and intuitions. Goethe and Schelling were both very much interested in science and thought that their philosophy could uncover the hidden, inner meaning of nature. For Goethe the goal was "That I may detect the inmost force which binds the world, and guides its course."

By the time conservation of energy was established and generally accepted, however, nature-philosophy was no longer popular. Scientists who had previously been influenced by it, including Mayer, now strongly

Johann Wolfgang von Goethe (1749-1832)
Goethe thought that his color theory (which most modern scientists consider useless) exceeded in importance all his literary works.

Friedrich von Schelling (1775-1854)

opposed it. In fact, some hard-headed scientists at first doubted the law of conservation of energy simply because of their distrust of nature-philosophy. For example, William Barton Rogers, founder of the Massachusetts Institute of Technology, wrote in 1858:

> To me it seems as if many of those who are discussing this question of the conservation of force are plunging into the fog of mysticism.

However, the law was so quickly and successfully put to use in physics that its philosophical origins were soon forgotten.

This episode is a reminder of a lesson we learned before: In the ordinary day-to-day work of scientists, experiment and mathematical theory are the usual guides. But in making a truly major advance in science, philosophical speculation often also plays an important role.

Mayer and Joule were only two of at least a dozen people who, between 1832 and 1854, proposed in some form the idea that energy is conserved. Some expressed the idea vaguely; others expressed it quite clearly. Some arrived at their belief mainly through philosophy; others from a practical concern with engines and machines, or from laboratory investigations; still others from a combination of factors. Many, including Mayer and Joule, worked quite independently of one another. The idea of energy conservation was somehow "in the air," leading to essentially simultaneous, separate discovery.

The wide acceptance of the law of conservation of energy owes much to the influence of a paper published in 1847. This was two years before Joule published the results of his most precise experiments. The author, a young German physician and physicist named Hermann von Helmholtz, entitled his work "On the Conservation of Force." Helmholtz boldly asserted the idea that others were only vaguely expressing; namely, "that it is impossible to create a lasting motive force out of nothing." He restated this theme even more clearly many years later in one of his popular lectures:

> We arrive at the conclusion that Nature as a whole possesses a store of force which cannot in any way be either increased or diminished, and that, therefore, the quantity of force in Nature is just as eternal and unalterable as the quantity of matter. Expressed in this form, I have named the general law 'The Principle of the Conservation of Force.'

Any machine or engine that does work (provides energy) can do so only by drawing from some source of energy. The machine cannot supply more energy than it obtains from the source. When the source runs out, the machine will stop working. Machines and engines can only *transform* energy; they cannot create it or destroy it.

Hermann von Helmholtz (1821-1894)

Helmholtz's paper, "Zur Erhaltung der Kraft," was tightly reasoned and mathematically sophisticated. It related the law of conservation of energy to the established principles of Newtonian mechanics and thereby helped make the law scientifically respectable.

SG 10.33

Q26 The significance of German nature philosophy in the history of science is that it

(a) was the most extreme form of the mechanistic viewpoint

(b) was a reaction against excessive speculation

Energy Conservation on Earth

Nuclear reactions inside the earth produce energy at a rate of 3×10^{13}W

The nuclear reactions in the sun produce energy at a rate of 3.5×10^{27}W

The earth receives about 17×10^{16}W from the sun, of which about $\frac{1}{3}$ is immediately reflected — mostly by clouds and the oceans; the rest is absorbed, converted to heat, and ultimately radiated into outer space as infrared radiation. Of that part of the solar energy which is not reflected, . . .

. . . 5×10^{16}W heats dry land

. . . 3×10^{16}W heats the air, producing winds, waves, etc.

. . . 4×10^{16}W evaporates water

. . . 1.5×10^{13}W is used by marine plants for photosynthesis

. . . 3×10^{13}W is used by land plants for photosynthesis

Most of the energy given to water is given up again when the water condenses to clouds and rain; but every second about 10^{15} Joules remains as gravitational potential energy of the fallen rain.

Ancient green plants have decayed and left a store of about 2.2×10^{23} Joules in the form of oil, gas, and coal. This store is being used at a rate of 5×10^{12}W.

Present-day green plants are being used as food for man and animals, at a rate of 2×10^{13}W. Agriculture uses about $\frac{1}{10}$ of this, and people ultimately consume 3×10^{11}W as food.

Some of this energy is used to produce 10^{11}W of hydroelectric power

12×10^{11}W is used in generating 4×10^{11}W of electrical power

9×10^{11}W is used in combustion engines. About $\frac{3}{4}$ of this is wasted as heat; less than 3×10^{11}W appears as mechanical power

3×10^{12}W is used for heating; this is equally divided between industrial and domestic uses.

Direct use as raw materials for plastics and chemicals accounts for 2×10^{11}W

Controlled nuclear reactions produce 2×10^{10}W in electrical power

5×10^{11}W

electrochemistry   light   communication   mechanical power

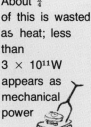

(c) stimulated speculation about the unity of natural phenomena

(d) delayed progress in science by opposing Newtonian mechanics

Q27 Discoveries in electricity and magnetism early in the nineteenth century contributed to the discovery of the law of conservation of energy because

(a) they attracted attention to the transformation of energy from one form to another

(b) they made it possible to produce more energy at less cost

(c) they revealed what happened to the energy that was apparently lost in steam engines

(d) they made it possible to transmit energy over long distances

Q28 The development of steam engines helped the discovery of the law of conservation of energy because

(a) steam engines produce a large amount of energy

(b) the caloric theory could not explain how steam engines worked

(c) the precise idea of work was developed to rate steam engines

(d) the internal energy of a steam engine was always found to be conserved

---

10.10 A precise and general statement of energy conservation

We can now try to pull many of the ideas in this chapter together into a precise statement of the law of conservation of energy. It would be pleasingly simple to call heat "internal" energy associated with temperature. We could then add heat to the potential and kinetic energy of a system, and call this sum the total energy that is conserved. In fact this works well for a great variety of phenomena, including the experiments of Joule. But difficulties arise with the idea of the heat "content" of a system. For example, when a solid is heated to its melting point, further heat input causes melting *without increasing the temperature*. (You may have seen this in the experiment on Calorimetry.) So simply adding the idea of heat as one form of a system's energy will not give us a complete general law. To get *that*, we must invent some additional terms with which to think.

Instead of "heat," let us use the idea of an *internal energy*, an energy in the system that may take forms not directly related to temperature. We can then use the word "heat" to refer only to a *transfer* of energy between a system and its surroundings. (In a similar way, the term *work* is not used to describe something contained in the system. Rather, it describes the transfer of energy from one system to another.)

Yet even these definitions do not permit a simple statement like "heat input to a system increases its internal energy, and work done on a system increases its mechanical energy." For heat input to a system can have effects other than increasing internal energy. In a steam engine, for example, heat input increases the mechanical energy of the piston. Similarly, *work* done on a system can have effects other than increasing

If you do not want to know what the detailed difficulties are, you can skip to the conclusion in the last paragraph on the next page.

The word "heat" is used rather loosely, even by physicists. This restriction on its meaning is not necessary in most contexts, but it is important for the discussion in this section.

mechanical energy. In rubbing your hands together, for example, the work you do increases the internal energy of the skin of your hands.

Therefore, a general conservation law of energy must include *both* work and heat transfer. Further, it must deal with change in the *total energy* of a system, not with a "mechanical" part and an "internal" part.

As we mentioned before in discussing conservation laws, such laws can be expressed in two ways: (a) in terms of an isolated system, in which the total quantity of something does not change, or (b) in terms of how to measure the increases and decreases of the total quantity in an open (or non-isolated) system. The two ways of expressing the law are logically related by the definition of "isolated." For example, conservation of momentum can be expressed either: (a) If no net outside force acts on a system, then the total $m\vec{v}$ of the system is constant; or (b) If a net outside force $\vec{F}$ acts on a system for a time $\Delta t,$ the change in the total $m\vec{v}$ of the system is $\vec{F} \times \Delta t.$ In (a), the absence of the net force is a condition of isolation. In (b), one describes how the presence of a net force affects momentum. Form (b) is obviously more generally useful.

A similar situation exists for the law of conservation of energy. We can say that the total energy of a system remains constant if the system is isolated. (By isolated we mean that no work is done on or by the system, and no heat passes between the system and its surroundings.) Or we can say that the *change* in energy of a *non*-isolated system is equal to the net work done on the system plus the net heat added to it. More precisely, we can let ΔW stand for the net work on the system, which is all the work done *on* the system minus all the work done *by* the system. We can let ΔH represent the net heat transfer to the system, or the heat added to the system minus the heat lost by the system. Then the change in *total* energy of the system, $\Delta E,$ is given by

$$\Delta E = \Delta W + \Delta H$$

This is a simple and useful form of the law of conservation of energy, and is sometimes called *the first law of thermodynamics.*

This general expression includes as special cases the preliminary versions of the conservation law given earlier in the chapter. If there is no heat transfer at all, then $\Delta H = 0$, and so $\Delta E = \Delta W.$ In this case, the change in energy of a system equals the net work done on it. On the other hand, if work is done neither on nor by a system, then $\Delta W = 0$, and $\Delta E = \Delta H.$ Here the change in energy of a system is equal to the net heat transfer.

We still lack a description of the part of the total energy of a system that we have called heat (or better, "internal" energy). So far we have seen only that an increase in internal energy is sometimes associated with an increase in temperature. We also mentioned the long-held suspicion that internal energy involves the motion of the "small parts" of bodies. We will take up this problem in detail in Chapter 11.

Special case of an isolated system:

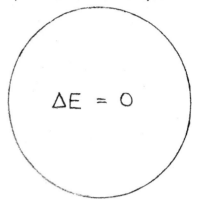

In general:

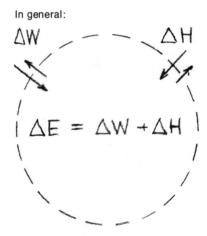

Thermodynamics is the study of the relation between heat and mechanical energy.

Q29 The first law of thermodynamics is

(a) true only for steam engines

(b) true only when there is no friction

(c) a completely general statement of conservation of energy

(d) the only way to express conservation of energy

Q30 Define ΔE, ΔW, and ΔH for a system.

Q31 What two ways are there for changing the total energy of a system?

10.11 Faith in the conservation of energy

For over a century, the law of conservation of energy has stood as one of the most fundamental laws of science. We encounter it again and again in this course, in studying electricity and magnetism, the structure of the atom, and nuclear physics. Throughout the other sciences, from chemistry to biology, and throughout engineering studies, the same law applies. Indeed, no other law so clearly brings together the various scientific fields, giving all scientists a common set of concepts.

The principle of conservation of energy has been immensely successsful. It is so firmly believed that it seems almost impossible that any new discovery could disprove it. Sometimes energy seems to appear or disappear in a system, without being accounted for by changes in known forms of energy. In such cases, physicists prefer to assume that some hitherto unknown kind of energy is involved, rather than consider seriously the possibility that energy is not conserved. We have already pointed out Leibniz's proposal that energy could be dissipated among "the small parts" of bodies. He advanced this idea specifically in order to maintain the principle of conservation of energy in inelastic collisions and frictional processes. His faith in energy conservation was justified. Other evidence showed that "internal energy" changed by just the right amount to explain observed changes in external energy.

SG 10.39, 10.40

Another recent example is the "invention" of the neutrino by the physicist Wolfgang Pauli in 1933. Experiments had suggested that energy disappeared in certain nuclear reactions. But Pauli proposed that a tiny particle, named the "neutrino" by Enrico Fermi, was produced in these reactions. Unnoticed, the neutrino carried off some of the energy. Physicists accepted the neutrino theory for more than twenty years even though neutrinos could not be detected by any method. Finally, in 1956, neutrinos were detected in experiments using the radiation from a nuclear reactor. (The experiment could not have been done in 1933, since no nuclear reactor existed until nearly a decade later.) Again, faith in the law of conservation of energy turned out to be justified.

The theme of "conservation" is so powerful in science that we believe it will always be justified. We believe that any apparent exceptions to the law will sooner or later be understood in a way which does not require us to give up the law. At most, they may lead us to discover new forms of energy making the law even more general and powerful.

The French mathematician and philosopher Henri Poincaré expressed this idea back in 1903 in his book *Science and Hypothesis:*

> . . . the principle of conservation of energy signifies simply that there is *something* which remains constant. Indeed, no matter what new notions future experiences will give us of the world, we are sure in advance that there will be something which will remain constant, and which we shall be able to call *energy*.

Today it is agreed that the discovery of conservation laws was one of the most important achievements of science. They are powerful and valuable tools of analysis. All of them basically affirm that, whatever happens within a system of interacting bodies, certain measurable quantities will remain constant as long as the system remains isolated.

The list of known conservation laws has grown in recent years. The area of fundamental (or "elementary") particles has yielded much of this new knowledge. Some of the newer laws are imperfectly and incompletely understood. Others are on uncertain ground and are still being argued.

Below is a list of conservation laws as it now stands. One cannot say that the list is complete or eternal. But it does include the conservation laws that make up the working tool-kit of physicists today. Those which are starred are discussed in the basic text portions of this course. The others are treated in supplemental (optional) units, for example, the Supplemental Unit entitled *Elementary Particles*.

1. Linear momentum*
2. Energy (including mass)*
3. Angular momentum (including spin)
4. Charge*
5. Electron-family number
6. Muon-family number
7. Baryon-family number
8. Strangeness number
9. Isotopic spin

Numbers 5 through 9 result from work in nuclear physics, high energy physics, or elementary or fundamental particle physics. If this aspect interests you, you will find the essay "Conservation Laws" (in the Reader entitled *The Nucleus*) worth reading at this stage. The first seven of the laws in the above listing are discussed in this selection.

10.1 The Project Physics materials particularly appropriate for Chapter 10 include:

Experiments
Conservation of Energy
Measuring the Speed of a Bullet
Temperature and Thermometers
Calorimetry
Ice Calorimetry

Activities
Student Horsepower
Steam Powered Boat
Predicting the Range of an Arrow

Film Loops
Finding the Speed of a Rifle Bullet – I
Finding the Speed of a Rifle Bullet – II
Recoil
Colliding Freight Cars
Dynamics of a Billiard Ball
A Method of Measuring Energy – Nail Driven into Wood
Gravitational Potential Energy
Kinetic Energy
Conservation of Energy – Pole Vault
Conservation of Energy – Aircraft Takeoff

Reader Articles
The Steam Engine Comes of Age
The Great Conservation Principles

Transparencies
Slow Collisions
The Watt Engine

10.2 A man carries a heavy load across the level floor of a building. Draw an arrow to represent the force he applies to the load, and one to represent the direction of his motion. By the definition of work given, how much work does he do on the load? Do you feel uncomfortable about this result? Why?

10.3 The speed of an object is always *relative* — that is, it will be different when measured from different reference frames. Since kinetic energy depends on speed, it too is only a relative quantity. If you are interested in the idea of the relativity of kinetic energy, consider this problem: An object of mass m is accelerated uniformly by a force F through a distance d, changing its speed from v_1 to v_2. The work done, Fd, is equal to the change in kinetic energy $\frac{1}{2}mv_2{}^2 - \frac{1}{2}mv_1{}^2$. (For simplicity, assume the case of motion in only one direction along a straight line.) Now: describe this event from a reference frame which is itself moving with speed u along the same direction.
(a) What are the speeds as observed in the new reference frame?
(b) Are the kinetic energies observed to have the same value in both reference frames?
(c) Does the *change* in kinetic energy have the same value?
(d) Is the calculated amount of work the same? Hint: by the Galilean relativity principle, the magnitude of the acceleration – and therefore force – will be the same when

viewed from frames of reference moving uniformly relative to each other.)
(e) Is the change in kinetic energy still equal to the work done?
(f) Which of the following are "invariant" for changes in reference frame (moving uniformly relative to one another)?
  i. the quantity $\frac{1}{2}mv^2$
  ii. the quantity Fd
  iii. the relationship $Fd = \Delta(\frac{1}{2}mv^2)$
(g) Explain why it is misleading to consider kinetic energy as something a body *has*, instead of only a quantity calculated from measurements.

10.4 An electron of mass about 9.1×10^{-31} kg is traveling at a speed of about 2×10^8 m/sec toward the screen of a television set. What is its kinetic energy? How many electrons like this one would be needed for a total kinetic energy of one joule?

10.5 Estimate the kinetic energy of each of the following: (a) a pitched baseball (b) a jet plane (c) a sprinter in a 100-yard dash (d) the earth in its motion around the sun.

10.6 A 200-kilogram iceboat is supported by a smooth surface of a frozen lake. The wind exerts on the boat a constant force of 400 newtons while the boat moves 900 meters. Assume that frictional forces are negligible, and that the boat starts from rest. Find the speed attained at the end of a 900 meter run by each of the following methods:

(a) Use Newton's second law to find the acceleration of the boat. How long does it take to move 900 meters? How fast will it be moving then?
(b) Find the final speed of the boat by equating the work done on it by the wind and the increase in its kinetic energy. Compare your result with your answer in (a).

10.7 A 2-gram bullet is shot into a tree stump. It enters at a speed of 300 m/sec and comes to rest after having penetrated 5 cm in a straight line.
(a) What was the change in the bullet's kinetic energy?
(b) How much work did the tree do on the bullet?
(c) What was the average force during impact?

10.8 Refer back to SG 9.20. How much work does the golf club do on the golf ball? How much work does the golf ball do on the golf club?

10.9 A penny has a mass of about 3.0 grams and is about 1.5 millimeters thick. You have 50 pennies which you pile one above the other.
(a) How much more gravitational potential energy has the top penny than the bottom one?
(b) How much more have all 50 pennies together than the bottom one alone?

10.10 (a) How high can you raise a book weighing 5 newtons if you have available one joule of energy?

(b) How many joules of energy are needed just to lift a 727 jet airliner weighing 7×10^5 newtons (fully loaded) to its cruising altitude of 10,000 meters?

10.11 As a home experiment, hang weights on a rubber band and measure its elongation. Plot the force vs. stretch on graph paper. How could you measure the stored energy?

10.12 For length, time and mass there are standards (for example, a standard meter). But energy is a "derived quantity," for which no standards need be kept. Nevertheless, assume someone asks you to supply him one joule of energy. Describe in as much detail as you can how you would do it.

10.13 (a) Estimate how long it would take for the earth to fall up 1 meter to a 1-kg stone if this stone were somehow rigidly fixed in space.
(b) Estimate how far the earth will actually move up while a 1-kg stone falls 1 meter from rest.

10.14 The photograph below shows a massive lead wrecking ball being used to demolish a wall. Discuss the transformations of energy involved.

10.15 This discussion will show that the *PE* of an object is relative to the frame of reference in which it is measured. The boulder in the photograph on page 37 was not lifted to its perch—rather the rest of the land has eroded away. leaving it where it may have been almost since the formation of the earth. Consider the question "What is the gravitational potential energy of the system boulder + earth?" You can easily calculate what the change in potential energy would be if the rock fell—it would be the product of the rock's weight and the distance it fell. But would that be the actual value of the gravitational energy that had been stored in the boulder-earth system? Imagine that there happened to be a deep mine shaft nearby and the boulder fell into the shaft. It would then fall much farther reducing the gravitational potential energy much more. Apparently the amount of energy stored depends on how far you imagine the boulder can fall.

(a) What is the greatest possible decrease in gravitational potential energy the isolated system boulder + earth could have?
(b) Is the system earth + boulder really isolated?
(c) Is there a true absolute bottom of gravitational potential energy for any system that includes the boulder and the earth?

These questions suggest that potential energy, like kinetic energy, is a relative quantity. The value of *PE* depends on the location of the (resting) frame of reference from which it is measured. This is not a serious problem, because we are concerned only with *changes* in energy. In any given problem, physicists will choose some convenient reference for the "zero-level" of potential energy, usually one that simplifies calculations. What would be a convenient zero-level for the gravitational potential energy of
(a) a pendulum?
(b) a roller coaster?
(c) a weight oscillating up and down a spring?
(d) a planet in orbit around the sun?

10.16 The figure below (not drawn to scale) shows a model of a carnival "loop-the-loop." A car starting from a platform above the top of the loop coasts down and around the loop without falling off the track. Show that to traverse the

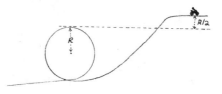

loop successfully, the car must start from a height at least one-half a radius above the top of the loop. Hint: The car's weight must not be greater than the centripetal force required to keep it on the circular path at the top of the loop.

10.17 Discuss the conversion between kinetic and potential forms of energy in the system of a comet orbiting around the sun.

10.18 Sketch an addition to one of the steam engine diagrams of a mechanical linkage that would open and close the valves automatically.

10.19 Show that if a constant propelling force F keeps a vehicle moving at a constant speed v (against the friction of the surrounding) the power required is equal to Fv.

10.20 The Queen Mary, one of Britain's largest steamships, has been retired to a marine museum on our west coast after completing 1,000 crossings of the Atlantic. Her mass is 81,000 tons (75 million kilograms) and her maximum engine power of 234,000 horsepower (174 million watts) allows her to reach a maximum speed of 30.63 knots (16 meters per second).

(a) What is her kinetic energy at full speed?

(b) Assume that at maximum speed all the power output of her engines goes into over-coming water drag. If the engines are suddenly stopped, how far will the ship coast before stopping? (Assume water drag is constant.)

(c) What constant force would be required to bring her to a stop from full speed within 1 nautical mile (2000 meters)?

(d) The assumptions made in (b) are not valid for the following reasons:

  1. Only about 60% of the power delivered to the propellor shafts results in a forward thrust to the ship; the rest results in friction and turbulence, eventually warming the water.

  2. Water drag is less for lower speed than for high speed.

  3. If the propellors are not free-wheeling, they add an increased drag.

  Which of the above factors tend to increase, which to decrease the coasting distance?

(e) Explain why tugboats are important for docking big ships.

10.21 Devise an experiment to measure the power output of

(a) a man riding a bicycle

(b) a motorcycle

(c) an electric motor.

10.22 Refer to the table of "Typical Power Ratings" on p. 46.

(a) What advantages would Newcomen's engine have over a "turret windmill"?

(b) What advantage would you expect Watt's engine (1778) to have over Smeaton's engine (1772)?

10.23 Besides horsepower, another term used in Watt's day to describe the performance of steam engines was *duty*. The duty of a steam engine was defined as the distance in feet that an engine can lift a load of one million pounds, using one bushel of coal as fuel. For example, Newcomen's engine had a duty of 4.3: it could perform 4.3 million foot-pounds of work by burning a bushel of coal. Which do you think would have been more important to the engineers building steam engines—increasing the horsepower or increasing the duty?

10.24 A modern term that is related to the "duty" of an engine is *efficiency*. The efficiency of an engine (or any device that transforms energy from one form to another) is defined as the percentage of the energy input that appears as useful output.

(a) Why would it have been impossible to find a value for the efficiency of an engine before Joule?

(b) The efficiency of "internal combustion" engines is seldom greater than 10%. For example, only about 10% of the chemical energy released in burning gasoline in an automobile engine goes into moving the automobile. What becomes of the other 90%?

10.25 Engine A operates at a greater power than engine B does, but its efficiency is less. This means that engine A does (a) more work with the same amount of fuel, but more slowly (b) less work with the same amount of fuel, but more quickly (c) more work with the same amount of fuel and does it faster (d) less work with the same amount of fuel and does it more slowly.

10.26 A table of rates for truck transportation is given below. How does the charge depend on the amount of work done?

Truck Transportation (1965)

Weight	Moving rates (including pickup and delivery) from Boston to:		
	Chicago (967 miles)	Denver (1969 miles)	Los Angeles (2994 miles)
100 lbs	$ 18.40	$ 24.00	$ 27.25
500	92.00	120.00	136.25
1000	128.50	185.50	220.50
2000	225.00	336.00	406.00
4000	383.00	606.00	748.00
6000	576.00	909.00	1122.00

10.27 Consider the following hypothetical values for a paddle-wheel experiment like Joule's: a 1-kilogram weight descends through a distance of 1 meter, turning a paddle-wheel immersed in 5 kilograms of water.

(a) About how many times must the weight be allowed to fall in order that the temperature of the water will be increased by $\frac{1}{2}$ Celsius degree?

(b) List ways you could modify the experiment so that the same temperature rise would be produced with fewer falls of the weight? (There are at least three possible ways.)

10.28 While traveling in Switzerland, Joule attempted to measure the difference in temperature of the water at the top and at the bottom of a waterfall. Assuming that the amount of heat produced at the bottom is equal to the decrease in gravitational potential energy, calculate roughly the temperature difference you would expect to observe between the top and bottom of a waterfall about 50 meters high, such as Niagra Falls. Does it matter how much water goes down the fall?

10.29 Find the power equivalent in watts or in

horsepower of one of the activities listed in the table on p. 53.

10.30 About how many kilograms of hamburgers would you have to eat to supply the energy for a half-hour of digging? Assume that your body is 20% efficient.

10.31 When a person's food intake supplies less energy than he uses, he starts "burning" his own stored fat for energy. The oxidation of a pound of animal fat provides about 4,300 kilocalories of energy. Suppose that on your present diet of 4,000 kilocalories a day you neither gain nor lose weight. If you cut your diet to 3,000 kilocalories and maintain your present physical activity, how long would it take to reduce your mass by 5 pounds?

10.32 In order to engage in normal light work, a person in India has been found to need on the average about 1,950 kilocalories of food energy a day, whereas an average West European needs about 3,000 kilocalories a day. Explain how each of the following statements makes the difference in energy need understandable.

(a) The average adult Indian weighs about 110 pounds; the average adult West European weighs about 150 pounds.

(b) India has a warm climate.

(c) The age distribution of the population for which these averages have been obtained is different in the two areas.

10.33 No other concept in physics has the economic significance that "energy" does. Discuss the statement: "We could express energy in dollars just as well as in joules or calories."

10.34 Show how the conservation laws for energy and for momentum can be applied to a rocket during the period of its lift off.

10.35 Discuss the following statement: "During a typical trip, all the chemical energy of the gasoline used in an automobile is used to heat up the car, the road and the air."

10.36 Show how all the equations we have given in Chapter 10 to express conservation of energy are special cases of the general statement $\Delta E = \Delta W + \Delta H$. Hint: let one or more of the terms equal zero.)

10.37 (a) Describe the procedure by which a space capsule can be changed from a high circular orbit to a lower circular orbit.

(b) How does the kinetic energy in the lower orbit compare with that in the higher orbit?

(c) How does the gravitational potential energy for the lower orbit compare with that of the higher orbit?

(d) It can be shown (by using calculus) that the change in gravitational potential energy in going from one circular orbit to another will be *twice* the change in kinetic energy. How, then, will the total energy for the lower circular orbit compare with that for the higher orbit?

(e) How do you account for the change in total energy?

10.38 Any of the terms in the equation $\Delta E = \Delta H + \Delta W$ can have negative values.

(a) What would be true for a system for which
i. ΔE is negative?
ii. ΔH is negative?
iii. ΔW is negative?

(b) Which terms would be negative for the following systems?
i. a man digging a ditch
ii. a car battery while starting a car
iii. an electric light bulb just after it is turned on
iv. an electric light bulb an hour after it is turned on
v. a running refrigerator
vi. an exploding firecracker

10.39 In each of the following, trace the chain of energy transformations from the sun to the energy in its final form:

(a) A pot of water is boiled on an electric stove.

(b) An automobile accelerates from rest on a level road, climbs a hill at constant speed, and comes to stop at a traffic light.

(c) A windmill pumps water out of a flooded field.

10.40 Show how the law of conservation of energy applies to the motion of each of the situations listed in SG 9.39 and 9.40, p. 27.

Bubbles of gas from high-pressure tanks expand as
the pressure decreases on the way to the surface.

CHAPTER ELEVEN

The Kinetic Theory of Gases

11.1 An overview of the chapter

During the 1840's, many scientists recognized that heat is not a substance, but a form of energy which can be converted into other forms. Two of these scientists, James Prescott Joule and Rudolf Clausius, went a step further. They based this advance on the fact that heat can produce mechanical energy and mechanical energy can produce heat. Therefore, they reasoned, the "heat energy" of a substance is simply the kinetic energy of its atoms and molecules. In this chapter we will see that this idea is largely correct. It forms the basis of the *kinetic-molecular theory of heat.*

However, even the idea of atoms and molecules was not completely accepted in the nineteenth century. If such small bits of matter really existed, they would be too small to observe even in the most powerful microscopes. Since scientists could not observe molecules, they could not check directly the hypothesis that heat is molecular kinetic energy. Instead, they had to derive from this hypothesis predictions about the behavior of measurably large samples of matter. Then they could test these predictions by experiment. For reasons which we will explain, it is easiest to test such hypotheses by observing the properties of gases. Therefore, this chapter deals mainly with the kinetic theory as applied to gases.

The development of the kinetic theory of gases in the nineteenth century led to the last major triumph of Newtonian mechanics. The method involved using a simple theoretical model of a gas. Newton's laws of motion were applied to the gas molecules assumed in this model as if they were tiny billiard balls. This method produced equations that related the easily observable properties of gases—such as pressure, density, and temperature—to properties not directly observable—such as the sizes and speeds of molecules. For example, the kinetic theory:

SG 11.1

Molecules are the smallest pieces of a substance—they may be combinations of atoms of simpler substances.

(1) explained rules that had been found previously by trial-and-error methods. (An example is "Boyle's law," which relates the pressure and the volume of a gas.)

(2) predicted new relations. (One surprising result was that the friction between layers of gas moving at different speeds increases with temperature, but is independent of the density of the gas.)

(3) led to values for the sizes and speeds of gas molecules.

Thus the successes of kinetic theory showed that Newtonian mechanics provided a way for understanding the effects and behavior of invisible molecules.

But applying Newtonian mechanics to a mechanical model of gases resulted in some predictions that did *not* agree with the facts. That is, the model is not valid for all phenomena. According to kinetic theory, for example, the energy of a group of molecules should be shared equally among all the different motions of the molecules and their atoms. But the properties of gases predicted from this "equal sharing" principle clearly disagreed with experimental evidence. Newtonian mechanics could be applied successfully to a wide range of motions and collisions of molecules in a gas. But it did not work for the motions of atoms inside molecules. It was not until the twentieth century that an adequate theory of the behavior of atoms— "quantum mechanics"—was developed. (Some ideas from quantum mechanics are discussed in Unit 5.)

Kinetic theory based on Newtonian mechanics also had trouble dealing with the fact that most phenomena are not reversible. An inelastic collision is an irreversible process. Other examples are the mixing of two gases, or scrambling an egg. In Newtonian theory, however, the reverse of any event is just as reasonable as the event itself. Can irreversible processes be described by a theory based on Newtonian theory? Or do they involve some new fundamental law of nature? In discussing this problem from the viewpoint of kinetic theory, we will see how the concept of "randomness" entered physics.

Modern physicists do not take too seriously the "billiard ball" idea of gas molecules—nor did most nineteenth century physicists. All models oversimplify the actual facts. Therefore, the simple assumptions of a model often need adjustment in order to get a theory that agrees well with experimental data. Nevertheless the kinetic theory is still very useful. Physicists are fond of it, and often present it as an example of how a physical theory should be developed. Section 11.5 gives one of the mathematical derivations from the model used in kinetic theory. This derivation is not given to be memorized in detail; it simply illustrates mathematical reasoning based on models. Physicists have found this method very useful in understanding many natural phenomena.

Q1 Early forms of the kinetic molecular theory were based on the assumption that heat energy is
(a) a liquid
(b) a gas
(c) the kinetic energy of molecules
(d) made of molecules

Q2 True or false: In the kinetic theory of gases, as developed in the nineteenth century, it was assumed that Newton's laws of motion apply to the motion and collisions of molecules.

Q3 True or false: In the twentieth century, Newtonian mechanics was found to be applicable not only to molecules but also to the atoms inside molecules.

11.2 A model for the gaseous state

What are the differences between a gas and a liquid or solid? We know by observation that liquids and solids have definite volume. Even if their shapes change, they still take up the same amount of space. A gas, on the other hand, will expand to fill any container (such as a room). If not confined, it will leak out and spread in all directions. Gases have low densities compared to liquids and solids—typically about 1,000 times smaller. Gas molecules are usually relatively far apart from one another, and they only occasionally collide. In the kinetic theory model, forces between molecules act only over very short distances. Therefore, gas molecules are considered to be moving freely most of the time. In liquids, the molecules are closer together; forces act among them continually and keep them from flying apart. In solids the molecules are usually even closer together, and the forces between them keep them in a definite orderly arrangement.

The initial model of a gas is a very simple model. The molecules are considered to behave like miniature billiard balls—that is, tiny spheres or clumps of spheres which exert no force at all on each other except when they make contact. Moreover, all the collisions of these spheres are assumed to be perfectly elastic. Thus, the total kinetic energy of two spheres is the same before and after they collide.

Note that the word "model" is used in two different senses in science. In Chapter 10, we mentioned the model of Newcomen's engine which James Watt was given to repair. That was a *working model*. It actually did function, although it was much smaller than the original engine, and contained some parts made of different materials. But now we are discussing a *theoretical model* of a gas. This model exists only in our imagination. Like the points, lines, triangles, and spheres studied in geometry, this theoretical model can be discussed mathematically. The results of such a discussion may help us to understand the real world of experience.

In order to emphasize that our model is a theoretical one, we will use the word "particle" instead of "atom" or "molecule." There is now no doubt that atoms and molecules exist and have their own definite properties. The particles in the kinetic theory model, on the other hand, are idealized and imaginary. We imagine such objects as perfectly elastic spheres, whose supposed properties are hopefully similar to those of actual atoms and molecules.

Our model represents the gas as consisting of *a large number of very*

Balloon for carrying apparatus used for weather forecasting.

Gases can be confined without a container. A star, for example, is a mass of gas confined by gravitational force. Another example is the earth's atmosphere.

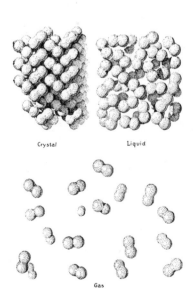

Crystal   Liquid

Gas

A very simplified "model" of the three states of matter:
(From *General Chemistry*, second edition, by Linus Pauling, W. H. Freeman and Company, © 1953.)

The word "gas" was originally derived from the Greek word *chaos*; it was first used by the Belgian chemist Jan Baptista van Helmont (1580-1644).

small particles in rapid, disordered motion. Let us define some of these terms. "A large number" means something like a billion billion (10^{18}) or more particles in a sample as small as a bubble in a soft drink. "Very small" means a diameter about a hundred-millionth of a centimeter (10^{-10} meter). "Rapid motion" means an average speed of a few hundred miles per hour. What is meant by "disordered" motion? Nineteenth-century kinetic theorists assumed that each individual molecule moved in a definite way, determined by Newton's laws of motion. Of course, in practice it is impossible to follow a billion billion particles at the same time. They move in all directions, and each particle changes its direction and speed during collision with another particle. Therefore, we cannot make a definite prediction of the motion of any one *individual* particle. Instead, we must be content with describing the *average* behavior of large collections of particles. We still believe that from moment to moment each individual molecule behaves according to the laws of motion. But it turns out to be easier to describe the *average* behavior if we assume complete ignorance about any *individual* motions. To see why this is so, consider the results of flipping a large number of coins all at once. It would be very hard to predict how a single coin would behave. But if you assume they behave randomly, you can confidently predict that flipping a million coins will give approximately 50% heads and 50% tails. The same principle applies to molecules bouncing around in a container. You can safely bet that about as many are moving in one direction as in another. Further, the particles are equally likely to be found in any cubic centimeter of space inside the container. This is true no matter where such a region is located, and even though we do not know where a given particle is at any given time. "Disordered," then, means that velocities and positions are distributed randomly. Each molecule is just as likely to be moving to the right as to the left (or in any other direction). And it is just as likely to be near the center as near the edge (or any other position).

In summary, we are going to discuss the properties of a model of a gas. The model is imagined to consist of a large number of very small particles in rapid, disordered motion. The particles move freely most of the time, exerting forces on one another only when they collide. The model is designed to represent the structure of real gases in many ways. However, it is simplified in order to make calculations manageable. By comparing the results of these calculations with the observed properties of gases, we can estimate the speeds and sizes of molecules.

On the opposite page you will find a more detailed discussion of the idea of random fluctuations.

SG 11.2

The idea of disorder is elaborated in the *Reader 3* articles "The Law of Disorder," "The Law," "The Arrow of Time," and "Randomness in the Twentieth Century."

Q4 In the kinetic theory, particles are thought to exert significant forces on one another
  (a) only when they are far apart
  (b) only when they are close together
  (c) all the time
  (d) never

Q5 Why was the kinetic theory first applied to gases rather than to liquids or solids?

Averages and Fluctuations

Molecules are too small, too numerous, and too fast for us to measure the speed of any one molecule, or its kinetic energy, or how far it moves before colliding with another molecule. For this reason the kinetic theory of gases concerns itself with making predictions about *average* values. The theory enables us to predict quite precisely the *average* speed of the molecules in a sample of gas, or the *average* kinetic energy, or the *average* distance the molecules move between collisions.

Any measurement made on a sample of gas reflects the combined effect of billions of molecules, averaged over some interval of time. Such average values measured at different times, or in different parts of the sample, will be slightly different. We assume that the molecules are moving randomly. Thus we can use the mathematical rules of statistics to estimate just how different the averages are likely to be. We will call on two basic rules of statistics for random samples:

1. Large variations away from the average are less likely than small variations. (For example, if you toss 10 coins you are less likely to get 9 heads and 1 tail than to get 6 heads and 4 tails.)

2. Percentage variations are likely to be smaller for large samples. (For example, you are likely to get nearer to 50% heads by flipping 1,000 coins than by flipping just 10 coins.)

A simple statistical prediction is the statement that if a coin is tossed many times, it will land "heads" 50 percent of the time and "tails" 50 percent of the time. For small sets of tosses there will be many "fluctuations" (variations) to either side of the predicted average of 50% heads. Both statistical rules are evident in the charts at the right. The top chart shows the percentage of heads in sets of 30 tosses each. Each of the 10 black squares represents a set of 30 tosses. Its position along the horizontal scale indicates the percent of heads. As we would expect from rule 1, there are more values near the theoretical 50% than far from it. The second chart is similar to the first, but here each square represents a set of *90* tosses. As before, there are more values near 50% than far from it. And, as we would expect from rule 2, there are fewer values far from 50% than in the first

chart.

The third chart is similar to the first two, but now each square represents a set of 180 tosses. Large fluctuations from 50% are less common still than for the smaller sets.

Statistical theory shows that the *average* fluctuation from 50% shrinks in proportion to the square root of the number of tosses. We can use this rule to compare the average fluctuation for sets of, say, 30,000,000 tosses with the average fluctuation for sets of 30 tosses. The 30,000,000-toss sets have 1,000,000 times as many tosses as the 30-toss sets. Thus, their average fluctuation in percent of heads should be 1,000 times smaller!

These same principles hold for fluctuations from average values of any randomly-distributed quantities, such as molecular speed or distance between collisions. Since even a small bubble of air contains about a quintillion (10^{18}) molecules, fluctuations in the average value for any isolated sample of gas are not likely to be large enough to be measurable. A measurably large fluctuation is not *impossible,* but extremely unlikely.

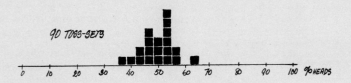

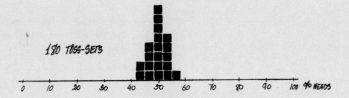

11.3 The speeds of molecules

The basic idea of the kinetic theory is that heat is related to the kinetic energy of molecular motion. This idea had been frequently suggested in the past. However, many difficulties stood in the way of its general acceptance. Some of these difficulties are well worth mentioning. They show that not all good ideas in science (any more than outside of science) are immediately successful.

SG 11.3

In 1738, the Swiss mathematician Daniel Bernoulli showed how a kinetic model could explain a well-known property of gases. This property is described by Boyle's law: as long as the temperature does not change, the pressure of a gas is proportional to its density. Bernoulli assumed that the pressure of a gas is simply a result of the impacts of individual molecules striking the wall of the container. If the density of the gas were twice as great there would be twice as many molecules per cubic centimeter. Thus, Bernoulli said, there would be twice as many molecules striking the wall per second, and hence twice the pressure. Bernoulli's proposal seems to have been the first step toward the modern kinetic theory of gases. Yet it was generally ignored by other scientists in the eighteenth century. One reason for this was that Newton had proposed a different theory in his *Principia* (1687). Newton showed that Boyle's law *could* be explained by a model in which particles at rest exert forces that repel neighboring particles. Newton did not claim that he had proved that gases really *are* composed of such repelling particles. But most scientists, impressed by Newton's discoveries, simply assumed that his treatment of gas pressure was also right. (As it turned out, it was not.)

Pressure is defined as the perpendicular force on a surface divided by the area of the surface.

The kinetic theory of gases was proposed again in 1820 by an English physicist, John Herapath. Herapath rediscovered Bernoulli's results on the relations between pressure and density of a gas and the speeds of the particles. But Herapath's work also was ignored by most other scientists. His earlier writings on the kinetic theory had been rejected for publication by the Royal Society of London. Despite a long and bitter battle Herapath did not succeed in getting recognition for his theory.

James Prescott Joule, however, did see the value of Herapath's work. In 1848 he read a paper to the Manchester Literary and Philosophical Society in which he tried to revive the kinetic theory. Joule showed how the speed of a hydrogen molecule could be computed (as Herapath had done). He reported a value of 2,000 meters per second at 0°C, the freezing temperature of water. This paper, too, was ignored by other scientists. For one thing, physicists do not generally look in the publications of a "literary and philosophical society" for scientifically important papers. But evidence for the equivalence of heat and mechanical energy continued to mount. Several other physicists independently worked out the consequences of the hypothesis that heat energy in a gas is the kinetic energy of molecules. Rudolf Clausius in Germany published a paper in 1856 on "The Nature of the Motion we call Heat." This paper established the basic principles of kinetic theory essentially in the form we accept today. Soon afterward, James Clerk Maxwell in Britain and Ludwig Boltzmann in Austria set forth the full mathematical details of the theory.

The Maxwell velocity distribution. It did not seem likely that all molecules in a gas would have the same speed. In 1859 Maxwell applied the mathematics of probability to this problem. He suggested that the speeds of molecules in a gas are distributed over all possible values. Most molecules have speeds not very far from the average speed. But some have much lower speeds and some much higher speeds.

A simple example will help you to understand Maxwell's distribution of molecular speeds. Suppose a marksman shoots a gun at a practice target many times. Some bullets will probably hit the bullseye. Others will miss by smaller or larger amounts, as shown in (a) in the sketch below. We count the number of bullets scattered at various distances to the left and right of the bullseye in (b). Then we can make a graph showing the number of bullets at these distances as shown in (c).

TARGET PRACTICE EXPERIMENT
(a) Scatter of holes in target; (b) target marked off in distance intervals left and right of center; (c) graph of number of holes per strip to left and right of center; (d) For a very large number of bullets and narrow strips, the envelope of the graph often closely approximates the mathematical curve called the "normal distribution" curve.

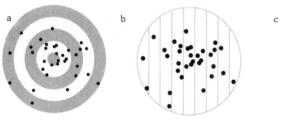
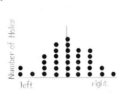
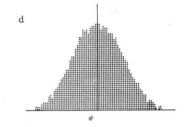

This graph showing the distribution of hits illustrates a general principle of statistics, namely, if any quantity varies randomly about an average value, the graph showing the distribution of variations will resemble the one shown in (d) above in the margin. There will be a peak at the average value and a smooth decline on either side. A similar "bell-shaped curve," as it is called, describes the distribution of many kinds of physical measurements. The *normal distribution law* applies even to large groups of people. For example, consider the distribution of heights in a large crowd. Such a distribution results from the combined effect of a great many *independent* factors. A person's height, for example, depends upon many independent genes as well as environmental factors. Thus the distribution of heights will closely follow a normal distribution. The velocity of a gas molecule is determined by a very large number of independent collisions. So the distribution of velocities is also smoothly "bell-shaped."

Maxwell's distribution law for molecular velocities in a gas is shown in the margin in graphical form for three different temperatures. The curve is not symmetrical since no molecule can have less than zero speed, but some have very large speeds. For a gas at any given temperature, the "tail" of each curve is much longer on the right (high speeds) than on the left (low speeds). As the temperature increases, the peak of the curve

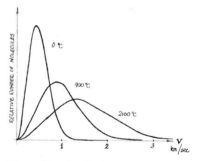

Maxwell's distribution of speeds in gases at different temperatures.

shifts to higher speeds. Then the speed distribution becomes more broadly spread out.

What evidence do we have that Maxwell's distribution law really applies to molecular speeds? Several successful predictions based on this law gave indirect support to it. But not until the 1920's was a direct experimental check possible. Otto Stern in Germany, and later Zartmann in the United States, devised a method for measuring the speeds in a beam of molecules. (See the illustration of Zartmann's method on the next page.) Stern, Zartmann, and others found that molecular speeds are indeed distributed according to Maxwell's law. Virtually all of the individual molecules in a gas change speed as they collide again and again. Yet if a confined sample of gas is isolated, the *distribution* of speeds remains very much the same. For the tremendous number of molecules in almost any sample of gas, the *average* speed has an extremely stable value.

SG 11.4

SG 11.5

Q6 In the kinetic theory of gases, it is assumed that the pressure of a gas on the walls of the container is due to
  (a) gas molecules colliding with one another
  (b) gas molecules colliding against the walls of the container
  (c) repelling forces exerted by molecules on one another
Q7 The idea of speed distribution for gas molecules means that
  (a) each molecule always has the same speed
  (b) there is a wide range at speeds of gas molecules
  (c) molecules are moving fastest near the center of the gas

---

11.4 The sizes of molecules

Is it reasonable to suppose that gases consist of molecules moving at speeds up to several hundred meters per second? If this model were correct, gases should mix with each other very rapidly. But anyone who has studied chemistry knows that they do not. Suppose hydrogen sulfide or chlorine is generated at the end of a large room. Several minutes may pass before the odor is noticed at the other end. But according to our kinetic-theory calculations, each of the gas molecules should have crossed the room hundreds of times by then. Something must be wrong with our kinetic-theory model.

Rudolf Clausius recognized this as a valid objection to his own version of the kinetic theory. His 1856 paper had assumed that the particles are so small that they can be treated like mathematical points. If this were true, particles would almost never collide with one another. However, the observed *slowness* of diffusion and mixing convinced Clausius to change his model. He thought it likely that the molecules of a gas are not vanishingly small, but of a finite size. Particles of finite size moving very rapidly would often collide with one another. An individual molecule might have an instantaneous speed of several hundred meters per second. But it changes its direction of motion every time it collides with another molecule. The more often it collides with other molecules, the less likely it

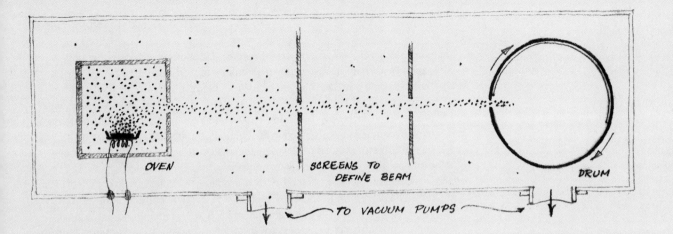

Direct Measurement of Molecular Speeds

A narrow beam of molecules is formed by letting molecules of a hot gas pass through a series of slits. In order to keep the beam from spreading out, collisions with randomly moving molecules must be avoided. Therefore, the source of gas and the slits are housed in a highly evacuated chamber. The molecules are then allowed to pass through a slit in the side of a cylindrical drum which can be spun very rapidly. The general scheme is shown in the drawing above.

As the drum rotates, the slit moves out of the beam of molecules. No more molecules can enter until the drum has rotated through a whole revolution. Meanwhile the molecules in the drum continue moving to the right, some moving fast and some moving slowly.

Fastened to the inside of the drum is a sensitive film which acts as a detector. Any molecule striking the film leaves a mark. The faster molecules strike the film first, before the drum has rotated very far.

The slower molecules hit the film later, after the drum has rotated farther, in general, molecules of different speeds strike different parts of the film. The darkness of the film at any point is proportional to the number of molecules which hit it there. Measurement of the darkening of the film shows the relative distribution of molecular speeds. The speckled strip at the right represents the unrolled film, showing the impact position of molecules over many revolutions of the drum. The heavy band indicates where the beam struck the film before the drum started rotating. (It also marks the place to which infinitely fast molecules would get once the drum was rotating.)

A comparison of some experimental results with those predicted from theory is shown in the graph. The dots show the experimental results and the solid line represents the predictions from the kinetic theory.

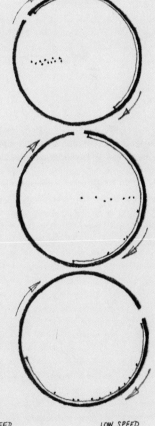

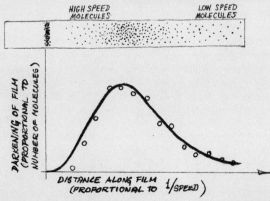

HIGH SPEED MOLECULES LOW SPEED MOLECULES

DARKENING OF FILM (PROPORTIONAL TO NUMBER OF MOLECULES)

DISTANCE ALONG FILM (PROPORTIONAL TO $\frac{1}{SPEED}$)

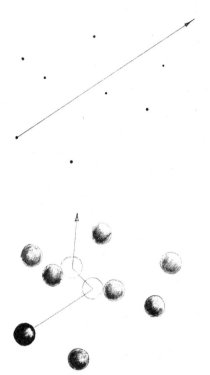

The larger the molecules are, the more likely they are to collide with each other.

SG 11.6

is to move very far in any one direction. How often collisions occur depends on how crowded the molecules are and on their size. For most purposes one can think of molecules as being relatively far apart and of very small size. But they are just large enough and crowded enough to get in one another's way. Realizing this, Clausius could modify his model to explain why gases mix so slowly. Further, he derived a precise quantitative relationship between the molecule's size and the average distance they moved between collisions.

Clausius now was faced with a problem that plagues every theoretical physicist. If a simple model is modified to explain better the observed properties, it becomes more complicated. Some plausible adjustment or approximation may be necessary in order to make any predictions from the model. If the predictions disagree with experimental data, one doesn't know whether to blame a flaw in the model or calculation error introduced by the approximations. The development of a theory often involves a compromise between adequate explanation of the data, and mathematical convenience.

Nonetheless, it soon became clear that the new model was a great improvement over the old one. It turned out that certain other properties of gases also depend on the size of the molecules. By combining data on several such properties it was possible to work backwards and find fairly reliable values for molecular sizes. Here we can only report the result of these calculations. Typically, the diameter of gas molecules came out to be of the order of 10^{-10} meters to 10^{-9} meters. This is not far from the modern values—an amazingly good result. After all, no one previously had known whether a molecule was 1,000 times smaller or bigger than that. In fact, as Lord Kelvin remarked:

> The idea of an atom has been so constantly associated with incredible assumptions of infinite strength, absolute rigidity, mystical actions at a distance and indivisibility, that chemists and many other reasonable naturalists of modern times, losing all patience with it, have dismissed it to the realms of metaphysics, and made it smaller than 'anything we can conceive.'

SG 11.7
SG 11.8

Kelvin showed that other methods could also be used to estimate the size of atoms. None of these methods gave results as reliable as did the kinetic theory. But it was encouraging that they all led to the same order of magnitude (within about 50%).

Q8 In his revised kinetic-theory model Clausius assumed that the particles have a finite size, instead of being mathematical points, because
 (a) obviously everything must have some size
 (b) it was necessary to assume a finite size in order to calculate the speed of molecules.
 (c) the size of a molecule was already well known before Clausius' time
 (d) a finite size of molecules could account for the slowness of diffusion.

11.5 Predicting the behavior of gases from the kinetic theory

One of the most easily measured characteristics of a confined gas is pressure. Our experience with balloons and tires makes the idea of air pressure seem obvious; but it was not always so.

Galileo, in his book on mechanics, *Two New Sciences* (1638), noted that a lift-type pump cannot raise water more than 34 feet. This fact was well known. Such pumps were widely used to obtain drinking water from wells and to remove water from mines. We already have seen one important consequence of this limited ability of pumps to lift water out of deep mines. This need provided the initial stimulus for the development of steam engines. Another consequence was that physicists became curious about why the lift pump worked at all. Also, why should there be a limit to its ability to raise water?

Air Pressure. The puzzle was solved as a result of experiments by Torricelli (a student of Galileo), Guericke, Pascal, and Boyle. By 1660, it was fairly clear that the operation of a "lift" pump depends on the pressure of the air. The pump merely reduces the pressure at the top of the pipe. It is the pressure exerted by the atmosphere on the pool of water below which forces water up the pipe. A good pump can reduce the pressure at the top of the pipe to nearly zero. Then the atmospheric pressure can force water up to about 34 feet above the pool—but no higher. Atmospheric pressure at sea level is not great enough to support a column of water any higher. Mercury is almost 14 times as dense as water. Thus, ordinary pressure on a pool of mercury can support a column only $\frac{1}{14}$ as high, about $2\frac{1}{2}$ feet (0.76 meter). This is a more convenient height for laboratory experiments. Therefore, much of the seventeenth-century research on air pressure was done with a column of mercury, or mercury "barometer." The first of these was designed by Torricelli.

The height of the mercury column which can be supported by air pressure does not depend on the diameter of the tube. That is, it depends not on the total amount of mercury, but only on its height. This may seem strange at first. To understand it, we must understand the difference between *pressure* and *force*. Pressure is defined as the magnitude of the force acting perpendicularly on a surface divided by the area of that surface: $P = F_{\perp}/A$. Thus a large force may produce only a small pressure if it is spread over a large area. For example, you can walk on snow without sinking in it if you wear snowshoes. On the other hand, a small force can produce a very large pressure if it is concentrated on a small area. Women's spike heel shoes have ruined many a wooden floor or carpet. The pressure at the place where the heel touched the floor was greater than that under an elephant's foot.

In 1661 two English scientists, Richard Towneley and Henry Power, discovered an important basic relation. They found that *the pressure exerted by a gas is directly proportional to the density of that gas.* Using P for pressure and D for density, we can write this relationship as $P \propto D$ or $P = kD$ where k is some constant. For example, if the density of a given quantity of air is doubled (say by compressing it), its pressure also doubles. Robert Boyle confirmed this relation by extensive experiments. It is an empirical rule, now generally known as *Boyle's Law*. But the law

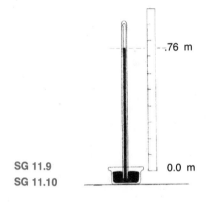

SG 11.9
SG 11.10

Torricelli's barometer is a glass tube standing in a pool of mercury. The top most part of the tube is empty of air. The air pressure on the pool supports the weight of the column of mercury in the tube up to a height of about $2\frac{1}{2}$ feet (0.76 meter).

SG 11.11
SG 11.12

holds true only under special conditions.

The effect of temperature on gas pressure. Boyle recognized that if the temperature of a gas changes during an experiment, the relation $P = kD$ no longer applies. For example, the pressure exerted by a gas in a closed container increases if the gas is heated, even though its density stays constant.

Many scientists throughout the eighteenth century investigated the expansion of gases by heat. The experimental results were not consistent enough to establish a quantitative relation between density (or volume) and temperature. But eventually, evidence for a surprisingly simple general law appeared. The French chemist Joseph-Louis Gay-Lussac (1778-1850) found that all the gases he studied—air, oxygen, hydrogen, nitrogen, nitrous oxide, ammonia, hydrogen chloride, sulfur dioxide, and carbon dioxide—changed their volume in the same way. If the pressure remained constant, then the change in volume was proportional to the change in temperature. On the other hand, if the volume remained constant, the change in pressure was proportional to the change in temperature.

A single equation summarizes all the experimental data obtained by Boyle, Gay-Lussac, and many other scientists. It is known as the *ideal gas law*:

$$P = kD(t + 273°)$$

Here t is the temperature on the Celsius scale. The proportionality constant k depends only on the kind of gas (and on the units used for P, D and t).

We call this equation the *ideal* gas law because it is not completely accurate for real gases except at very low pressures. Thus, it is not a law of physics in the same sense as the law of conservation of momentum. Rather, it simply gives an experimental and approximate summary of the observed properties of real gases. It does not apply when pressure is so high, or temperature so low, that the gas is nearly changing to a liquid.

Why does the number 273 appear in the ideal gas law? Simply because we are measuring temperature on the Celsius scale. If we had chosen to use the Fahrenheit scale, the equation for the ideal gas law would be

$$P = k'D(t + 460°)$$

where t is the temperature measured on the Fahrenheit scale. In other words, the fact that the number is 273 or 460 has no great importance. It just depends on our choice of a particular scale for measuring temperature. However, it *is* important to note what would happen if t were decreased to $-273°$C or $-460°$F. Then the entire factor involving temperature would be zero. And, according to the ideal gas law, the pressure of any gas would also fall to zero at this temperature. The chemical properties of the gas no longer makes sense. Real gases become liquid long before a temperature of $-273°$C is reached. Both experiment and thermodynamic theory indicate that it is impossible actually to cool anything—gas, liquid, or solid—down to precisely

On the Celsius scale, water freezes at 0° and boils at 100°, when the pressure is equal to normal atmospheric pressure. On the Fahrenheit scale, water freezes at 32° and boils at 212°. Some of the details involved in defining temperature scales are part of the experiment Temperature and Thermometers in the *Handbook*.

If the pressure were kept constant, then according to the ideal gas law the *volume* of a sample of gas would shrink to zero at $-273°$C.

this temperature. However, a series of cooling operations has produced temperatures less than 0.0001 degree above this limit.

In view of the unique meaning of this lowest temperature, Lord Kelvin proposed a new temperature scale. He called it the *absolute temperature scale,* and put its zero at −273°C. Sometimes it is called the Kelvin scale. The temperature of −273°C is now referred to as 0°K on the absolute scale, and is called the *absolute zero* of temperature.

The ideal gas law may now be written in simpler form:

$$P = kDT$$

T is the temperature in degrees Kelvin and k is the proportionality constant.

The equation $P = kDT$ summarizes *experimental facts* about gases. Now we can see whether the kinetic-theory model offers a *theoretical* explanation for these facts.

Kinetic explanation of gas pressure. According to the kinetic theory, the pressure of a gas results from the continual impacts of gas particles against the container wall. This explains why pressure is proportional to density: the greater the density, the greater the number of particles colliding with the wall. But pressure also depends on the *speed* of the individual particles. This speed determines the force exerted on the wall during each impact and the frequency of the impacts. If the collisions with the wall are perfectly elastic, the law of conservation of momentum will describe the results of the impact. The detailed reasoning for this procedure is worked out on pages 82 and 83. This is a beautifully simple application of Newtonian mechanics. The result is clear: applying Newtonian mechanics to the kinetic molecular model of gases leads to the conclusion that $P = \frac{1}{3}D(v^2)_{av}$ where $(v^2)_{av}$ is the average of the squared speed of the molecules.

So we have two expressions for the pressure of a gas. One summarizes the experimental facts, $P = kDT$. The other is derived by Newton's laws from a theoretical model, $P = \frac{1}{3}D(v^2)_{av}$. The *theoretical* expression will agree with the *experimental* expression only if $kT = \frac{1}{3}(v^2)_{av}$. This would mean that *the temperature of a gas is proportional to* $(v^2)_{av}$. The mass *m* of each molecule is a constant, so we can also say that the temperature is proportional to $\frac{1}{2}m(v^2)_{av}$. In equation form, $T \propto \frac{1}{2}m(v^2)_{av}$. You should recall that $\frac{1}{2}m(v^2)$ is our expression for kinetic energy. Thus, the kinetic theory leads to the conclusion that the temperature of a gas is proportional to the average kinetic energy of its molecules! We already had some idea that raising the temperature of a material somehow affected the motion of its "small parts." We were aware that the higher the temperature of a gas, the more rapidly its molecules are moving. But the conclusion $T \propto \frac{1}{2}m(v^2)_{av}$ is a precise quantitative relationship derived from the kinetic model and empirical laws.

Many different kinds of experimental evidence support this conclusion, and therefore also support the kinetic-theory model. Perhaps the best evidence is the motion of microscopic particles suspended in a gas or liquid,

This "absolute zero" point on the temperature scale has been found to be −273.16° Celsius (459.69° F).

For our purposes it is sufficiently accurate to say the absolute temperature of any sample (symbolized by the letter *T* and measured in degrees Kelvin, or °K) is equal to the Celsius temperature *t* plus 273°:
$$T = t + 273°$$
The boiling point of water, for example, is 373°K on the absolute scale.

SG 11.13, 11.14

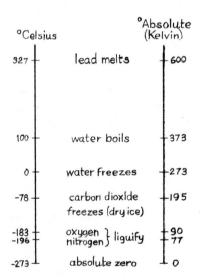

Comparison of the Celsius and absolute temperature scales.

Deriving an Expression For Pressure From the Kinetic Theory

We begin with the model of a gas described in Section 11.2: "a large number of very small particles in rapid, disordered motion." We can assume here that the particles are points with vanishingly small size, so that collisions between them can be ignored. If the particles did have finite size, the results of the calculation would be slightly different. But the approximation used here is accurate enough for most purposes.

The motions of particles moving in all directions with many different velocities are too complex as a starting point for a model. So we fix our attention first on one particle that is simply bouncing back and forth between two opposite walls of a box. Hardly any molecules in a real gas would actually move like this. But we will begin here in this simple way, and later in this chapter extend the argument to include other motions. This later part of the argument will require that one of the walls be movable. So let us arrange for that wall to be movable, but to fit snugly into the box.

In SG 9.24 we saw how the laws of conservation of momentum and energy apply to cases like this. When a very light particle hits a more massive object, like our wall, very little kinetic energy is transferred. If the collision is elastic, the particle will reverse its direction with very little change in speed. In fact, if a force on the outside of the wall keeps it stationary against the impact from inside, the wall will not move during the collisions. Thus *no work* is done on it, and the particles rebound without any change in speed.

How large a force will these particles exert on the wall when they hit it? By Newton's third law the average force acting on the wall is equal and opposite to the average force with which the wall acts on the particles. The force on each particle is equal to the product of its mass times its acceleration ($\vec{F} = m\vec{a}$), by Newton's second law. As shown in Section 9.4, the force can also be written as

$$\vec{F} = \frac{\Delta(m\vec{v})}{\Delta t}$$

where $\Delta(m\vec{v})$ is the change in momentum. Thus, to find the average force acting on the wall we need to find the change in momentum per second due to molecule-wall collisions.

Imagine that a particle, moving with speed v_x (the component of $\vec{v}$ in the x direction) is about to collide with the wall at the right. The component of the particle's momentum in the x direction is $m\vec{v}_x$. Since the particle collides elastically with the wall, it rebounds with the same speed. Therefore, the momentum in the x direction after the collision is $m(-\vec{v}_x) = -m\vec{v}_x$. The change in the

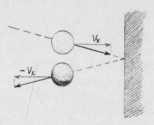

momentum of the particle as a result of this collision is

$$\frac{\text{final}}{\text{momentum}} - \frac{\text{initial}}{\text{momentum}} = \frac{\text{change in}}{\text{momentum}}$$

$$(-mv_x) \quad - \quad (mv_x) \quad = \quad (-2mv_x)$$

Note that all the vector quantities considered in this derivation have only two possible directions: to the right or to the left. We can therefore indicate direction by using a + or a −

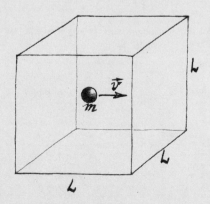

sign respectively.

Now think of a single particle of mass m moving in a cubical container of volume L^3 as shown in the figure.

The time between collisions of one particle with the right-hand wall is the time required to cover a distance $2L$ at a speed of v_x; that is, $2L/v_x$. If $2L/v_x$ = the time between collisions,

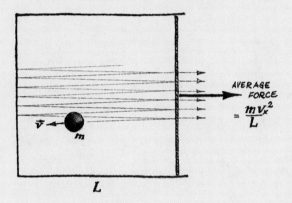

then $v_x/2L$ = the number of collisions per second. Thus, the change in momentum per second is given by

(change in   (number of   (change in
momentum in ×   collisions   =   momentum per
one collision)   per second)   second)

$$(-2mv_x) \quad \times \quad (v_x/2L) \quad = \quad \frac{-mv_x^2}{L}$$

The net force equals the rate of change of momentum. Thus, the average force acting on the molecule (due to the wall) is equal to $-mv_x^2/L$; and by Newton's third law, the average force acting on the wall (due to the molecule) is equal to $+mv_x^2/L$. So the average pressure on the wall due to the collisions made by one molecule moving with speed v_x is

$$P = \frac{F}{A} = \frac{F}{L^2} = \frac{mv_x^2}{L^3} = \frac{mv_x^2}{V}$$

where V (here L^3) is the volume of the cubical container.

Actually there are not one but N molecules in the container. They do not all have the same speed, but we need only the average speed in

order to find the pressure they exert. More precisely, we need the average of the square of their speeds in the x direction. We call this quantity $(v_x^2)_{av}$. The pressure on the wall due to N molecules will be N times the pressure due to one molecule, or

$$P = \frac{nm(v_x^2)_{av}}{V}$$

In a real gas, the molecules will be moving in all directions, not just in the x direction. That

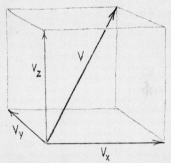

is, a molecule moving with speed v will have three components: v_x, v_y, and v_z. If the motion is random, then there is no preferred direction of motion for a large collection of molecules, and $(v_x^2)_{av} = (v_y^2)_{av} = (v_z^2)_{av}$. It can be shown from a theorem in geometry that $v^2 = v_x^2 + v_y^2 + v_z^2$. These last two expressions can be combined to give

$$(v^2)_{av} = 3(v_x^2)_{av}$$
$$\text{or} \qquad (v_x^2)_{av} = \tfrac{1}{3}(v^2)_{av}$$

By substituting this expression for $(v_x^2)_{av}$ in the pressure formula, we get

$$P = \frac{Nm \times 1/3(v^2)_{av}}{V}$$
$$= \frac{1}{3}\frac{Nm}{V}(v^2)_{av}$$

Notice now that Nm is the total mass of the gas and therefore Nm/V is just the density D. So

$$P = \tfrac{1}{3}D(v^2)_{av}$$

This is our theoretical expression for the pressure P exerted on a wall by a gas in terms of its density D and the molecular speed v.

SG 11.15

Brownian motion was named after the English botanist. Robert Brown, who in 1827 observed the phenomenon while looking at a suspension of the microscopic grains of plant pollen. The same kind of motion of particles ("thermal motion") exists also in liquids and solids. but there the particles are far more constrained than in gases.

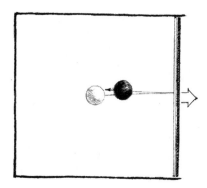

This phenomenon can be demonstrated by means of the expansion cloud chamber, cooling of CO_2 fire extinguisher, etc. The "wall" is here the air mass being pushed away.

Diesel engines have no spark plugs; ignition is produced by temperature rise during the high compression of the air-fuel vapor mixture.

called *Brownian Movement*. The gas or liquid molecules themselves are too small to be seen directly. But their effects on a larger particle (for example, a particle of smoke) can be observed through the microscope. At any instant, molecules moving at very different speeds are striking the larger particle from all sides. Nevertheless, so many molecules are taking part that their total effect *nearly* cancels. Any remaining effect changes in magnitude and direction from moment to moment. Hence the impact of the invisible molecules makes the visible particle "dance" in the viewfield of the microscope. The hotter the gas, the more lively the motion, as the equation $T \propto \frac{1}{2}m(v^2)_{av}$ predicts.

This experiment is simple to set up and fascinating to watch. You should do it as soon as you can in the laboratory. It gives visible evidence that the smallest parts of all matter in the universe are in a perpetual state of lively, random motion. In the words of the twentieth-century physicist Max Born, we live in a "restless universe."

But we need a more extensive argument in order to make confident quantitative predictions from kinetic theory. We know by experience that when a gas is compressed or expanded very slowly, its temperature changes hardly at all. Thus Boyle's simple law ($P = kD$) applies. But when a gas is compressed or condensed rapidly, the temperature does change. Then, only the more general gas law ($P = kDT$) applies. Can our model explain this?

In the model used on the special pages, particles were bouncing back and forth between the walls of a box. Every collision with the wall was perfectly elastic, so the particles rebounded with no loss in speed. Suppose we suddenly reduce the outside force that holds one wall in place. What will happen to the wall? The force exerted on the wall by the collisions of the particles will now be greater than the outside force. Therefore, the wall will move outward.

As long as the wall was stationary, the particles did no work on it, and the wall did no work on the particles. But now the wall moves in the same direction as the force exerted on it by the particles. Thus, the particles must be doing work on the wall. The energy needed to do this work must come from somewhere. But the only available source of energy here is the kinetic energy ($\frac{1}{2}mv^2$) of the particles. In fact, we can show that molecules colliding perfectly elastically with a receding wall rebound with slightly less speed (see SG 11.16). Therefore the kinetic energy of the particles must decrease. But the relationship $T \propto \frac{1}{2}m(v^2)_{av}$ implies that the temperature of the gas will then drop. And this is exactly what happens!

If we increase the outside force on the wall instead of decreasing it, just the opposite happens. The gas is suddenly compressed as the wall moves inward, doing work on the particles and increasing their kinetic energy. As $\frac{1}{2}mv^2$ goes up, we expect the temperature of the gas to rise—which is just what happens when we compress a gas quickly.

The model also predicts that, for *slow* motion of the wall, Boyle's law applies. However, the gas must not be insulated from its surroundings. Suppose we keep the surroundings of the gas at a constant temperature—for example, by immersing the gas container in a large water bath. Small changes in the temperature of the gas will then be cancelled by exchange of heat with the surroundings. Whenever the kinetic energy of the molecules momentarily decreases (as during expansion), the temperature of the gas will drop below that of its surroundings. Unless the walls of the container are heat insulators, heat will then flow into the gas until its temperature rises to that of the surroundings. Whenever the kinetic energy momentarily increases (as during compression), the temperature of the gas will rise above that of its surroundings. Heat will then flow out of the gas until its temperature falls to the temperature of the surroundings. This natural tendency of heat to flow from hot bodies to cold bodies explains why the average kinetic energy of the particles remains nearly constant when gas is slowly compressed or expanded.

SG 11.17–11.22

Q9   The relationship between the density and pressure of a gas expressed by Boyle's law, $P = kD$, holds true
(a) for any gas under any conditions
(b) for some gases under any conditions
(c) only if the temperature is kept constant
(d) only if the density is constant

Q10   If a piston is pushed rapidly into a container of gas, what will happen to the kinetic energy of the molecules of gas? What will happen to the temperature of the gas?

Q11   Which of the following conclusions result only when the ideal gas law and the kinetic theory model are *both* considered to apply?
(a) P is proportional to T.
(b) P is proportional to $(v^2)_{av}$.
(c) $(v^2)_{av}$ is proportional to T.

11.6 The second law of thermodynamics and the dissipation of energy

We have seen that the kinetic-theory model can explain the way a gas behaves when it is compressed or expanded, warmed or cooled. In the late nineteenth century, the model was refined to take into account many effects we have not discussed. There proved to be limits beyond which the model breaks down. For example, radiated heat comes to us from the sun through the vacuum of space. This is not explainable in terms of the thermal motion of particles. But in most cases the model worked splendidly, explaining the phenomena of heat in terms of the ordinary

SG 11.23

"Our life runs down in sending up
    the clock.
The brook runs down in sending
    up our life.
The sun runs down in sending up
    the brook.
And there is something sending
    up the sun.
It is this backward motion toward
    the source,
Against the stream, that most we
    see ourselves in,
It is from this in nature we are
    from.
It is most us."
[Robert Frost, *West-Running Brook*]

Sadi Carnot (1796–1832)

Modern steam engines have a
theoretical limit of about 35%
efficiency—but in practice they
seldom have better than 20%.

motions of particles. This was indeed a triumph of Newtonian mechanics. It fulfilled much of the hope Newton had expressed in the *Principia:* that all phenomena of nature could be explained in terms of the motion of the small parts of matter. In the rest of this chapter we will touch briefly on the further development of thermodynamic theory. (Additional discussion appears in several articles in *Reader 3.*)

The first additional concept arose out of a basic philosophical theme of the Newtonian cosmology: the idea that the world is like a machine whose parts never wear out, and which never runs down. This idea inspired the search for conservation laws applying to matter and motion. So far in this text, it might seem that this search has been successful. We can measure "matter" by mass, and "motion" by momentum or by kinetic energy. By 1850 the law of conservation of mass had been firmly established in chemistry. In physics, the laws of conservation of momentum and of energy had been equally well established.

Yet these successful conservation laws could not banish the suspicion that somehow the world *is* running down, the parts of the machine *are* wearing out. Energy may be conserved in burning fuel, but it loses its *usefulness* as the heat goes off into the atmosphere. Mass may be conserved in scrambling an egg, but its organized *structure* is lost. In these transformations, something is conserved, but something is also lost. Some processes are irreversible—they will not run backwards. There is no way to *un*scramble an egg, although such a change would not violate mass conservation. There is no way to draw smoke and hot fumes back onto a blackened stick, forming a new, unburned match.

The first attempts to find quantitative laws for such irreversible processes were stimulated by the development of steam engines. During the eighteenth and nineteenth centuries, engineers steadily increased the efficiency of steam engines. Recall that *efficiency* refers to the amount of mechanical work obtainable from a given amount of fuel energy. (See Section 10.6.) In 1824 a young French engineer, Sadi Carnot, published a short book entitled *Reflections on the Motive Power of Fire.* Carnot raised the question: Is there a maximum possible efficiency of an engine? Conservation of energy, of course, requires a limit of 100%, since energy output can never be greater than energy input. But, by analyzing the flow of heat in engines, Carnot proved that the maximum efficiency actually is always *less* than 100%. That is, the useful energy output can never even be as much as the input energy. There is a fixed limit on the amount of mechanical energy obtainable from a given amount of heat by using an engine. This limit can never be exceeded regardless of what substance—steam, air, or anything else—is used in the engine.

In addition to this limit on efficiency even for ideal engines, real engines operate at still lower efficiency in practice. For example, heat leaks from the hot parts of the engine to the cooler parts. Usually, this heat bypasses the part of the engine where it could be used to generate mechanical energy.

Carnot's analysis of steam engines shows that there is an *unavoidable* waste of mechanical energy, even under ideal circumstances. The total amount of energy in the high-temperature steam is *conserved* as it passes through the engine. But while part of it is transformed into useful mechanical energy, the rest is discharged in the exhaust. It then joins the relatively low temperature pool of the surrounding world. Carnot reasoned that there always must be some such "rejection" of heat from any kind of engine. This rejected heat goes off into the surroundings and becomes unavailable for useful work.

These conclusions about heat engines became the basis for the *Second Law of Thermodynamics*. This law has been stated in various ways, all of which are roughly equivalent. It expresses the idea that it is impossible to convert a given amount of heat fully into work.

Carnot's analysis implies more than this purely negative statement, however. In 1852, Lord Kelvin asserted that the second law of thermodynamics applies even more generally. There is, he said, a universal tendency in nature toward the "degradation" or "dissipation" of energy. Another way of stating this principle was suggested by Rudolph Clausius, in 1865. Clausius introduced a new concept, *entropy* (from the Greek word for transformation). In thermodynamics, entropy is defined quantitatively in terms of temperature and heat transfer. But here we will find it more useful to associate entropy with *disorder*. Increases in entropy occur with increasing disorder of motion in the parts of a system.

For example, think of a falling ball. If its temperature is very low, the random motion of its parts is very low too. Thus, the motion of all particles during the falling is mainly downward (and hence "ordered"). The ball strikes the floor and bounces several times. During each bounce, the mechanical energy of the ball decreases and the ball warms up. Now the random thermal motion of the parts of the heated ball is far more vigorous. Finally, the ball as a whole lies still (no "ordered" motion). The disordered motion of its molecules (and of the molecules of the floor where it bounced) is all the motion left. According to the entropy concept, *all* motion of whole bodies will run down like this. In other words, as with the bouncing ball, all motions tend from ordered to disordered. In fact, entropy can be defined mathematically as a measure of the disorder of a system (though we will not go into the mathematics here). The general version of the second law of thermodynamics, as stated by Clausius, is therefore quite simple: *the entropy of an isolated system always tends to increase*.

Irreversible processes are processes for which entropy increases. For example, heat will not flow by itself from cold bodies to hot bodies A ball lying on the floor will not somehow gather the kinetic energy of its randomly moving parts and suddenly leap up. An egg will not unscramble itself. An ocean liner cannot be powered by an engine that takes heat from the ocean water and exhausts ice cubes. All these and many other events could occur without violating any principles of Newtonian mechanics, including the law of conservation of energy. But they do not happen; they are "forbidden" by the second law of thermodynamics. (We say "forbidden" in the sense that Nature does not show that such things happen. Hence, the second law, formulated by the human mind, describes

The first law of thermodynamics, or the general law of conservation of energy. does not forbid the full conversion of heat into mechanical energy. The second law is an additional constraint on what can happen in nature.

SG 11.24-11.26

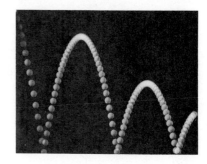

Two illustrations from Flammarion's novel, *Le Fin du Monde*.

"La miserable race humaine pêrira par le froid."

"Ce sera la fin."

SG 11.27

well what Nature does or does not do.)

We haven't pointed it out yet, but *all* familiar processes are to some degree irreversible. Thus, Lord Kelvin predicted that all bodies in the universe would eventually reach the same temperature by exchanging heat with each other. When this happened, it would be impossible to produce any useful work from heat. After all, work can only be done by means of heat engines when heat flows from a hot body to a cold body. Finally, the sun and other stars would cool, all life on earth would cease, and the universe would be dead.

This general "heat-death" idea, based on predictions from thermodynamics, aroused some popular interest at the end of the nineteenth century. It appeared in several books of that time, such as H. G. Wells' *The Time Machine*. The French astronomer Camille Flammarion wrote a book describing ways in which the world would end. The American historian Henry Adams had learned about thermodynamics through the writings of one of America's greatest scientists, J. Willard Gibbs. Adams attempted to extend the application of the second law from physics to human history in a series of essays entitled *The Degradation of the Democratic Dogma*.

Q12 The presumed "heat death of the universe" refers to a state
(a) in which all mechanical energy has been transformed into heat energy
(b) in which all heat energy has been transformed into other forms of energy
(c) in which the temperature of the universe decreases to absolute zero
(d) in which the supply of coal and oil has been used up.

Q13 Which of the following statements agrees with the second law of thermodynamics?
(a) Heat does not naturally flow from cold bodies to hot bodies.
(b) Energy tends to transform itself into less useful forms.
(c) No engine can transform all its heat input into mechanical energy.
(d) Most processes in nature are reversible.

11.7 Maxwell's demon and the statistical view of the second law of thermodynamics

Is there any way of avoiding the "heat death?" Is irreversibility a basic law of physics, or only an approximation based on our limited experience of natural processes?

The Austrian physicist Ludwig Boltzmann investigated the theory of irreversibility. He concluded that the tendency toward dissipation of energy is not an *absolute* law of physics that holds rigidly always. Rather, it is only a *statistical* law. Think of a can of air containing about 10^{22} molecules. Boltzmann argued that, of all conceivable arrangements of the gas molecules at a given instant, nearly all would be almost completely "disordered." Only a relatively few arrangements would have most of the molecules moving in the same direction. And even if a momentarily ordered arrangement of molecules occurred by chance, it would soon become less ordered by collisions, etc. Fluctuations from complete disorder will of course occur. But the greater the fluctuations, the less likely it is to occur. For collections of particles as large as 10^{22}, the chance of a fluctuation large enough to be measurable is vanishingly small. It is *conceivable* that a cold kettle of water will heat up on its own after being struck by only the most energetic molecules in the surrounding air. It is also *conceivable* that air molecules will "gang up" and strike only one side of a rock, pushing it uphill. But such events, while conceivable, are *utterly improbable*.

For *small* collections of particles, however, it is a different story. For example, it is quite probable that the average height of people on a bus will be considerably greater or less than the national average. In the same way, it is probable that more molecules will hit one side of a microscopic particle than the other side. Thus we can observe the "Brownian movement" of microscopic particles. Fluctuations are an important aspect of the world of very small particles. But they are virtually undetectable for any large collection of molecules familiar to us in the everyday world.

Still, the second law is different in character from all the other fundamental laws of physics we have studied so far. The difference is that it deals with probabilities, not uncertainties.

Maxwell proposed an interesting "thought experiment" to show how the second law of themodynamics could be violated or disobeyed. It involved an imaginary being who could observe individual molecules and sort them out in such a way that heat would flow from cold to hot. Suppose a container of gas is divided by a diaphragm into two parts, **A** and **B**. Initially the gas in **A** is hotter than the gas in **B**. This means that the molecules in **A** have greater average *KE* and therefore greater average speeds than those in **B**. However, the speeds are distributed according to

Consider also a pool table—the ordered motion of a cue ball moving into a stack of resting ones gets soon "randomized."

To illustrate Boltzmann's argument, consider a pack of cards when it is shuffled. Most possible arrangements of the cards after shuffling are fairly disordered. If we start with an ordered arrangement—for example, the cards sorted by suit and rank—then shuffling would almost certainly lead to a more disordered arrangement. (Nevertheless it does occasionally happen that a player is dealt 13 spades—even if no one has stacked the deck.)

Drawing by Steinberg; © 1963, The New Yorker Magazine, Inc.

How Maxwell's "demon" could use a small, massless door to *increase* the order of a system and make heat flow from a cold gas to a hot gas.

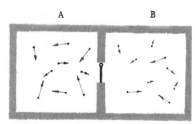

Initially the average *KE* of molecules is greater in *A*.

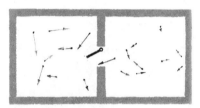

Only fast molecules are allowed to go from *B* to *A*.

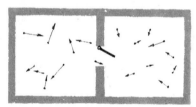

Only slow molecules are allowed to go from *A* to *B*.

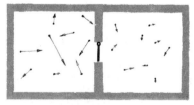

As this continues, the average *KE* in *A* increases and the average *KE* in *B* decreases.

SG 11.28

Maxwell's distribution (Section 11.3). Therefore many molecules in **A** have speeds less than the average in **A**.

"Now conceive a finite being," Maxwell suggested, "who knows the paths and velocities of all the molecules by simple inspection but who can do no work except open and close a hole in the diaphragm by means of a slide without mass." (If the slide or door has no mass, no work will be needed to move it.) This "finite being" observes the molecules in **A**. When he sees one coming whose speed is less than the average speed of the molecules in **B,** he opens the hole and lets it go into **B**. Now the average speed of the molecules of **B** is even lower than it was before. Next, the "being" watches for a molecule of **B** with a speed greater than the average speed in **A**. When he sees one, he opens the hole to let the molecule go into **A**. Now the average speed in **A** is even higher than it was before. Maxwell concludes:

> Then the number of molecules in **A** and **B** are the same as at first, but the energy in **A** is increased and that in **B** diminished, that is, the hot system has got hotter and the cold colder and yet no work has been done, only the intelligence of a very observant and neat-fingered being has been employed.

In the same way, a group of such beings could keep watch over a swarm of randomly moving molecules. By allowing passage to those molecules moving only in some given direction, they could establish a region of orderly molecular motion.

The imaginary "being who knows the paths and velocities of all the molecules" has come to be known as "Maxwell's demon." Maxwell's thought experiment shows that if there were any way to sort out individual molecules, the tendency to increasing entropy could be reversed. Some biologists have suggested that certain large molecules, such as enzymes, may function in just this way. They may influence the motions of smaller molecules, building up ordered molecular systems in living beings. This would help to explain why growing plants or animals do not tend toward higher disorder, while lifeless objects do.

As interesting as this suggestion is, it shows a misunderstanding of the second law of thermodynamics. The second law doesn't say that the order can never (or is extremely unlikely to) increase in *any* system. It makes that claim only for an isolated, or closed system. The order of *part* of a closed system may increase, but only if the order of the *other parts* decreases by as much or more. This point is made nicely in the following passage from a UNESCO document on environmental pollution.

> Some scientists used to feel that the occurrence, reproduction, and growth of order in living systems presented an exception to the second law. This is no longer believed to be so. True, the living system may increase in order, but only by diffusing energy to the surroundings and by converting complicated molecules (carbohydrates, fats) called food into simple

molecules (CO_2, H_2O). For example, to maintain a healthy human being at constant weight for one year requires the degradation of about 500 kilograms (one half ton) of food, and the diffusion into the surroundings (from the human and the food) of about 500,000 kilocalories (two million kilojoules) of energy. The "order" in the human may stay constant or even increase, but the order in the surroundings decreases much, much more. Maintenance of life is an expensive process in terms of generation of disorder, and no one can understand the full implications of human ecology and environmental pollution without understanding that first.

Q14 In each of the following pairs, which situation is more ordered?
(a) an unbroken egg; a scrambled egg.
(b) a glass of ice and warm water; a glass of water at uniform temperature.
Q15 True or false?
(a) Maxwell's demon was able to get around the second law of thermodynamics.
(b) Scientists have made a Maxwell demon.
(c) Maxwell believed that his demon actually existed.

James Clerk Maxwell (1831–1879)

11.8 Time's arrow and the recurrence paradox

Late in the nineteenth century, a small but influential group of scientists began to question the basic philosophical assumptions of Newtonian mechanics. They even questioned the very idea of atoms. The Austrian physicist Ernst Mach argued that scientific theories should not depend on assuming the existence of things (such as atoms) which could not be directly observed. Typical of the attacks on atomic theory was the argument used by the mathematician Ernst Zermelo and others against kinetic theory. Zermelo believed that: (1) The second law of thermodynamics is an absolutely valid law of physics because it agrees with all the experimental data. However, (2) kinetic theory allows the possibility of exceptions to this law (due to large fluctuations). Therefore, (3) kinetic theory must be wrong. It is an interesting historical episode on a point that is still not quite settled.

The critics of kinetic theory pointed to two apparent contradictions between kinetic theory and the principle of dissipation of energy. These were the *reversibility paradox* and the *recurrence paradox*. Both paradoxes are based on possible exceptions to the second law; both could be thought to cast doubt on the kinetic theory.

The *reversibility* paradox was discovered in the 1870's by Lord Kelvin and Josef Loschmidt, both of whom supported atomic theory. It was not regarded as a serious objection to the kinetic theory until the 1890's. The paradox is based on the simple fact that Newton's laws of motion are reversible in time. For example, if we watch a motion picture of a

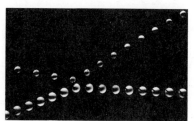

The reversibility paradox: Can a model based on reversible events explain a world in which so many events are irreversible? (Also see photographs on next page.)

bouncing ball, it is easy to tell whether the film is being run forward or backward. We know that the collisions of the ball with the floor are inelastic, and that the ball rises less high after each bounce. If, however, the ball made perfectly elastic bounces, it would rise to the same height after each bounce. Then we could not tell whether the film was being run forward or backward. In the kinetic theory, molecules *are* assumed to make perfectly elastic collisions. Imagine that we could take a motion picture of gas molecules colliding elastically according to this assumption. When showing this motion picture, there would be no way to tell whether it was being run forward or backward. Either way would show valid sequences of collisions. But—and this is the paradox—consider motion pictures of interactions involving large objects, containing many molecules. One can immediately tell the difference between forward (true) and backward (impossible) time direction. For example, a smashed lightbulb does not reassemble itself in real life, though a movie run backward can make it appear to do so.

The kinetic theory is based on laws of motion which are reversible for each individual molecular interaction. How, then, can it explain the existence of *irreversible* processes on a large scale? The existence of such processes seems to indicate that time flows in a definite direction—from past to future. This contradicts the possibility implied in Newton's laws of motion: that it does not matter whether we think of time as flowing forward or backward. As Lord Kelvin expressed the paradox,

> If . . . the motion of every particle of matter in the universe were precisely reversed at any instant, the course of nature would be simply reversed for ever after. The bursting bubble of foam at the foot of a waterfall would reunite and descend into the water; the thermal motions would reconcentrate their energy, and throw the mass up the fall in drops reforming into a close column of ascending water. Heat which had been generated by the friction of solids and dissipated by conduction, and radiation with absorption, would come again to the place of contact, and throw the moving body back against the force to which it had previously yielded. Boulders would recover from the mud the materials required to rebuild them into their previous jagged forms, and would become reunited to the mountain peak from which they had formerly broken away. And if also the materialistic hypothesis of life were true, living creatures would grow backwards, with conscious knowledge of the future, but no memory of the past, and would become again unborn. But the real phenomena of life infinitely transcend human science; and speculation regarding consequences of their imagined reversal is utterly unprofitable.

Kelvin himself, and later Boltzmann, used statistical probability to explain why we do not observe such large-scale reversals. There are almost infinitely many possible disordered arrangements of water molecules at the bottom of a waterfall. Only an extremely small number of these arrangements would lead to the process described above. Reversals of this kind are possible *in principle,* but for all practical purposes they are out of the question.

The answer to Zermelo's argument is that his first claim is incorrect. The second law of thermodynamics is not an absolute law, but a statistical law. It assigns a very low probability to ever detecting any overall increase in order, but does not declare it impossible.

However, another small possibility allowed in kinetic theory leads to a situation that seems unavoidably to contradict the dissipation of energy. The *recurrence paradox* revived an idea that appeared frequently in ancient philosophies and present also in Hindu philosophy to this day: the myth of the "eternal return." According to this myth, the long-range history of the world is cyclic. All historical events eventually repeat themselves, perhaps many times. Given enough time, even the matter that people were made of will eventually reassemble by chance. Then people who have died may be born again and go through the same life. The German philosopher Friedrich Nietzsche was convinced of the truth of this idea. He even tried to prove it by appealing to the principle of conservation of energy. He wrote:

> If the universe may be conceived as a definite quantity of energy, as a definite number of centres of energy—and every other concept remains indefinite and therefore useless—it follows therefrom that the universe must go through a calculable number of combinations in the great game of chance which constitutes its existence. In infinity [of time], at some moment or other, every possible combination must once have been realized; not only this, but it must have been realized an infinite number of times.

If the number of molecules is finite, there is only a finite number of possible arrangements of molecules. Hence, somewhere in infinite time the same combination of molecules is bound to come up again. At the same point, all the molecules in the universe would reach exactly the same arrangement they had at some previous time. All events following this point would have to be exactly the same as the events that followed it before. That is, if any single instant in the history of the universe is ever exactly repeated, then the entire history of the universe will be repeated. And, as a little thought shows, it would then be repeated over and over again to infinity. Thus, energy would *not* endlessly become dissipated. Nietzsche claimed that this view of the eternal return disproved the "heat death" theory. At about the same time, in 1889, the French mathematician Henri Poincaré published a theorem on the possibility of recurrence in mechanical systems. According to Poincaré, even though the universe might undergo a heat death, it would ultimately come alive again:

> A bounded world, governed only by the laws of mechanics, will always pass through a state very close to its initial state. On the other hand, according to accepted experimental laws (if one

SG 11.29

The World's great age begins anew,
  The golden years return,
The earth doth like a snake renew
  His winter weeds outworn . . .
Another Athens shall arise
  And to remoter time
Bequeath, like sunset to the skies,
  The splendour of its prime . . .
[Percy Bysshe Shelley, "Hellas" (1822)]

Lord Kelvin (1824–1907)

SG 11.30-11.32

attributes absolute validity to them, and if one is willing to press their consequences to the extreme), the universe tends toward a certain final state, from which it will never depart. In this final state, from which will be a kind of death, all bodies will be at rest at the same temperature.

. . . the kinetic theories can extricate themselves from this contradiction. The world, according to them, tends at first toward a state where it remains for a long time without apparent change; and this is consistent with experience; but it does not remain that way forever; . . . it merely stays there for an enormously long time, a time which is longer the more numerous are the molecules. This state will not be the final death of the universe, but a sort of slumber, from which it will awake after millions of centuries.

According to this theory, to see heat pass from a cold body to a warm one, it will not be necessary to have the acute vision, the intelligence, and the dexterity of Maxwell's demon; it will suffice to have a little patience.

SG 11.33

Poincaré was willing to accept the possibility of a violation of the second law after a very long time. But others refused to admit even this possibility. In 1896, Zermelo published a paper attacking not only the kinetic theory but the mechanistic world view in general. This view, he asserted, contradicted the second law. Boltzmann replied, repeating his earlier explanations of the statistical nature of irreversibility.

The final outcome of the dispute between Boltzmann and his critics was that both sides were partly right and partly wrong. Mach and Zermelo were correct in believing that Newton's laws of mechanics cannot fully describe molecular and atomic processes. (We will come back to this subject in Unit 5.) For example, it is only approximately valid to describe gases in terms of collections of frantic little billiard balls. But Boltzmann was right in defending the usefulness of the molecular model. The kinetic theory is very nearly correct except for those properties of matter which involve the structure of molecules themselves.

In 1905, Albert Einstein pointed out that the fluctuations predicted by kinetic theory could be used to calculate the rate of displacement for particles in "Brownian" movement. Precise quantitative studies of Brownian movement confirmed Einstein's theoretical calculations. This new success of kinetic theory—along with discoveries in radioactivity and atomic physics—persuaded almost all the critics that atoms and molecules do exist. But the problems of irreversibility and of whether the laws of physics must distinguish between past and future survived. In new form, these issues still interest physicists today.

This chapter concludes the application of Newtonian mechanics to individual particles. The story was mainly one of triumphant success. Toward the end, however, we have hinted that, like all theories, Newtonian mechanics has serious limitations. These will be explored later.

The last chapter in this unit covers the successful use of Newtonian mechanics in the case of mechanical wave motion. This will complete the list of possibilities of particle motion. In Unit 1 we treated the motion of single particles or isolated objects. The motion of a system of objects bound by a

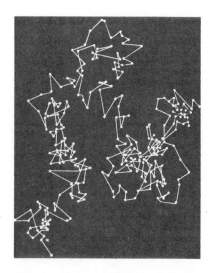

Record of a particle in Brownian motion. Successive positions, recorded every 20 seconds, are connected by straight lines. The actual paths between recorded positions would be as erratic as the overall path.

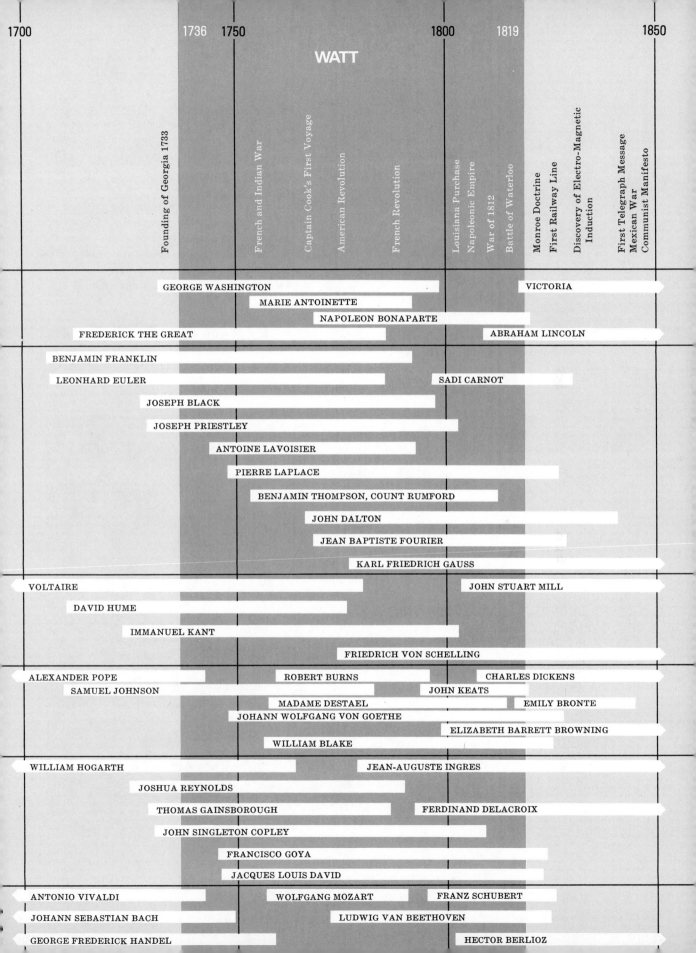

1700	1736	1750	1800	1819	1850

WATT

Founding of Georgia 1733

French and Indian War

Captain Cook's First Voyage

American Revolution

French Revolution

Louisiana Purchase
Napoleonic Empire
War of 1812
Battle of Waterloo

Monroe Doctrine
First Railway Line

Discovery of Electro-Magnetic Induction

First Telegraph Message
Mexican War
Communist Manifesto

GEORGE WASHINGTON

VICTORIA

MARIE ANTOINETTE

NAPOLEON BONAPARTE

FREDERICK THE GREAT

ABRAHAM LINCOLN

BENJAMIN FRANKLIN

LEONHARD EULER

SADI CARNOT

JOSEPH BLACK

JOSEPH PRIESTLEY

ANTOINE LAVOISIER

PIERRE LAPLACE

BENJAMIN THOMPSON, COUNT RUMFORD

JOHN DALTON

JEAN BAPTISTE FOURIER

KARL FRIEDRICH GAUSS

VOLTAIRE

JOHN STUART MILL

DAVID HUME

IMMANUEL KANT

FRIEDRICH VON SCHELLING

ALEXANDER POPE

ROBERT BURNS

CHARLES DICKENS

SAMUEL JOHNSON

JOHN KEATS

MADAME DESTAEL

EMILY BRONTE

JOHANN WOLFGANG VON GOETHE

ELIZABETH BARRETT BROWNING

WILLIAM BLAKE

WILLIAM HOGARTH

JEAN-AUGUSTE INGRES

JOSHUA REYNOLDS

THOMAS GAINSBOROUGH

FERDINAND DELACROIX

JOHN SINGLETON COPLEY

FRANCISCO GOYA

JACQUES LOUIS DAVID

ANTONIO VIVALDI

WOLFGANG MOZART

FRANZ SCHUBERT

JOHANN SEBASTIAN BACH

LUDWIG VAN BEETHOVEN

GEORGE FREDERICK HANDEL

HECTOR BERLIOZ

force of interaction, such as the Earth and Sun, was treated in Unit 2 and in Chapters 9 and 10 of this unit. In this chapter we discussed the motions of a system of a very large number of separate objects. Finally, in Chapter 12 we will study the action of many particles going back and forth together as a wave passes.

Q16 The kinetic energy of a falling stone is transformed into heat when the stone strikes the ground. Obviously this is an irreversible process; we never see the heat transform into kinetic energy of the stone, so that the stone rises off the ground. We believe that the process is irreversible because

SG 11.34
SG 11.35

    (a) Newton's laws of motion prohibit the reversed process.
    (b) the probability of such a sudden ordering of molecular motion is extremely small.
    (c) the reversed process would not conserve energy.
    (d) the reverse process would violate the second law of thermodynamics.

The ruins of a Greek temple at Delphi are an elegant testimony to the continual encroachment of disorder.

11.1 The Project Physics materials particularly appropriate for Chapter 11 include:

Experiments
Monte Carlo Experiment on Molecular Collisions
Behavior of Gases

Activities
Drinking Duck
Mechanical Equivalent of Heat
A Diver in a Bottle
Rockets
How to Weigh a Car with a Tire Pressure Gauge
Perpetual-Motion Machines

Film Loop
Reversibility of Time

Reader Articles
The Barometer Story
The Great Molecular Theory of Gases
Entropy and the Second Law of Thermodynamics
The Law of Disorder
The Law
The Arrow of Time
James Clerk Maxwell
Randomness and the Twentieth Century

11.2 The idea of randomness can be used in predicting the results of flipping a large number of coins. Give some other examples where randomness is useful.

11.3 The examples of early kinetic theories given in Sec. 11.3 include only *quantitative* models. Some of the underlying ideas are thousands of years old. Compare the kinetic molecular theory of gases to these Greek ideas expressed by the Roman poet Lucretius in about 60 B.C.:

If you think that the atoms can stop and by their stopping generate new motions in things, you are wandering far from the path of truth. Since the atoms are moving freely through the void, they must all be kept in motion either by their own weight or on occasion by the impact of another atom. For it must often happen that two of them in their course knock together and immediately bounce apart in opposite directions, a natural consequence of their hardness and solidity and the absence of anything behind to stop them . . . .

It clearly follows that no rest is given to the atoms in their course through the depths of space. Driven along in an incessant but variable movement, some of them bounce far apart after a collision while others recoil only a short distance from the impact. From those that do not recoil far, being driven into a closer union and held there by the entanglement of their own interlocking shapes, are composed firmly rooted rock, the stubborn strength of steel and the like. Those others that move freely through larger tracts of space, springing far apart and carried far by the rebound — these provide for us thin air and blazing sunlight. Besides these, there are many other

atoms at large in empty space which have been thrown out of compound bodies and have nowhere even been granted admittance so as to bring their motions into harmony.

11.4 Consider these aspects of the curves showing Maxwell's distribution of molecular speeds:
(a) All show a peak.
(b) The peaks move toward higher speed at higher temperatures.
(c) They are not symmetrical, like normal distribution curves.
Explain these characteristics on the basis of the kinetic model.

11.5 The measured speed of sound in a gas turns out to be nearly the same as the average speed of the gas molecules. Is this a coincidence? Discuss.

11.6 How did Clausius modify the simple kinetic model for a gas? What was he able to explain with this new model?

11.7 Benjamin Franklin observed in 1765 that a teaspoonful of oil would spread out to cover half an acre of a pond. This helps to give an estimate of the upper limit of the size of a molecule. Suppose that one cubic centimeter of oil forms a continuous layer one molecule thick that just covers an area on water of 1000 square meters.
(a) How thick is the layer?
(b) What is the size of a single molecule of the oil (considered to be a cube for simplicity)?

11.8 Knowing the size of molecules allows us to compute the number of molecules in a sample of material. If we assume that molecules in a solid or liquid are packed close together, something like apples in a bin, then the total volume of a material is approximately equal to the volume of one molecule times the number of molecules in the material.
(a) Roughly how many molecules are there in 1 cubic centimeter of water? (For this approximation, you can take the volume of a molecule to be d^3 if its diameter is d.)
(b) The density of a gas (at 1 atmosphere pressure and 0°C) is about 1/1000 the density of a liquid. Roughly how many molecules are there in 1 cc. of gas? Does this estimate support the kinetic model of a gas as described on p. 82?

11.9 How high could water be raised with a lift pump on the moon?

11.10 At sea level, the atmospheric pressure of air ordinarily can balance a barometer column of mercury of height 0.76 meters or 10.5 meters of water. Air is approximately a thousand times less dense than liquid water. What can you say about the minimum height to which the atmosphere goes above the Earth?

11.11 How many atmospheres of pressure do you exert on the ground when you stand on flat-heeled shoes? skis? skates? (1 atmosphere is about 15 lbs/in.)

11.12 From the definition of density, $D = M/V$ (where M is the mass of a sample and V is its volume), write an expression relating pressure P and volume V of a gas.

11.13 Show how all the proportionalities describing gas behavior on p. 79 are included in the ideal gas law: $P = kD (t + 273°)$

11.14 The following information appeared in a pamphlet published by an oil company:

HOW'S YOUR TIRE PRESSURE?

If you last checked the pressure in your tires on a warm day, one cold morning you may find your tires seriously underinflated.

The Rubber Manufacturers Association warns that tire pressures drop approximately one pound for every 10-degree dip in outside air. If your tires register 24 pounds pressure on an 80-degree day, for example, they'll have only 19 pounds pressure when the outside air plunges to 30° Fahrenheit.

If you keep your car in a heated garage at 60°, and drive out into a 20 degrees-below-zero morning, your tire pressure drops from 24 pounds to 18 pounds.

Are these statements consistent with the ideal gas law? (Note: The pressure registered on a tire gauge is the pressure *above* normal atmospheric pressure of about 15 pounds/sq. in.)

11.15 Distinguish between two uses of the word "model" in science.

11.16 If a light particle rebounds from a massive, stationary wall with almost no loss of speed, then, according to the principle of Galilean relativity, it would still rebound from a *moving* wall without changing speed as seen in *the frame of reference of the moving piston.* Show that the rebound speed as measured *in the laboratory* would be less from a retreating wall (as is claimed at the bottom of p. 84).
(Hint: First write an expression relating the particle's speed relative-to-the-wall to its speed relative-to-the-laboratory.)

11.17 What would you expect to happen to the temperature of a gas that was released from a

container in empty space (that is, with nothing to push back)?

11.18 List some of the directly observable properties of gases.

11.19 What aspects of the behavior of gases can the kinetic molecular theory be used to explain successfully?

11.20 Many products are now sold in spray cans. Explain in terms of the kinetic theory of gases why it is dangerous to expose the cans to high temperatures.

11.21 When a gas in an enclosure is compressed by pushing in a piston, its temperature increases.

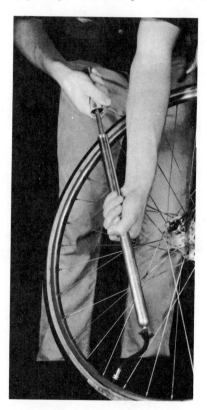

Explain this fact in two ways:
(a) by using the first law of thermodynamics.
(b) by using the kinetic theory of gases.
The compressed air eventually cools down to the same temperature as the surroundings. Describe this heat transfer in terms of molecular collisions.

11.22 From the point of view of the kinetic theory, how can one explain (a) that a hot gas would not cool itself down while in a perfectly insulating container? (b) how a kettle of cold water, when put on the stove, reaches a boiling temperature. (Hint: At a given temperature the molecules in and on the walls of the solid container are also in motion, although, being part of a solid, they do not often get far away.)

11.23 In the *Principia* Newton expressed the hope that all phenomena could be explained in terms of the motion of atoms. How does Newton's view compare with this Greek view expressed by Lucretius in about 60 B.C.?

I will now set out in order *the stages by which the initial concentration of matter laid the foundations of earth and sky*, of the ocean depths and the orbits of sun and moon. Certainly the atoms did not post themselves purposefully in due order by an act of intelligence, nor did they stipulate what movements each should perform. But multitudinous atoms, swept along in multitudinous courses through infinite time by mutual clashes and their own weight, have come together in every possible way and realized everything that could be formed by their combinations. So it comes about that a voyage of immense duration, in which they have experienced every variety of movement and conjunction, has at length brought together those whose sudden encounter normally forms the starting-point of substantial fabrics — earth and sea and sky and the races of living creatures.

11.24 Clausius' statement of the second law of thermodynamics is: "Heat will not of its own accord pass from a cooler to a hotter body." Give examples of the operation of this law. Describe how a refrigerator can operate, and show that it does not contradict the Clausius statement.

11.25 There is a tremendous amount of internal energy in the oceans and in the atmosphere. What would you think of an invention that purported to draw on this source of energy to do mechanical work? (For example, a ship that sucked in sea water and exhausted blocks of ice, using the heat from the water to run the ship.)

11.26 Imagine a room that is perfectly insulated so that no heat can enter or leave. In the room is a refrigerator that is plugged into an electric outlet in the wall. If the door of the refrigerator is left open, what happens to the temperature of the room?

11.27 Since there is a tendency for heat to flow from hot to cold, will the universe eventually reach absolute zero?

11.28 Does Maxwell's demon get around the second law of thermodynamics? List the assumptions in Maxwell's argument. Which of them do you believe are likely to be true?

11.29 Since all the evidence is that molecular motions are random, one might expect that any given arrangement of molecules will recur if one just waited long enough. Explain how a paradox arises when this prediction is compared with the second law of thermodynamics.

11.30 (a) Explain what is meant by the statement that Newton's laws of motion are time-reversible.

(b) Describe how a paradox arises when the time-reversibility of Newton's laws of motion is compared with the second law of thermodynamics.

11.31 If there is a finite probability of an exact repetition of a state of the universe, there is also a finite probability of its exact opposite — that is, a state where molecules are in the same position but with reversed velocities. What would this imply about the subsequent history of the universe?

11.32 List the assumptions in the "recurrence" theory. Which of them do you believe to be true?

11.33 Some philosophical and religious systems of the Far East and the Middle East include the ideas of the eternal return. If you have read about some of these philosophies, discuss what analogies exist with some of the ideas in the last part of this chapter. Is it appropriate to take the existence of such analogies to mean there is some direct connection between these philosophical and physical ideas?

11.34 Where did Newtonian mechanics run into difficulties in explaining the behavior of molecules?

11.35 What are some advantages and disadvantages of theoretical models?

CHAPTER TWELVE

Waves

12.1 Introduction

The world is continually criss-crossed by waves of all sorts. Water waves, whether giant rollers in the middle of the ocean or gently-formed rain ripples on a still pond, are sources of wonder or pleasure. If the earth's crust shifts, violent waves in the solid earth cause tremors thousands of miles away. A musician plucks a guitar string and sound waves pulse against our ears. Wave disturbances may come in a concentrated bundle like the shock front from an airplane flying at supersonic speeds. Or the disturbances may come in succession like the train of waves sent out from a steadily vibrating source, such as a bell or a string.

SG 12.1

All of these are *mechanical* waves, in which bodies or particles physically move back and forth. But there are also wave disturbances in electric and magnetic fields. In Unit 4, you will learn that such waves are responsible for what our senses experience as light. In all cases involving waves, however, the effects produced depend on the flow of energy as the wave moves forward.

So far in this text we have considered motion in terms of individual particles. In this chapter we begin to study the cooperative motion of collections of particles in "continuous media" moving in the form of mechanical waves. We will see how closely related are the ideas of particles and waves which we use to describe events in nature.

A comparison will help us here. Look at a black and white photograph in a newspaper or magazine with a magnifying glass. You will see that the picture is made up of many little black dots printed on a white page (up to 20,000 dots per square inch). Without the magnifier, you do not see the individual dots. Rather, you see a pattern with all possible shadings between completely black and completely white. These two views emphasize different aspects of the same thing. In much the same way, the physicist can sometimes choose between two (or more) ways of viewing events. For the most part, a particle view has been emphasized in

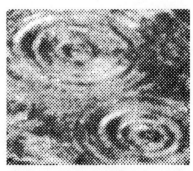

A small section from the lower right of the photograph on the opposite page.

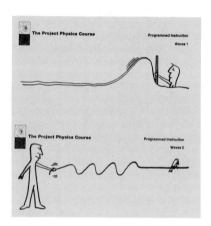

the first three units of the *Text*. In Unit 2 for example, we treated each planet as a particle undergoing the sun's gravitational attraction. We described the behavior of the solar system in terms of the positions, velocities, and accelerations of point-like objects. For someone interested only in planetary motions, this is fine. But for someone interested in, say, the chemistry of materials on Mars, it is not very helpful.

In the last chapter we saw two different descriptions of a gas. One was in terms of the behavior of the individual particles making up the gas. We used Newton's laws of motion to describe what each *individual* particle does. Then we used average values of speed or energy to describe the behavior of the gas. But we also discussed concepts such as pressure, temperature, heat, and entropy. These refer directly to a sample of gas *as a whole*. This is the viewpoint of thermodynamics, which does not depend on assuming Newton's laws or even the existence of particles. Each of these viewpoints served a useful purpose and helped us to understand what we cannot directly see.

Now we are about to study waves, and once again we find the possibility of using different points of view. Most of the waves discussed in this chapter can be described in terms of the behavior of particles. But we also want to understand waves as disturbances traveling in a continuous medium. We want, in other words, to see both the forest and the trees—the picture as a whole, not only individual dots.

12.2 Properties of waves

Suppose that two people are holding opposite ends of a rope. Suddenly one person snaps the rope up and down quickly once. That "disturbs" the rope and puts a hump in it which travels along the rope toward the other person. We can call the traveling hump one kind of a wave, a *pulse*.

Originally, the rope was motionless. The height of each point on the rope depended only upon its position along the rope, and did not change in time. But when one person snaps the rope, he creates a rapid change in the height of one end. This disturbance then moves away from its source. The height of each point on the rope depends upon time as well as position along the rope.

The disturbance is a pattern of *displacement* along the rope. The motion of the displacement pattern from one end of the rope toward the other is an example of a *wave*. The hand snapping one end is the *source* of the wave. The rope is the *medium* in which the wave moves. These four terms are common to all mechanical wave situations.

Consider another example. When a pebble falls into a pool of still liquid, a series of circular crests and troughs spreads over the surface. This moving displacement pattern of the liquid surface is a wave. The pebble is the source, the moving pattern of crests and troughs is the wave, and the liquid surface is the medium. Leaves, sticks, or other objects floating on the surface of the liquid bob up and down as each wave passes. But they do not experience any net displacement on the average.

No *material* has moved from the wave source, either on the surface or among the particles of the liquid. The same holds for rope waves, sound waves in air, etc.

As any one of these waves moves through a medium, the wave produces a changing displacement of the successive parts of the medium. Thus we can refer to these waves as *waves of displacement*. If we can see the medium and recognize the displacements, then we can see waves. But waves also may exist in media we cannot see (such as air). Or they may form as disturbances of a state we cannot detect with our eyes (such as pressure, or an electric field).

You can use a loose spring coil to demonstrate three different kinds of motion in the medium through which a wave passes. First, move the end of the spring from side to side, or up and down as in sketch (a) in the margin. A wave of side-to-side or up-and-down displacement will travel along the spring. Now push the end of the spring back and forth, along the direction of the spring itself, as in sketch (b). A wave of back-and-forth displacement will travel along the spring. Finally, twist the end of the spring clockwise and counterclockwise, as in sketch (c). A wave of angular displacement will travel along the spring. Waves like those in (a), in which the displacements are perpendicular to the direction the wave travels, are called *transverse* waves. Waves like those in (b), in which the displacements are in the direction the wave travels, are called *longitudinal* waves. And waves like those in (c), in which the displacements are twisting in a plane perpendicular to the direction the wave travels, are called *torsional* waves.

All three types of wave motion can be set up in solids. In fluids, however, transverse and torsional waves die out very quickly, and usually cannot be produced at all. So sound waves in air and water are longitudinal. The molecules of the medium are displaced back and forth along the direction that the sound travels.

It is often useful to make a graph of wave patterns in a medium. However, a graph on paper always has a transverse appearance, even if it represents a longitudinal or torsional wave. For example, the graph at the right represents the pattern of compressions in a sound wave in air. The sound waves are longitudinal, but the graph line goes up and down. This is because the graph represents the increasing and decreasing density of the air. It does *not* represent an up-and-down motion of the air.

To describe completely transverse waves, such as those in ropes, you must specify the *direction* of displacement. Longitudinal and torsional waves do not require this specification. The displacement of a longitudinal wave can be in only one direction—along the direction of travel of the wave. Similarly, the angular displacements of a torsional wave can be around only one axis—the direction of travel of the wave. But the displacements of a transverse wave can be in any and all of an infinite number of directions. The only requirement is that they be at right angles to the direction of travel of the wave. You can see this by shaking one end of a rope randomly instead of straight up and down or straight left and right. For simplicity, our diagrams of rope and spring waves here show transverse displacements consistently in only one of all the possible planes.

When the displacement pattern of a transverse wave does lie in a

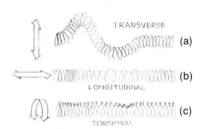

"Snapshots" of three types of waves. In (c), small markers have been put on the top of each coil in the spring.

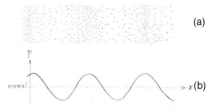

(a) "Snapshot" representation of a sound wave progressing to the right. The dots represent the density of air molecules. (b) Graph of air pressure *P* vs. position *x* at the instant of the snapshot.

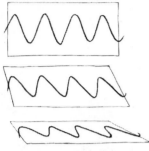

Three of the infinitely many different polarization planes of a transverse wave.

single plane, we say the wave is *polarized*. For waves on ropes and springs, we can observe the polarization directly. Thus, in the photograph on the previous page, the waves the person makes are in the horizontal plane. However, whether we can see the wave directly or not, there is a general test for polarization. The test involves finding some effect of the wave which depends on the angular position of a medium or obstacle through which it travels. An example of the principle is illustrated in the diagram below. Here, the transmission of a rope wave depends on the angle at which a slotted board is held. Each of the three sketches begins with the same wave approaching the obstacle (top line). Whether the wave passes through (bottom line) depends on the angle the slot makes with the plane of the rope's mechanical motion.

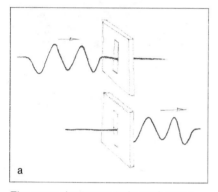

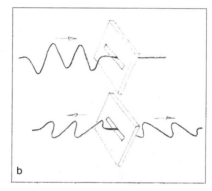

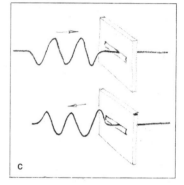

a   b   c

The same short wave train on the rope approaches the slotted board in each of the three sketches (top). Depending on the orientation of the slot, the train of waves (a) goes entirely through the slot; (b) is partly reflected and partly transmitted with changed angles of rope vibration; or (c) is completely reflected.

In general, if some effect of a wave depends similarly on the angular position of an obstacle or medium, the wave must be polarized. Further, we can conclude that the wave is transverse rather than longitudinal or torsional. Some interesting and important examples of this principle will be presented in Chapter 13.

All three kinds of wave—longitudinal, transverse, and torsional—have an important characteristic in common. The disturbances move away from their sources through the media and *continue on their own*. We stress this particular characteristic by saying that these waves *propagate*. This means more than just that they "travel" or "move." An example will clarify the difference between waves which propagate and those which do not. You probably have read some description of the great wheat plains of our Middle West, Canada, or Central Europe. Such descriptions usually mention the "beautiful, wind-formed waves that roll for miles across the fields." The medium for such a wave is the wheat, and the disturbance is the swaying motion of the wheat. This disturbance does indeed travel, but it does *not* propagate. That is, the disturbance does not originate at a source and then go on by *itself*. Rather, it must be continually fanned by the wind. When the wind stops, the disturbance does not roll on, but stops, too. The traveling "waves" of swaying wheat are not at all the same as our rope and water waves. We will concentrate on waves that do originate at sources and propagate themselves. For the purposes of this chapter, *waves are disturbances which propagate in a medium.*

Q1 What kinds of mechanical waves can propagate in a solid?
Q2 What kinds of mechanical waves can propagate in a fluid?
Q3 What kinds of mechanical waves can be polarized?
Q4 Suppose that a mouse runs along under a rug, causing a bump
in the rug that travels with the mouse across the room. Is this moving
disturbance a propagating wave?

12.3 Wave propagation

Waves and their behavior are perhaps best studied by beginning with
large mechanical models and focusing our attention on pulses. Consider
for example a freight train, with many cars attached to a powerful
locomotive, but standing still. If the locomotive now starts abruptly, it
sends a displacement wave running down the line of cars. The shock of
the starting displacement proceeds from locomotive to caboose, clacking
through the couplings one by one. In this example, the locomotive is the
source of the disturbance, while the freight cars and their couplings are
the medium. The "bump" traveling along the line of cars is the wave. The
disturbance proceeds all the way from end to end, and with it goes *energy*
of displacement and motion. Yet no particles of matter are transferred that
far; each car only jerks ahead a bit.

A very important point: energy transfer can occur without matter transfer.

How long does it take for the effect of a disturbance created at one
point to reach a distant point? The time interval depends upon the speed
with which the disturbance or wave propagates. That, in turn, depends
upon the type of wave and the characteristics of the medium. In any case,
the effect of a disturbance is never transmitted instantly over any distance.
Each part of the medium has inertia, and each portion of the medium is
compressible. So time is needed to transfer energy from one part to the
next.

An engine starting abruptly can start a displacement wave along a line of cars.

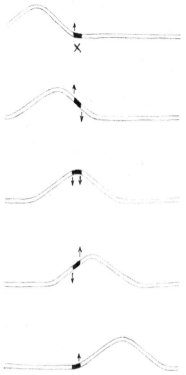

A rough representation of the forces at the ends of a small section of rope as a transverse pulse moves past.

SG 12.2

The exact meaning of stiffness and density factors is different for different kinds of waves and different media. For tight strings, for example, the stiffness factor is the tension T in the string, and the density factor is the mass per unit length, m/l. The propagation speed v is given by

$$v = \sqrt{\frac{T}{m/l}}$$

The same comments apply also to transverse waves. The series of sketches in the margin represents a wave on a rope. Think of the sketches as frames of a motion picture film, taken at equal time intervals. The material of the rope does *not* travel along with the wave. But each bit of the rope goes through an up-and-down motion as the wave passes. Each bit goes through exactly the same motion as the bit to its left, except a little later.

Consider the small section of rope labeled X in the diagrams. When the pulse traveling on the rope first reaches X, the section of rope just to the left of X exerts an upward force on X. As X is moved upward, a restoring downward force is exerted by the next section. The further upward X moves, the greater the restoring forces become. Eventually X stops moving upward and starts down again. The section of rope to the left of X now exerts a restoring (downward) force, while the section to the right exerts an upward force. Thus, the trip down is similar, but opposite, to the trip upward. Finally, X returns to the equilibrium position and both forces vanish.

The time required for X to go up and down—the time required for the pulse to pass by that portion of the rope—depends on two factors. These factors are the *magnitude of the forces* on X, and the *mass* of X. To put it more generally: the speed with which a wave propagates depends on the *stiffness* and on the *density* of the medium. The stiffer the medium, the greater will be the force each section exerts on neighboring sections. Thus, the greater will be the propagation speed. On the other hand, the greater the density of the medium, the less it will respond to forces. Thus, the slower will be the propagation. In fact, the speed of propagation depends on the *ratio* of the stiffness factor and the density factor.

Q5 What is transferred along the direction of wave motion?

Q6 On what two properites of a medium does wave speed depend?

12.4 Periodic waves

Many of the disturbances we have considered up to now have been sudden and short-lived. They were set up by a single disturbance like snapping one end of a rope or suddenly bumping one end of a train. In each case, we see a single wave running along the medium with a certain speed. We call this kind of wave a *pulse*.

Now let us consider *periodic waves*—continuous regular rhythmic disturbances in a medium, resulting from *periodic vibrations* of a source. A good example of a periodic vibration is a swinging pendulum. Each swing is virtually identical to every other swing, and the swing repeats over and over again in time. Another example is the up-and-down motion of a weight at the end of a spring. The maximum displacement from the position of equilibrium is called the *amplitude A,* as shown on page 107. The time taken to complete one vibration is called the *period T*. The number of vibrations per second is called the *frequency f.*

What happens when such a vibration is applied to the end of a rope? Suppose that one end of a rope is fastened to the oscillating (vibrating) weight. As the weight vibrates up and down, we observe a wave propagating along the rope. The wave takes the form of a series of moving crests and troughs along the length of the rope. The source executes "simple harmonic motion" up and down. Ideally, every point along the length of the rope executes simple harmonic motion in turn. The wave travels to the right as crests and troughs follow one another. But each point along the rope simply oscillates up and down at the same frequency as the source. The amplitude of the wave is represented by A. The distance between any two consecutive crests or any two consecutive troughs is the same all along the length of the rope. This distance, called the *wavelength* of the periodic wave, is represented by the Greek letter λ (lambda).

If a single pulse or a wave crest moves fairly slowly through the medium, we can easily find its *speed*. In principle all we need is a clock and a meter stick. By timing the pulse or crest over a measured distance, we get the speed. But it is not always simple to observe the motion of a pulse or a wave crest. As is shown below, however, the speed of a periodic wave can be found indirectly from its frequency and wavelength.

As a wave progresses, each point in the medium oscillates with the frequency and period of the source. The diagram in the margin illustrates a periodic wave moving to the right, as it might look in snapshots taken every $\frac{1}{4}$ period. Follow the progress of the crest that started out from the extreme left at $t = 0$. The time it takes this crest to move a distance of one wavelength is *equal* to the time required for one complete oscillation. That is, the crest moves one wavelength λ in one period of oscillation T. The speed v of the crest is therefore

$$v = \frac{\text{distance moved}}{\text{corresponding time interval}} = \frac{\lambda}{T}$$

All parts of the wave pattern propagate with the same speed. Thus the speed of any one crest is just the speed of the wave. We can say, therefore, that the speed v of the wave is

$$v = \frac{\text{wavelength}}{\text{period of oscillation}} = \frac{\lambda}{T}$$

But $T = 1/f$, where f = frequency (see *Text*, Chapter 4, page 108). Therefore $v = f\lambda$, or wave speed = frequency × wavelength.

We can also write this relationship as $\lambda = v/f$ or $f = v/\lambda$. These expressions imply that, for waves of the same speed, the frequency and wavelength are inversely proportional. That is, a wave of twice the frequency would have only half the wavelength, and so on. This inverse relation of frequency and wavelength will be useful in other parts of this course.

The diagram below represents a periodic wave passing through a medium. Sets of points are marked which are moving "in step" as the periodic wave passes. The crest points C and C' have reached maximum

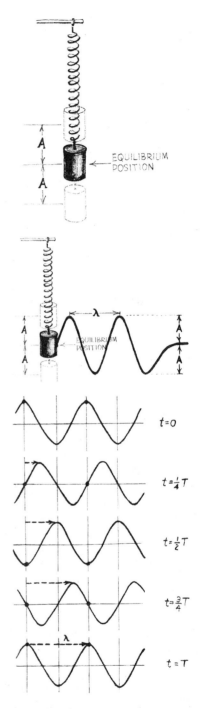

The wave generated by a simple harmonic vibration is a *sine* wave. A "snapshot" of the displacement of the medium would show it has the same shape as a graph of the sine function familiar in trigonometry. This shape is frequently referred to as "sinusoidal."

displacement positions in the upward direction. The trough points *D* and *D'* have reached maximum displacement positions in the downward direction. The points *C* and *C'* have identical displacements and velocities at any instant of time. Their vibrations are identical, and in unison. The same is true for the points *D* and *D'*. Indeed there are infinitely many such points along the medium which are vibrating identically when this wave passes. Note that *C* and *C'* are a distance λ apart, and so are *D* and *D'*.

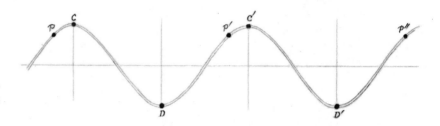

A "snapshot" of a periodic wave moving to the right. Letters indicate sets of points with the same phase.

Points that move "in step" such as *C* and *C'*, are said to be *in phase* with one another. Points *D* and *D'* also move in phase. Points separated from one another by distances of λ, 2λ, 3λ, . . . and *n*λ (where *n* is any whole number) are all in phase with one another. These points can be anywhere along the length of the wave. They need not correspond with only the highest or lowest points. For example, points such as *P*, *P'*, *P''*, are all in phase with one another. Each is separated from the next by a distance λ.

Some of the points are exactly *out* of step. For example, point *C* reaches its maximum upward displacement at the same time that *D* reaches its maximum downward displacement. At the instant that *C* begins to go down, *D* begins to go up. Points such as these are called one-half period *out of phase* with respect to one another; *C* and *D'* also are one-half period out of phase. Any two points separated from one another by distances of λ/2, 3λ/2, 5λ/2, . . . are one-half period out of phase.

Q7 Of the wave variables—frequency, wavelength, period, amplitude and polarization—which ones describe

(1) *space* properties of waves?

(2) *time* properties of waves?

Q8 A wave with the displacement as smoothly and simply varying from point to point as that shown in the last illustration above is called a sine wave. How might the "wavelength" be defined for a periodic wave that isn't a sine wave?

Q9 A vibration of 100 cycles per second produces a wave.

(1) What is the wave frequency?

(2) What is the period of the wave?

(3) If the wave speed is 10 meters per second what is the wavelength? (If necessary, look back to find the relationship you need to answer this.)

Q10 If points *X* and *Y* on a periodic wave are one-half period "out of phase" with each other, which of the following *must* be true?

(a) *X* oscillates at half the frequency at which *Y* oscillates.
(b) *X* and *Y* always move in opposite directions.
(c) *X* is a distance of one-half wavelength from *Y*.

12.5 When waves meet: the superposition principle

So far, we have considered single waves. What happens when two waves encounter each other in the same medium? Suppose two waves approach each other on a rope, one traveling to the right and one traveling to the left. The series of sketches in the margin shows what would happen if you made this experiment. The waves pass through each other without being modified. After the encounter, each wave looks just as it did before and is traveling just as it was before. This phenomenon of passing through each other unchanged can be observed with all types of waves. You can easily see that it is true for surface ripples on water. (Look back, for example, to the opening photograph for the chapter.) You could reason that it must be true for sound waves also, since two conversations can take place across a table without distorting each other. (Note that when *particles* encounter each other, they collide. Waves can pass through each other.)

But what happens during the time when the two waves overlap? The displacements they provide add up. At each instant, the displacement of each point in the overlap region is just the *sum* of the displacements that would be caused by each of the two waves separately. An example is shown in the margin. Two waves travel toward each other on a rope. One has a maximum displacement of 0.4 cm upward and the other a maximum displacement of 0.8 cm upward. The total maximum upward displacement of the rope at a point where these two waves pass each other is 1.2 cm.

What a wonderfully simple behavior, and how easy it makes everything! Each wave proceeds along the rope making its own contribution to the rope's displacement no matter what any other wave is doing. We can easily determine what the rope looks like at any given instant. All we need to do is add up the displacements caused by each wave at each point along the rope at that instant. This property of waves is called the *superposition principle*. Another illustration of wave superposition is shown on page 110. Notice that when the displacements are in opposite directions, they tend to cancel each other. One of the two directions of displacement may always be considered negative. Check the diagrams with a ruler. You will find that the net displacement (solid line) is just the sum of the individual displacements (broken lines).

The superposition principle applies no matter how many separate waves or disturbances are present in the medium. In the examples just given, only two waves are present. But we would find by experiment that the superposition principle works equally well for three, ten, or any number of waves. Each wave makes its own contribution, and the net result is simply the sum of all the individual contributions.

We can turn the superposition principle around. If waves add as we

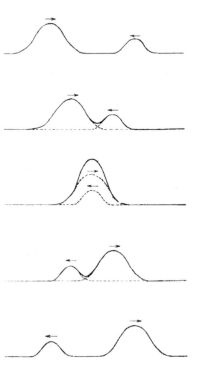

The superposition of two rope waves at a point. The dashed curves are the contributions of the individual waves.

have described, then we can think of a complex wave as the sum of a set of simpler waves. In the diagram below (right), a complex pulse has been analyzed into a set of three simpler pulses. In 1807 the French mathematician Jean-Baptiste Fourier advanced a very useful theorem. Fourier stated that any continuing periodic oscillation, however complex, could be analyzed as the sum of simpler, regular wave motions. This, too, can be demonstrated by experiment. The sounds of musical instruments have been analyzed in this way also. Such analysis makes it possible to "imitate" instruments electronically by combining just the right proportions of simple vibrations.

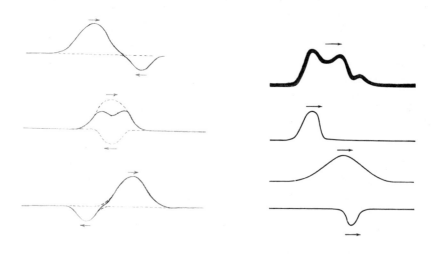

SG 12.4-12.8

Q11 Two periodic waves of amplitudes A_1 and A_2 pass through a point P. What is the greatest displacement of P?

Q12 What is the displacement of a point produced by two waves together if the displacements produced by the waves separately at that instant are $+5$ cm and -6 cm?

12.6 A two-source interference pattern

The photograph at the right (center) shows ripples spreading from a vibrating source touching the water surface in a "ripple tank." The drawing to the left of it shows a "cut-away" view of the water level pattern at a given instant.

The third photograph (far right) introduces a phenomenon which will play an important role in later parts of the course. It shows the pattern of ripples on a water surface which is disturbed by *two* vibrating sources. The two small sources go through their up and down motions together. That is, they are in phase. Each creates its own set of circular, spreading ripples. The photograph catches the pattern made by the overlapping sets of waves at one instant. It is called an *interference pattern*.

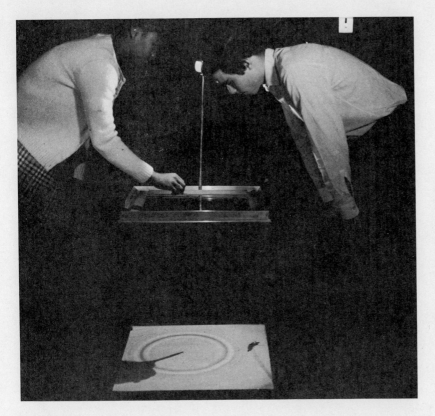

The ripple tank shown in the photograph at the left is being used by students to observe a circular pulse spreading over a thin layer of water. When a vibrating point source is immersed at the edge of the tank, it produces periodic wave trains of crests and troughs, somewhat as shown in the "cut-away" drawing at the left below. The center figure below is an instantaneous photograph of the shadows of ripples produced by a vibrating point source. The crests and troughs on the water surface show up in the image as bright and dark circular bands. Below right, there were two point sources vibrating in phase. The overlapping waves create an interference pattern.

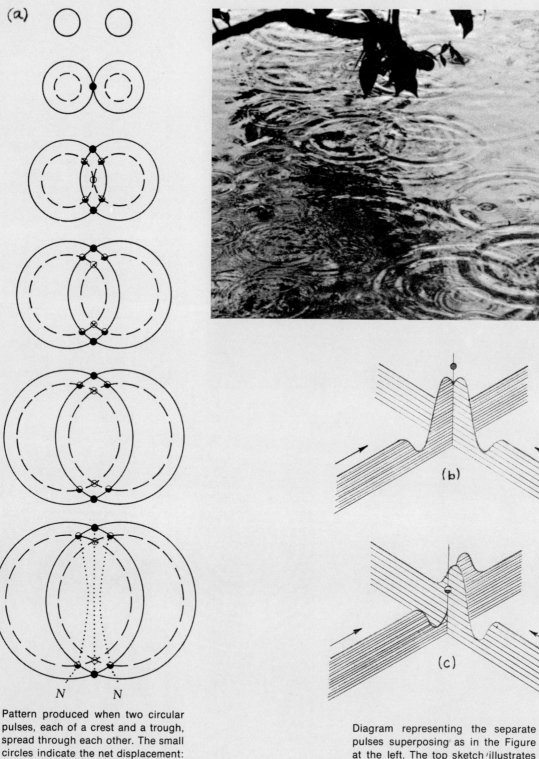

(a)

Pattern produced when two circular pulses, each of a crest and a trough, spread through each other. The small circles indicate the net displacement:

● = double height peak
◒ = average level
○ = double depth trough

Diagram representing the separate pulses superposing as in the Figure at the left. The top sketch illustrates two crests about to arrive at the vertical line. The bottom sketch illustrates a crest about to arrive together with a trough.

N   N

(b)

(c)

We can interpret what we see in this photograph in terms of what we already know about waves. And we can predict how the pattern will change with time. First, tilt the page so that you are viewing the interference pattern from a glancing direction. You will see more clearly some nearly straight gray bands. This feature can be explained by the superposition principle.

Suppose that two sources produce identical pulses at the same instant. Each pulse contains one crest and one trough. (See page 112 at the left.) In each pulse the height of the crest above the undisturbed or average level is equal to the depth of the trough below. The sketches show the patterns of the water surface after equal time intervals. As the pulses spread out, the points at which they overlap move too. In the figure we have placed a completely darkened circle wherever a crest overlaps another crest. A half-darkened circle marks each point where a crest overlaps a trough. A blank circle indicates the meeting of two troughs. According to the superposition principle, the water level should be highest at the completely darkened circles (where the crests overlap). It should be lowest at the blank circles, and at average height at the half-darkened circles. Each of the sketches on page 112 represents the spatial pattern of the water level at a given instant.

At the points marked with darkened circles in (a), the two pulses arrive in phase, as indicated in (b). At points indicated by blank circles, the pulses also arrive in phase. In either case, the waves reinforce each other, causing a *greater* amplitude of either the crest or the trough. Thus, they are said to *interfere constructively*. In this case, all such points are at the same distance from each source. As the ripples spread, the region of maximum disturbance moves along the central dotted line in (a).

At the points in (a) marked with half-darkened circles, the two pulses arrive completely out of phase, as shown in (c). Here the waves cancel and so are said to interfere *destructively,* leaving the water surface undisturbed. The lines N in (a) show the path along which the overlapping pulses meet when they are just out of phase. All along these lines there is no change or displacement of the water level. Note that all points on these lines are one-crest-trough distance ($\frac{1}{2}\lambda$) further from one source than from the other.

When periodic waves of equal amplitude are sent out instead of single pulses, overlap occurs all over the surface. All along the central dotted line there is a doubled disturbance amplitude. All along the side lines the water height remains undisturbed. Depending on the wavelength and the distance between the sources, there can be many such lines of constructive and destructive interference.

Now we can interpret the ripple tank interference pattern on page 111. The "gray bands" are areas where waves cancel each other, called *nodal* lines. These bands correspond to lines N in the simple case of pulses instead of periodic waves. Between these bands are other bands where crest and trough follow one another, where the waves reinforce. These are called *antinodal* lines.

Look closely at the diagram on page 114. It explains what is happening in the lower right hand photograph on page 111. Notice its symmetry. The central band labeled A_0 is an antinode where

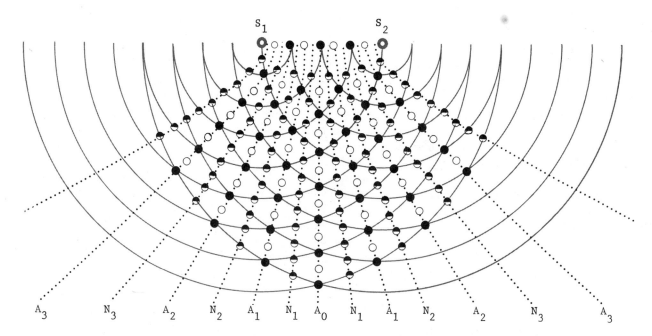

Analysis of interference pattern similar to that of the lower right photograph on p. 111 set up by two in-phase periodic sources. (Here S₁ and S₂ are separated by four wavelengths.) The letters A and N designate antinodal and nodal lines. The dark circles indicate where crest is meeting crest, the blank circles where trough is meeting trough, and the half-dark circles where crest is meeting trough.

reinforcement is complete. The other lines of maximum constructive interference are labeled A_1, A_2, A_3, etc. Points on these lines move up and down *much more* than they would because of waves from either source alone. The lines labeled N_1, N_2, etc. represent bands along which there is maximum destructive interference. Points on these lines move up and down *much less* than they would because of waves from either source alone. Compare the diagram with the photograph and identify antinodal lines and nodal lines.

Whenever we find such an interference pattern, we know that it is set up by overlapping waves from two sources. For water waves, the interference pattern can be seen directly. But whether visible or not, all waves can set up interference patterns—including earthquake waves, sound waves, or x rays. For example, suppose two loudspeakers are working at the same frequency. By moving about and listening in front of the loudspeakers, you can find the nodal regions where destructive interference causes only little sound to be heard. You also can find the antinodal regions where a strong signal comes through.

The beautiful symmetry of these interference patterns is not accidental. Rather, the whole pattern is determined by the wavelength λ and the source separation S_1S_2. From these we could calculate the angles at which the nodal and antinodal lines radiate out to either side of A_0. Conversely, we might know S_1S_2 and might have found these angles by probing around in the two-source interference pattern. If so, we can calculate the wavelength even if we can't see the crests and troughs of the waves directly. This is very useful, for most waves in nature can't be directly seen. So their wavelength has to be found in just this way: letting waves set up an interference pattern, probing for the nodal and antinodal lines, and calculating λ from the geometry.

The figure at the right shows part of the pattern of the diagram on the opposite page. At any point P on an *antinodal* line, the waves from the two sources arrive *in phase*. This can happen only if P is equally far from S_1 and S_2, or if P is some whole number of wavelengths farther from one source than from the other. In other words, the difference in distances $(S_1P - S_2P)$ must equal $n\lambda$, λ being the wavelength and n being zero or any whole number. At any point Q on a *nodal* line, the waves from the two sources arrive exactly *out of phase*. This occurs because Q is an odd number of half-wavelengths ($\frac{1}{2}\lambda$, $\frac{3}{2}\lambda$, $\frac{5}{2}\lambda$, etc.) farther from one source than from the other. This condition can be written $S_1Q - S_2Q = (n + \frac{1}{2})\lambda$.

The distance from the sources to a detection point may be much larger than the source separation d. In that case, there is a simple relationship between the node position, the wavelength λ, and the separation d. The wavelength can be calculated from measurements of the positions of nodal lines. The details of the relationship and the calculation of wavelength are described on the next page.

This analysis allows us to calculate from simple measurements made on an interference pattern the wavelength of any wave. It applies to water ripples, sound, light, etc. You will find this method very useful in later units. One important thing you can do now is find λ for a real case of interference of waves in the laboratory. This practice will help you later in finding the wavelengths of other kinds of waves.

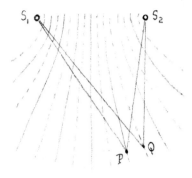

$$S_1P - S_2P = n\lambda$$

$$S_1Q - S_2Q = (n + \tfrac{1}{2})\lambda$$

Since the sound wave patterns in space are three-dimensional, the nodal or antinodal regions in this case are two-dimensional surfaces. For example, they are *planes*, not lines.

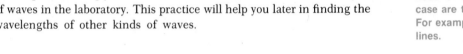

Q13   Are nodal lines in interference patterns regions of cancellation or reinforcement?

Q14   What are antinodal lines? antinodal points?

Q15   Nodal points in an interference pattern are places where
(a) the waves arrive "out of phase"
(b) the waves arrive "in phase"
(c) the point is equidistant from the wave sources
(d) the point is one-half wavelength from both sources.

Q16   Under what circumstances do waves from two in-phase sources arrive at a point out of phase?

12.7 Standing waves

If both ends of a rope are shaken with the same frequency and same amplitude, an interesting thing happens. The interference of the identical waves coming from opposite ends results in certain points on the rope not moving at all! In between these nodal points, the rope oscillates up and down. But there is no apparent propagation of wave patterns in either direction along the rope. This phenomenon is called a *standing wave* or *stationary wave*. (With the aid of Transparency T-27, using the superposition principle, you can see that this effect is just what would be expected from the addition of the two oppositely traveling waves.) The important thing to remember is that the standing oscillation we observe is

Calculating λ from an Interference Pattern

$d = (S_1S_2)$ = separation between S_1 and S_2. (S_1 and S_2 may be actual sources that are in phase, or two slits through which a previously prepared wave front passes.)

$\ell = OQ$ = distance from sources to a far-off line or screen placed parallel to the two sources.

x = distance from center axis to point P along the detection line.

$L = OP$ = distance to point P on detection line measured from sources.

Waves reaching P from S_1 have traveled farther than waves reaching P from S_2. If the extra distance is λ (or 2λ, 3λ, etc.), the waves will arrive at P in phase. Then P will be a point of strong wave disturbance. If the extra distance is $\frac{1}{2}\lambda$ (or $\frac{3}{2}\lambda$, $\frac{5}{2}\lambda$, etc.), the waves will arrive out of phase. Then P will be a point of weak or no wave disturbance.

With P as center we draw an arc of a circle of radius PS_2; it is indicated on the figure by the dotted line S_2M. Then line segment PS_2 = line segment PM. Therefore the extra distance that the wave from S travels to reach P is the length of the segment SM.

Now if d is very small compared to ℓ, as we can easily arrange in practice, the circular arc S_2M will then be a very small piece of a large diameter circle—or nearly a straight line. Also, the angle S_1MS_2 is very nearly 90°. Thus, the triangle S_1S_2M can be regarded as a right triangle. Furthermore, angle S_1S_2M is equal to angle POQ. Then right triangle S_1S_2M is a similar triangle POQ.

$$\frac{S_1M}{S_1S_2} = \frac{x}{OP} \quad \text{or} \quad \frac{S_1M}{d} = \frac{x}{L}$$

If the distance ℓ is large compared to x, the distances ℓ and L are nearly equal, and we can write

$$\frac{S_1M}{d} = \frac{x}{L}$$

But S_1M is the extra distance traveled by the wave from source S_1. For P to be a point of maximum wave disturbance, S_1M must be equal to $n\lambda$ (where $n = 0$ if P is at Q, and $n = 1$ if P is at the first maximum of wave disturbance found to one side of Q, etc.). So the equation becomes

$$\frac{n\lambda}{d} = \frac{x}{\ell}$$

$$\text{and} \quad \lambda = \frac{dx}{n\ell}$$

This important result says that if we measure the source separation d, the distance ℓ, and the distance x from the central line to a wave disturbance maximum, we can calculate the wavelength λ.

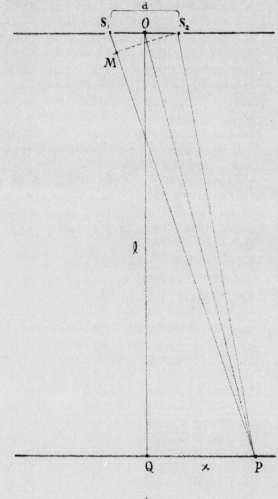

really the effect of two *traveling* waves.

To make standing waves on a rope, there do not have to be two people shaking the opposite ends. One end can be tied to a hook on a wall. The train of waves sent down the rope by shaking one end will reflect back from the fixed hook. These reflected waves interfere with the new, oncoming waves and can produce a standing pattern of nodes and oscillation. In fact, you can go further and tie both ends of a string to hooks and pluck (or bow) the string. From the plucked point a pair of waves go out in opposite directions and then reflect back from the ends. The interference of these reflected waves traveling in opposite directions can produce a standing pattern just as before. The strings of guitars, violins, pianos, and all other stringed instruments act in just this fashion. The energy given to the strings sets up standing waves. Some of the energy is then transmitted from the vibrating string to the body of the instrument. The sound waves sent forth from there are at essentially the same frequency as the standing waves on the string.

The vibration frequencies at which standing waves can exist depend on two factors. One is the speed of wave propagation along the string. The other is the length of the string. The connection between length of string and musical tone was recognized over two thousand years ago. This relationship contributed greatly to the idea that nature is built on mathematical principles. Early in the development of musical instruments, people learned how to produce certain pleasing harmonies by plucking strings. These harmonies result if the strings are of equal tautness and diameter and if their lengths are in the ratios of small whole numbers. Thus the length ratio 2:1 gives the octave, 3:2 the musical fifth, and 4:3 the musical fourth. This striking connection between music and numbers encouraged the Pythagoreans to search for other numerical ratios or harmonies in the universe. The Pythagorean ideal strongly affected Greek science and many centuries later inspired much of Kepler's work. In a general form, the ideal flourishes to this day in many beautiful applications of mathematics to physical experience.

Using the superposition principle, we can now define the harmonic relationship much more precisely. First, we must stress an important fact about standing wave patterns produced by reflecting waves from the boundaries of a medium. We can imagine an unlimited variety of waves traveling back and forth. But, in fact, *only certain wavelengths (or frequencies) can produce standing waves* in a given medium. In the example of a stringed instrument, the two ends are fixed and so must be nodal points. This fact puts an upper limit on the length of standing waves possible on a fixed rope of length L. Such waves must be those for which one-half wavelength just fits on the rope ($L = \lambda/2$). Shorter waves also can produce standing patterns having more nodes. But *always*, some whole number of one-half wavelengths must just fit on the rope ($L = \lambda/2$).

We can turn this relationship around to give an expression for all possible wavelengths of standing waves on a fixed rope:

$$\lambda_n = \frac{2L}{n}$$

A vibrator at the left produces a wave train that runs along the rope and reflects from the fixed end at the right. The sum of the oncoming and the reflected waves is a standing wave pattern.

Lyre player painted on a Greek vase in the 5th century B.C.

SG 12.13

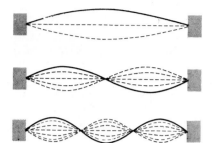

Film Loops 38—43 show a
variety of standing waves, including
waves on a string, a drum, and in a
tube of air.

Mathematically inclined students are
encouraged to pursue the topic of
waves and standing waves, for
example, Science Study Series
paperbacks *Waves and the Ear* and
Horns, Strings and Harmony.

See the *Reader 3* articles "Musical
Instruments and Scales" and
"Founding a Family of Fiddles."

SG 12.16

Or simply, $\lambda_n \propto 1/n$. That is, if λ_1 is the longest wavelength possible, the other possible wavelengths will be $\frac{1}{2}\lambda_1, \frac{1}{3}\lambda_1, \dots 1/n\,\lambda_1$. Shorter wavelengths correspond to higher frequencies. Thus, *on any bounded medium, only certain frequencies of standing waves can be set up.* Since frequency f is inversely proportional to wavelength, $f \propto 1/\lambda$, we can rewrite the expression for all possible standing waves as

$$f_n \propto n$$

The lowest possible frequency of a standing wave is usually the one most strongly present when the string vibrates after being plucked or bowed. If f_1 represents this lowest possible frequency, then the other possible standing waves would have frequencies $2f_1, 3f_1, \dots nf_1$. These higher frequencies are called "overtones" of the "fundamental" frequency f_1. On an "ideal" string, there are in principle an unlimited number of such frequencies, all simple multiples of the lowest frequency.

In real media, there are practical upper limits to the possible frequencies. Also, the overtones are not exactly simple multiples of the fundamental frequency. That is, the overtones are not strictly "harmonic." This effect is still greater in more complicated systems than stretched strings. In a saxophone or other wind instrument, an *air column* is put into standing wave motion. The overtones produced may not be even approximately harmonic.

As you might guess from the superposition principle, standing waves of different frequencies can exist in the same medium at the same time. A plucked guitar string, for example, oscillates in a pattern which is the superposition of the standing waves of many overtones. The relative oscillation energies of the different instruments determine the "quality" of the sound they produce. Each type of instrument has its own balance of overtones. This is why a violin sounds different from a trumpet, and both sound different from a soprano voice—even if all are sounding at the same fundamental frequency.

Q17   When two identical waves of same frequency travel in opposite directions and interfere to produce a standing wave, what is the motion of the medium at
   (1) the nodes of the standing wave?
   (2) the places between nodes, called "antinodes" or loops, of the standing wave?

Q18   If the two interfering waves have wavelength λ, what is the distance between the nodal points of the standing wave?

Q19   What is the wavelength of the longest traveling waves which can produce a standing wave on a string of length L?

Q20   Can standing waves of *any* frequency, as long as it is higher than the fundamental, be set up in a bounded medium?

In the Film Loop *Vibration of a Drum*, a marked rubber "drumhead" is seen vibrating in several of its possible modes. Below are pairs of still photographs from three of the symmetrical modes and from an antisymmetrical mode.

12.8 Wave fronts and diffraction

Waves can go around corners. For example, you can hear a voice coming from the other side of a hill, even though there is nothing to reflect the sound to you. We are so used to the fact that sound waves do this that we scarcely notice it. This spreading of the energy of waves into what we would expect to be "shadow" regions is called *diffraction.*

Once again, water waves will illustrate this behavior most clearly. From among all the arrangements that can result in diffraction, we will concentrate on two. The first is shown in the second photograph in the margin at the left. Straight water waves (coming from the top of the picture) are diffracted as they pass through a narrow slit in a straight barrier. Notice that the slit is less than one wavelength wide. The wave emerges and spreads in all directions. Also notice the *pattern* of the diffracted wave. It is basically the same pattern a vibrating point source would set up if it were placed where the slit is.

The bottom photograph shows the second barrier arrangement we want to investigate. Now there are two narrow slits in the barrier. The pattern resulting from superposition of the diffracted waves from both slits is the same as that produced by two point sources vibrating in phase. The same kind of result is obtained when many narrow slits are put in the barrier. That is, the final pattern just matches that which would appear if a point source were put at the center of each slit, with all sources in phase.

We can describe these and all other effects of diffraction if we understand a basic characteristic of waves. It was first stated by Christian Huygens in 1678 and is now known as *Huygens' principle.* But in order to state the principle, we first need the definition of a *wave front.*

For a water wave, a wave front is an imaginary line along the water's surface. Every point along this line is in exactly the same stage of vibration. That is, all points on the line are *in phase.* Crest lines are wave fronts, since all points on the water's surface along a crest line are in phase. Each has just reached its maximum displacement upward, is momentarily at rest, and will start downward an instant later.

The simplest wave fronts are straight lines parallel to each other, as in the top part of the center photograph at the left. Or they may be circular, as in the bottom part of the same photograph. Sound waves are somewhat different. Since a sound wave spreads not over a surface but in three dimensions, its wave fronts become very nearly spherical surfaces. At large distances from the source, however, the radius of a spherical wave front is also large. Thus, any small section of the wave front is nearly flat. All circular and spherical wave fronts become virtually straight-line or flat-plane fronts at great distances from their sources.

Now Huygens' principle, as it is generally stated today, is that *every point on a wave front may be considered to behave as a point source for waves generated in the direction of the wave's propagation.* As Huygens said:

> There is the further consideration in the emanation of these waves, that each particle of matter in which a wave spreads, ought not to communicate its motion only to the next

Diffraction of ripples around the edge of a barrier.

Diffraction of ripples through a narrow opening.

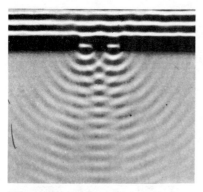

Diffraction of ripples through two narrow openings.

particle which is in the straight line drawn from the (source),
but that it also imparts some of it necessarily to all others
which touch it and which oppose themselves to its movement.
So it arises that around each particle there is made a wave of
which that particle is the center.

The diffraction patterns seen at slits in a barrier are certainly
consistent with Huygens' principle. The wave arriving at the barrier
causes the water in the slit to oscillate. The oscillation of the water in the
slit acts as a source for waves traveling out from it in all directions. When
there are two slits and the wave reaches both slits in phase, the oscillating
water in each slit acts like a point source. The resulting interference
pattern is similar to the pattern produced by waves from two point sources
oscillating in phase.

Or consider what happens behind a breakwater wall as in the aerial
photograph of the harbor below. By Huygens' principle, water oscillation
near the end of the breakwater sends circular waves propagating into the
"shadow" region.

We can understand all diffraction patterns if we keep both Huygens'
principle and the superposition principle in mind. For example, consider a
slit wider than one wavelength. In this case the pattern of diffracted
waves contains nodal lines (see the series of four photographs in the
margin).

The figure on p. 122 helps to explain why nodal lines appear. There
must be points like P that are just λ farther from side A of the slit than
from side B. That is, there must be points P for which AP differs from BP

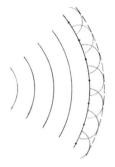

Each point on a wave front can be
thought of as a point source of waves.
The waves from all the point sources
interfere constructively only along
their envelope, which becomes the
new wave front.

When part of the wave front is blocked,
the constructive interference of waves
from points on the wave front extends
into the "shadow" region.

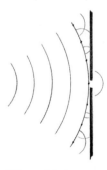

When all but a very small portion of a
wave front is blocked, the wave propagating away from that small portion
is nearly the same as from a point
source.

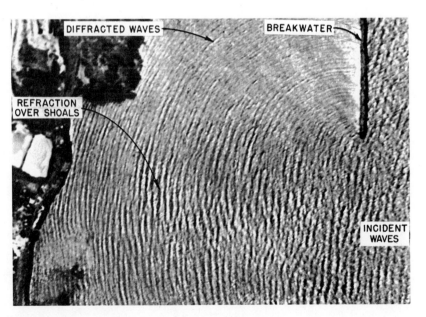

DIFFRACTED WAVES

BREAKWATER

REFRACTION
OVER SHOALS

INCIDENT
WAVES

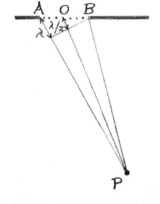

by exactly λ. For such a point, *AP* and *OP* differ by one-half wavelength, λ/2. By Huygens' principle, we may think of points *A* and *O* as in-phase point sources of circular waves. But since *AP* and *OP* differ by λ/2, the two waves will arrive at *P* completely out of phase. So, according to the superposition principle, the waves from *A* and *O* will cancel at point *P*.

But this argument also holds true for the pair of points consisting of the first point to the right of *A* and the first to the right of *O*. In fact, it holds true for *each* such matched pair of points, all the way across the slit. The waves originating at each such pair of points all cancel at point *P*. Thus, *P* is a nodal point, located on a nodal line. On the other hand, if the slit width is less than λ, then there can be *no* nodal point. This is obvious, since no point can be a distance λ farther from one side of the slit than from the other. Slits of widths less than λ behave nearly as point sources. The narrower they are, the more nearly their behavior resembles that of point sources.

We can easily compute the wavelength of a wave from the interference pattern set up where diffracted waves overlap. For example, we can analyze the two-slit pattern on page 120 exactly as we analyzed the two-source pattern in Section 12.6. This is one of the main reasons for our interest in the interference of diffracted waves. By locating nodal lines formed beyond a set of slits, we can calculate λ even for waves that we cannot see.

For two-slit interference, the larger the wavelength compared to the distance between slits, the more the interference pattern spreads out. That is, as λ increases or *d* decreases, the nodal and antinodal lines make increasingly large angles with the straight-ahead direction. Similarly, for single-slit diffraction, the pattern spreads when the ratio of wavelength to the slit width increases. In general, diffraction of longer wavelengths is more easily detected. Thus, when you hear a band playing around a corner, you hear the bass drums and tubas better than the piccolos and cornets—even though they actually are playing equally loud.

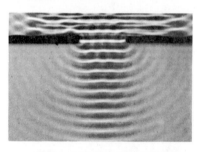

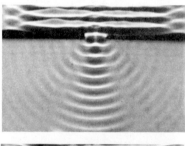

Q21 What characteristic do all points on a wave front have in common?

Q22 State Huygens' principle.

Q23 Why can't there be nodal lines in a diffraction pattern from an opening less than one wavelength wide?

Q24 What happens to the diffraction pattern from an opening as the wavelength of the wave increases?

Q25 Can there be diffraction without interference? Interference without diffraction?

12.9 Reflection

We have seen that waves can pass through one another and spread around obstacles in their paths. Waves also are reflected, at least to some degree, whenever they reach any boundary of the medium in which they travel. Echoes are familiar examples of the reflection of sound waves. All waves share the property of reflection. Again, the superposition principle will help us understand what happens when reflection occurs.

Suppose that one end of a rope is tied tightly to a hook securely fastened to a massive wall. From the other end, we send a pulse wave down the rope toward the hook. Since the hook cannot move, the force exerted by the rope wave can do no work on the hook. Therefore, the energy carried in the wave cannot leave the rope at this fixed end. Instead, the wave bounces back—is *reflected*—ideally with the same energy.

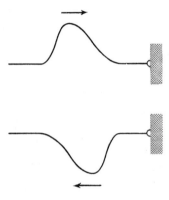

What does the wave look like after it is reflected? The striking result is that the wave seems to flip upside down on reflection. As the wave comes in from left to right and encounters the fixed hook, it pulls up on it. By Newton's third law, the hook must exert a force on the rope in the opposite direction while reflection is taking place. The details of how this force varies in time are complicated. The net effect is that an inverted wave of the same form is sent back down the rope.

Two-dimensional water-surface waves exhibit a fascinating variety of reflection phenomena. There may be variously shaped crest lines, variously shaped barriers, and various directions from which the waves approach the barrier. If you have never watched closely as water waves are reflected from a fixed barrier, you should do so. Any still pool or water-filled wash basin or tub will do. Watch the circular waves speed outward, reflect from rocks or walls, run through each other, and finally die out. Dip your fingertip into and out of the water quickly, or let a drop of water fall from your finger into the water. Now watch the circular wave approach and then bounce off a straight wall or a board. The long side of a tub is a good straight barrier.

The sketches in the margin picture the results of reflection from a straight wall. Three crests are shown. You may see more or fewer than three clear crests in your observations, but that does not matter. In the upper sketch, the outer crest is approaching the barrier at the right. The next two sketches show the positions of the crests after first one and then

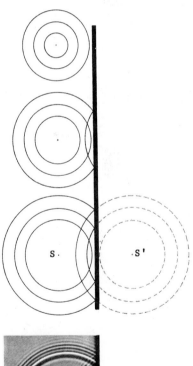

SG 12.21

two of them have been reflected. Notice the dashed curves in the last sketch. They attempt to show that the reflected wave appears to originate from a point S′ that is as far behind the barrier as S is in front of it. The imaginary source at point S′ is called the *image* of the source S.

We mention the reflection of circular waves first, because that is what one usually notices first when studying water waves. But it is easier to see a general principle for explaining reflection by observing a straight wave front, reflected from a straight barrier. The ripple-tank photograph at the left shows one instant during such a reflection. (The wave came in from the upper left at an angle of about 45°.) The sketches below show in more detail what happens as the wave crests reflect from the straight barrier. The first sketch shows three crests approaching the barrier. The last sketch shows the same crests as they move away from the barrier after the encounter. The two sketches between show the reflection process at two different instants during reflection.

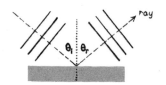

The description of wave behavior is often made easier by drawing lines perpendicular to the wave fronts. Such lines, called *rays*, indicate the direction of propagation of the wave. Notice the drawing at the left, for example. Rays have been drawn for a set of wave crests just before reflection and just after reflection from a barrier. The straight-on direction, perpendicular to the reflecting surface, is shown by a dotted line. The ray for the *incident* crests makes an angle θ_i with the straight-on direction. The ray for the *reflected* crests makes an angle θ_r with it. The *angle of reflection* θ_r is equal to the *angle of incidence* θ_i : that is, $\theta_r = \theta_i$. This is an experimental fact, which you can verify for yourself.

SG 12.22

Many kinds of wave reflectors are in use today, from radar antennae to infrared heaters. Figures (a) and (b) below show how straight-line waves reflect from two circular reflectors. A few incident and reflected rays are shown. (The dotted lines are perpendicular to the barrier surface.) Rays reflected from the half circle (a) head off in all directions. However, rays reflected from a small segment of the circle (b) come close to

SG 12.23–12.25

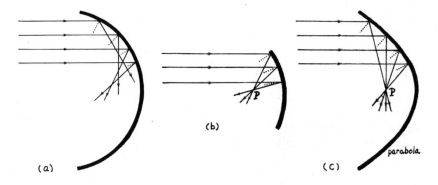

(a)   (b)   (c) *parabola*

meeting at a single point. And a barrier with the shape of a parabola (c) focuses straight-line waves precisely at a point. Similarly, a parabolic surface reflects plane waves to a sharp focus. An impressive example is a radio telescope. Its huge parabolic surface reflects faint radio waves from space to focus on a detector.

The wave paths indicated in the sketches could just as well be reversed. For example, spherical waves produced at the focus become plane waves when reflected from a parabolic surface. The flashlight and automobile headlamp are familiar applications of this principle. In them, white-hot wires placed at the focus of parabolic reflectors produce almost parallel beams of light.

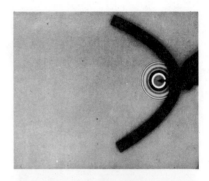

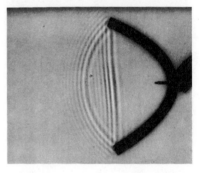

Q26   What is a "ray"?

Q27   What is the relationship between the angle at which a wave front strikes a barrier and the angle at which it leaves?

Q28   What shape of reflector can reflect parallel wave fronts to a sharp focus?

Q29   What happens to wave fronts originating at the focus of such a reflecting surface?

Above: A ripple tank shadow showing how circular waves produced at the focus of a parabolic wall are reflected from the wall into straight waves.

Left: the parabolic surface of a radio telescope reflects radio waves from space to a detector supported at the focus.

Below: the filament of a flashlight bulb is at the focus of a parabolic mirror, so the reflected light forms a nearly parallel beam.

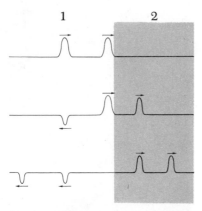

Pulses encountering a boundary between two different media. The speed of propagation is less in medium 2.

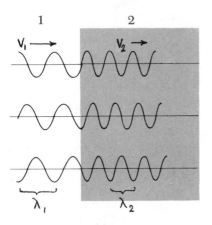

Continuous wave train crossing the boundary between two different media. The speed of propagation is less in medium 2.

SG 12.26

12.10 Refraction

What happens when a wave propagates from one medium to another medium in which its speed of propagation is different? We begin with the simple situation pictured in the margin. Two one-dimensional pulses approach a boundary separating two media. The speed of the propagation in medium 1 is greater than it is in medium 2. We might imagine the pulses to be in a light rope (medium 1) tied to a relatively heavy rope (medium 2). Part of each pulse is reflected at the boundary. This reflected component is flipped upside down relative to the original pulse. You will recall the inverted reflection at a hook in a wall discussed earlier. The heavier rope here tends to hold the boundary point fixed in just the same way. But we are not particularly interested here in the reflected wave. We want to see what happens to that part of the wave which continues into the second medium.

As shown in the figure, the transmitted pulses are closer together in medium 2 than they are in medium 1. Is it clear why this is so? The speed of the pulses is less in the heavier rope. So the second pulse is catching up with the first while the second pulse is still in the light rope and the first is already in the heavy rope. In the same way, each separate pulse is itself squeezed into a narrower form. That is, while the front of the pulse is entering the region of less speed, the back part is still moving with greater speed.

Something of the same sort happens to a periodic wave at such a boundary. The figure at the left pictures this situation. For the sake of simplicity, we have assumed that all of the wave is transmitted, and none of it reflected. Just as the two pulses were brought closer and each pulse was squeezed narrower, the periodic wave pattern is squeezed together too. Thus, the wavelength λ_2 of the transmitted wave is shorter than the wavelength λ_1 of the incoming, or incident, wave.

Although the wavelength changes when the wave passes across the boundary, the frequency of the wave cannot change. If the rope is unbroken, the pieces immediately on either side of the boundary must go up and down together. The frequencies of the incident and transmitted waves must, then, be equal. So we can simply label both of them f.

We can write our wavelength, frequency, and speed relationship for both the incident and transmitted waves separately:

$$\lambda_1 f = v_1, \text{ and } \lambda_2 f = v_2$$

If we divide one of these equations by the other, eliminating the f's, we get

$$\frac{\lambda_1}{\lambda_2} = \frac{v_1}{v_2}$$

This equation tells that the ratio of the wavelengths in the two media equals the ratio of the speeds.

The same sort of thing happens when water ripples cross a boundary.

Experiments show that the ripples move more slowly in shallower water. A piece of plate glass is placed on the bottom of a ripple tank to make the water shallower there. This creates a boundary between the deeper and shallower part (medium 1 and medium 2). Figure (a) below shows the case where this boundary is parallel to the crest lines of the incident wave. As with rope waves, the wavelength of water waves in a medium is proportional to the speed in that medium.

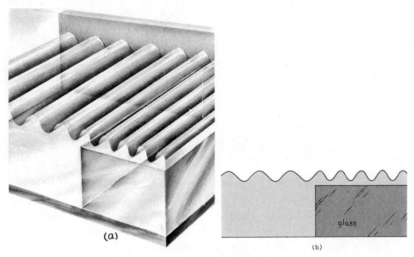

(a)

(b)

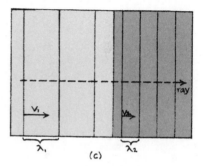

(c)

Water waves offer a possibility not present for rope waves. We can arrange to have the crest lines approach the boundary at any angle, not only head-on. The photograph below right shows such an event. A ripple tank wave approaches the boundary at the angle of incidence θ_i. The wavelength and speed of course change as the wave passes across the boundary. But the *direction* of the wave propagation changes too. Figure (d) in the margin shows how this comes about. As each part of a crest line in medium 1 enters medium 2, its speed decreases and it starts to lag behind. In time, the directions of the whole set of crest lines in medium 2 are changed from their directions in medium 1.

This phenomenon is called *refraction*. It occurs whenever a wave passes into a medium in which the wave velocity is reduced. The wave fronts are turned (refracted) so that they are more nearly parallel to the

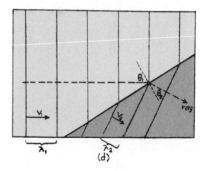

(d)

SG 12.27–12.31

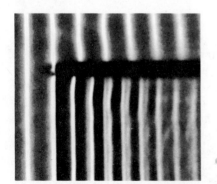

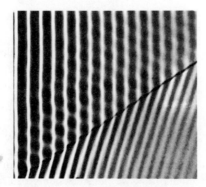

Left: ripples on water (coming from the left) encounter the shallow region over the corner of a submerged glass plate.

Right: ripples on water (coming from the left) encounter a shallow region over a glass plate placed at an angle to the wavefronts.

Aerial photograph of the refraction of ocean waves approaching shore.

The slowing of star light by increasingly dense layers of the atmosphere produces refraction that changes the apparent position of the star.

boundary. (See the photographs at the bottom of the previous page.) This accounts for something that you may have noticed if you have been at an ocean beach. No matter in what direction the waves are moving far from the shore, when they come near the beach their crest-lines are nearly parallel to the shoreline. A wave's speed is steadily reduced as it moves into water that gets gradually more shallow. So the wave is refracted continuously as if it were always crossing a boundary between different media, as indeed it is. The refraction of sea waves is so great that wave crests can curl around a small island with an all-beach shoreline and provide surf on all sides. (See the photograph on page 139.)

Q30 If a periodic wave slows down on entering a new medium, what happens to (1) its frequency? (2) its wavelength? (3) its direction?

Q31 Complete the sketch in the margin to show roughly what happens to a wave train that enters a new medium where its speed is greater.

12.11 Sound waves

Look again at the bottom figure in the margin of p. 103.

Sound waves are mechanical disturbances that propagate through a medium, such as the air. Typically, sound waves are longitudinal waves, producing changes of density and pressure in the medium through which they travel. The medium may be a solid, liquid, or gas. If the waves strike the ear, they can produce the sensation of hearing. The biology and psychology of hearing, as well as the physics of sound, are important to the science of acoustics. But here, of course, we will concentrate on sound as an example of wave motion. Sound has all the properties of wave motion that we have considered so far. It exhibits refraction, diffraction, and the same relations among frequency, wavelength, and propagation speed and interference. Only the property of polarization is missing, because sound waves are longitudinal, not transverse.

Vibrating sources for sound waves may be as simple as a tuning fork or as complex as the human larynx with its vocal cords. Tuning forks and some special electronic devices produce a steady "pure tone." Most of the energy in such a tone is in simple harmonic motion at a single frequency. The "pitch" of a sound we hear goes up as the frequency of the wave increases.

People can hear sound waves with frequencies between about 20 and 20,000 cycles per second. Dogs can hear over a much wider range (15-50,000 cps). Bats, porpoises, and whales generate and respond to frequencies up to about 120,000 cps.

Loudness (or "volume") of sound is, like pitch, a psychological variable. Loudness is strongly related to the *intensity* of the sound. Sound intensity is a physical quantity. It is defined in terms of *power flow*, such as the number of watts per square centimeter transmitted through a surface perpendicular to the direction of motion of a wave front. The human ear can perceive a vast range of intensities of sound. The table below illustrates this range. It begins at a level of 10^{-16} watts per square centimeter (relative intensity = 1). Below this "threshold" level, the normal ear does not perceive sound.

RELATIVE INTENSITY	SOUND
1	Threshold of hearing
10^1	Normal breathing
10^2	Leaves in a breeze
10^3	
10^4	Library
10^5	Quiet restaurant
10^6	Two-person conversation
10^7	Busy traffic
10^8	Vacuum cleaner
10^9	Roar of Niagara Falls
10^{10}	Subway train
10^{11}	
10^{12}	Propeller plane at takeoff
10^{13}	Machine-gun fire
10^{14}	Small jet plane at takeoff
10^{15}	
10^{16}	Wind tunnel
10^{17}	Space rocket at lift-off

Levels of noise intensity about 10^{12} times threshold intensity can be felt as a tickling sensation in the ear. Beyond 10^{13} times threshold intensity, the sensation changes to pain and may damage the unprotected ear.

SG 12.32

It has always been fairly obvious that sound takes time to travel from source to receiver. Light and sound are often closely associated in the same event—lightning and thunder, for instance. In all such cases, we perceive the sound later. By timing echoes over a known distance, the French mathematician Marin Mersenne in 1640 first computed the speed

Noise and the Sonic Boom

The world seems to be increasingly loud with unpleasant, manmade noise. At worst it is a major nuisance and may be tiring, painful, and sometimes even physically harmful. Loud, prolonged noise can produce temporary deafness. Very loud noise, kept up for a long time, can produce some degree of permanent deafness, especially deafness with respect to high-frequency sounds.

Often the simplest way of reducing noise is by *absorbing* it after it is produced but before it reaches your ears. Like all sound, noise is the energy of back and forth motion of the medium through which the noise goes. Noisy machinery can be muffled by padded enclosures in which the energy of noise is changed to heat energy, which then dissipates. In a house, a thick rug on the floor can absorb 90% of room noise. (A foot of fresh snow is an almost perfect absorber of noise outdoors. Cities and countrysides are remarkably hushed after a snowfall.)

In the last few years a new kind of noise has appeared: the sonic boom. An explosion-like sonic boom is produced whenever an object travels through air at a speed greater than the speed of sound (supersonic speed). Sound travels in air at about 700 miles per hour. Many types of military airplanes can travel at two or three times this speed. Flying at such speeds, the planes unavoidably and continually produce sonic booms. SST (Supersonic Transport) planes are now in civilian use in some countries. The unavoidable boom raises important questions. What is the price of technological "progress"? Who gains, and what fraction of the population? Who and how many pay the price? *Must* we pay it—must SST's be used? How much say has the citizen in decisions that affect his environment so violently?

The formation of a sonic boom is similar to the formation of a wake by a boat. Consider a simple point source of waves. If it remains in the same position in a medium, the wave it produces spreads out symmetrically around it, as in diagram 1. But if the source of the disturbance is *moving* through the medium, each new crest starts from a different point, as in diagram 2.

Notice that the wavelength has become shorter in front of the object and longer behind it. (This is called the *Doppler effect.*) In diagram 3, the source is moving through the medium *faster than the wave speed.* Thus the crests and the corresponding troughs overlap and interfere with one another. The interference is mostly destructive everywhere except on the line tangent to the wave fronts, indicated in diagram 4. The result is a wake that spreads like a wedge away from the moving source, as in the photograph below.

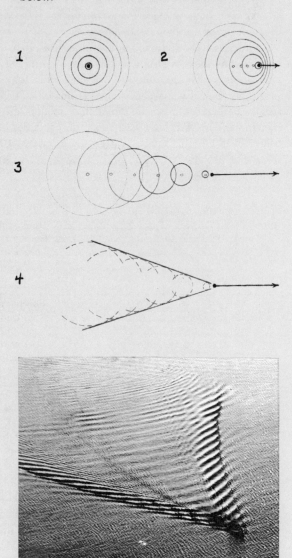

All these concepts apply not only to water waves but also to sound waves, including those disturbances set up in air by a moving plane as the wind and body push the air out of the way. If the source of sound is moving faster than the speed of sound wave, then there is a cone-shaped wake (in 3-dimensions) that spreads away from the source.

Actually two cones of sharp pressure change are formed: one originating at the front of the airplane and one at the rear, as indicated in the graph at the right.

Because the double shock wave follows along behind the airplane, the region on the ground where people and houses may be struck by the boom (the "sonic-boom carpet," or "bang-zone"), is as long as the supersonic flight path itself. In such an area, typically thousands of miles long and 50 miles wide, there may be millions of people. Tests made with airplanes flying at supersonic speed have shown that a single such cross-country flight by a 350-ton supersonic transport plane would break many thousands of dollars worth of windows, plaster walls, etc., and cause fright and annoyance to millions of people. Thus the supersonic flight of such planes may have to be confined to over-ocean use — though it may even turn out that the annoyance to people on shipboard, on islands, etc., is so great that over-ocean flights, too, will have to be restricted.

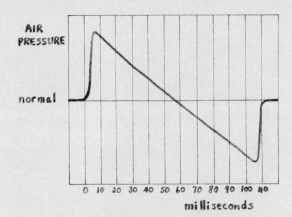

This curve represents the typical sonic boom from an airplane flying at supersonic speed (speed greater than about 700 mph). The pressure rises almost instantly, then falls relatively slowly to below-normal pressure, then rises again almost instantaneously. The second pressure rise occurs about 0.1 second after the first one, making the boom sound "double."

Double-cone shock wave, or sonic boom, produced by an airplane that is travelling (at 13-mile altitude) at three times the speed of sound. Building B is just being hit by shock wave, building A was struck a few seconds ago, and building C will be hit a few seconds later.

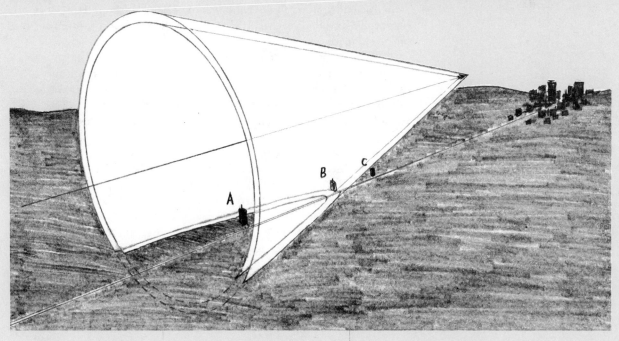

of sound in air. But it took another seventy years before William Derham in England, comparing the flash and noise from cannons across 12 miles, came close to the modern measurements.

Sound in air at 68°F moves at 1,125 feet per second (about 344 meters per second or 770 mph). As for all waves, the speed of sound waves depends on the properties of the medium—the temperature, density, and elasticity. Sound waves generally travel faster in liquids than in gases, and faster still in solids. In sea water, their speed is about 4,890 ft/sec; in steel, about 16,000 ft/sec; in quartz, about 18,000 ft/sec.

Interference of sound waves can be shown in a variety of ways. In a large hall with hard, sound-reflecting surfaces, there will be "dead" spots. At these spots, sound waves coming together after reflection cancel each other. Acoustic engineers must consider this in designing the shape, position, and materials of an auditorium. Another interesting and rather different example of sound interference is the phenomenon known as *beats*. When two notes of slightly different frequency are heard together, they interfere. This interference produces beats, a rhythmic pulsing of the sound. Piano tuners and string players use this fact to tune two strings to the same pitch. They simply adjust one string or the other until the beats disappear.

Refraction of sound by different layers of air explains why we sometimes see lightning without hearing thunder. Similar refraction of sound occurs in layers of water of different temperatures. .This sometimes causes problems in using *sonar* (*s*ound *n*avigation *a*nd *r*anging) devices at sea. Sonic refraction is used for a variety of purposes today. Geologists use them to study the earth's deep structure and to locate fossil fuels and minerals. Very intense sound waves are produced in the ground (as by dynamite blasts). The sound waves travel through the earth and are received by detection devices at different locations. The path of the waves, as refracted by layers in the earth, can be calculated from the relative intensities of sound received. From knowledge of the paths, estimates can be made of the composition of the layers.

We have already mentioned diffraction as a property of sound waves. Sound waves readily bend around corners and barriers to reach the listener within range. Sound waves reflect, as do rope or water waves, wherever they encounter a boundary between different media. Echo chamber effects (which can be artificially produced by electronics) have become familiar to listeners who enjoy popular music. The "live" sound of a bare room results from multiple reflections of waves which normally would be absorbed by furniture, rugs, and curtains. The architechtural accidents called "whispering galleries" show vividly how sound can be focused by reflection from curved surfaces. Laboratory rooms which greatly reduce reflections are called *anechoic* chambers. All these effects are of interest in the study of acoustics. Moreover, the proper acoustical design of public buildings is now recognized as an important function by most good architects.

In this chapter we have explained the basic phenomena of mechanical waves, ending with the theory of sound propagation. These explanations were considered the final triumph of Newtonian mechanics as applied to the transfer of energy of particles in motion. Most of the general principles

SG 12.33–12.35

The article "Silence, Please" in *Reader 3* is an amusing fantasy about wave superposition.

The acoustic properties of a hall filled with people are very different from those of the empty hall. Acoustical engineers sometimes fill the seats with felt-covered sandbags while making tests.

An anechoic chamber being used for research in acoustics. Sound is almost completely absorbed during multiple reflections among the wedges of soft material that cover the walls.

The concert hall of the University of Illinois Krannert Center for the Performing Arts was accoustically designed for unamplified performances.

of acoustics were discovered in the 1870's. Since then the study of acoustics has become involved with such fields as quantum physics. But perhaps its most important influence on modern physics has been its effect on the imagination of scientists. The successes of acoustics encouraged them to take seriously the power of the wave viewpoint—even in fields far from the original one, the mechanical motion of particles that move back and forth or up and down in a medium.

Q32 List five wave behaviors that can be demonstrated with sound waves.

Q33 Why can't sound waves be polarized?

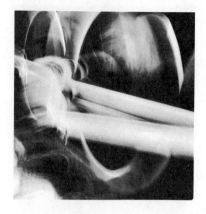

EPILOGUE   Seventeenth-century scientists thought they could eventually explain all physical phenomena by reducing them to matter and motion. This mechanistic viewpoint became known as the Newtonian worldview or Newtonian cosmology, since its most impressive success was Newton's theory of planetary motion. Newton and other scientists of his time proposed to apply similar methods to other problems, as we mentioned in the Prologue to this unit.

The early enthusiasm for this new approach to science is vividly expressed by Henry Power in his book *Experimental Philosophy* (1664). Addressing his fellow natural philosophers (or scientists, as we would now call them), he wrote:

> You are the enlarged and elastical Souls of the world, who, removing all former rubbish, and prejudicial resistances, do make way for the Springy Intellect to flye out into its desired Expansion . . .
>
> . . . This is the Age wherein (me-thinks) Philosophy comes in with a Spring-tide . . . I see how all the old Rubbish must be thrown away, and carried away with so powerful an Inundation. These are the days that must lay a new Foundation of a more magnificent Philosophy, never to be overthrown: that will Empirically and Sensibly canvass the *Phaenomena* of Nature, deducing the causes of things from such Originals in Nature, as we observe are producible by Art, and the infallible demonstration of Mechanicks; and certainly, this is the way, and no other, to build a true and permanent Philosophy.

In Power's day there were many people who did not regard the old Aristotelian cosmology as rubbish. For them, it provided a comforting sense of unity and interrelation among natural phenomena. They feared that this unity would be lost if everything was reduced simply to atoms moving randomly through space. The poet John Donne, in 1611, complained bitterly of the change already taking place in cosmology:

> And new Philosophy calls all in doubt,
> The Element of fire is quite put out;
> The Sun is lost, and th' earth, and no man's wit
> Can well direct him where to looke for it.
> And freely men confesse that this world's spent,
> When in the Planets, and the Firmament
> They seeke so many new; then see that this
> Is crumbled out againe to his Atomies.
> 'Tis all in peeces, all coherence gone;
> All just supply, and all Relation. . .

Newtonian physics provided powerful methods for analyzing the world and uncovering the basic principles of motion for individual pieces of matter. But the richness and complexity of processes in the real world seemed infinite. Could Newtonian physics deal as successfully with these real events as with ideal processes in a hypothetical vacuum? Could the perceptions of colors, sounds, and smells really be reduced to "nothing but" matter and motion? In the seventeenth century, and even in the eighteenth century, it was too soon to expect Newtonian physics to answer these questions. There was still too much work to do in establishing the basic principles of mechanics and applying them to astronomical problems. A full-scale attack on the properties of matter and energy had to wait until the nineteenth century.

This unit covered several successful applications and extensions of Newtonian mechanics which were accomplished by the end of the nineteenth century. For example, we discussed the conservation laws, new explanations of the properties of heat and gases, and estimates of some properties of molecules. We introduced the concept of energy, linking mechanics to heat and to sound. In Unit 4 we will show similar links to light, electricity, and magnetism. We also noted that applying mechanics on a molecular level requires statistical ideas and presents questions about the direction of time.

Throughout most of this unit we have emphasized the application of mechanics to separate pieces or molecules of matter. But scientists found that the molecular model was not the only way to understand the behavior of matter. Without departing from basic Newtonian cosmology, scientists could also interpret many phenomena (such as sound and light) in terms of wave motions in continuous matter. By the middle of the nineteenth century it was generally believed that all physical phenomena could be explained by a theory that was built on the use of either particles or waves. In the next unit, we will discover how much or how little validity there was in this belief. We will begin to see the rise of a new viewpoint in physics, based on the field concept. Then, in Unit 5, particles, waves, and fields will come together in the context of twentieth-century physics.

12.1 The Project Physics materials particularly appropriate for Chapter 12 include:

Experiments
  Sound
Activities
  Standing Waves on a Drum and a Violin
  Moiré Patterns
  Music and Speech Activities
  Measurement of the Speed of Sound
  Mechanical Wave Machines
Film Loops
  Superposition
  Standing Waves in a String
  Standing Waves in a Gas
  Four loops on vibrations
Reader Articles
  Silence, Please
  Frontiers of Physics Today: Acoustics
  Waves
  What is a Wave
  Musical Instruments and Scales
  Founding a Family of Fiddles

12.2 Some waves propagate at such a high speed that we are usually not aware of any delay in energy transfer. For example, the delay between the flash and the "bang" in watching lightning or fireworks seems peculiar, because the propagation time for sounds produced near us is not noticeable. Give an example of a compression wave in a solid, started by an action at one end, that propagates so quickly that we are not aware of any delay before an effect at the other end.

12.3 Describe the differences in phase of oscillation of various parts of your body as you walk. What points are exactly in phase? Which points are exactly $\frac{1}{2}$ cycle out of phase? Are there any points $\frac{1}{4}$ cycle out of phase?

12.4 Pictured are two pulse waves (A and B) on a rope at the instants before and after they

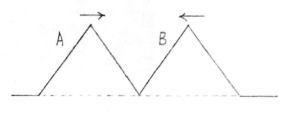

overlap (t_1 and t_2). Divide the elapsed time between t_1 and t_2 into four equal intervals and

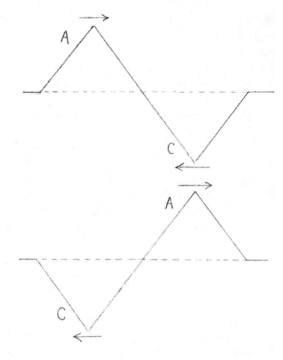

plot the shape of the rope at the end of each interval.

12.5 Repeat Exercise 12.3 for the two pulses (A and C) pictured at the top.

12.6 The wave below propagates to the right along a rope. What is the shape of the wave propagating to the left that could for an instant cancel this one completely?

12.7 The velocity of a portion of rope at some instant as transverse waves are passing through it is the superposition of the velocities of waves passing through that portion. Is the kinetic energy of a portion of the rope the superposition of the kinetic energies of waves passing through that region? Justify your answer.

12.8 Graphically superpose the last three curves of the figure on p. 110 to find their sum (which should be the original curve).

12.9 What shape would the nodal regions have for sound waves from two loudspeakers?

12.10 Imagine a detection device for waves is moved slowly to either the right or left of the point labeled A_0 in the figure on p. 114. Describe what the detection device would register.

12.11 What kind of interference pattern would you expect to see if the separation between two in-phase sources were less than the wavelength λ? Where would the nodal and antinodal lines be if the two in-phase sources were separated by the distance λ? By $\lambda/2$? Convince yourself that one additional nodal line appears on each side of the central antinodal line whenever the separation between the two in-phase sources is increased by one wavelength.

12.12 Derive an equation, similar to $n\lambda l = dx_n$, for *nodal* points in a two-source interference pattern (where d is the separation of the sources, l the distance from the sources, and x_n the distance of the nth node from the center line).

12.13 If you suddenly disturbed a stretched rubber hose or slinky with a frequency that precisely matched a standing wave frequency, would standing waves appear immediately? If not, what factors would determine the time delay?

12.14 Different notes are sounded with the same guitar string by changing its vibrating length (that is, pressing the string against a brass ridge). If the full length of the string is L, what lengths must it be shortened to in order to sound (a) a "musical fourth," (b) a "musical fifth," (c) an "octave"?

12.15 Standing sound waves can be set up in the air in an enclosure (like a bottle or an organ pipe). In a pipe that is closed at one end, the air molecules at the closed end are not free to be displaced, so the standing wave must have a displacement node at the closed end. At the open end, however, the molecules are almost completely free to be displaced, so the standing waves must have an antinode near the open end.
(a) What will be the wavelength of the fundamental standing wave in a pipe of length L closed at one end? (Hint: What is the longest wave that has a node and an antinode a distance L apart?)
(b) What is a general expression for possible wavelengths of standing waves in a pipe closed at one end?
(c) Answer (a) and (b) for the case of a pipe open at *both* ends.

12.16 Imagine a spherical blob of jello in which you can set up standing vibrations. What would be some of the possible modes of vibration? (Hint: what possible symmetrical nodal surfaces could there be?)

12.17 Suppose that straight-line ripple waves approach a thin straight barrier which is a few wavelengths long and which is oriented with its length parallel to the wavefronts. What do you predict about the nature of the diffraction pattern along a straight line behind the barrier which is perpendicular to the barrier and passes through the center of the barrier? Why do people who design breakwaters need to concern themselves with diffraction effects?

12.18 A megaphone directs sound along the megaphone axis if the wavelength of the sound is

small compared to the diameter of the opening. Estimate the upper limit of frequencies which are diffracted at a cheerleader's megaphone opening. Can you hear what a cheerleader shouts even though you are far off the axis of the megaphone?

12.19 Explain why it is that the narrower a slit in a barrier is, the more nearly it can act like a point source of waves.

12.20 If light is also a wave, then why have you not seen light being diffracted by the slits, say those of a picket fence, or diffracted around the corner of houses?

12.21 By actual construction with a ruler and compass on a tracing of the photograph on p. 127, show that rays for the reflected wave front appear to come from S'. Show also that this is consistent with $\theta_r = \theta_i$.

12.22 A straight-line wave approaches a right-angle reflecting barrier as shown in the figure. Find the shape, size, and direction of propagation of the wave after it has been completely reflected by the barrier.

12.23 With ruler and compass reproduce part (b) of the figure at the bottom of p. 124 and find the distance from the circle's center to the point P in terms of the radius of the circle r. Make the radius of your circle much larger than the one in the figure. (Hint: the dotted lines are along radii.)

12.24 Convince yourself that a parabolic reflector will actually bring parallel wave-fronts to a sharp focus. Draw a parabola $y = kx^2$ (choosing any convenient value for k) and some parallel rays along the axis as in part (c) of the Figure at the bottom of p. 124. Construct line segments perpendicular to the parabola where the rays hit it, and draw the reflected rays at equal angles on the other side of these lines.

12.25 The *focal length* of a curved reflector is the distance from the reflector to the point where parallel rays are focused. Use the drawing in SG 12.24 to find the focal length of a parabola in terms of k.

12.26 Recalling that water surface waves travel slower in shallow water, what would you expect to happen to the shape of the following wave as it

continues to the right? Pay particular attention to the region of varying depth. Can you use the line of reasoning above to give at least a partial explanation of the cause of breakers near a beach?

12.27 A straight-line wave in a ripple tank approaches a boundary between deep and shallow water as shown. Describe the shape of the wave as it passes through the boundary and then as it continues in the shallow water.

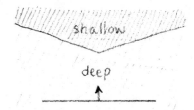

12.28 On the opposite page is an aerial photograph of ocean waves entering from the upper right and encountering a small island. Describe the wave phenomena demonstrated by this encounter.

12.29 The diagram below shows two successive positions, *AB* and *CD*, of a wave train of sound or light, before and after crossing an air-glass boundary. The time taken to go from *AB* to *DC* is one period of the wave.

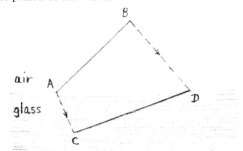

(a) Indicate and label an angle equal to angle of incidence θ_A.
(b) Indicate and label an angle equal to angle of refraction θ_B.
(c) Label the wavelength in air λ_A.
(d) Label the wavelength in glass λ_B.
(e) Show that $v_A/v_B = \lambda_A/\lambda_B$.
(f) If you are familiar with trigonometry, show that $\sin\theta_A/\sin\theta_B = \lambda_A/\lambda_B$.

12.30 A periodic ripple-tank wave passes through a straight boundary between deep and shallow water. The angle of incidence at the boundary is 45° and the angle of refraction is 30°. The propagation speed in the deep water is 0.35 m/sec, and the frequency of the wave is 10 cycles per sec. Find the wavelengths in the deep and shallow water.

12.31 Look at Figure (d) on p. 127. Convince yourself that if a wave were to approach the boundary between medium 1 and medium 2 from below, along the same direction as the refracted ray in the figure, it would be refracted along the direction of the incident ray in the figure. This is another example of a general rule: if a wave follows a set of rays in one direction, then a wave can follow the same set of rays in the opposite direction. In other words, wave paths are reversible.

12.32 Suppose that in an extremely quiet room you can barely hear a buzzing mosquito at a distance of one meter.
(a) What is the sound power output of the mosquito?
(b) How many mosquitoes would it take to supply the power for one 100-watt reading lamp?
(c) If the swarm were at ten meters' distance, what would the sound be like? (Sound intensity diminishes in proportion to the square of the distance from a point source.)

12.33 How can sound waves be used to map the floors of oceans?

12.34 Estimate the wavelength of a 1000 cycles per second sound wave in air; in water; in steel (refer to data in text). Do the same if $f = 10,000$ cps. Design the dimensions of an experiment to show two-source interference for 1000 cps sound waves.

12.35 Waves reflect from an object in a definite direction only when the wavelength is small compared to the dimensions of the object. This is true for sound waves as well as for any other. What does this tell you about the sound frequencies a bat must generate if it is to catch a moth or a fly? Actually some bats can detect the presence of a wire about 0.12 mm in diameter. Approximately what frequency does that require?

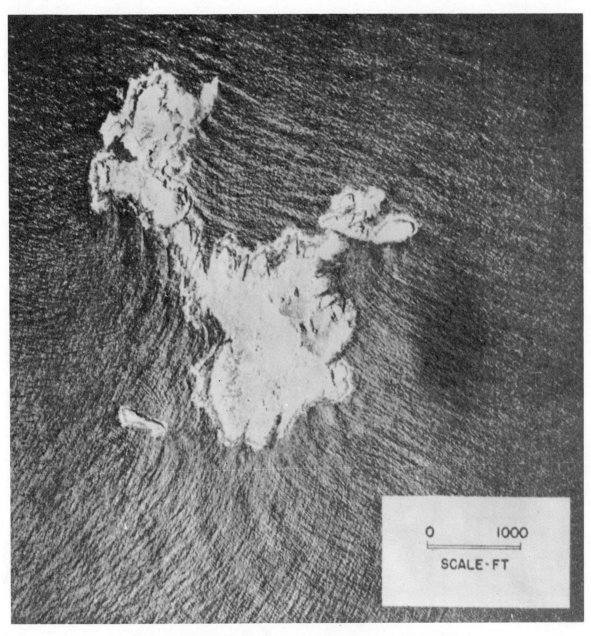

Refraction, reflection, and diffraction of waves around Farallon Island, California. There are breakers all around the coast. The swell coming from top right rounds both sides of the island, producing a crossed pattern below. The small islet 'radiates' the waves away in all directions. (U.S. Navy photograph.)

PROJECT PHYSICS

4

Light and Electromagnetism

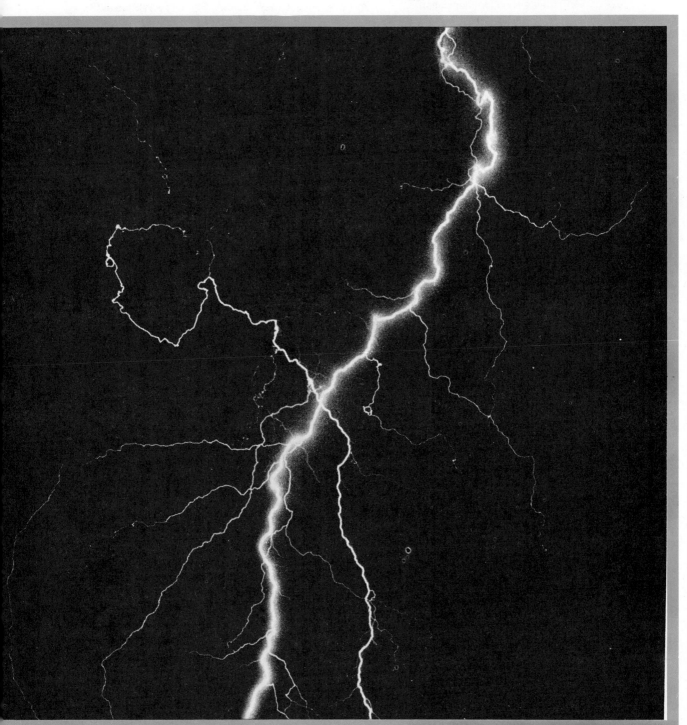

Experiments

4-1   Refraction of a Light Beam
4-2   Young's Experiment—The Wavelength
        of Light
4-3   Electric Forces I
4-4   Electric Forces II—Coulomb's Law
4-5   Forces on Currents
4-6   Currents, Magnets and Forces
4-7   Electron Beam Tube
4-8   Electron Beam tubes II
4-9   Waves and Communication

Activities

Thin Film Interference
Handkerchief Diffraction Grating
Photographing Diffraction Patterns
Poisson's Spot
Photographic Activities
Color
Polarized Light
Making an Ice Lens
Detecting Electric Fields
Voltaic Pile
An 11¢ Battery
Measuring Magnetic Field Intensity
More Perpetual Motion Machines
Transistor Amplifier
Inside a Radio Tube
An Isolated North Magnetic Pole?
Faraday Disk Dynamo
Generator Jump Rope
Simple Meters and Motors
Simple Meter-Generator Demonstration
Physics Collage
Bicycle Generator
Lapis Polaris, Magnes
Microwave Transmission Systems
Science and the Artist—The Story Behind a
   Science Stamp
Bell Telephone Science Kits

Film Loop

L44   Standing Electromagnetic Waves

Transparencies

T30   The Speed of Light
T31 $\vec{E}$ Field Inside Conducting Spheres
T32   Magnetic Fields and Moving Charges
T33   Forces Between Current Carriers
T34   The Electromagnetic Spectrum

Reader Articles

1   *Letter from Thomas Jefferson, June 1799*
      by Thomas Jefferson
2   *On the Method of Theoretical Physics*
      by Albert Einstein
3   *Systems, Feedback, Cybernetics*
      by V. Lawrence Parsegian and others
4   *Velocity of Light*
      by A. A. Michelson
5   *Popular Applications of Polarized Light*
      by William A. Shurcliff and Stanley S.
      Ballard
6   *Eye and Camera*
      by George Wald
7   *The Laser—What It Is and Does*
      by J. M. Carroll
8   *A Simple Electric Circuit: Ohm's Law*
      by Albert V. Baez
9   *The Electronic Revolution*
      by Arthur C. Clarke
10   *The Invention of the Electric Light*
      by Matthew Josephson
11   *High Fidelity*
      by Edgar Villchur
12   *The Future of Direct Current Power
      Transmission*
      by N. L. Allen
13   *James Clerk Maxwell, Part II*
      by James R. Newman
14   *On the Induction of Electric Currents*
      by James Clerk Maxwell
15   *The Relationship of Electricity and
      Magnetism*
      by D. K. C. MacDonald
16   *The Electromagnetic Field*
      by Albert Einstein and Leopold Infeld
17   *Radiation Belts Around the Earth*
      by James Van Allen
18   *A Mirror for the Brain*
      by W. Grey Walter
19   *Scientific Imagination*
      by Richard P. Feynman, Robert B.
      Leighton and Matthew Sands
20   *Lenses and Optical Instruments*
      by Physical Science Study Committee
21   *Baffled!*
      by Keith Waterhouse

Contents TEXT, UNIT 4

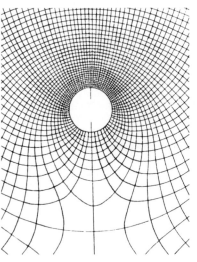

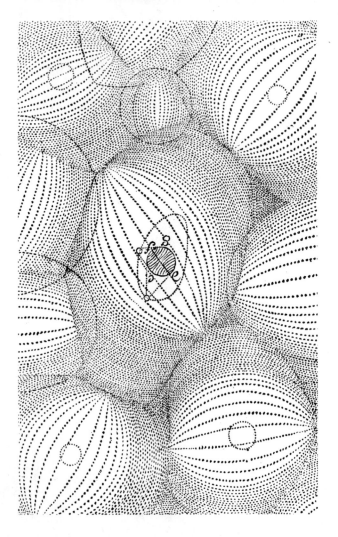

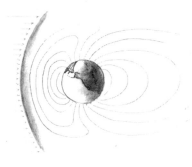

It was inconceivable to many scientists that one body could directly affect another across empty space. They devised a variety of schemes to fill the space in between with something that would transmit the effect first with material "ether,"—later with mathematical "fields." Some of these schemes are illustrated on this page. Descartes, 17th century (bottom left); Euler, 18th century (top left); Maxwell, 19th century (top right). Above is a drawing copied from *The New York Times* (1967) representing the magnetic field around the earth. It is not the more symmetrical field the earth would have on its own, but as disturbed by the field due to streams of charged particles from the sun.

UNIT **4**

Light and Electromagnetism

CHAPTERS

PROLOGUE The conviction that the world and everything in it consists of *matter in motion* drove scientists to search for mechanical models for light and electromagnetism. That is, they tried to imagine how the effects of light, electricity, and magnetism could be explained in detail as the action of material objects. (For example, consider the way light bounces off a mirror. A model for this effect might picture light as consisting of particles of matter that behave somewhat like tiny ping-pong balls.) Such mechanical models were useful for a while, but in the long run proved far too limited. Still, the search for them led to many new discoveries, which in turn brought about important changes in science, technology, and society. These discoveries and their effects form the subject of this unit. In this Prologue we sketch the development of various models and briefly indicate their effect on our present ideas of the physical world.

From the seventeenth century on there were two competing models for light. One model tried to explain light in terms of particles, the other in terms of waves. In the first half of the nineteenth century the wave model won general acceptance, because it was better able to account for newly discovered optical effects. Chapter 13 tells the story of the triumph of the wave theory of light. The wave theory remained supreme until the early part of the twentieth century, when it was found (as we will see in Unit 5) that neither waves nor particles alone could account for all the behavior of light.

As experiments established that electric and magnetic forces have some characteristics in common with gravitational forces, scientists developed new theories of electricity and magnetism. Modeled on Newton's treatment of gravitation, these new theories assumed that there are forces between electrified and magnetized bodies which vary inversely with the square of the distance. This assumption was found to account for many observations. Of course, the drafters of these theories also assumed that bodies can exert forces over a distance without having to touch one another.

Action-at-a-distance theories were remarkably successful in providing a quantitative explanation for some aspects of electromagnetism. However, they did not at the time provide a really complete explanation. Instead, another means of description, based on the idea of *fields,* became widely accepted by the end of the nineteenth century. It is now generally believed to be the best way to discuss *all* physical forces. We introduce the field concept in Chapter 14 and develop it further in the last chapter of the unit.

Many scientists felt that action-at-a-distance theories, however accurate in prediction, failed to give a satisfactory physical explanation of how one body exerts a force on another. Newton himself was reluctant to assume that one body can act on another through empty space. In a letter to Richard Bentley he wrote:

The text of this letter is reproduced exactly as Newton wrote it.

> Tis unconceivable to me that inanimate brute matter should (without the mediation of something else wch is not material) operate upon & affect other matter without mutual contact; . . . And this is one reason why I desire you would not ascribe innate gravity to me. That gravity should be innate inherent & essential to matter so yt one body may act upon another at a distance through a vacuum wthout the mediation of any thing else by & through wch their action or force may be conveyed from one point to another is to me so great an absurdity that I believe no man who has in philosophical matters any competent faculty of thinking can ever fall into it.

Some seventeenth-century scientists were less cautious than Newton. They proposed that objects are surrounded by atmospheres that extend to the most distant regions and transmit gravitational, electric, and magnetic forces from one body to another. The atmospheres proposed at this time were not made a part of a quantitative theory. But in the nineteenth century the atmosphere concept was revived. Numerous attempts were made to develop mathematically the properties of a medium that would transmit the waves of light. The name "luminiferous ether" was given to this hypothetical "light-bearing" substance.

The rapid discovery of new electrical and magnetic effects in the first half of the nineteenth century stimulated the scientific imagination. Michael Faraday (1791-1867), who made many of the important discoveries, developed a model with lines of force assigned to the space surrounding electrified and magnetized bodies. Faraday showed how these lines of force could account for many electromagnetic effects.

In a paper he wrote at age 17, William Thomson (1824-1907) showed how the equations used to formulate and solve a problem in electrostatics could also be used to solve a heat-flow problem. *Electrostatics* deals with the effects of forces between charges at rest. At the time, it was most simply and effectively treated by assuming that electrical forces can act at a distance. On the other hand, the flow of heat was generally held to result

William Thomson (Lord Kelvin) was a Scottish mathematical physicist. He contributed to the fields of electricity, mechanics, and thermodynamics and to such practical developments as an improved ship's compass and the first Atlantic cable. The Kelvin scale of absolute temperature is named for him.

from the action of parts that touch. Thomson showed that the same mathematical formulation could be used for theories based on completely different physical assumptions. Perhaps, then, it was more important to find correct mathematical tools than to choose a particular mathematical model.

James Clerk Maxwell (1831-1879), inspired by Faraday's physical models and by Thomson's mathematics, attempted to develop a mathematical theory of electromagnetism. Maxwell first assumed an imaginary ether filled with gears and idler wheels. Then he gradually worked out a set of equations that described the properties of electric and magnetic fields. These equations were later found to be remarkably successful. They described quite accurately the electric and magnetic effects already known to occur. Moreover, they led Maxwell to predict new effects based on the idea of a propagating wave disturbance in electric and magnetic fields. The speed he predicted for such electromagnetic waves was nearly the same as the measured speed of light. This similarity suggested to him that light might *be* an electromagnetic wave.

The field concept, together with the concept of energy, provides a way of treating the action of one body on another without speaking of action at a distance or of a material medium that transmits the action. The field concept has proved its usefulness over and over again during the twentieth century.

See Maxwell's article "Action at a Distance" in *Reader 4.*

Radio telescope at the National Radio Astronomy Observatory, Greenbank, West Virginia.

CHAPTER THIRTEEN

Light

13.1 Introduction

What is light? At first, this may seem a rather trivial question. After all, hardly anything is more familiar to us. We see by means of light. We also live by light, for without it there would be no photosynthesis, and photosynthesis is the basic source of energy for most life on earth. Light brings us most of our information about the world around us, both on the earth and out to the most distant reaches of space. Because our world is largely defined by light, its behavior has always fascinated us. How fast does it travel? How does it cross empty space? What is color?

Light is a form of energy. The physicist can describe a beam of light by measurable values of its speed, wavelength or frequency, and intensity. But to physicists, as to all people, light of course also means brightness and shade, the beauty of summer flowers and fall foliage, of red sunsets and of the canvases painted by masters. These are simply different ways of appreciating light. One way concentrates on light's measurable aspects; this approach has been enormously fruitful in physics and technology. The other way asks about our aesthetic responses when we view light in nature or art. Still another way of considering light centers upon the biophysical process of vision.

These aspects of light are not easily separated. Thus, in the early history of science, light presented more subtle and more elusive problems than did most other aspects of physical experience. Early ideas on its nature often confused light with vision. This confusion is still evident in young children. When playing hide-and-go-seek, some of them "hide" by covering their eyes with their hands; apparently they think that they cannot be seen when they cannot see. The association of vision with light persists into the language of the adult world. We talk about the sun "peeping out of the clouds" or the stars "looking down."

Behold the Light emitted from the Sun,
　What more familiar, and what more unknown;
　While by its spreading Radiance it reveals
　All Nature's Face, it still itself conceals . . .

[Richard Blackmore, *Creation* II, 1715.]

SG 13.1

Some Greek philosophers believed that light travels in straight lines at high speed and contains particles which stimulate the sense of vision when they enter the eye. For centuries after the Greek era, limited attention was paid to the nature of light, and this particle model survived almost intact. But around 1500, Leonardo da Vinci, noting a similarity between sound echoes and the reflection of light, speculated that light might have a wave character.

A decided difference of opinion about the nature of light emerged among scientists of the seventeenth century. Some, including Newton, favored a model largely based on the idea of light as a stream of particles. Others, including Huygens, supported a wave model. By the late nineteenth century, there appeared to be overwhelming evidence in support of the wave model. In this chapter we will look at the question *How appropriate is a wave model in explaining the observed behavior of light?* That is, we will take the wave model as a hypothesis and examine the evidence that supports it. We must remember that any scientific model, hypothesis, or theory has two chief functions: to explain what is known, and to make predictions that can be tested experimentally. We will discuss both of these aspects of the wave model. The result will be rather surprising. The wave model turns out to work splendidly for all properties of light known before the twentieth century. But in Chapter 18 we will find that for some purposes we must adopt a particle model. Then in Chapter 20 we will combine *both* models, merging two apparently opposite theories.

We have already mentioned the ancient opinion—later proved by experiment—that light travels in straight lines and at high speed. Our daily use of mirrors convinces us that light can also be reflected. Light also can be refracted, and it shows the phenomena of interference and diffraction. You studied all of these properties in Chapter 12, where we discussed the behavior of waves. If necessary, you should refresh your memory about the basic ideas of that chapter before going on to the study of light. We will also encounter other phenomena—dispersion, polarization, and scattering—which we so far have given little or no consideration. As you will see, these also fit into our wave model, and in fact provide strong experimental support for it.

Before discussing these various aspects of light's behavior and how they support our hypothesis of a wave model, let us first consider the propagation of light. Then we can take up two characteristics—reflection and refraction—which can be explained by either a corpuscular (particle) model or a wave model. Of course, the discussion in this text should be supplemented whenever possible by laboratory experiments and other activities, selections from the readers, films and loops, transparencies, etc.

Indeed, this is a good moment to remind you of an important point: this course stresses the use of many media to learn physics. It therefore differs from many other courses with which you may be familiar, and which rely most heavily on a text only. In this course, the text will sometimes only motivate or put into context parts of the materials that are much better learned through experiments, class discussion, etc., than through reading about them. This is especially true of optics (the science

There is no sharp general distinction among model, hypothesis, and theory. Roughly we can say that a model (whether mechanical or mathematical) is a rather limited conception to explain a particular observed phenomenon. A hypothesis is a statement that usually can be directly or indirectly tested. A theory is a more general construction, putting together one or more models and several hypotheses to explain many effects or phenomena that previously seemed unrelated.

In addition, a Supplemental Unit has been prepared which deals entirely with Optics.

Light beams travel in straight lines

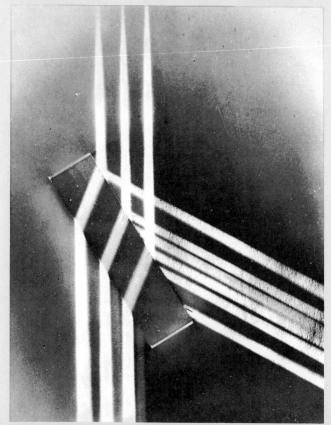

of light), electricity, and magnetism—the subjects of Unit 4. This text is intended to provide a general map, which you will fill out in a way that will make the study of physics more valid and exciting than reading alone could do.

13.2 Propagation of light

SG 13.2

There is ample evidence that light travels in straight lines. The fact that one cannot see "around the corner" of an obstacle is one obvious example of such evidence. A shadow cast by the sun has the sharply defined outlines given by a large but very distant light source. Similarly, sharp shadows are cast by smaller sources closer by. The distant sun and the nearby small source are approximate *point* sources of light. Such point sources produce sharp shadows.

Images as well as shadows can demonstrate that light travels in straight lines. Before the invention of the modern camera with its lens system, a light-tight box with a pinhole in the center of one face was widely used. As the *camera obscura,* the device was highly popular in the Middle Ages. Leonardo da Vinci probably used it as an aid in his sketching. In one of his manuscripts he says that "a small aperture in a window shutter projects on the inner wall of the room an image of the bodies which are beyond the aperture." He includes a sketch to show how the straight-line propagation of light explains the formation of an image.

Camera obscura is a Latin phrase meaning "dark chamber."

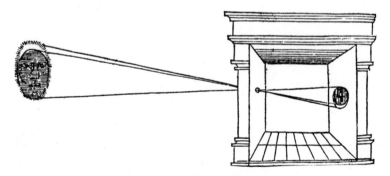

First published illustration of a *camera obscura*; observing a solar eclipse in January 1544, from a book by the Dutch physician and mathematician Gemma Frisius.

It is often convenient to use a straight line to represent the direction in which light travels. The pictorial device of an infinitely thin *ray* of light is useful for thinking about light, but no such rays actually exist. A light beam emerging from a good-sized hole in a screen is as wide as the hole. You might expect that if we made the hole extremely small we would get a very narrow beam of light—ultimately just a single ray. But we don't! Diffraction effects (such as you observed for water and sound waves in Chapter 12) appear when the beam of light passes through a small hole (see opposite). So an infinitely thin ray of light, although it is pictorially useful, cannot be produced in practice. But we can still use the idea in order to *represent the direction* in which a train of parallel waves in a beam of light is traveling.

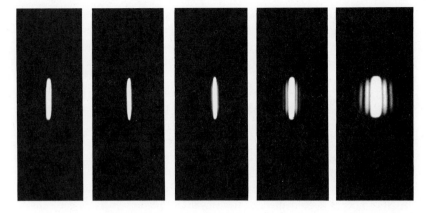

An attempt to produce a "ray" of light. To make the pictures at the left, a parallel beam of red light was directed through increasingly narrow slits to a photographic plate. (Of course, the narrower the slit, the less the light that gets through. This was compensated for by longer exposures in these photographic exposures.) The slit widths, from left to right, were 1.5 mm, 0.7 mm, 0.4 mm, 0.2 mm, and 0.1 mm.

Actually the beam of light produced by a laser comes as close as possible to the ideal case of a thin, parallel bundle of rays. As we will learn later in this unit (Chapter 15), light is produced by the vibrations of electrons within the atoms of its source. In most light sources, ranging from incandescent and fluorescent bulbs to the sun and stars, the atoms vibrate independently of one another. Each of the vibrating atoms produces an individual wavelet, and the sum of the wavelets from all the vibrating atoms makes up the total emerging light beam. As a result, light from such sources spreads out in all directions. A more or less parallel beam of light can be produced by using a set of pinholes, or with mirrors or lenses, as found, for instance, in flashlights, automobile headlights, and searchlights. However, as you can quickly determine for yourself, the beams of light they produce still diverge noticeably.

SG 13.3

In contrast, lasers are designed in such a way that their atoms vibrate and produce light in unison with one another, rather than individually and at random. As a result, the atoms produce their wavelets simultaneously; this can yield a total beam of considerable intensity and much more nearly monochromatic (that is, of a single color) than the light from any conventional source. In addition, since the individual wavelets from the atoms of a laser are produced simultaneously, they are able to interfere with each other constructively to produce a beam of light which is narrow and very nearly parallel. In fact, such light spreads out so little that beams from lasers, when directed at the surface of the moon a quarter-million miles away, have been found to produce spots of light only a few feet in diameter.

Given that light seems to travel in straight lines, can we tell how fast it goes? Galileo discussed this problem in his *Two New Sciences* (published 1638). He pointed out that everyday experiences might lead us to conclude that light propagates instantaneously. But these experiences, when analyzed more closely, really show only that light travels much faster than sound. For example, "when we see a piece of artillery fired, at a great distance, the flash reaches our eyes without lapse of time; but the sound reaches the ear only after a noticeable interval." But how do we really know whether the light moved "without lapse of time" unless we have some accurate way of measuring the lapse of time?

See also *Reader 4* article, "The Laser—What it is and does."

Galileo then described an experiment by which two persons on distant hills flashing lanterns might measure the speed of light. (This experiment is to be analyzed in SG 13.4.) He concluded that the speed of light is probably finite, not infinite. But he was not able to estimate a definite value for it.

SG 13.4

Experimental evidence was first successfully related to a finite speed for light by a Danish astronomer, Ole Römer. Detailed observations of Jupiter's satellites had shown an unexplained irregularity in the times recorded between successive eclipses of the satellites by the planet. Such an eclipse was expected to occur at 45 seconds after 5:25 A.M. on November 9, 1676. In September of that year, Römer announced to the Academy of Sciences in Paris that the eclipse would be ten minutes late. On November 9, astronomers at the Royal Observatory in Paris carefully observed the eclipse. Though skeptical of Römer's mysterious prediction, they reported that the eclipse did occur late, just as he had foreseen.

Later, Römer revealed the theoretical basis of his prediction to the baffled astronomers at the Academy of Sciences. He explained that the originally expected time of the eclipse had been calculated from observations made when Jupiter was near the earth. But now Jupiter had moved farther away. The delay in the eclipse occurred simply because light from Jupiter takes time to reach the earth. And, obviously, this time interval must be larger when the relative positions of Jupiter and the earth in their orbits are larger. In fact, Römer estimated that it takes about 22 minutes for light to cross the earth's own orbit around the sun.

Shortly after this, the Dutch physicist Christian Huygens used Römer's data to make the first calculation of the speed of light. He combined Römer's value of 22 minutes for light to cross the earth's orbit with his own estimate of the diameter of the earth's orbit. (This distance could be estimated for the first time in the seventeenth century, as a result of the advances in astronomy described in Unit 2.) Huygens obtained a value which, in modern units, is about 2×10^8 meters per second. This is about two-thirds of the presently accepted value (see below). The error in Huygens' value was due mainly to Römer's overestimate of the time interval. We now know that it takes light only about 16 minutes to cross the earth's orbit.

The importance of Römer's work was not so much that it led to a particular value of the speed of light, but rather that it established that the propagation of light is not instantaneous but takes a finite time, and that he obtained a value of the right order of magnitude.

The speed of light has been measured in many different ways since the seventeenth century. (See the article "Velocity of Light" in *Reader 4*.) Since the speed is very great, it is necessary to use either a very long distance or a very short time interval or both. The earlier methods were based on measurements of astronomical distances. In the nineteenth century, rotating slotted wheels and mirrors made it possible to measure very short time intervals so that distances of a few miles could be used. The development of electronic devices in the twentieth century allowed measurement of even shorter time intervals. Today the speed of light is one of the most accurately known physical constants. But because of the importance of the value of the speed of light in modern physical theories, physicists are continuing to improve their methods of measurement.

The most accurate recent measurements indicate that the speed of light in vacuum is 299,792,456.2 meters per second. The uncertainty of this value is thought to be about 1 meter per second, or 0.000001%. The

speed of light is usually represented by the symbol c, and for most
purposes it is sufficient to use the approximate value c = 3 × 10⁸ meters
per second.

SG 13.5

SG 13.6

Q1   Can a beam of light be made increasingly narrow by passing it
through narrower and narrower slits?

Q2   What reason did Römer have for thinking that the eclipse of a
particular satellite of Jupiter would be observed later than expected?

Q3   What was the most important outcome of Römer's work?

Two narrow beams of light, coming
from the upper left, strike a block of
glass. Can you account for the other
effects?

13.3 Reflection and refraction

What happens when light traveling in one medium (say air) hits the
boundary of another medium (say glass)? The answers to this question
depend on whether we adopt a particle or a wave theory of light. So here
we have a chance to test which theory is better.

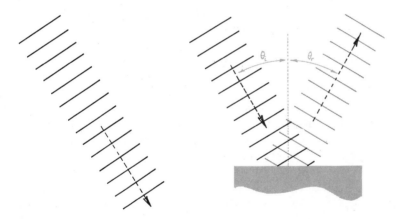

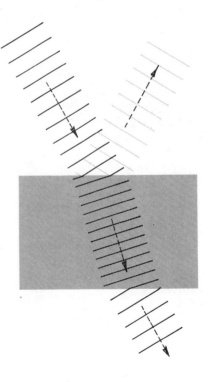

We have already discussed reflection and refraction from the wave
viewpoint in Chapter 12. We need only recall the results obtained there
and apply them to light.

1. A ray may be taken as the line drawn perpendicular to a wave's
crest lines. Such a ray represents the direction in which a train of parallel
waves is traveling.

2. In reflection, the angle of incidence (θ_i) is equal to the angle of
reflection (θ_r).

3. Refraction involves a change of wavelength and speed of the wave
as it goes into another medium. When the speed decreases, the
wavelength decreases, and the ray bends in a direction toward a line
perpendicular to the boundary. This bending toward the perpendicular is
observed when a ray of light goes from air to glass.

What about explaining the same observations by means of the particle

SG 13.7–13.12

The incident, reflected, and refracted
rays are all in the same plane, a
plane perpendicular to the surface.

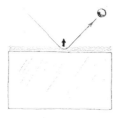

SG 13.13

The surface of a mirror as shown by an electron microscope. The surface is a three-micron thick aluminum film. The magnification here is nearly 26,000. (μ stands for micron; where $1\mu = 10^{-6}$ meter.)

model? To test this model, we must first consider the nature of the surface of glass. Though apparently smooth, it is actually a wrinkled surface. A powerful microscope would show it to have endless hills and valleys. If particles of light were at all similar to little balls of matter, then on striking such a wrinkled surface they would scatter in all directions. They would not be reflected and refracted as shown on page 11. Therefore, Newton argued, there must actually be "some feature of the body which is evenly diffused over its surface and by which it acts upon the ray without immediate contact." Obviously, in the case of reflection, the acting force would have to be one which repelled the particles of light. Similarly, a force which attracted light particles instead of repelling them could explain refraction. As a particle of light approached a boundary of another medium, it would first have to overcome the repelling force. If it did that, it would then meet an attractive force in the medium which would pull it into the medium. Since the attractive force would be a vector with a component in the direction of the particle's original motion, the particle's speed would increase. So if the ray of particles were moving at an oblique angle to the boundary, it would change direction as it entered the medium, bending toward the line perpendicular to the boundary.

According to the *particle* model, therefore, we can make the following statements about reflection and refraction.

1. A ray represents the direction in which the particles are moving.

2. In reflection, the angles of incidence and reflection are equal. This prediction can be derived by applying the Law of Conservation of Momentum (Chapter 9) to particles repelled by a force as shown on the last sketch on the previous page (see also SG 13.7).

3. Refraction involves a change of speed of the particles as they enter another medium. In particular, when an attractive power acts, *the speed increases* and the ray is bent into the medium.

Compare these features of the particle model with the corresponding features of the wave model (above). The only difference is in the predicted speed for a refracted ray. We *observe* that a ray is bent toward the perpendicular line when light goes from air into water. The particle theory *predicts* that light has a *greater* speed in the second medium. The wave theory *predicts* that light has a *lower* speed.

You might think that it would be fairly easy to devise an experiment to determine which prediction is correct. All one has to do is measure the speed light has after it has entered water and compare it with the speed of light in air. But in the late seventeenth and early eighteenth centuries, when Huygens was supporting the wave model and Newton a particle model, no such experiment was possible. The only available way of measuring the speed of light was an astronomical one. Not until the middle of the nineteenth century did Armand H. L. Fizeau and Jean B. L. Foucault measure the speed of light in water. The results agreed with the predictions of the wave model: the speed of light is less in water than in air.

Actually, by the time these experiments were done, most physicists had already accepted the wave model for other reasons (see below). The Foucault-Fizeau experiments of 1850 were widely regarded as driving the last nail in the coffin of the Newtonian particle theory.

Q4 What evidence showed conclusively that Newton's particle model for light could not explain all aspects of refraction?

Q5 If light has a wave nature, what changes take place in the speed, wavelength, and frequency of light on passing from air into water?

13.4 Interference and diffraction

From the time of Newton until the early nineteenth century, most physicists favored the particle theory of light. Newton's own prestige contributed greatly to this support. Early in the nineteenth century, however, the wave theory was revived by Thomas Young. In experiments made between 1802 and 1804, Young found that light shows the phenomenon of *interference*. (Interference patterns were discussed in Section 12.6 in connection with water waves.) The particle theory of light could not easily explain such patterns. But Young's famous "double-slit experiment" provided convincing evidence that light does have properties that are explainable only in terms of waves.

Young's experiment must be done in the lab, rather than just talked about, but we will describe it briefly here. Basically, it involves splitting a single beam of light into two beams. The split beams are then allowed to overlap, and the two wave trains interfere—constructively in some places and destructively in others. To simplify our interpretation of the experiment, we will assume that it is done with light that has a single definite wavelength λ.

Young used a black screen with a small hole punched in it to produce a narrow beam of sunlight in a dark room. In the beam he placed a

Thomas Young (1773-1829) was an English linguist, physician, and expert in many fields of science. At the age of fourteen he was familiar with Latin, Greek, Hebrew, Arabic, Persian, French, and Italian, and later was one of the first scholars successful at decoding Egyptian hieroglyphic inscriptions. He studied medicine in England, Scotland, and Germany. While still in medical school he made original studies of the eye, and later developed the first version of what is now known as the three-color theory of vision. He also did research in physiology on the functions of the heart and arteries, and studied the human voice mechanism, through which he became interested in the physics of sound and sound waves.

Young then turned to optics, and showed that many of Newton's experiments with light could be explained in terms of a simple wave theory of light. This conclusion was strongly attacked by some scientists in England who were upset by the implication that Newton might be wrong.

Thomas Young's original drawing showing interference effects in overlapping waves. The alternate regions of reinforcement and cancellation in the drawing can be seen best by placing your eye near the right edge and sighting at a grazing angle along the diagram.

A Polaroid photograph taken through a Project Physics magnifier placed about 30 cm behind a pair of closely spaced slits. The slits were illuminated with a narrow but bright light source.

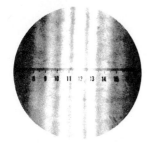

SG 13.14

Augustin Jean Fresnel (1788-1827) was an engineer of bridges and roads for the French government. In his spare time he carried out extensive experimental and theoretical work in optics. Fresnel developed a comprehensive wave model of light that successfully accounted for reflection, refraction, interference, and polarization. He also designed a lens system for lighthouses that is still used today.

SG 13.15

second black screen with two narrow slits cut in it, close together. Beyond this screen he placed a white screen. The light coming through each slit was diffracted and spread out into the space beyond the screen. The light from each slit interfered with the light from the other, and the interference pattern showed on the white screen. Where interference was constructive, there was a bright band on the screen. Where interference was destructive, the screen remained dark.

It is remarkable that Young actually found, by experiment, numerical values for the very short wavelength of light. Here is his result:

> From a comparison of various experiments, it appears that the breadth of the undulations constituting the extreme red light must be supposed to be, in air, about one 36 thousandth of an inch, and those of the extreme violet about one 60 thousandth.

In announcing his results, Young took special pains to forestall criticism from followers of Newton, who was generally considered a supporter of the particle theory. He pointed out that Newton himself had made several statements favoring a theory of light that had some aspects of a wave theory. Nevertheless, Young was not taken seriously. It was not until 1818, when the French physicist Augustin Fresnel proposed his own mathematical wave theory, that Young's research began to get the credit it deserved. Fresnel also had to submit his work for approval to a group of physicists who were committed to the particle theory. One of them, the mathematician Simon Poisson, tried to refute Fresnel's wave equations. If these equations really did describe the behavior of light, Poisson said, a very peculiar thing ought to happen when a small solid disk is placed in a beam of light. Diffraction of the light waves all around the edge of the round disk should lead to constructive interference at the center. In turn, this constructive interference should produce a bright spot in the center of the disk's shadow on a white screen placed at certain distances behind the disk. But the particle theory of light allowed no room for ideas such as diffraction and constructive interference. Further, such a bright spot had never been reported, and even the very idea of a bright spot in the center of a shadow seemed absurd. For all of these reasons, Poisson announced that he had refuted the wave theory.

Fresnel accepted the challenge, however, and immediately arranged for Poisson's prediction to be tested by experiment. The result was that a bright spot *did* appear in the center of the shadow, as predicted by Poisson on the basis of Fresnel's wave theory.

Gradually, scientists realized the significance of the Young double-slit experiment and the Poisson bright spot. Support for the particle theory of light began to crumble away. By 1850 the wave model of light was generally accepted. Physicists had begun to concentrate on working out the mathematical consequences of this model and applying it to the different properties of light.

Q6 How did Young's experiments support the wave model of light?

Q7 In what way is diffraction involved in Young's experiments?

Q8 What phenomenon was predicted by Poisson on the basis of Fresnel's wave theory?

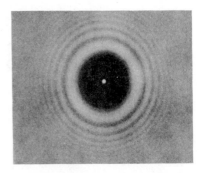

Diffraction pattern due to an opaque circular disk, showing the Poisson bright spot in the center of the shadow. Note also the bright and dark fringes of constructive and destructive interference. (You can make similar photographs yourself—see the activity "Poisson's Spot" in the *Handbook*.)

13.5 Color

The coloring agents found in prehistoric painting and pottery show us that humans have appreciated color since earliest times. But no scientific theory of color was developed before the time of Newton. Until then, most of the accepted ideas about color had come from artist-scientists like da Vinci, who based their ideas on experiences with mixing pigments.

Unfortunately, the lessons learned in mixing pigments rarely apply to the mixing of different-colored light beams. In ancient times, it was thought that light from the sun was "pure light." Color resulted from adding impurity, as when "pure light" was refracted in glass.

Newton became interested in colors when, as a student at Cambridge University, he set out to construct an astronomical telescope. One troublesome defect of the telescope was a fuzzy ring of color that always surrounded the image formed by the telescope lens. Perhaps in an attempt to understand this particular defect, Newton began his extensive study of color.

In 1672, at the age of 29, Newton published a theory of color in the *Philosophical Transactions* of The Royal Society of London. This was his first published scientific paper. He wrote:

> . . . in the beginning of the Year 1666 (at which time I applyed myself to the grinding of Optick glasses of other figures than *Spherical*,) I procured me a Triangular glass-Prisme, to try therewith the celebrated *Phaenomena* of *Colours*. And in order thereto haveing darkened my chamber, and made a small hole in my window-shuts, to let in a convenient quantity of the Suns light, I placed my Prisme at his entrance, that it might be thereby refracted to the opposite wall. It was at first a very pleasing divertisement, to view the vivid and intense colours produced thereby. . . .

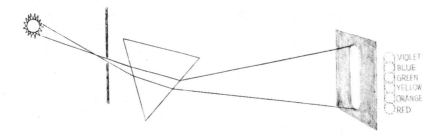

VIOLET
BLUE
GREEN
YELLOW
ORANGE
RED

The drawing at the left is based on Newton's diagram of the refraction of sunlight by a prism.

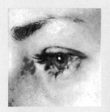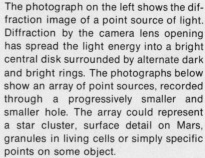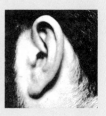

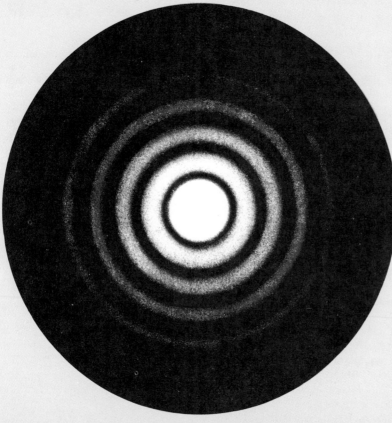

Diffraction and Detail

The photograph on the left shows the diffraction image of a point source of light. Diffraction by the camera lens opening has spread the light energy into a bright central disk surrounded by alternate dark and bright rings. The photographs below show an array of point sources, recorded through a progressively smaller and smaller hole. The array could represent a star cluster, surface detail on Mars, granules in living cells or simply specific points on some object.

The diffraction of the waves from the edges of the hole limits the detail of information that it is possible to receive. As the hole through which we observe the array below becomes smaller, the diffraction image of each point spreads out and begins overlapping the diffraction images of other points. When the diffraction patterns for the points overlap sufficiently, it is impossible to distinguish between them.

This problem of diffraction has many practical consequences. We obtain most of the information about our environment by means of waves (light, sound, radio, etc.) which we receive through some sort of hole: the pupil of the eye, the entrance to the ear or a microphone, the aperture of an optical telescope or radio telescope, etc. In all these cases, then, diffraction places a limit on the detail with which the sources of waves can be discriminated.

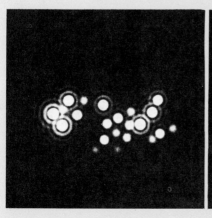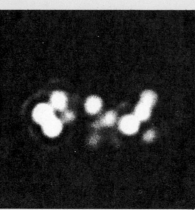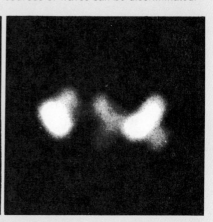

The cylindrical beam of "white" sunlight from the circular opening passed through the prism and produced an elongated patch of colored light on the opposite wall. This patch was violet at one end, red at the other, and showed a continuous gradation of colors in between. For such a pattern of colors, Newton invented the name *spectrum*.

But, Newton wondered, where do the colors come from? And why is the image spread out in an elongated patch rather than circular? Newton passed the light through different thicknesses of the glass, changed the size of the hole in the window shutter, and even placed the prism outside the window. But none of these changes had any effect on the spectrum. Perhaps some unevenness or irregularity in the glass produced the spectrum, Newton thought. To test this possibility, he passed the colored rays from one prism through a similar second prism turned upside down. If some irregularity in the glass caused the beam of light to spread out, then passing this beam through the second prism should spread it out even more. Instead, the second prism, when properly placed, brought the colors *back together* fairly well. A spot of *white* light was formed, as if the light had not passed through either prism.

By such a process of elimination, Newton convinced himself of a belief that he probably had held from the beginning: *white light is composed of colors*. The prism does not manufacture or add the colors; they were there all the time, but mixed up so that they could not be distinguished. When white light passes through a prism, each of the component colors is refracted at a different angle. Thus, the beam is spread into a spectrum.

As a further test of this hypothesis, Newton cut a small hole in a screen on which a spectrum was projected. In this way, light of a single color could be separated out and passed through a second prism. He found that the second prism had no further effect on this single-color beam, aside from refracting it more. Once the first prism had done its job of separating the colored components of white light, the second prism could not change the color of the components.

Summarizing his conclusions, Newton wrote:

> Colors are not *Qualifications of Light* derived from
> Refraction or Reflection of natural Bodies (as 'tis generally
> believed) but Original and Connate Properties, which in divers
> Rays are divers. Some Rays are disposed to exhibit a Red
> Colour and no other; some a Yellow and no other, some a
> Green and no other, and so of the rest. Nor are there only
> Rays proper and particular to the more Eminent Colours, but
> even to all their intermediate gradations.

Apparent colors of objects. So far Newton had discussed only the colors of rays of light. But in a later section of his paper he raised the important question: why do objects appear to have different colors? Why is the sky blue, the grass green, a paint pigment yellow or red? Newton proposed a very simple answer:

> That the Colours of all Natural Bodies have no other

As is suggested in the diagram below, the recombination of colors by a second prism is not complete. Newton himself noted: "The prisms also must be placed very near to one another; for if their distance be so great, the colours begin to appear in the light, before its incidence on the second prism, these colours will not be destroyed by the contrary refractions of that prism."

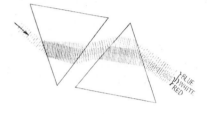

Most colors observed for real materials are "body" colors, produced by selective absorption of light which penetrates a little beyond the surface before being scattered back. This explains why the light transmitted by colored glass has the same color as the light reflected from it. Thin metallic films, however, have "surface" color, resulting from selective regular reflection. Thus the transmitted light will be the complement of the reflected light. For example, the light transmitted by a thin film of gold is bluish-green, while that reflected is yellow.

SG 13.16

Origin than this, that they . . . Reflect one sort of Light in greater plenty than another.

In other words, a red pigment looks red to us because when white sunlight falls on it, the pigment absorbs most of the rays of other colors of the spectrum and reflects mainly the red to our eyes.

According to Newton's theory, color is not a property of an object by itself. Rather, color depends on how the object reflects and absorbs the various colored rays that strike it. Newton backed up this hypothesis by pointing out that an object may appear to have a different color when a different kind of light shines on it. For example, consider a pigment that reflects much more red light than green or blue light. When illuminated by white light, it will reflect mostly the red component of the white light, and so will appear red. But if it is illuminated with blue light, there is no red for it to reflect, and it can reflect only a very little of the blue light. Thus, it will appear to be dark and slightly blue. Newton wrote:

> I have experimented in a dark Room, by illuminating those Bodies with uncompounded [pure] light of divers Colours. For by that means any Body may be made to appear of any Colour. They have there no appropriate Colour, but ever appear of the Colour of the Light cast upon them, but yet with this difference, that they are most brisk and vivid in the Light of their own Day-light Colour.

Reactions to Newton's theory. Newton's theory of color met with violent opposition at first. Other British scientists, especially Robert Hooke, objected that postulating a different kind of light for each color was unnecessary. It would be simpler to assume that the different colors were produced from pure white light by some kind of modification. For example, the wave front might be twisted so that it is no longer perpendicular to the direction of motion.

Newton was aware of the flaws in Hooke's theory, but he disliked public controversy. In fact, he waited until after Hooke's death in 1703 to publish his own book, *Opticks* (1704), in which he reviewed the properties of light.

Newton's *Principia* was a much more important work from a purely scientific viewpoint. But his *Opticks* had also considerable influence on the literary world. English poets gladly celebrated the discoveries of their country's greatest scientist. Most poets, of course, were only dimly aware of the significance of Newton's theory of gravity. The technical details of the geometric axioms and proofs of the *Principia* were beyond them. But Newton's theory of colors and light provided good material for poetic fancy, as in James Thomson's, "To the Memory of Sir Isaac Newton" (1727).

> . . . First the flaming red,
> Springs vivid forth; the tawny orange next;
> And next delicious yellow; by whose side
> Fell the kind beams of all-refreshing green.
> Then the pure blue, that swells autumnal skies,

OPTICKS:

OR, A

TREATISE

OF THE

REFLEXIONS, REFRACTIONS,

INFLEXIONS and COLOURS

O F

L I G H T.

ALSO

Two **TREATISES**

OF THE

SPECIES and MAGNITUDE

O F

Curvilinear Figures.

LONDON,

Printed for SAM. SMITH, and BENJ. WALFORD, Printers to the Royal Society, at the *Prince's Arms* in St. *Paul's* Church-yard. MDCCIV.

Title page from the first edition of Newton's *Opticks* (1704), in which he described his theory of light.

Ethereal played; and then, of sadder hue,
Emerged the deepened indigo, as when
The heavy-skirted evening droops with frost;
While the last gleamings of refracted light
Died in the fainting violet away.

Leaders of the nineteenth-century Romantic movement in literature, and the German "Nature Philosophers" did not think so highly of Newton's theory of color. The scientific procedure of dissecting and analyzing natural phenomena by experiments was distasteful to them. They preferred to speculate about the unifying principles of all natural forces, hoping somehow to grasp nature as a whole. The German philosopher Friedrich Schelling wrote in 1802:

> Newton's *Opticks* is the greatest illustration of a whole structure of fallacies which, in all its parts, is founded on observation and experiment.

The German poet and Nature Philosopher Goethe (mentioned in Chapter 11) spent many years trying to overthrow Newton's theory of colors. Using his own observations, as well as passionate arguments, Goethe insisted on the purity of white light in its natural state. He rejected Newton's hypothesis that white light is a mixture of colors. Instead, he suggested, colors may be produced by the interaction of white light and its opposite, darkness. Goethe's observations on color perception were of some value to science. But his theory of the physical nature of color could not stand up under detailed experiment. Newton's theory of color remained firmly established.

SG 13.17

To the nineteenth-century physicists who were trying to use Newton's theory to explain newly-discovered color phenomena, Goethe addressed the following poem:

May ye chop the light in pieces
Till it hue on hue releases;
May ye other pranks deliver,
Polarize the tiny sliver
Till the listener, overtaken,
Feels his senses numbed
    and shaken–
Nay, persuade us shall ye never
Nor aside us shoulder ever,
Steadfast was our dedication–
We shall win the consummation.

Q9   How did Newton show that white light was not "pure"?

Q10   Why could Newton be confident that, say, green light was not itself composed of different colors of light?

Q11   How would Newton explain the color of a blue shirt?

Q12   Why was Newton's theory of color attacked by the Nature Philosophers?

SG 13.18, 13.19

13.6 Why is the sky blue?

Newton suggested that the apparent colors of natural objects depend on which color is most strongly reflected or scattered to the viewer by the object. In general, there is no simple way of predicting from the surface structure, chemical composition, etc., what colors a substance will reflect or scatter. However, the blue color of the clear sky can be explained by a fairly simple argument.

As Thomas Young showed experimentally (Section 13.4), different wavelengths of light correspond to different colors. The wavelength of light may be specified in units of Ångstrom (Å), equal to 10^{-10} meters. The range of the spectrum visible to humans is from about 4000 Å for violet light to about 7000 Å for red light. (7000 Å is of the order of 10^{-3} mm, a figure worth remembering.)

The Ångstrom unit is named after Anders Jonas Ångstrom, a Swedish astronomer who, in 1862, used spectroscopic techniques to detect the presence of hydrogen in the sun.

Small obstacles can scatter the energy of an incident wave in all directions, and the amount of scattering depends on the wavelength. This fact can be demonstrated by simple experiments with water waves in a ripple tank. As a general rule, *the larger the wavelength is compared to the size of the obstacle, the less is the wave scattered by the obstacle*. For particles smaller than one wavelength, the amount of scattering of light varies inversely with the fourth power of the wavelength. For example, the wavelength of red light is about twice the wavelength of blue light. Therefore, the scattering of red light is about 1/16th as much as the scattering of blue light.

The amount of scattering of different waves by a tiny obstacle is indicated here for three wavelengths.

RED

GREEN

BLUE

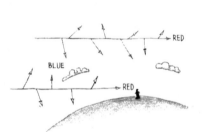

RED

BLUE

RED

An observer looking at a sunset on a hazy day is receiving primarily *un-*scattered colors such as red; whereas if the observer looks overhead, he will be receiving primarily scattered colors, the most dominant of which is blue.

If light is scattered by particles considerably larger than one wavelength (such as water droplets in a cloud), there isn't much difference in the scattering of different wavelengths. So we receive the mixture we perceive as white.

Now we can understand why the sky is blue. Light from the sun is scattered by air molecules and particles of dust in the sky. These particles are usually very small compared to the wavelengths of visible light. Thus, light of short wavelengths—blue light—is much more strongly scattered by the particles than light of longer wavelengths. When you look up into a clear sky, it is mainly this scattered light that enters your eye. The range of scattered short wavelengths (and the color sensitivity of the human eye) lead to the sensation of blue. On the other hand, suppose you look at a sunset on a very hazy day. You receive a beam that has had the blue light completely scattered out, while the longer wavelengths have *not* been scattered out. So you perceive the sun as reddish.

If the earth had no atmosphere, the sky would appear black and stars would be visible by day. In fact, starting at altitudes of about ten miles, where the atmosphere becomes quite thin, the sky does look black and stars can be seen during the day, as astronauts have found.

Sometimes the air contains dust particles or water droplets as large as the wavelength of visible light (about 10^{-6} meter). If so, colors other than blue may be strongly scattered. For example, the quality of sky coloring changes with the water-vapor content of the atmosphere. On clear, dry days the sky is a much deeper blue than on clear days with high humidity. The intensely blue skies of Italy and Greece, which have inspired poets and painters for centuries, are a result of exceptionally dry air.

The blue-grey haze that often covers large cities is caused mainly by particles emitted by internal combustion engines (cars, trucks) and by industrial plants. Even when idling, a typical automobile engine emits more than 100 billion particles per second. Most of these particles are invisible, ranging in size from 0.005 to 1 micron (one micron is equal to 10^{-6} meters). Such particles provide a framework to which gases, liquids, and other solids adhere. These larger particles then scatter light and produce haze. Gravity has little effect on the particles until they become very large by collecting more matter. They may remain in the atmosphere for months if not cleaned out by repeated rain, snow, or winds. The influences of such clouds of haze or smog on the climate and on human health are substantial.

Q13   How does the scattering of light waves by tiny obstacles depend on the wavelength?

Q14   How would you explain the color of the earth's sky? What do you expect the sky to look like on the moon? Why?

13.7 Polarization

Hooke and Huygens proposed that light is in many ways like sound—that is, that light is a wave propagated through a medium. Newton could not accept this proposal, and argued that light must also have some particle-like properties. He noted two properties of light that, he thought, could not be explained unless light had particle properties. First, a beam of light is propagated in straight lines, while waves such as sound spread out in all directions and go around corners. This objection could not be answered until early in the nineteenth century, when Young measured the wavelength of light and found it to be extremely small. Even the wavelength of red light, the longest wavelength of the visible spectrum, is less than a thousandth of a millimeter. As long as a beam of light shines on objects or through holes of ordinary size (a few millimeters or more in width), the light will appear to travel in straight lines. Diffraction and scattering effects don't become strikingly evident until a wave passes over an object or through a hole whose size is about equal to or smaller than the wavelength.

Newton's second objection was based on the phenomenon of "polarization" of light. In 1669, the Danish scientist Erasmus Bartholinus discovered that crystals of Iceland spar (calcite) could split a ray of light into two rays. Writing or small objects viewed through the crystal looked double.

Newton thought this behavior could be explained by assuming that light is made up of particles that have different "sides"—for example, rectangular cross-sections. The double images, he thought, represent a sorting out of light particles which had entered the medium with different orientations.

Around 1820, Young and Fresnel gave a far more satisfactory explanation of polarization, using a modified wave theory of light. Before then, scientists had generally assumed that light waves, like sound waves, must be *longitudinal*. (And, as Newton believed, longitudinal waves could not have any directional property.) Young and Fresnel showed that if light waves are *transverse,* this could account for the phenomenon of polarization.

In a transverse wave, the motion of the medium itself is always perpendicular to the direction of propagation of the wave (see Chapter 12).

**Iceland Spar Crystal
Double Refraction**

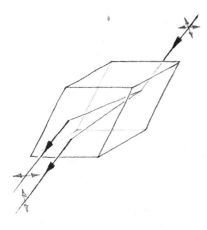

Double refraction by a crystal of Iceland spar. The "unpolarized" incident light can be thought of as consisting of two polarized components. The crystal separates these two components, transmitting them through the crystal in different directions and with different speeds.

A. unpolarized wave on a rope

B. polarized wave on a rope

This does not mean that the motion of the medium is always in the same direction. In fact, it could be in any direction in a plane perpendicular to the direction of propagation. However, if the motion of the medium *is* mainly in one direction (for example, vertical), we say that the wave is *polarized*. (Thus a polarized wave is really the *simplest* kind of transverse wave. An unpolarized transverse wave is more complicated, since it is a mixture of various transverse motions.) The way in which Iceland spar separates an unpolarized light beam into two polarized beams is sketched in the margin.

Scientific studies of polarization continued throughout the nineteenth century. Practical applications, however, were frustrated, mainly because polarizing substances like Iceland spar were scarce and fragile. One of the best polarizers was "herapathite," or sulfate of iodo-quinine, a synthetic crystal. The needle-like herapathite crystals absorb light that is polarized in the direction of the long crystal axis. But the crystals absorb very little of the light polarized in a direction at 90° to the long axis.

Herapathite crystals were so fragile that there seemed to be no way of using them. But in 1928, Edwin H. Land, while still a freshman in college, invented a polarizing plastic sheet he called "Polaroid." His first polarizer was a plastic film in which many microscopic crystals of herapathite were imbedded. When the plastic was stretched, the needle-like crystals lined up in one direction. Thus, they all acted on incoming light in the same way.

Later, Land improved Polaroid by using polymeric molecules composed mainly of iodine in place of the herapathite crystals.

Some properties of a polarizing material are easily demonstrated. Hold a polarizing sheet—for example, the lens of a pair of polarizing sunglasses—in front of a light source. Then look at the first polarizing sheet through a second one. Rotate the first sheet. You will notice that, as you do so, the light alternately brightens and dims. You must rotate the sheet through an angle of 90° to go from maximum brightness to maximum dimness.

The eyes of bees and ants are sensitive to the polarization of scattered light from the clear sky. This enables a bee to navigate by the sun, even when the sun is low on the horizon or obscured. Following the bees' example, engineers have equipped airplanes with polarization indicators for use in Arctic regions. (See *Reader 4* article, "Popular Applications of Polarized Light.")

How can this be explained? The light that strikes the first sheet is originally unpolarized—that is, a mixture of waves polarized in various directions. The first sheet transmits only those waves that are polarized in one direction, and absorbs the rest. The transmitted wave going toward the second sheet is now polarized in one direction. Whenever this direction coincides with the direction of the long molecules in the second sheet, the wave will be absorbed by the second sheet. (That is, the wave will set up vibrations within the molecules of the crystals and will lose most of its energy.) However, if the direction is *perpendicular* to the long axis of the crystal molecules, the polarized light will go through the second sheet without much absorption.

SG 13.20, 13.21

Interference and diffraction effects required a wave model for light. To explain polarization phenomena, the wave model was made more specific. It was shown that polarization could be explained if light waves were transverse. This model for light explains well enough all the characteristics of light considered so far. But we will see in Unit 5 that it turned out to require even further extension.

Q15   What two objections did Newton have to a wave model?

Q16   What phenomena have we discussed that agree with a wave model of light?

Q17   Have we proved that light can have *no* particle properties?

13.8 The ether

One thing seems clearly to be missing from our wave model for light. In Chapter 12, we discussed waves as disturbances that propagate in some substance or "medium," such as a rope or water. What is the medium for the propagation of light waves?

Is air the medium for light waves? No, because light can pass through airless space, as it does between the sun or other stars and the earth. Even before it was definitely known that there is no air between the sun and the earth, Robert Boyle had tried the experiment of pumping almost all of the air out of a glass container. He found that the objects inside remained visible.

It was difficult to think of a disturbance without specifying what was being disturbed. So it was natural to propose that a medium for the propagation of light waves existed. This medium was called the *ether*.

In the seventeenth and eighteenth centuries the ether was imagined to be an invisible fluid of very low density. This fluid could penetrate all matter and fill all space. It might somehow be associated with the "effluvium" (something that "flows out") that was imagined to explain magnetic and electric forces. But light waves must be transverse in order to explain polarization, and transverse waves usually propagate only in a *solid* medium. A liquid or a gas cannot transmit transverse waves for any significant distance, for the same reason that you cannot "twist" a liquid or a gas. So nineteenth-century physicists assumed that the ether must be a solid.

As stated in Chapter 12, the speed of propagation increases with the stiffness of the medium, and decreases with its density. The speed of propagation of light is very high compared to other kinds of waves, such as sound. Therefore, the ether was thought to be a very stiff solid with a very low density.

Yet it seems absurd to say that a stiff, solid ether fills all space. We know that the planets move without slowing down, so apparently they encounter no resistance from a stiff ether. And, of course, we ourselves feel no resistance when we move around in a space that transmits light freely.

Without ether, the wave-theory seemed improbable. But the ether

"Ether" was originally the name for Aristotle's fifth element, the pure transparent fluid that filled the heavenly sphere. It was later called "quintessence" (see Sections 2.1 and 6.4).

In order to transmit transverse waves, the medium must have some tendency to return to its original shape when it has been deformed by a transverse pulse. As Thomas Young remarked on one such ether model, "It is at least very ingenious, and may lead us to some satisfactory computations; but it is attended by one circumstance which is perfectly *appalling* in its consequences. . . . It is only to solids that such a *lateral* resistance has ever been attributed: so that . . . it might be inferred that the luminiferous ether, pervading all space, and penetrating almost all substances, is not only high elastic, but absolutely solid!!!"

itself had absurd properties. Until early in this century, this problem remained unsolved, just as it had for Newton. We will see how, following Einstein's modification of the theory of light, the problem came to be solved.

Q18 Why was it assumed that an "ether" existed which transmitted light waves?

Q19 What remarkable property must the ether have if it is to be the mechanical medium for the propagation of light?

"Entrance to the Harbor", a painting by Georges Seurat (1888). Art historians believe that Seurat's techniques of pointillism, the use of tiny dots of pure color to achieve all effects in a painting, reflects his understanding of the physical nature of light.

13.1 The Project Physics learning materials particularly appropriate for Chapter 13 include:

Experiments
  Refraction of a Light Beam
  Young's Experiment – the Wavelength of Light
Activities
  Thin Film Interference
  Handkerchief Diffraction Grating
  Photographic Diffraction Patterns
  Poisson's Spot
  Photographing Activities
  Color
  Polarized Light
  Make an Ice Lens
Reader Articles
  Experiments and Calculations Relative to
    Physical Optics
  Velocity of Light
  Popular Applications of Polarized Light
  Eye and Camera
  Lenses and Optical Instruments
In addition the following Project Physics materials can be used with Unit 4 in general:
Reader Articles
  Action at a Distance
  Maxwell's Letters: A Collection
Film
  People and Particles

13.2 A square card, 3 cm on a side, is held 10 cm from a small penlight bulb, and its shadow falls on a wall 15 cm behind the card. What is the size of the shadow on the wall? (A diagram of the situation will be useful.)

13.3 The row of photographs on page 9 shows what happens to a beam of light that passes through a narrow slit. The row of photographs on page 122 of Chapter 12 shows what happens to a train of water wave that passes through a narrow opening. Both sets of photographs illustrate single-slit diffraction, but the photographs are not all similar in appearance. Explain the difference in appearance of the photographs, and how they are similar.

13.4 An experiment to determine whether or not the propagation of light is instantaneous is described by Galileo as follows:

Let each of two persons take a light contained in a lantern, or other receptacle, such that by the interposition of the hand, the one can shut off or admit the light to the vision of the other. Next let them stand opposite each other at a distance of a few cubits and practice until they acquire such skill in uncovering and occulting their lights that the instant one sees the light of his companion he will uncover his own. After a few trials the response will be so prompt that without sensible error (svario) the uncovering of one light is immediately followed by the uncovering of the other, so that as soon as one exposes his light he will instantly see that of the other. Having acquired skill at this short distance let the two experimenters, equipped as before

take up positions separated by a distance of two or three miles and let them perform the same experiment at night, noting carefully whether the exposures and occultations occur in the same manner as at short distances; if they do, we may safely conclude that the propagation of light is instantaneous but if time is required at a distance of three miles which, considering the going of one light and the coming of the other, really amounts to six, then the delay ought to be easily observable . . . .

But later he states:

In fact, I have tried the experiment only at a short distance, less than a mile, from which I have not been able to ascertain with certainty whether the appearance of the opposite light was instantaneous or not; but if not instantaneous, it is extraordinarily rapid . . . .

(a) Why was Galileo unsuccessful in the above experiment?
(b) How would the experiment have to be altered to be successful?
(c) What do you think is the longest time that light might have taken in getting from one observer to the other without the observers detecting the delay? Use this estimate to arrive at a lower limit for the speed of light that is consistent with Galileo's description of the result.
(d) Why do you suppose that the first proof of the finite speed of light was based on celestial observations rather than terrestrial observations?

13.5 A convenient unit for measuring astronomical distances is the *light year,* defined to be the distance that light travels in one year. Calculate the number of meters in a light year to two significant figures.

13.6 Suppose a space vehicle had a speed 1/1000 that of light. How long would it take to travel the 4.3 light years from the earth to the closest known star other than the sun, Proxima Centauri. Compare the speed given for the space vehicle with the speed of approximately 10 km/sec maximum speed (relative to the earth) that a space capsule reaches on an earth-moon trip.

13.7 Newton supposed that the reflection of light off shiny surfaces is due to "some feature of the body which is evenly diffused over its surface and by which it acts upon the ray without contact." The simplest model for such a feature would be a repulsive force which acts only in a direction perpendicular to the surface. In this problem you are to show how this model—together with the laws of mechanics—predicts that the angles of incidence and reflection must be equal. Proceed as follows:
(a) Draw a clear diagram showing the incident and reflected rays. Also show the angles of incidence and reflection (θ_1 and θ_2). Sketch a coordinate system on your diagram that has an x-axis parallel to the surface and a y-axis perpendicular to the

surface. Note that the angles of incidence and reflection are defined to be the angles between the incident and reflected rays and the y-axis.

(b) Supposing that the incident light consists of particles of mass m and speed v, what is the kinetic energy of a single particle? Write mathematical expressions for the x and y components of the momentum of an incident light particle.

(c) If the repulsive force due to the reflecting surface does no work on the particle and acts only perpendicular to the surface, which of the quantities that you have described in part (b) is conserved?

(d) Show algebraically that the speed u of the reflected particle is the same as the speed y of the incident particle.

(e) Write mathematical expressions for the components of the momentum of the reflected particle.

(f) Show algebraically that θ_1 and θ_2 must be equal angles.

13.8 In the diagram below, find the shortest path from point A to any point on the surface M and then to point B. Solve this by trial and error, perhaps by experimenting with a short piece of string held at one end by a tack at point A. (A possible path is shown but it is not necessarily the shortest one.) Notice that the shortest distance between A, M and B is also the *least-time* path for a particle traveling at a constant speed from A to M to B. What path would light take from A to M to B? Can you make a statement of the law of reflection in terms of this principle instead of in terms of angles?

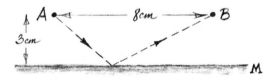

13.9 What is the shortest mirror in which a 6-foot-tall man can see himself entirely? (Assume that both he and the mirror are vertical and that he places the mirror in the most favorable position.) Does it matter how far away he is from the mirror? Do your answers to these questions depend on the distance from his eyes to the top of his head?

13.10 Suppose the reflecting surfaces of every visible object were somehow altered so that they completely absorbed any light falling on them; how would the world then appear to you?

13.11 Objects are visible as a whole if their surfaces reflect light, enabling our eyes to intercept cones of reflected light diverging from *each part* of the surface. The accompanying diagram shows such a cone of light (represented by two diverging rays) entering the eye from a book.

Draw clear straight-line diagrams to show how a pair of diverging rays can be used to help explain the following phenomena.

(a) The mirror image of an object appears to be just as far behind the mirror as the object is in front of the mirror.

(b) A pond appears shallower than it actually is.

(c) A coin is placed in an empty coffee mug so that the coin cannot *quite* be seen. The coin becomes visible if the mug is filled with water.

13.12 Due to atmospheric refraction we see the sun in the evening for some minutes after it is really below the horizon, and also for some minutes before it is actually above the horizon in the morning.

(a) Draw a simple diagram to illustrate how this phenomenon occurs.

(b) What would sunset be like on a planet with a very thick and dense (but still transparent) atmosphere?

13.13 In a particle theory of light, refraction could be explained by assuming that the particle was accelerated by an attractive force as it passed from air or vacuum toward a medium such as glass. Assume that this accelerating force could act on the particle *only* in a direction perpendicular to the surface. Use vector diagrams to show that the speed of the particle in the glass would have to be greater than in air.

13.14 Plane parallel waves of single-wavelength light illuminate the two narrow slits, resulting in an interference pattern of alternate bright and dark fringes being formed on the screen. The bright fringes represent zones of constructive

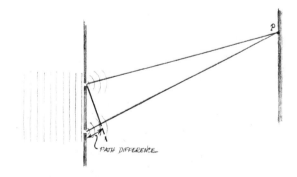

interference. Hence they appear at a point such as P on the diagram above only if the diffracted waves from the two slits arrive at P in phase. The diffracted waves will be in phase at point P only if the path difference is a whole number of wavelengths (that is, only if the path difference equals $m\lambda$ where $m = 0, 1, 2, 3 \ldots$).

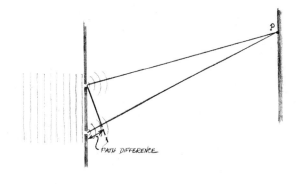

PATH DIFFERENCE

(a) What path difference results in destructive interference at the screen?

(b) The separation between two successive bright fringes depends on the wavelengths of the light used. Would the separation be greater for red light or for blue light?

(c) For a particular color of light, how would the pattern change if the distance of the screen from the slits is increased? (Hint: make two diagrams.)

(d) What changes occur in the pattern if the slits are moved closer together? (Hint: make two diagrams.)

(e) What happens to the pattern if the slits themselves are made more narrow?

13.15 Recalling diffraction and interference phenomena from Chapter 12, show how the wave theory of light can explain the bright spot found in the center of the shadow of a disk illuminated by a point source.

DISK   BRIGHT SPOT

SCREEN

13.16 It is now a familiar observation that clothing of certain colors appears different in artificial light and in sunlight. Explain why.

13.17 Another poem by James Thomson (1728):

Meantime, refracted from yon eastern cloud,
Bestriding earth, the grand ethereal bow
Shoots up immense; and every hue unfold,
In fair proportion running from the red
To where the violet fades into the sky.

Here, awe-ful Newton, the dissolving clouds
Form, fronting on the sun, thy showery prism;
And to the sage-instructed eye unfold
The various twine of light, by thee disclosed
From the white mingling blaze.

How do you think it compares with the poem on p. 18 (a) as poetry? (b) as physics?

13.18 Green light has a wavelength of approximately 5×10^{-7} meters. What frequency corresponds to this wavelength? Compare this frequency to the carrier frequency of the radio waves broadcast by a radio station you listen to.

13.19 The arts sometimes reflect contemporary ideas in science; the following poem is an excellent example of this.

Some range the colours as they parted fly.
Clear-pointed to the philosophic eye;
The flaming red, that pains the dwelling gaze,
The stainless, lightsome yellow's gilding rays;
The clouded orange, that betwixt them glows,
And to kind mixture tawny lustre owers;
All-chearing green, that gives the spring its dye:
The bright transparent blue, that robes the sky;
And indigo, which shaded light displays,
And violet, which in the view decays.
Parental hues, whence others all proceed;
An ever-mingling, changeful, countless breed,
Unravel'd, variegated, lines of light,
When blended, dazzling in promiscuous white.
[Richard Savage (1697-1743), *The Wanderer*]

(a) Would you or would you not classify the poet Richard Savage as a "nature philosopher"? Why?

(b) Compare this poem with the one in SG 13.17 by James Thomson; which *poet* do you think displayed the better understanding of physics of his time? Which *poem* do you prefer?

13.20 One way to achieve privacy in apartments facing each other across a narrow courtyard while still allowing residents to enjoy the view of the courtyard and the sky above the courtyard is to use polarizing sheets placed over the windows. Explain how the sheets must be oriented for maximum effectiveness.

13.21 To prevent car drivers from being blinded by the lights of approaching autos, polarizing sheets could be placed over the headlights and windshields of every car. Explain why these sheets would have to be oriented the same way on every vehicle and must have their polarizing axis at 45° to the vertical.

An inside view of "Hilac" (heavy ion linear accelerator) at Berkeley, California. In this device electric fields accelerate charged atoms to high energies.

CHAPTER FOURTEEN

Electric and Magnetic Fields

14.1 Introduction

The subject "electricity and magnetism" makes up a large part of modern physics, and has important connections with almost all other areas of physics, chemistry, and engineering. It would be impossible to cover this subject fully in the time available in an introductory course. Here we will consider only a few main topics, which will serve as a foundation for later chapters. Major applications of the information in this chapter will appear later: the development of electrical technology (Chapter 15), the study of the nature of light and electromagnetic waves (Chapter 16), and the study of properties of atomic and subatomic particles (Unit 5).

SG 14.1

In this chapter we will first treat electric charges and the forces between them. Our discussion will be brief, because the best way to learn about this subject is not by reading but by doing experiments in the laboratory (see Experiment 4-3 in the *Handbook*). Next, we will show how the idea of a "field" simplifies the description of electric and magnetic effects. Then we will take up electric currents, which are made up of moving charges. By combining the concept of field with the idea of potential energy, we can establish quantitative relations between current, voltage, and power, These relations will be needed for the practical applications discussed in Chapter 15.

Finally, at the end of this chapter, we will come to the relation between electricity and magnetism. This relation has very important consequences for both technology and basic physical theory. We will begin by studying a simple physical phenomenon: the interaction between moving charges and magnetic fields.

14.2 The curious properties of lodestone and amber: Gilbert's *De Magnete*

Two natural substances, amber and lodestone, have aroused interest since ancient times. Amber is sap that long ago oozed from certain softwood trees, such as pine. Over many centuries, it hardened into a semitransparent solid ranging in color from yellow to brown. It is a handsome ornamental stone when polished, and it sometimes contains the remains of insects that were caught in the sticky sap. Ancient Greeks recognized a strange property of amber: if rubbed vigorously against cloth, it can attract nearby objects such as bits of straw or grain seeds.

Lodestone is a mineral that also has unusual properties. It attracts iron. Also, when suspended or floated, a piece of lodestone always turns to one particular position—a north-south direction. The first known written description of the navigational use of lodestone as a compass in Western countries dates from the late twelfth century, but its properties were known even earlier in China. Today, lodestone would be called magnetized iron ore.

The histories of lodestone and amber are the early histories of magnetism and electricity. The modern developments in these subjects began in 1600 with the publication in London of William Gilbert's book *De Magnete*. Gilbert (1544-1603) was an influential physician, who served as Queen Elizabeth's chief physician. During the last twenty years of his life, he studied what was already known of lodestone and amber. He made his own experiments to check the reports of other writers and summarized his conclusions in *De Magnete*. The book is a classic in scientific literature, primarily because it was a thorough and largely successful attempt to test complex speculation by detailed experiment.

Gilbert's first task in his book was to review and criticize what had previously been written about lodestone. He discussed various theories about the cause of magnetic attraction. One of the most popular theories was suggested by the Roman author Lucretius:

Lucretius was one of the early writers on atomic theory; see the Prologue to Unit 5.

> Lucretius . . . deems the attraction to be due to this, that as there is from all things a flowing out ("efflux" or "effluvium") of minutest bodies, so there is from iron an efflux of atoms into the space between the iron and the lodestone—a space emptied of air by the lodestone's atoms (seeds); and when these begin to return to the lodestone, the iron follows, the corpuscles being entangled with each other.

Gilbert himself did not accept the effluvium theory as an explanation for magnetic attraction, although he thought it might apply to electrical attraction.

When it was discovered that lodestones and magnetized needles or iron bars tend to turn in a north-south direction, many authors offered explanations. But, says Gilbert,

> . . . they wasted oil and labor, because, not being practical in the research of objects of nature, being acquainted only with books, being led astray by certain erroneous physical systems,

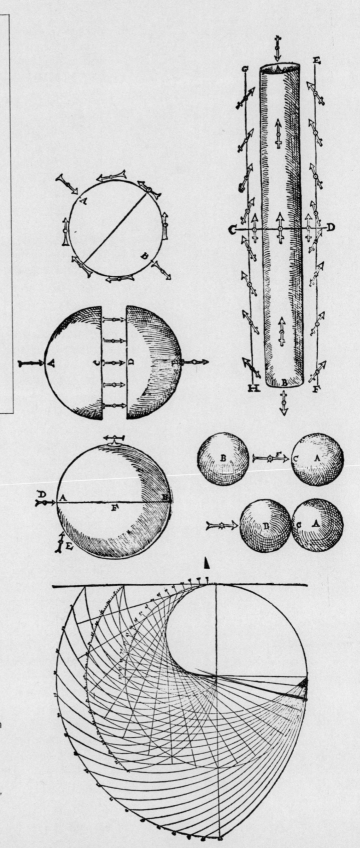

The title page of the third edition (1633) of Gilbert's book is reproduced above. Early in the book Gilbert makes the following statement:

> Before we expound the causes of magnetic movements and bring forward our demonstrations and experiments touching matters that for so many ages have lain hid . . . we must formulate our new and till now unheard-of view of the earth, and submit it to the judgment of scholars.

Gilbert proposed an elaborate analogy between the earth and a spherical lodestone. At the right are reproduced some of the drawings Gilbert used to illustrate his experiments with magnetized needles and spheres of iron and lodestone. Toward the end of the book, he presents the diagram at the right, which shows the angle at which a magnetic needle would "dip" toward the earth's surface (represented by the central circle) at different latitudes. The section of *De Magnete* in which this diagram appears is titled: *How to find . . . the latitude of any place by means of the following diagram, turned into a magnetic instrument, in any part of the world, without the help of the heavenly bodies, sun, planets, or fixed stars, and in foggy weather as well as in darkness.*

and having made no magnetical experiments, they constructed certain explanations on a basis of mere opinions, and old-womanishly dreamt the things that were not. Marcilius Ficinus chews the cud of ancient opinions, and to give the reason of the magnetic direction seeks its cause in the constellation Ursa . . . Paracelsus declares that there are stars which, gifted with the lodestone's power, do attract to themselves iron . . . All these philosophers . . . reckoning among the causes of the direction of the magnet, a region of the sky, celestial poles, stars . . . mountains, cliffs, vacant space, atoms, attractional . . . regions beyond the heavens, and other like unproved paradoxes, are world-wide astray from the truth and are blindly wandering.

Gilbert himself proposed the real cause of the lining-up of a suspended magnetic needle or lodestone: the earth itself is a lodestone. Gilbert also did a clever experiment to show that his hypothesis was a likely one. Using a large piece of natural lodestone in the shape of a sphere, he showed that a small magnetized needle placed on the surface of the lodestone acts just as a compass needle does at different places on the earth's surface. (In fact, Gilbert called his lodestone the *terrella,* or "little earth.") If the directions along which the needle lines up are marked with chalk on the lodestone, they form meridian circles. Like the lines of equal longitude on a globe of the earth, these circles converge at two opposite ends that may be called "poles." At the poles, the needle points perpendicular to the surface of the lodestone (see page 31). Halfway between, along the "equator," the needle lies along the surface. Small bits of iron wire placed on the spherical lodestone also line up in these same directions.

The immensely important idea of "field" was introduced into physics by Michael Faraday early in the nineteenth century, and developed further by Kelvin and Maxwell (see Sections 14.4 and 16.2).

Discussion of the actions of magnets now generally uses the idea that magnets set up "fields" all around themselves. The field can act on other objects, near or distant. Gilbert's description of the force exerted on the needle by his spherical lodestone was a step toward the modern field concept:

> The terrella's force extends in all directions . . . . But whenever iron or other magnetic body of suitable size happens within its sphere of influence it is attracted; yet the nearer it is to the lodestone the greater the force with which it is borne toward it.

"Electric" comes from the Greek word *electron,* meaning "amber."

Gilbert also included a discussion of electricity in his book. He introduced the word *electric* as the general term for "bodies that attract in the same way as amber." Gilbert showed that electric and magnetic forces are different. For example, a lodestone always attracts iron or other magnetic bodies. An electric object exerts its attraction only when it has been recently rubbed. On the other hand, an electric object can attract small pieces of many different substances. But magnetic forces act only between a few types of substances. Objects are attracted to a rubbed electric object along lines directed toward one center region. But magnets always have *two* regions (poles) toward which other magnets are attracted.

Gilbert went beyond summarizing the known facts of electricity and magnets. He suggested new research problems that were pursued by others for many years. For example, he proposed that while the poles of two lodestones might either attract or repel each other, electric bodies could never exert repelling forces. But in 1646, Sir Thomas Browne published the first account of electric repulsion. To systematize such observations a new concept, *electric charge,* was introduced. In the next section we will see how this concept can be used to describe the forces between electrically charged bodies.

Q1 How did Gilbert demonstrate that the earth behaves like a spherical lodestone?

Q2 How does the attraction of objects by amber differ from the attraction by lodestone?

14.3 Electric charges and electric forces

As Gilbert strongly argued, the facts of electrostatics must be learned in the laboratory rather than by just reading about them. This section, therefore, is only a brief outline to prepare you for your own experience with the phenomena.

The behavior of amber was discussed earlier. When rubbed, it mysteriously acquires the property of picking up small bits of grain, cork, paper, hair, etc. To some extent all materials show this effect when rubbed, including rods made of glass or hard rubber, or strips of plastic. There are two other important basic observations: (a) When two rods of the same material are rubbed with something made of another material, the rods *repel* each other. Examples that were long ago found to work especially well are two glass rods rubbed with silk cloth, or two hard rubber rods rubbed with fur. (b) When two rods of *different* material are rubbed—for example, a glass rod rubbed with silk, and a rubber rod rubbed with fur—the two rods may *attract* each other.

These and thousands of similar experimentally observable facts can be summarized in a systematic way by adopting a very simple model. While we are describing a *model* for electrostatic attraction and repulsion, remember that this model is *not* an experimental fact which you can observe separately. It is, rather, a set of invented ideas which help us describe and summarize what we see happening. It is easy to forget this important difference between experimentally observable facts and invented explanations. Both are needed, but they are not the same thing! The model we will adopt consists of the concept of "charge" and three rules. An object that is rubbed and given the property of attracting small bits of matter will be said to "be electrically charged" or to "have an electric charge." Further, we imagine that there are two kinds of charge. All objects showing electrical behavior are imagined to have either one or the other of the two kinds of charge. The three rules are:

Benjamin Franklin (1706-1790), American statesman, inventor, scientist, and writer. He was greatly interested in the phenomena of electricity; his famous kite experiment and invention of the lightning rod gained him wide recognition. He is shown here observing the behavior of a bell whose clapper is connected to a lightning rod.

(1) There are only two kinds of electric charge.

(2) Two objects charged alike (that is, having the same kind of charge) repel each other.

(3) Two objects charged oppositely attract each other.

When two different uncharged materials are rubbed together (for example, the glass rod and the silk cloth) they acquire opposite kinds of charge. Benjamin Franklin, who did many experiments with electric charges, proposed a mechanical model for such phenomena. In his model, charging an object electrically involved the transfer of an "electric fluid" that was present in all matter. When two objects were rubbed together, some electric fluid from one passed into the other. One body then had an extra amount of fluid and the other a lack of fluid. An excess of fluid produced one kind of electric charge—which Franklin called "positive." A lack of the same fluid produced the other kind of electric charge—which he called "negative."

Previously, some theorists had proposed "two-fluid" models involving both a "positive fluid" and a "negative fluid." Normal matter contained equal amounts of these two fluids, so that they cancelled out each other's effects. When two different objects were rubbed together, a transfer of fluids occurred. One object received an excess of positive fluid and the other received an excess of negative fluid.

There was some dispute between advocates of one-fluid and two-fluid models. But both sides agreed to speak of the two kinds of electrical charges as "+" or "−." It was not until the late 1890's that experimental evidence gave convincing support to any model for "electric charge." There were, as it turned out, elements of truth in both one-fluid and two-fluid models. The story will be told in some detail in Unit 5. For the present, we can say that there are in fact two different material "fluids." But the "negative fluid" moves around much more easily than the "positive fluid." So most of the electric phenomena we have been discussing actually involve an excess or lack of the mobile "negative fluid"—or, in modern terms, an excess or lack of electrons.

Franklin thought of the electric fluid as consisting of tiny particles, and that is the present view, too. Consequently, the word "charge" is often used in the plural. For example, we usually say "electric charges transfer from one body to another."

What is amazing in electricity, and indeed in other parts of physics, is that so few concepts are needed to deal with so many different observations. For example, we do not need to invent a third or fourth kind of charge in addition to "+" and "−." That is to say no observation of charged objects requires some additional type of charge that might have to be called "÷" or "×."

Even the behavior of an *un*charged body can be understood in terms of + and − charges. Any piece of matter large enough to be visible can be considered to contain a large amount of electric charge, both positive and negative. If the positive charge is equal to the negative charge, the piece of matter will appear to have zero charge—no charge at all. The effects of the positive and negative charges simply cancel each other when they are added together or are acting together. (This is one advantage of calling the two kinds of charge positive and negative rather then, say, x and y.)

When we talk about the electric charge on an object we usually mean the slight *excess* (or net) of either positive or negative charge that happens to be on that object.

The electric force law. What is the "law of force" between electric charges? In other words, how does the force depend on the *amount of* charge and on the *distance* between the charged objects?

The first evidence of the nature of such a force law was obtained in an indirect way. About 1775, Benjamin Franklin noted that a small cork hanging near the outside of an electrically charged metal can was strongly attracted. But when he lowered the cork by a thread into the can, he found that no force was experienced by the cork no matter what its position inside the can.

Franklin did not understand why the walls of the can did not attract the cork when it was inside, but did when it was outside. He asked his friend Joseph Priestley to repeat the experiment.

Priestley verified Franklin's results, and went on to reach a brilliant conclusion from them. He remembered from Newton's *Principia* that gravitational forces behave in a similar way. Inside a hollow planet, the net gravitational force on an object (the sum of all the forces exerted by all parts of the planet) would be exactly zero. This result also follows mathematically from the law that the gravitational force between any two individual pieces of matter is inversely proportional to the square of the distance between them. Priestley therefore proposed that forces exerted by charges vary inversely as the square of the distance, just as do forces exerted by massive bodies. (Zero force inside a hollow conductor is discussed on page 38.) We call the force exerted between bodies owing to the fact that they are charged "electric" force, just as we call the force between uncharged bodies "gravitational" force. (But remember that all forces are known to us by their mechanical effects—by the push or acceleration they cause on material objects!)

Priestley's proposal was based on reasoning by analogy, that is, by reasoning from a parallel, well demonstrated case. Such reasoning alone could not *prove* that electrical forces are inversely proportional to the square of the distance between charges. But it strongly encouraged other physicists to test Priestley's hypothesis by experiment.

The French physicist Charles Coulomb provided direct experimental evidence for the inverse-square law for electric charges suggested by Priestley. Coulomb used a *torsion balance* which he had invented. A diagram of the balance appears on the following page. A horizontal, balanced insulating rod is suspended by a thin silver wire. The wire twists when a force is exerted on the end of the rod and the twisting effect can be used as a measure of the force.

Coulomb attached a charged body A to one end of the rod and placed another charged body B near it. The electrical force exerted on A by B caused the wire to twist. By measuring the twisting effect for different separations between the centers of spheres A and B, he found that the force between spheres varied in proportion to $1/R^2$:

$$F_{el} \propto \frac{1}{R^2}$$

Our experience with Newton's law of gravitation is affecting our question. We are assuming that the force depends only on a single property and on distance.

Joseph Priestley (1773-1804), a Unitarian minister and physical scientist, was persecuted in England for his radical political ideas. One of his books was burned, and a mob looted his house because of his sympathy with the French Revolution. He moved to America, the home of Benjamin Franklin, who had stimulated Priestley's interest in science. Primarily known for his identification of oxygen as a separate element which is involved in combustion and respiration, he also experimented in electricity. In addition, he can claim to be the developer of carbonated drinks (soda-pop).

Charles Augustin Coulomb (1738-1806) was born into a family of high social position and grew up in an age of political unrest. He studied science and mathematics and began his career as a military engineer. His book *The Theory of Simple Machines* gained him membership in the French Academy of Sciences. While studying machines Coulomb invented his torsion balance, with which he carried out intensive investigations on the mechanical forces due to electrical charges.

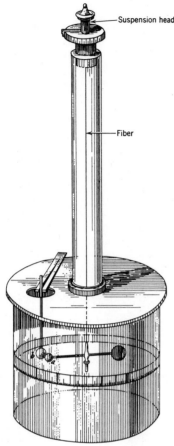

Suspension head

Fiber

Coulomb's Torsion Balance

That two equally large spheres
share the available charge equally
might have been guessed by what
is called "argument by symmetry."
There is no evident reason why the
charge should not be distributed
symmetrically, and therefore divided
equally, among equal spheres. But
such a guess based on a symmetry
argument must always be confirmed
by separate experiment, as it was in
this case.

SG 14.2

Thus he directly confirmed Priestley's suggestion. *The electric force of
repulsion for like charges, or attraction for unlike charges, varies
inversely as the square of the distance between charges.*

Coulomb also demonstrated how the magnitude of the electric force
depends on the magnitudes of the charges. There was not yet any
accepted method for measuring quantitatively the amount of charge on an
object. (In fact, nothing we have said so far would suggest how to
measure the magnitude of the charge on a body.) Yet Coulomb used a
clever technique based on symmetry to compare the effects of different
amounts of charge. He first showed that if a charged metal sphere
touches an uncharged sphere of the same size, the second sphere
becomes charged also. We might say that, at the moment of contact
between the objects, some of the charge from the first "flows" or is
"conducted" to the second. Moreover, after contact has been made the two
spheres are found to share the original charge *equally*. (This is
demonstrated by the observable fact that they exert equal forces on some
third charged body.) Using this principle, Coulomb started with a given
amount of charge on one sphere. He then shared this charge by contact
among several other identical but uncharged spheres. Thus, he could
produce charges of one-half, one-quarter, one-eighth, etc., of the original
amount. In this way, Coulomb varied the charges on the two original test
spheres independently, then measured the change in force between them.
He found that, for example, when the charges on the two spheres are
both reduced by one-half, the force between the spheres is reduced to
one-quarter its previous value. In general, he found that the magnitude of
the electric force is proportional to the *product* of the charges. We can use
the symbols q_A and q_B for the net charge on bodies A and B. The
magnitude F_{el} of the electric force that each exerts on the other is
proportional to $q_A \times q_B$, and may be written as $F_{el} \propto q_A q_B$.

Coulomb summarized his results in a single equation which describes
the electric forces that two small charged spheres A and B exert on each
other:

$$F_{el} = k \frac{q_A q_B}{R^2}$$

R represents the distance between the centers and k is a constant whose
value depends on the units of charge and length that are used. This form
of the law of force between two electric charges is now called Coulomb's
Law. We will discuss the value of k below. For the moment, note one
beautiful fact about Coulomb's Law: it has exactly the same form as
Newton's Law of Universal Gravitation! Yet these two great laws arise
from completely different sets of observations and apply to completely
different kinds of phenomena. Why they should match so exactly is to this
day a fascinating puzzle, and another reminder of the basic simplicity of
nature.

The unit of charge. We can use Coulomb's Law to define a unit of
charge. For example, we could assign k a value of exactly 1. We could
then define a unit charge so that two unit charges separated by a unit

distance exert a unit force on each other. There actually is a set of units based on this choice. However, we will find another system of electrical units—the "MKSA" system—more convenient to use. In this system the unit of charge is derived not from electrostatics but from the unit of current, the *ampere*. (This will be discussed in Section 14.12.) The unit of charge is called the *coulomb*. It is defined as the amount of charge that flows past a point in a wire in one second when the current is equal to one ampere. In Section 14.6 we will see that 1 coulomb corresponds to the charge of $1/1.6 \times 10^{19}$ electrons.

The ampere, or "amp," is a familiar unit frequently used to describe the current in electrical appliances. The effective amount of current in a common 100-watt light bulb is approximately one ampere. Therefore, the amount of charge that goes through the bulb in one second is about 1 coulomb. It might seem that a coulomb is a fairly small amount of charge. However, one coulomb of *net* charge collected in one place is unmanageably large! In the light bulb, one coulomb of negative charge moves through the filament each second. However, these negative charges are passing through a more or less stationary arrangement of *positive* charges in the filament. Thus, the *net* charge on the filament is zero at every moment.

Taking the coulomb (1 coul) as the unit of charge, we can find the constant k in Coulomb's Law experimentally. We simply measure the force between known charges separated by a known distance. The value of k turns out to equal about nine billion newton-meters squared per coulomb squared (9×10^9 Nm²/coul²). So two objects, each with a *net* charge of one coulomb, separated by a distance of one meter, would exert forces on each other of nine billion newtons. This force is roughly the same as a weight of one million tons! We never observe such large forces because we cannot actually collect so much net charge in one place. Nor can we exert enough force to bring two such charges so close together. The mutual repulsion of like charges is so strong that it is difficult to keep a charge of more than a thousandth of a coulomb on an object of ordinary size. If you rub a pocket comb on your sleeve enough to produce a spark when the comb is brought near a conductor (such as a sink faucet), the net charge on the comb will be far less than one millionth of a coulomb. Lightning discharges usually take place when a cloud has accumulated a net charge of a few hundred coulombs distributed over its very large volume.

Electrostatic induction. We have noted, and you have probably observed, that an electrically charged object can often attract small pieces of paper. But the paper itself has no net charge; it exerts no force on other pieces of paper. At first sight then, its attraction to the charged object might seem to contradict Coulomb's law. After all, the force ought to be zero if either q_A or q_B is zero. But we can explain the attraction if we recall that uncharged objects contain equal amounts of positive and negative electric charges. And when a charged body is brought near a neutral object, it may rearrange the positions of some of the charges in the neutral object. The negatively charged comb does this when held near a piece of paper. Some of the positive charges in the paper shift toward

The Project Physics documentary film *People and Particles* shows an experiment designed to show whether Coulomb's law applies to charges at distances as small as 10^{-15} cm. (It does.)

Meter-Kilogram-Second-Ampere

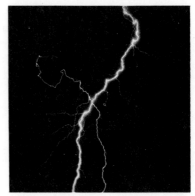

A stroke of lightning is, on the average, about 40,000 amperes, and transfers about 1 coulomb of charge between the cloud and the ground.

SG 14.3

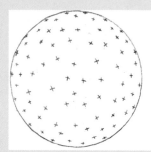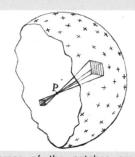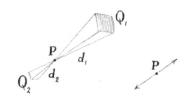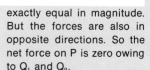

Consider any point charge P inside an even, spherical distribution of charges. For any small patch of charges with total charge Q_1 on the sphere there is a corresponding patch on the other side of P with total charge Q_2. But the areas of the patches are directly proportional to the squares of the distances from P, hence the total charges Q_1 and Q_2 are also *directly* proportional to the squares of the distances from P.

The electric field due to each patch of charge is proportional to the area of the patch, and *inversely* proportional to the square of the distance from P. So the distance and area factors cancel—the forces on P due to the two patches at P are exactly equal in magnitude. But the forces are also in opposite directions. So the net force on P is zero owing to Q_1 and Q_2.

Since this is true for all pairs of charge patches, the net electric field at P is zero.

Electric shielding

In general, charges on a closed conducting surface arrange themselves so that the electric force inside is zero just as they do on a sphere as shown in the diagrams above. Even if the conductor is placed in an electric field, the surface charges will rearrange themselves so as to keep the net force zero everywhere inside. Thus, the region inside any closed conductor is "shielded" from any *external* electric field. This is a very important practical principle.

Whenever stray electric fields might disturb the operation of some electric equipment, the equipment can be enclosed by a shell of conducting material. Some uses of electric shielding can be seen in the photographs of the back of a TV receiver, below.

Closeup of a tube in the tuning section of the TV set on the left. Surrounding the tube is a collapsible metal shield. Partly shielded tubes can be seen elsewhere in that photo.

A section of shielded cable such as is seen in use in the photo above, showing how the two wires are surrounded by a conducting cylinder woven of fine wires.

the side of the paper nearest the comb, and a corresponding amount of negative charge shifts toward the other side. The paper still has no *net* electric charge. But some of the positive charges are slightly *closer* to the comb than the corresponding negative charges are. So the attraction to the comb is greater than the repulsion. (Remember that the force gets weaker with the square of the distance, according to Coulomb's law. The force would be only one fourth as large if the distance were twice as large.) In short, there is a net attraction of the charged body for the neutral object. This explains the old observation of the effect rubbed amber had on bits of grain and the like.

A charged body *induces* a shift of charge on the nearby neutral body. Thus, the rearrangement of electric charges inside or on the surface of a neutral body caused by the influence of a nearby charged object is called *electrostatic induction*. In Chapter 16 we will see how the theory of electrostatic induction played an important role in the development of the theory of light.

Q3 In the following sentences, underline the words or phrases that do not simply describe observable facts, but that have been specifically "invented" to help understand such observations.

(a) Like charges repel each other. A body that has a net positive charge repels any body that has a net positive charge. That is, two glass rods that have both been rubbed will tend to repel each other. A body that has a net negative charge repels any other body that has a net negative charge.

(b) Unlike charges attract each other. A body that has a net positive charge attracts any body that has a net negative charge and vice versa.

Q4 What experimental fact led Priestley to propose that electrical force and gravitational forces change with distance in a similar way?

Q5 What two facts about the force between electric charges did Coulomb demonstrate?

Q6 If the distance between two charged objects is doubled, how is the electrical force between them affected?

Q7 Are the coulomb and ampere both units of charge?

SG 14.4
SG 14.5

14.4 Forces and fields

Gilbert described the action of the lodestone by saying it had a "sphere of influence" surrounding it. He meant that any other magnetic body coming inside this sphere would be attracted. Further, the strength of the attractive force would be greater at places closer to the lodestone. In modern language, we would say that the lodestone is surrounded by a *magnetic field*.

The word "field" is used in many ways. Let us discuss some familiar kinds of fields, and then gradually develop the idea of physical fields as used in science. This exercise should remind us that most terms in physics are really adaptations—with important changes—of commonly used words. Velocity, acceleration, force, energy, and work are examples you have already encountered in this course.

One ordinary use of the concept of field is illustrated by the "playing field" in various sports. The football field, for example, is a place where teams compete according to rules which confine the important action to the area of the field. "Field" in this case means a *region of interaction*.

In international politics, we speak of "spheres" or "fields" of influence. A field of political influence is also a region of interaction. But unlike a playing field, it has no sharp boundary line. A country usually has greater influence on some countries and less influence on others. So in the political sense, "field" refers also to an *amount* of influence—more in some places and less in others. Further, the field has a *source*—the country that exerts the influence.

There are similarities here to the concept of field as used in physics. But there is also an important difference: to define a field in physics, it must be possible to assign a numerical value of field strength to every point in the field. This part of the field idea will become clearer if we discuss some situations that are more directly related to the study of physics. First we will talk about them in everyday language, then in terms of physics.

The Situation	*Description of your experience*
(a) You are walking along the sidewalk toward a street lamp at night.	"The brightness of light is increasing."
(b) You stand on the sidewalk as an automobile moves down the street with its horn blaring.	"The sound gets louder and then softer."
(c) On a hot summer day, you walk barefoot out of the sunshine and into the shade on the sidewalk.	"The sidewalk is cooler here than in the sunshine."

We can describe these experiences in terms of fields:

(a) The street lamp is surrounded by a field of illumination. The closer you move to the lamp, the stronger is the field of illumination as registered on your eye or on a lightmeter you might be carrying. For every point in the space around the street lamp, we could assign a number that represents the strength of the field of illumination at that place.

(b) The automobile horn is surrounded by a sound field. You are standing still in your frame of reference (the sidewalk). A pattern of field values goes past you with the same speed as the car. We can think of the sound field as steady but moving with the horn. At any instant we could

assign a number to each point in the field to represent the intensity of
sound. At first the sound is faintly heard as the weakest part of the field
reaches you. Then the more intense parts of the field go by, and the
sound seems louder. Finally, the loudness diminishes as the sound field
and its source (the horn) move away.

(c) In this case you are walking in a temperature field. This field is
intense where the sidewalk is in the sunshine and weaker where it is in
the shade. Again, we could assign a number to each point in the field to
represent the temperature at that point.

Notice that the first two fields are each produced by a single source.
In (a) the source is a stationary street lamp; in (b) it is a moving horn. In
both cases the field strength gradually increases as your distance from the
source decreases. But in the third case (c) the field is produced by a
complicated combination of influences: the sun, clouds in the sky, the
shadow cast by nearby buildings, and other factors. Yet the description of
the field itself is just as simple as for a field produced by a single source:
one numerical value is associated with each point in the field.

So far, all examples were simple *scalar* fields. No direction was
involved in the value of the field at each point. On the next page are
maps of two fields for the layer of air over North America on two
consecutive days. But there is a very important difference between the
field mapped at the left and that mapped at the right. The air pressure
field (on the left) is a scalar field; the wind velocity field (on the right) is
a vector field. For each point in the pressure field a single number—a
scalar quantity—gives the value of the field at that point. But for each
point in the wind velocity field the value of the field is given by both a
numerical value (magnitude) and a *direction*—that is, by a vector.

One use of these field maps is that they can help in more or less
accurately predicting what conditions might be in the field on the next
day. Also, by superimposing the maps for pressure and velocity, we can
discover how these two kinds of field are related to each other.

Physicists actually use the term "field" in three different senses: (1)
the value of the field *at a point* in space; (2) the set or collection of all
values everywhere in the space where that field exists; (3) the region of
space in which the field has values. In reading the rest of this chapter,
you will not find it difficult to decide which meaning applies each time
the term is used.

The gravitational force field. Before returning to electricity and
magnetism, let us illustrate a bit further the idea of a field. A good
example is the gravitational force field of the earth. Recall that the force
$\vec{F}_{grav}$ exerted by the earth on any object above its surface acts in a
direction toward the center of the earth. So the field of force of
gravitational attraction is a *vector* field, which could be represented by
arrows pointing toward the center of the earth. In the illustration, a few
such arrows are shown, some near, some far from the earth.

The strength, or numerical magnitude, of the earth's gravitational
force field at any chosen point depends on the distance of the point from
the center of the earth. This follows from Newton's theory, which states
that the magnitude of the gravitational attraction is inversely proportional

Note that meteorologists have a
different convention for representing
vectors than we have been using.
What are the advantages and
disadvantages?

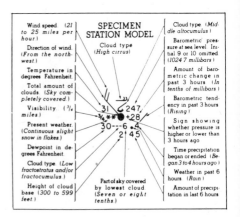

Key for a U.S. Weather Bureau Map.

Pressure and velocity fields

These maps, adapted from those of the U.S. Weather Bureau, depict two fields, air pressure at the earth's surface and high-altitude wind velocity, for two successive days. Locations at which the pressure is the same are connected by lines. The set of such pressure "contours" represents the overall field pattern. The wind velocity at a location is indicated by a line (showing direction) and feather lines—one for every 10 mph. (The wind velocity over the tip of Florida, for example, is a little to the east of due north and is approximately 30 mph.)

Air pressure at the earth's surface

Jan. 10

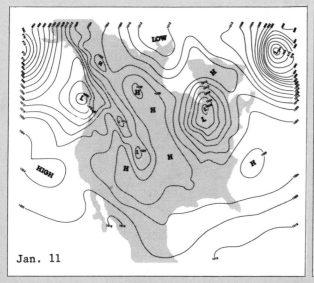

Jan. 11

High altitude wind velocity

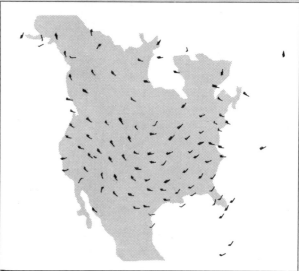

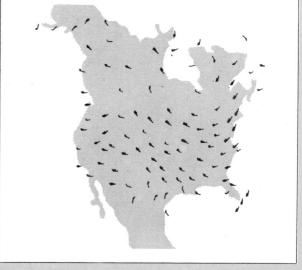

to the square of the distance R:

$$F_{\text{grav}} = G \times \frac{Mm}{R^2}$$

where M is the mass of the earth, m is the mass of the test body, R is the distance between the centers of earth and the other body, and G is the universal gravitational constant.

In this equation F_{grav} also depends on the mass of the test body. It would be more convenient to define a field that depends only on the properties of the source, whatever the mass of the test body. Then we could think of the field as existing in space and having a definite magnitude and direction at every point. The mass of the test body would not matter. In fact, it would not matter whether there were any test body present at all. As it happens, such a field is easy to define. By slightly rearranging the equation for Newton's law of gravitation, we can write:

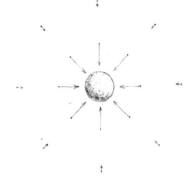

$$F_{\text{grav}} = m \left(\frac{Gm}{R^2} \right)$$

We then define the gravitational field strength $\vec{g}$ around a spherical body of mass M as having a magnitude GM/R^2 and a direction the same as the direction of $\vec{F}_{\text{grav}}$, so that:

$$\vec{F}_{\text{grav}} = m\vec{g}$$

where $g = GM/R^2$. Thus note that $\vec{g}$ at a point in space is determined by the source mass M and the distance R from the source, and does *not* depend on the mass of any test object.

The total or net gravitational force at a point in space is usually determined by more than one source. For example, the moon is acted on by the sun as well as by the earth, and to a smaller extent by the other planets. In order to define the field resulting from any configuration of massive bodies, we can take $\vec{F}_{\text{grav}}$ to be the *net* gravitational force due to *all* sources. We then *define* $\vec{g}$ in such a way that we can still write the simple relationship $\vec{F}_{\text{grav}} = m\vec{g}$. That is, we define $\vec{g}$ by the equation:

SG 14.6

$$\vec{g} = \frac{\vec{F}_{\text{grav}}}{m}$$

Thus the gravitational field strength at any point is the *ratio* of the net gravitational force $\vec{F}_{\text{grav}}$ acting on a test body at that point to the mass m of the test body.

Electric fields. The strength of any force field can be defined in a similar way. According to Coulomb's law, the electric force exerted by one relatively small charged body on another depends on the product of the *charges* of the two bodies. Consider a charge q placed at any point in the electric field set up by a charge Q. Coulomb's law, describing the force F_{el} experienced by q, can be written as:

$$F_{\text{el}} = k\frac{Qq}{R^2} \quad \text{or} \quad F_{\text{el}} = q\frac{kQ}{R^2}$$

Recall that F_{el} is *called* an "electric" force because it is caused by the presence of charges. But, as with all forces, we know it exists and can measure it only by its mechanical effects on bodies.

As in our discussion of the gravitational field, the expression for force here is broken into two parts. One part, kQ/R^2, depends only on the charge Q of the source and distance R from it. We can call this part "the electric field strength due to Q." The second part, q, is a property of the body being acted on. Thus we *define* the electric field strength $\vec{E}$, due to charge Q, as having magnitude kQ/R^2 and the same direction as $\vec{F}_{el}$. The electric force is then the product of the test charge and the electric field strength:

$$\vec{F}_{el} = q\vec{E} \qquad \text{and} \qquad \vec{E} = \frac{\vec{F}_{el}}{q}$$

The equation *defines* $\vec{E}$ for an electric force field. Thus the electric field strength $\vec{E}$ at a point in space is the *ratio* of the net electric force $\vec{F}_{el}$ acting on a test charge at that point to the magnitude q of the test charge. This definition applies whether the electric field results from a single point charge or from a complicated distribution of charges. The same kind of superposition principle holds which we have already seen many times. Fields set up by many sources superpose, forming a single net field. The vector specifying the magnitude of the net field at any point is simply the vector sum of the values of the fields due to each individual source.

So far we have passed over a complication that we did not encounter in dealing with gravitation. There are *two* kinds of electric charge, positive (+) and negative (−). The forces they experience when placed in the same electric field are opposite in direction. By agreement, scientists define the direction of the vector $\vec{E}$ as the direction of the force exerted by the field on a *positive* test charge. Given the direction and magnitude of the field vector $\vec{E}$ at a point, then by definition the force vector $\vec{F}_{el}$ acting on a charge q is $\vec{F}_{el} = q\vec{E}$. A positive charge, say +0.00001 coulombs, placed at this point will experience a force $\vec{F}_{el}$ in the same direction as $\vec{E}$ at that point. A negative charge, say −0.00001 coulombs, will experience a force of the same magnitude, but in the *opposite* direction. Changing the sign of q from + to − automatically changes the direction of $\vec{F}_{el}$ to the opposite direction.

SG 14.7
SG 14.8

SG 14.9

SG 14.10

Q8 What is the difference between a scalar field and a vector field? Give examples of each.

Q9 Describe how one can find, by experiment, the magnitude and the directions of:

(a) the gravitational field at a certain point in space

(b) the electric field at a certain point in space.

Q10 Why would the field strengths $\vec{g}$ and $\vec{E}$ for the test bodies be unchanged if m and q were doubled?

Q11 A negatively charged test body is placed in an electric field where the vector $\vec{E}$ is pointing downward. What is the direction of the force on the test body?

14.5 The smallest charge

In Section 14.3 we noted that an electrified comb can pick up a small piece of paper. Obviously, the electric force on the paper must exceed the gravitational force exerted on the paper by the earth. This observation indicates that electric forces in general are strong compared to gravitational forces. Using the same principle, we can balance the gravitational force on a microscopically small object (which still contains several billion atoms) against the electrical force on the same object when the object has a net electric charge of only a single electron! (The electron is one of the basic components of the atom. Other properties of atoms and electrons will be discussed in Unit 5.) This fact is the basis of a method for actually measuring the electron's charge. The method was first employed by the American physicist Robert A. Millikan in 1909. Millikan's experiment will be described in detail in Section 18.3. But we will discuss its basic principle here, since it provides such a clear connection between the ideas of force, field, and charge.

Suppose a small body of mass m—a tiny drop of oil or a small plastic sphere—has a net negative electric charge of magnitude q. We place the negatively charged body in an electric field E directed downward. A force $\vec{F}_{el}$ of magnitude qE is now exerted on the body in the *upward* direction. Of course, there is also a downward gravitational force $F_{grav} = mg$ on the object. The body will accelerate upward or downward, depending on whether the electric force or the gravitational force is greater. By adjusting the magnitude of the electric field strength $\vec{E}$ (that is, by changing the source that sets up $\vec{E}$), we can balance the two forces.

What happens when the two forces are balanced? Remember that if a zero *net* force acts on a body it can have no acceleration. That is, it would be at rest or continue to move at some constant velocity. In this case air resistance is also acting as long as the drop moves at all, and will soon bring the drop or sphere to rest. The drop will then be in equilibrium. In fact, it will be suspended in mid-air. When this happens, we record the magnitude of the electric field strength $\vec{E}$ which we had to apply to produce this condition.

Since now the electric force balances the gravitational force, the following must hold:

$$qE \;=\; mg$$

We can calculate the charge q from this equation if we know the quantities E, m and g, since

$$q = \frac{mg}{E}$$

This allows us to find, in the laboratory, what values of charge q a very small test object can carry.

Millikan used fine droplets of oil from an atomizer. The droplets became charged as they formed a spray. The oil was convenient because of the low rate of evaporation of the droplet.

When $m\vec{g}$ and $q\vec{E}$ are balanced, frictional forces remain until the body stops moving.

SG 14.11

Visualizing electric fields

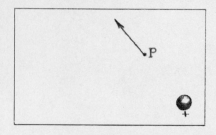 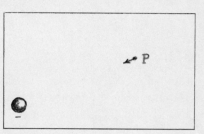 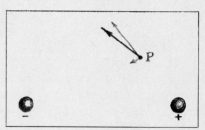

Only rarely will we be interested in the electric field of a single charged sphere. Usually we want to calculate the field values for a complicated array of charges. Unless we actually take some small test charge and move it around in the field to measure the force, we need a rule for adding the fields set up by separate sources. A wide variety of experiments indicates that, at any point in an electric field, the field strength produced by several sources *is just the vector sum* of the field strengths produced by each source alone.

A simple example is that of finding the net electric field strength produced by a pair of spheres with equal charges of opposite sign. The arrow in the first frame above indicates the field strength that would result at a point P from the presence of the (+) charge alone. The second frame shows the field strength that would result at the same point from the presence of the (−) charge alone. (The point P happens to be twice as far from the center of the positive charge, so the field strength is only $\frac{1}{4}$ as great in the second frame.) When both (+) and (−) charges are present, the net electric field strength at P is the vector sum of the individual electric field strengths. This sum is indicated in the third frame.

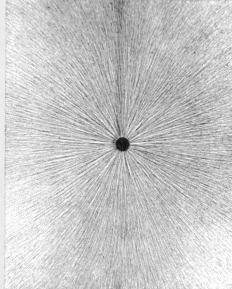

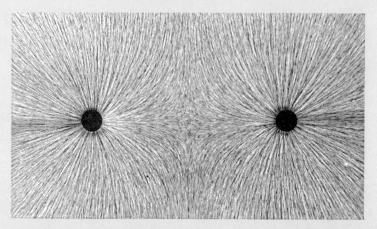

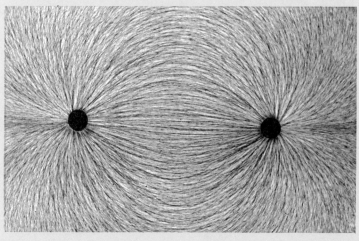

The photograph above shows bits of fine thread suspended in oil. At center is a charged object. Its electric field induces opposite charges on the two ends of each bit of thread which then tend to line up end-to-end along the direction of the field.
Top right: equal like charges.
Bottom right: equal opposite charges.

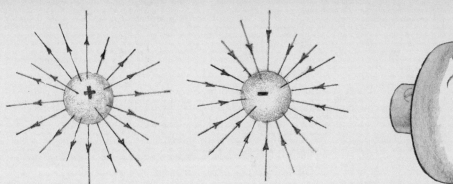

The "map" of a three-dimensional electric field is not easy to draw. A vector value can be assigned to the electric field strength $\vec{E}$ at every point in space. But obviously we cannot illustrate that—such a map would be totally black with arrows. A convention used for many years in physics involves drawing a small number of the infinitely many possible lines that indicate the *direction* of the field.

For example, the field around a charged sphere could be represented by a drawing like either of those above. Notice that the lines, which are drawn symmetrically around the sphere, are more closely spaced where the field is stronger. The lines can be drawn in three dimensions so that the density of lines in a given region represents the strength of the field in that region. These lines, therefore, represent both the local direction and local strength of the field. They are called "lines of force."

Around a single charged sphere the lines of force are straight and directed radially away from or toward the center. When charges are distributed in a more complicated way, the lines of force around them may be curved. The direction of the field strength $\vec{E}$ at a point is the *tangent* to the curved line of force at that point. Above, for example, we have drawn lines of force that represent the electric field between a charged fingertip and an oppositely charged doorknob. The electric field vector $\vec{E}$ at point P is directed along the tangent to the curved line of force at P, and represented by the arrow at P.

Note the difference: each line of force shows only direction, and terminates at a charged object or goes off to infinity. But the electric field vector $\vec{E}$ at each point P is represented by an arrow of length drawn to scale to indicate magnitude E.

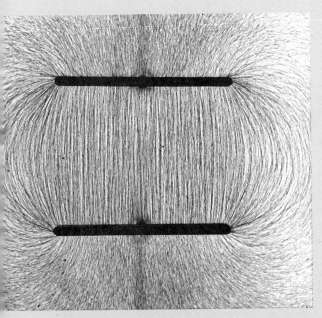

Oppositely charged plates. (Notice the *uniformity* of the field *between* the plates as compared with the *nonuniformity* at the *ends* of the plates.)

Oppositely charged cylinder and plate. (Notice the absence of field inside the cylinder, as indicated by lack of alignment of the fibers.)

The magnitude of the charge on the electron is symbolized by q_e, and its sign is negative. Any charge q is therefore given by $q = nq_e$ where n is the whole number of individual charges, each of magnitude q_e.

Hence 1 coulomb is the magnitude of the charge on $1/1.6 \times 10^{19}$ electrons.

SG 14.12 –14.14

When you do this, you will discover a remarkable fact: *all possible charges in nature are made up of whole multiples of some smallest charge.* We call this smallest possible charge the *magnitude of the charge on one electron.* By repeating the experiment many times with a variety of small charges, we can find the value of the charge on one electron (q_e). In effect, this is what Millikan did. He obtained the value of $q_e = 1.6024 \times 10^{-19}$ coulomb for the electron charge. (For most purposes we can use the value 1.6×10^{-19} coulomb.) This value agrees with the results of many other experiments done since then. No experiment has yet revealed the existence of a smaller unit of charge. (Some physicists have speculated, however, that there might be $\frac{1}{3} q_e$ associated with a yet-to-be-found subatomic particle called the "quark.")

Q12 How can the small oil drops or plastic spheres used in the Millikan experiment experience an electric force *upward* if the electric field is directed *downward*?

Q13 What do the results of the Millikan experiment indicate about the nature of electric charge?

14.6 The law of conservation of electric charge

For many centuries the only way to charge objects electrically was to rub them. In 1663, Otto von Guericke made and described a machine that would aid in producing large amounts of charge by rubbing:

> . . . take a sphere of glass which is called a phial, as large as a child's head; fill it with sulphur that has been pounded in a mortar and melt it sufficiently over a fire. When it is cooled again break the sphere and take out the globe and keep it in a dry place. If you think it best, bore a hole through it so that it can be turned around an iron rod or axle . . . .

When he rested his hand on the surface of the sulphur globe while rotating it rapidly, the globe acquired enough charge to attract small objects.

By 1750 electrical machines were far more powerful and vigorous research on the nature of electricity was going on in many places. Large glass spheres or cylinders were whirled on axles supported by heavy wooden frames. A stuffed leather pad was sometimes substituted for the human hands. The charge on the globe was often transferred to a large metal object (such as a gun barrel) suspended nearby.

These machines were powerful enough to deliver strong electrical shocks and to produce frightening sparks. In 1746 Pieter van Musschenbroek, a physics professor at Leyden, reported on an accidental and nearly fatal discovery in a letter which begins, "I wish to communicate to you a new, but terrible, experiment that I would advise you never to attempt yourself." Musschenbroek was apparently trying to capture electricity in a bottle, for he had a brass wire leading from a charged gun barrel to a jar filled with water. A student was holding the jar in one hand while Musschenbroek cranked the machine. When the student touched the brass wire with his free hand he received a tremendous shock. They repeated the experiment, this time with the student at the crank and Musschenbroek holding the jar. The jolt was even greater than before (the student must have been giving his all at the crank). Musschenbroek wrote later that he thought ". . . it was all up with me . . . ." and that he would not repeat the experience for the whole kingdom of France. Word of the experiment spread rapidly, and the jar came to be called a Leyden jar. In fact, Musschenbroek had inadvertently discovered that charge could be stored in a properly constructed solid object. Devices such as Leyden jars that have a capacity for storing electric charge, are now called *capacitors*.

The Leyden jar came to Benjamin Franklin's attention. He performed a series of experiments with it, and published his analysis of its behavior in 1747. In these experiments Franklin first showed that the effects of different kinds of charge (which we call positive and negative) can cancel each other. Because of this cancellation he concluded that positive and negative charges were not really different. As we mentioned before, Franklin thought that *one* kind of electricity was enough to explain all phenomena. He believed that a positive charge resulted from an excess of "electric fluid" or "electric fire," and a negative charge from a shortage of it.

This view led him to the powerful and correct idea that electric charge is neither created nor destroyed. Objects become positively or negatively charged by rearrangement of the electric charges already present in them. This is a matter of redistribution rather than creation. Similarly, positive and negative charges can cancel or neutralize each other's effect without being destroyed. This is the modern principle of *conservation of charge*. It is taken to be as basic a law of nature as are the conservation principles of momentum and of energy. The principle of Law of Conservation of Electric Charge can be stated in this way: *the net amount of electric charge in a closed system remains constant, regardless of what reactions occur in the system. Net amount of charge* is defined as the difference between the amounts of + and of − charge. (For example, a *net* charge of +1 coulomb would describe 1 coulomb of positive charge all by itself, or a combination of 11 coulombs of positive charge and 10 coulombs of negative charge.) If we take the + and − as actual numerical signs, instead of only convenient labels for two different kinds of charge, then the *net* charge can be called the *total* charge. Simply adding charges with + and − signs will then give the difference between the amounts of positive and negative charge.

The law or principle of conservation of electric charge is widely useful. Its applications range from designing circuits (see the *Reader 4* article, "Ohm's Law") to analyzing subatomic reactions (see the Project Physics Supplemental Unit *Elementary Particles*). One interesting possibility allowed by the electric charge conservation law is that charges can appear or disappear suddenly in a closed system—as long as the appearance or disappearance involve *equal* amounts of + and − charge. (An example of such a spontaneous appearance of + and − charges, in

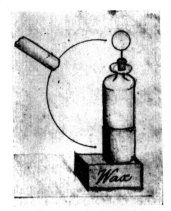

Franklin's drawing of a Leyden jar, standing on an insulating block of wax. The rod in the stopper was connected to a conducting liquid in the bottle. A charge given to the ball would hold through the non-conducting glass wall an equal amount of the opposite charge on the metal foil wrapped around the outside. It can hold a large charge because positive charges hold negative charges on the other side of a nonconducting wall.

Capacitors, familiar to anyone who has looked inside a radio, are descendents of the Leyden jar. They have many different functions in modern electronics.

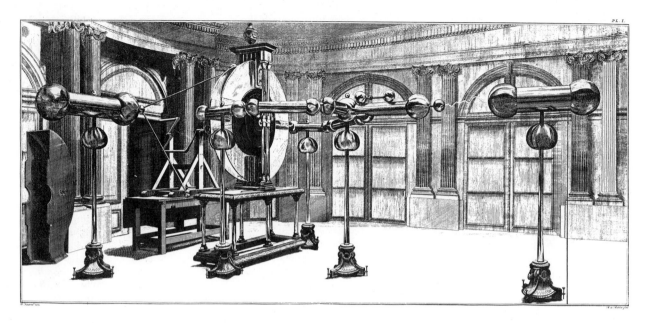

Electrostatic equipment of the 1700's.

the form of a negative electron and a positron, is a central part of the experiment in the Project Physics film *People and Particles*.)

Q14 What does the Law of Conservation of Electric Charge demand when, for example, a + charge appears inside a closed system?

14.7 Electric currents

SG 14.15

Touching a charged object to one end of a chain or gun barrel will cause the entire chain or barrel to become charged. The obvious explanation is that the charges move through and spread over the object. Electric charges move easily through some materials, called *conductors*. Metal conductors were most commonly used by the early experimenters, but salt solutions and very hot gases also conduct charge easily. Other materials, such as glass and dry fibers, conduct charge hardly at all. Such materials are called non-conductors or *insulators*. Dry air is a fairly good insulator. (Damp air is not—you may have difficulty keeping charges on objects in electrostatic experiments on a humid day.) But if the charge is great enough, even dry air around it suddenly will become a conductor, allowing a large amount of charge to shift through it. The heat and light caused by the sudden rush of charge produces a "spark." Sparks were the first obvious evidence of moving charges. Until late in the eighteenth century, a significant flow of charge—an *electric current*—could be produced only by discharging a Leyden jar. Such currents lasted only for the brief time it took for the jar to discharge.

In 1800, Alessandro Volta discovered a much better way of producing electric currents. Volta's method involved two different metals, each held with an insulating handle. When put into contact and then separated, one metal took on a positive charge and the other a negative charge. Volta reasoned that a much larger charge could be produced by stacking up several pieces of metal in alternate layers. This idea led him to undertake a series of experiments which produced an amazing finding, reported in a letter to the Royal Society in England in March of 1800:

Count Alessandro Volta (1745-1827) was given his title by Napoleon in honor of his electrical experiments. He was Professor of Physics at the University of Pavia, Italy. Volta showed that the electric effects previously observed by Luigi Galvani, in experiments with frog legs, were due to the metals and not to any special kind of "animal electricity." See the article "A Mirror for the Brain" in *Reader 4* for an account of this controversy.

> Yes! the apparatus of which I speak, and which will doubtless astonish you, is only an assemblage of a number of good conductors of different sorts arranged in a certain way. 30, 40, 60 pieces or more of copper, or better of silver, each in contact with a piece of tin, or what is much better, of zinc, and an equal number of layers of water or some other liquid which is a better conductor than pure water, such as salt water or lye and so forth, or pieces of cardboard or of leather, etc. well soaked with these liquids. . . .
>
> I place horizontally on a table or base one of the metallic plates, for example, one of the silver ones, and on this first plate I place a second plate of zinc; on this second plate I lay one of the moistened discs; then another plate of silver, followed immediately by another of zinc, on which I place again a moistened disc. I thus continue in the same way coupling a plate of silver with one of zinc, always in the same sense, that is to say, always silver below and zinc above or *vice versa,* according as I began, and inserting between these couples a moistened disc; I continue, I say, to form from several of these steps a column as high as can hold itself up without falling.

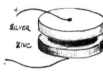

Voltaic "cell"

Volta showed that one end, or "terminal," of the pile was charged positive, and the other charged negative. He then attached wires to the first and last disks of his apparatus, which he called a "battery." Through these wires he obtained electricity with exactly the same effects as the electricity produced by rubbing amber, by friction in electrostatic machines, or by discharging a Leyden jar.

But most important of all, Volta's battery could produce a more or less *steady* electric current for a long period of time. Unlike the Leyden jar, it did not have to be charged from the outside after each use. Now the properties of electric currents as well as of static electric charges could be studied in a controlled manner. And this was the device needed to start the series of inventions that have so greatly changed civilization.

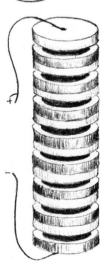

Voltaic "pile" or battery

Q15 In what ways was Volta's battery superior to a Leyden jar?

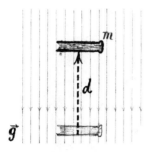

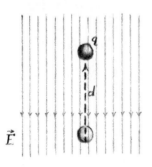

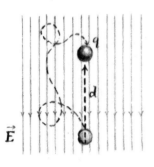

14.8 Electric potential difference

Sparks and heat are produced when the terminals of an electric battery are connected. These phenomena show that energy from the battery is being transformed into light, sound, and heat energy. The battery itself converts chemical energy to electrical energy. This, in turn, is changed to other forms of energy (such as heat) in the conducting path between the terminals. In order to understand electric currents and how they can be used to transport energy, we need a new concept which has the common name "voltage."

We learned in mechanics (Unit 3) that *change in potential energy* is equal to the work required to move an object frictionlessly from one position to another (Section 10.2). For example, a book's gravitational potential energy is greater when the book is on a shelf than when it is on the floor. The increase in potential energy is equal to the work done in raising the book from floor to shelf. This difference in potential energy depends on three factors: the mass *m* of the book, the magnitude of the gravitational field strength *g*, and the difference in height *d* between the floor and the shelf.

Similarly, the *electric* potential energy changes when work is done in moving an electric charge from one point to another in an electric field. Again, this change of potential energy $\Delta(PE)$ can be directly measured by the work that is done. The magnitude of this change in potential energy of course depends on the magnitude of the test charge *q*. But if we divide $\Delta(PE)$ by *q*, we get a quantity that does not depend on how large *q* is. Rather, it depends only on the intensity of the electric field and the location of the beginning and end points. This new quantity is called "electric potential difference." *Electric potential difference is defined as the ratio of the change in electrical potential energy $\Delta(PE)$ of a charge q to the magnitude of the charge.* In symbols,

$$V = \frac{\Delta(PE)}{q}$$

The units of electric potential difference are those of energy divided by charge, or joules per coulomb. The term used as the abbreviation for joules/coul is *volt*. The electrical potential difference (or "voltage") between two points is 1 volt if 1 joule of work is done in moving 1 coulomb of charge from one point to the other.

$$1 \text{ volt } = 1 \text{ joule/coulomb}$$

The potential difference between two points in a steady electric field depends on the location of the points. But it does *not* depend on the *path* followed by the test charge. Whether the path is short or long, direct or roundabout, the same work is done per unit charge. Similarly, a mountaineer does the same work per pound of mass in his pack against the gravitational field, whether he climbs straight up or spirals up along the slopes. Thus we can speak of the electrical potential difference

As is true for gravitational potential energy, there is no absolute zero level of electric potential energy. The *difference* in potential energy is the significant quantity. The symbol *V* is used both for "potential difference" as in the equation at the right, and as an abbreviation for volt, the unit of potential difference (as in 1 *V* = 1 J/coul).

SG 14.15–14.21

between two points in a field just as we spoke in Section 10.2 of the difference in gravitational potential energy between two points.

A simple case will help us to see the great importance of this definition of potential difference. Let us calculate the potential difference between two points in a uniform electric field of magnitude E produced by oppositely charged parallel plates. Work must be done in moving a positive charge q from one point to the other directly against the lines of electric force. The amount of work required is the product of the force F_{el} exerted on the charge (where $F_{el} = qE$), and the distance d through which the charge is moved. Thus,

$$\Delta(PE) = qEd$$

Substituting this expression for $\Delta(PE)$ in the definition of electric potential difference gives for the simple case of a uniform field:

$$V = \frac{\Delta(PE)}{q}$$
$$= \frac{qEd}{q}$$
$$= Ed$$

A $1\frac{1}{2}$-volt cell is one which has a potential difference of $1\frac{1}{2}$-volts between its two terminals. (This type of cell is often called a "battery," although technically a battery is the name for a group of connected cells.)

In practice it is easier to measure electric potential difference V (with a voltmeter) than to measure electric field strength E. The relationship above is most often useful in the form $E = V/d$, which can be used to find the intensity of a uniform electric field.

Electric potential energy, like gravitational potential energy, can be converted into kinetic energy. A charged particle placed in an electric field, but free of other forces, will accelerate. In doing so, it will increase its kinetic energy at the expense of electric potential energy. (In other words, the electric force on the charge acts in such a way as to push it toward a region of lower potential energy.) A charge q "falling" through a potential difference V increases its kinetic energy by qV if nothing is lost by friction (as in a vacuum tube). The *increase* in kinetic energy is equal to the *decrease* of potential energy. So the sum of the two at any moment remains constant. This is just one particular case of the general principle of energy conservation, though only electric forces are acting.

The conversion of electric potential energy to kinetic energy is used in *electron accelerators* (a common example is a television picture tube). An electron accelerator usually begins with an electron "gun." The "gun" has two basic parts: a wire and a metal can in an evacuated glass tube. The wire is heated red-hot, causing electrons to escape from its surface. The nearby can is charged positively, producing an electric field between the hot wire and the can. The electric field accelerates the electrons through the vacuum toward the can. Many electrons stick to the can, but some go shooting through a hole in one end of it. The stream of electrons emerging from the hole can be further accelerated or focused by additional cans. (You can make such an electron gun for yourself in the laboratory experiment *Electron Beam Tube.*) Such a beam of charged particles has a

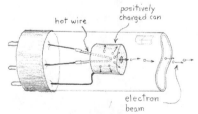

Electrically charged particles (electrons) are accelerated in an "electron gun" as they cross the potential difference between a hot wire (filament) and can in an evacuated glass tube.

Particle accelerators come in a wide variety of shapes and sizes. They can be as common as a 1,000-volt tube in an oscilloscope or 20,000-volt TV "guns," or as spectacular as the one shown below. (Or see the Cambridge Electron Accelerator, which was the scene for two Project Physics films, *People and Particles* and *Synchrotron.*)

K : kilo- (10^3)
M : mega- (10^6)
B : billion (10^9)
(B is often replaced by G : giga-)

SG 14.22

wide range of uses both in technology and in research. For example, it can make a fluorescent screen glow, as in a television picture tube or electron microscope. Or it can be used to break atoms apart, producing interesting particles for study, or x rays for medical purposes or research. When moving through a potential difference of one volt, an electron with a charge of 1.6×10^{-19} coulomb increases its kinetic energy by 1.6×10^{-19} joules. This amount of energy is called an "electron volt," abbreviated eV. Multiples are 1 KeV (= 1,000 eV), 1 MeV (= 10^6 eV) and 1 BeV (= 10^9 eV). Energies of particles in accelerators are commonly expressed in such multiples. In a TV tube, the electrons in the beam are accelerated across an electric potential difference of about 20,000 volts. Thus, each electron has an energy of about 20 KeV. The largest accelerator now operating gives (for research purposes) charged particles with kinetic energies of about 200 BeV.

Q16   How is the electric potential difference, or "voltage," between two points defined?

Q17   Does the potential difference between two points depend on the path followed in taking a charge from one to the other? Does it depend on the magnitude of the charge moved?

Q18   Is the electron volt a unit of charge, or potential difference (voltage), or what?

Below left: a section of the evacuated tube through which the electrons travel. The electrons are accelerated in steps by electric fields in a long line of accelerating cavities, similar to those in the photograph on page 28.

Below right: the site of Stanford University's 2-mile electron accelerator, in which electrons are given kinetic energies as great as 20 BeV.

14.9 Electric potential difference and current

The acceleration of an electron in a vacuum by an electric field is the simplest example of a potential difference affecting a charged particle. A more familiar example is electric current in a metal wire. In this arrangement the two ends of the wire are attached to the two terminals of a battery. Chemical changes inside a battery produce an electric field which continually drives charges to the terminals, one charged negatively, the other positive. The "voltage" of the battery tells us how much energy per unit charge is available when the charges move in any *external* path from one terminal to the other along the wire, for example.

Electrons in a metal do not move freely as they do in an evacuated tube, but continually interact with the metal atoms. So the relation between current and potential difference might seem more complicated in a wire than a vacuum tube. However, a simple relation first found by Georg Wilhelm Ohm is at least approximately valid for most metallic conductors: *the total current I in a conductor is proportional to the potential difference V applied between the two ends of the conductor.* Using the symbol I for the current and V for the potential difference, we can write:

$$I \propto V$$

or
$$I = constant \times V$$

This simple relation is called *Ohm's Law*. It is usually written in the form

$$I = \frac{V}{R}$$

where R is a constant called the *resistance* of the conducting path. Thus, Ohm's law assumes that the resistance of a given conducting path does not depend on current or voltage. Resistance *does* depend on the material and dimensions of the path, such as the length and diameter of a wire. But resistance is not strictly constant for any conducting path; it varies with changes in temperature, for example.

Ohm's law applies closely enough for practical technical work. But it does not have the general validity of the law of universal gravitation or Coulomb's law. In this course, we will use it mainly in lab work and in discussing electric light bulbs and power transmission in Chapter 15.

In metallic conductors, the moving charge is the negative electron, with the positive "mother" atom fixed. But all effects are the same as if positive charges were moving in the opposite direction. By an old convention, the latter is the direction usually chosen to describe the direction of current.

Close-up of part of the electric circuit in the TV set pictured on p. 38. These "resistors" have a fairly constant voltage-to-current ratio. (The value of the ratio is indicated by colored stripes.)

SG 14.23

Q19 How does the current in a metallic conductor change if the potential difference between the ends of the conductor is doubled?

Q20 What does it mean to say a resistor has a resistance of 5 *megohms* (5×10^6)?

Q21 How would you test whether Ohm's law applies to a given piece of wire?

14.10 Electric potential difference and power

Suppose a charge could move freely from one terminal to the other in an evacuated tube. The work done on the charge would then simply increase the kinetic energy of the charge. However, a charge moving through some material such as a wire transfers energy to the material by colliding with atoms. Thus at least some of the work goes into heat energy. A good example is a flashlight bulb. A battery forces charges through the filament wire in the bulb. The electric energy carried by the charges is converted to heat energy in the filament. The hot filament in turn radiates energy, a small fraction of which is in the form of visible light. Recall now that "voltage" (electric potential difference) is the amount of *work* done per unit of charge transferred. So the product of voltage and current gives the amount of *work* done per unit *time*:

$$V \text{ (joules/coulomb)} \times I \text{ (coulombs/sec)} = VI \text{ (joules/sec)}$$

Example: A small flashlight bulb connected to a 1.5-volt cell will have a current of about 0.1 ampere in its filament. At what rate is electric work being done to heat the filament in the bulb?

$P = VI$
 $= 1.5 \text{ volts} \times 0.1 \text{ amps}$
 $= 0.15 \text{ watts}$

(Only a small fraction of this power goes into the visible light energy radiated from the filament.)

But work done per unit time is called *power* (as defined in Section 10.6 of Unit 3 Text). The unit of power, equal to 1 joule/sec, is called a "watt." Using the definition of ampere (1 coulomb/sec) and volt (1 joule/coulomb), we can write the power P:

$$P \text{ (watts)} = V \text{ (volts)} \times I \text{ (amperes)}$$

What energy transformation does this work accomplish? As the positive charge moves to a lower potential level, it does work against material by colliding with atoms. The electric energy of the charge is converted to heat energy. If V is the voltage between the two ends of some material carrying a current I, the power converted to heat in the material is given by $P = VI$. This can be equally well expressed in terms of the resistance of the material substituting IR for V:

SG 14.24–14.27

$$P = IR \times I$$
$$P = I^2R$$

Thus, *the heat produced by a current is proportional to the square of the current.* Joule was the first to find this relationship experimentally. The discovery was part of his series of researches on conversion of different forms of energy (Section 10.8). The fact that heat production is proportional to the *square* of the current is very important in making practical use of electric energy. We will learn more about this in the next chapter.

Q22 What happens to the electrical energy used to move charge through a conducting material?

Q23 How does the power converted to heat in a conductor change if the current in the conductor is doubled?

14.11 Currents act on magnets

Early in the eighteenth century, reports began to appear that lightning changed the magnetization of compass needles and made magnets of knives and spoons. Some researchers believed that they had magnetized steel needles by discharging a Leyden jar through them. These reports suggested that electricity and magnetism were closely related in some way. But the casual observations were not followed up with deliberate, planned experiments that might have led to useful concepts and theories.

None of these early reports surprised the nineteenth-century Nature Philosophers in Europe. They were convinced that all phenomena observed in nature were only different effects of a single "force." Their belief in the unity of physical forces naturally led them to expect that electrical and magnetic forces were associated or related in some way.

The first concrete evidence of a connection between electricity and magnetism came in 1820, when Oersted performed an extremely important series of experiments. (See illustrations on next page.) Oersted placed a magnetic compass needle directly beneath a long horizontal conducting wire. The wire lay along the earth's magnetic north-south line, so that the magnetic needle was naturally lined up parallel to the wire. When Oersted connected the wire to the terminals of a battery, the compass needle swung toward an east-west orientation—nearly perpendicular to the wire! Charge at rest does not affect a magnet. But charge in motion (a current) does exert an odd kind of force on a magnet.

Oersted's results were the first ever found in which a force did *not* act along a line connecting the sources of the force. (Forces between planets, between electric charges, or between magnetic poles all act along such a line.) The force exerted between the current-carrying wire and each magnetic pole of the compass needle is not along the line from the wire to the pole. In fact, for the needle to twist as it does, the force must be acting *perpendicular* to such a line. The magnetic needle is *not* attracted or repelled by the wire, but is *twisted* sidewise by forces on its poles.

This was a totally new kind of effect. No wonder it had taken so long before anyone found the connection between electricity and magnetism. Closer examination revealed more clearly what was happening in this experiment. The long, straight current-carrying wire sets up a magnetic field. This field turns a small magnet so that the north-south line on the magnet is tangent to a circle whose center is at the wire and whose plane lies *perpendicular* to the wire. Thus, the current produces a *circular* magnetic field, not a centrally directed magnetic field as had been expected.

We define the direction of the magnetic field vector $\vec{B}$ at each point as *the direction of the force on the north-seeking pole of a compass needle placed at that point*. The force on the south-seeking pole will be in a direction exactly opposite to the field direction. A compass needle will respond to the opposite forces on its ends by turning until it points as closely as possible in the direction of the field. We can get a clue to the

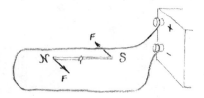

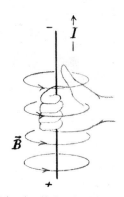

A useful rule: if the thumb points in the direction of the flow of charge, the fingers curl in the direction of the lines of the magnetic field $\vec{B}$. The magnitude of $\vec{B}$ is discussed in Sec. 14.13. Use the right hand for positive charge flow, left hand for negative charge flow.

Hans Christian Oersted (1777-1851), a Danish physicist, studied the writings of the Nature Philosopher Schelling and wrote extensively on philosophical subjects himself. In an essay published in 1813, he predicted that a connection between electricity and magnetism would be found. In 1820 he discovered that a magnetic field surrounds an electric current when he placed a compass under a current-carrying wire. In later years he vigorously denied the suggestion of other scientists that his discovery of electromagnetism had been accidental.

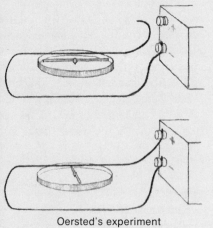

Oersted's experiment

To make the photograph below, a thick wire was inserted vertically through a horizontal sheet of cardboard, and tiny slivers of iron were sprinkled on a sheet. A strong current through the wire creates a magnetic field which causes the slivers to become magnetized and to line up in the direction of the field. Note that the magnetic lines of force encircle the wire.

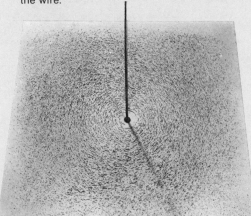

Left: an array of tiny compasses on a sheet of cardboard placed perpendicular to a brass rod. Right: when there is a strong current in the rod, the compass needles are deflected from their normal north-south line by the magnetic field set up by the current. This experiment, too, indicates that the lines of magnetic force due to the current are circular around the rod.

"shape" of the magnetic field around a current by sprinkling tiny slivers of iron on a sheet of paper through which the current-carrying wire is passing. The slivers become magnetized and behave like tiny compass needles, indicating the direction of the field. The slivers also tend to link together end-to-end. Thus, the pattern of slivers indicates magnetic lines of force around any current-carrying conductor or bar magnet. These lines form a "picture" of the magnetic field.

We can use a similar argument to find the "shape" of magnetic field produced by a current in a *coil* of wire, instead of a straight wire. To do this, we bend the wire into a loop so that it goes through the paper in two places. The magnetic effects of the different parts of the wire on the iron slivers produce a field pattern similar to that of a bar magnet. (See pages 62 and 63.)

Q24   Under what conditions can electric charges affect magnets?

Q25   What was surprising about the force a current exerted on a magnet?

Q26   How do we know that a current produces any magnetic field near it? What is the "shape" of the field anywhere near a straight conductor?

14.12 Currents act on currents

Oersted's experiment was one of those rare occasions when a discovery suddenly opens up an exciting new subject of research. In this case, no new equipment was needed. At once, dozens of scientists throughout Europe and America began intensive studies on the magnetic effects of electric currents. The work of André-Marie Ampère (1775–1836) stands out among all the rest. Ampère was called the "Newton of electricity" by James Clerk Maxwell, who decades later constructed a complete theory of electricity and magnetism. Ampère's work is filled with elegant mathematics. Without describing his theory in detail, we can trace some of his ideas and review some of his experiments.

Ampère's thoughts raced forward as soon as he heard Oersted's news. He began with a line of thought somewhat as follows: magnets exert forces on each other, and magnets and currents exert forces on each other. Do currents then exert forces on other currents? The answer is not necessarily yes. Arguing from symmetry is inviting and often turns out to be right. But the conclusions to which such arguments lead are not logically or physically necessary. Ampère recognized the need to let experiment answer his question. He wrote:

> When M. Oersted discovered the action which a current exercises on a magnet, one might certainly have suspected the existence of a mutual action between two circuits carrying currents; but this was not a necessary consequence; for a bar

Needle-like iron oxide crystals in the magnetic field of a bar magnet. The bar magnet is under the paper on which the iron oxide has been spread.

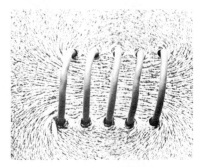

Iron filings in the magnetic field produced by current in a coil of wire.

SG 14.28

André-Marie Ampère (1775-1836) was born in a village near Lyons, France. There was no school in the village and Ampère was self-taught. His father was executed during the French Revolution, and Ampère's personal life was deeply affected by his father's death. Ampère became a professor of mathematics in Paris and made important contributions to physics, mathematics, and the philosophy of science. His self-portrait is reproduced above.

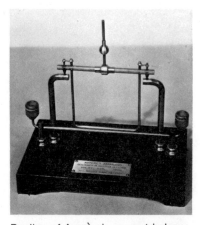

Replica of Ampère's current balance. The essential part is a fixed horizontal wire (foreground), and just behind it, hanging from a hinged support, a shorter segment of wire. Current is produced in both wires, and the force between them is measured.

of soft iron also acts on a magnetised needle, although there is not mutual action between two bars of soft iron.

And so Ampère put his hunch to the test. On September 30, 1820, within a week after word of Oersted's work reached France, Ampère reported to the French Academy of Sciences. He had indeed found that two parallel current-carrying wires exert forces on each other. They did so even though the wires showed no evidence of net electric charges.

Ampère made a thorough study of the forces between currents. He investigated how they depend on the distance between the wires, the relative positions of the wires, and the amount of current. In the laboratory you can repeat these experiments and work out the "force law" between two currents. We need not go into the quantitative details here, except to note that the force between currents can be used to measure how much current is flowing. In fact, the magnetic force between currents is now the quantity preferred for *defining* the unit of current. This unit is called the *ampere,* as mentioned in Section 14.3. One ampere is defined as the amount of current in each of two long straight parallel wires, set one meter apart, that causes a force of exactly 2×10^{-7} newtons to act on each meter of each wire.

Q27   What was Ampère's hunch?

Summary of Electric Units

QUANTITY	SYMBOL	UNIT
current	I	The *ampere* is the fourth fundamental unit in the so-called MKSA system (meter, kilogram, second, ampere) which is now widely used by physicists. For definition, see last paragraph.
charge	Q	The *coulomb* is defined as the amount of charge that flows in one second, when the current is 1 ampere.
potential difference	V	The *volt* is defined as the electric potential difference between two points such that 1 joule of work is done in moving 1 coulomb of charge between those points.
electric power	P	The *watt* is defined as the rate of energy flow (or work done per second, or "power") which corresponds to 1 joule per second. Thus a current of 1 ampere due to a potential difference of 1 volt corresponds to 1 watt power. The *kilowatt* is equal to 1,000 watts.
work	W	The *kilowatt-hour* is the amount of energy expended (work done) when one kilowatt of power is used for one hour. It is equal to 3,600,000 joules (1,000 joules/sec $\times$ 3,600 sec).
resistance	R	The *ohm* is defined as the resistance of a material which allows a current of just 1 ampere to pass through if the potential difference across the material is 1 volt.
electric field	$\vec{E}$	Electric field can be expressed either in terms of the force experienced by a unit charge (newtons per coulomb), or in terms of the rate at which the electric potential difference increases (volts per meter).
magnetic field	$\vec{B}$	The magnitude of magnetic field is defined in terms of the force experienced per meter of length by a conductor carrying a current of 1 ampere. The units are thus newtons per ampere-meter. Another common unit is the *gauss,* which equals 10^{-4} newtons/amp. meter.

14.13 Magnetic fields and moving charges

In the last two sections we discussed the interactions of currents with magnets and with each other. The concept of *magnetic field* greatly simplifies the description of these phenomena.

As we saw in studying Coulomb's law, electrically charged bodies exert forces on each other. When the charged bodies are at rest, we say that the forces are "electric" forces, or Coulomb forces. We imagine "electric fields" which act as the sources of these forces. But when the charged bodies are moving (as when two parallel wires carry currents), new forces *in addition to* the electric forces are present. We call these new forces "magnetic" and attribute them to "magnetic fields" set up by the moving charges.

Magnetic interaction of moving charged bodies is not as simple as electric interaction. Remember our description of Oersted's experiment. The direction of the force exerted by a current on a magnet is perpendicular both to the direction of the current and to the line between the magnet and current. For the moment, however, we will ignore the forces on current-carrying conductors. After all, we believe that the force on a wire is caused by forces on the individual electric charges moving in it. So let us see how such individual charges behave when moving freely in an external magnetic field. Once we have established some simple rules for the behavior of free charged particles, we can return to wires in the next chapter. There you will see how these simple rules are enough to explain the operation of electric generators and electric motors. (You will also see how these inventions changed civilization.)

The rules summarized in the remainder of this section are best learned in the laboratory. All you need is a magnet and a device for producing a beam of charged particles—for example, the "electron gun" described in Section 14.8. (Recommended procedures are described in the experiment *Electron Beam Tube* in the *Handbook*.)

The force on a moving charged body. Suppose we have a fairly uniform magnetic field $\vec{B}$, produced either by a bar magnet or by a current in a coil. How does this external field act on a moving, charged body? We find by experiment that the charge experiences a force, and that the force depends on three quantities: (1) the charge q on the body; (2) the velocity $\vec{v}$ of the body; (3) the strength of the external field $\vec{B}$ through which the body is moving.

The force depends not only on the *magnitude* of the velocity, but also on its *direction*. If the body is moving in a direction *perpendicular* to the field $\vec{B}$, the magnitude of the force is proportional to *both* of these quantities. That is,

$$F \propto qvB$$

which we can also write as

$$F = kqvB$$

where k is a proportionality constant that depends on the units chosen for

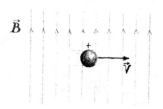

(a) When q moves with velocity $\vec{v}$ perpendicular to $\vec{B}$ we find that

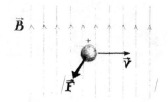

(b) there is a force $\vec{F}$ as shown, proportional to q, v, and B.

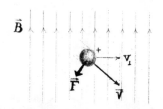

(c) If $\vec{v}$ is not $\perp$ to $\vec{B}$, there is a smaller force, proportional to $v_\perp$ instead of v.

Magnets and fields

The diagrams at the right represent the magnetic field of a current in a loop of wire. In the first diagram, some lines of force produced by opposite sides of the loops are drawn separately. One example is given of how the two fields add at point *P*. Some lines of force for the total field appear in the second diagram. Below at the right is a photograph of iron filings in the magnetic field of an actual current loop. Below at the left is the field of a series of coils, or helix.

In many applications, from doorbells to cyclotrons, magnetic fields are produced by coils of wire wound around iron cores. When a current is switched on, the iron core becomes magnetized and increases the strength of the field of the coil alone by a factor of 10^2 or 10^3. Such devices are called *electromagnets*.

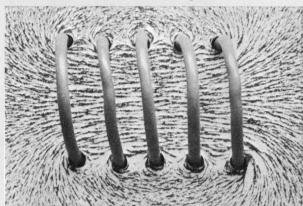

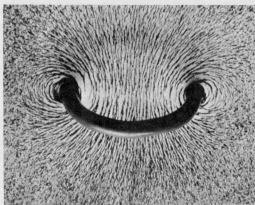

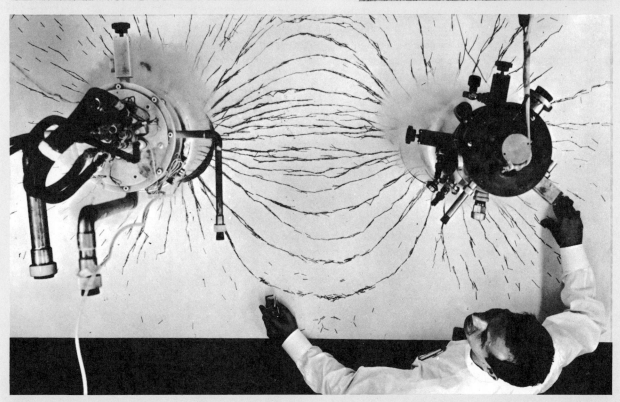

This electromagnet was used early in this century to deflect a beam of charged atoms sent through the tube at the top, in the gap between two sets of coils.

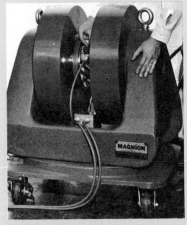

A modern electromagnet used in research when strong uniform fields are required.

The first electromagnet, invented by William Sturgeon in England in 1824, could lift a weight of nine pounds. In 1832, Joseph Henry constructed an electromagnet at Princeton which could hold up a weight of 3,600 pounds. Modern electromagnets (see above) which can typically lift 50,000 pounds of iron are widely used in industry, for example, to sort or load scrap metal.

In the two pictures at the left, iron nails line up in a strong magnetic field produced by large currents in superconducting coils, kept at 4° above absolute zero by liquid helium.

F, q, v, and B.

But if the charge is moving in a direction *parallel* to $\vec{B}$, there is no force! For all other directions of motion, the magnitude of the force is somewhere between the full value and zero. In fact, the force is proportional to the *component* of the velocity that is perpendicular to the field direction, $v_\perp$. So we can write a more general expression for the force:

$$F \propto qv_\perp B$$

$$\text{or} \qquad F = kqv_\perp B$$

A useful rule: if your fingers point along $\vec{B}$, and your thumb along $\vec{v}$, $\vec{F}$ will be in the direction your palm would push. For positive charges use the right hand, and for negative use the left hand.

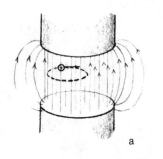

where k is the same constant as before. *The direction of the force is always perpendicular to the direction of the field. It is also perpendicular to the direction of motion of the charged body.*

The force exerted by an external magnetic field on a moving charged particle can be used to *define* the unit of magnetic field $\vec{B}$. This is done by taking the proportionality constant k as equal to one. This definition is convenient here, since we are dealing mainly with how magnetic fields act on moving charges (rather than with forces between bar magnets). So in the special case when $\vec{B}$ and $\vec{v}$ are *at right angles* to each other, the magnitude of the deflecting force becomes simply

$$F = qvB$$

The path of a charged body in a magnetic field. The force on a moving charged body in a magnetic field is always "off to the side." That is, the force is perpendicular to the body's direction of motion at every moment. Therefore, the magnetic force does not change the *speed* of the charged body. Rather, it changes the *direction* of the velocity vector. If a charged body is moving exactly perpendicular to a uniform magnetic field, there will be a constant sideways push. The body will move along a circular path, in a plane perpendicular to the direction of the magnetic field. If B is strong enough, the particle will be trapped in a circular orbit (as in sketch *a* in the margin).

What if the charged body's velocity has some component along the direction of the field but not exactly parallel to it? The body will still be deflected into a curved path, but the component of its motion *along* the field will continue undisturbed. So the particle will trace out a coiled (helical) path (as in sketch *b* in the margin). If the body is initially moving exactly parallel to the magnetic field, there is no deflecting force at all, since $v_\perp$ is zero.

Some important examples of the deflection of charged particles by magnetic fields are discussed in Unit 5 and the Supplemental Unit *The Nucleus*. These examples include particle accelerators and bubble chambers. Here we will mention one example of "coiled" motion: the Van Allen radiation belts. A stream of charged particles, mainly from the sun but also from outer space, continually sweeps past the earth. Many of these particles are deflected into spiral paths by the magnetic field of the earth, and become "trapped" in the earth's field. The extensive zones

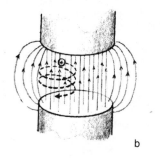

a

SG 14.29

SG 14.30

b

SG 14.31

containing these rapidly moving trapped particles are called the Van Allen belts. Particles from these zones sometimes work their way toward the earth's magnetic poles. When they hit the atmosphere, they excite the atoms of the gases to radiate light. This is the cause of the aurora ("northern lights" and "southern lights").

In this chapter we have discussed the interaction between currents and magnets and between magnetic fields and charged particles. At first reading, many students consider this topic to be a very abstract part of pure physics. Yet the study of these interactions has had important social and practical effects on the whole civilized world. We will look at some of these effects in the next two chapters.

Q28 Which of the following affect the *magnitude* of the deflecting force on a moving charged particle?
(a) the component of the velocity parallel to the magnetic field
(b) the component of the velocity perpendicular to the field
(c) the magnetic field $\vec{B}$ itself
(d) the magnitude of the charge
(e) the sign of the charge

Q29 Which of the items in the preceding question affect the direction of the deflecting force on the charged particle?

Q30 Why does the deflecting force on a moving charged particle not change the speed of the charged particle? Does it ever do any work on it?

Q31 What are differences between deflecting forces on a charged object due to gravity, due to an electric field, and due to a magnetic field?

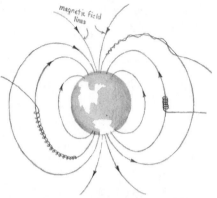

A simplified sketch of a variety of paths taken by charged particles in the earth's magnetic field. The Van Allen belts are regions of such trapped particles.

The American physicist James A. Van Allen directed the design of instruments carried by the first American satellite, Explorer I. See his article "Radiation Belts Around the Earth," in *Reader 4.*

SG 14.32, 14.33

The aurora photographed from Alaska. The glow is produced when the upper atmosphere is excited by charged particles trapped in the earth's magnetic field.

14.1 The Project Physics learning materials particularly appropriate for Chapter 14 include:

Experiments
  Electric Force I
  Electric Forces II
  Forces on Currents
  Currents, Magnets, and Forces
  Electron Beam Tube
  Electron Beam Tubes II

Activities
  Detecting Electric Fields
  Voltaic Pile
  An 11¢ Battery
  Measuring Magnetic Field Intensity
  More Perpetual Motion Machines
  Inside a Radio Tube
  An Isolated North Magnetic Pole?

Reader Articles
  Radiation Belts Around the Earth
  A Mirror for the Brain

14.2 How much must you alter the distances between two charged objects in order to keep the force on them constant, if you also
  (a) triple the net charge on each?
  (b) halve the net charge on each?
  (c) double the net charge on one and halve the net charge on the other?

14.3 How far apart in air must two charged spheres be placed, each having a net charge of 1 coulomb, so that the force on them is 1 newton?

14.4 If electrostatic induction does not involve the addition or subtraction of charged particles, but instead is just a redistribution of charged particles, how can attraction result from induction?

14.5 A carbon-coated (and therefore conducting) ping-pong ball hanging by a nylon (nonconducting) thread from a ring stand is touched with a finger to remove any slight charge it may have had. Then a negatively charged rod is brought up close to but *not touching* the ball. While the rod is held there the ball is momentarily touched with a finger; then the rod is removed. Does the ball now have a net charge? How would you test whether it has. If you think it has, make a few simple sketches to show how it became charged, indicating clearly what kind of charge it has been left with.

14.6 (a) Calculate the strength of the gravitational field of the moon at a point on its surface. The mass of the moon is taken to be 7.3×10^{22} kg and its radius is 1.74×10^6 m.
  (b) Calculate the gravitational field at a point near the surface of a small but extremely dense star, whose radius is 1.5×10^6 m and whose density is about 10^{22} kg/m^3.
  (c) The gravitational field of any uniform spherical shell is zero inside the shell.

Use this principle together with Newton's gravitational force law and the formula for the volume of a sphere ($\frac{4}{3}\pi r^3$) to find out how the gravitational field at a point P *inside* a solid spherical planet depends on the distance r from the center. (Assume the planet's density is uniform throughout.)

14.7 We speak of an electric field exerting a force on a charged particle placed in the field. What else can we say about this situation considering the fact that Newton's third law holds in this case too?

14.8 The three spheres A, B and C are fixed in the positions shown. Determine the direction of the net electrical force on sphere C, which is positively charged, if

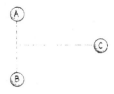

  (a) A and B carry equal positive charges.
  (b) A and B have charges of equal magnitude, but the charge on B is negative, and on A is positive.

14.9 An electric field strength exists at the earth's surface of about 100 N/coul, directed downward.
  (a) What is the net charge on the earth? (As Newton had shown for gravitational forces, the field of a uniformly charged sphere can be calculated by assuming all of the charge is concentrated at its center).
  (b) Because the earth is a conductor, most of the net charge is on the surface. What, roughly, is the average amount of net charge per square meter of surface? Does this seem large or small, compared to familiar static charges like those that can be produced on combs?

14.10 In oscilloscope tubes, a beam of electrons is deflected as it is passed between two pairs of oppositely charged plates. Each pair of plates, as can be seen in the photograph at the top of the following page, is shaped something like the

sketch to the right of the photograph. Sketch in roughly what you think the lines of force in the electric field between a pair of such oppositely charged plates would be like.

14.11 (a) Tell how the fact that the ball has a net charge squares with the Law of Conservation of Electric Charge. (b) Is air friction acting on the moving oildrop a help or a hindrance in the experiment described for measurement of the charge of the electron. Explain your answer briefly.

14.12 The magnitude of the electron's charge is 1.6 $\times 10^{-19}$ coulomb. How many electrons are required to make 1 coulomb of charge?

14.13 Calculate the ratio of the electrostatic force to the gravitational force between two electrons a distance of 10^{-10} meters apart. (The mass of the electron is approximately 10^{-30} kg; recall that $G = 6.7 \times 10^{-11}$ N·m²/kg².)

14.14 Electrical forces are similar in some respects to gravitational forces. So it is reasonable to imagine that charged particles such as the electron, may move in stable orbits around other charged particles. Then, just as the earth is a "gravitational satellite" of the sun, the electron would be an "electric satellite" of some *positively* charged particle. If this particle has a very large mass compared to the electron, we can assume it to remain stationary at the center of the electron's orbit. Suppose the particle has a charge equal in magnitude to the charge of the electron, and that the electron moves around in a circular orbit.
  (a) The centripetal force acting on the moving electron is provided by the electrical (Coulomb) force between the electron and the positively charged particle. Write an equation representing this statement. From this equation derive another equation showing how the kinetic energy of the electron is related to its distance from the positively charged particle.
  (b) Calculate the kinetic energy of the electron if the radius of its orbit were 10^{-10} meters.
  (c) What would be the speed of the electron if it had the kinetic energy you calculated in part (b)? (The mass of the electron is approximately 10^{-30} kg.)

14.15 A hard-rubber or plastic comb rubbed against wool can often be shown to be charged.

Why does a metal comb not readily show a net charge produced by rubbing unless it is held by an insulating handle?

14.16 What is the potential difference between two points in an electric field if 6×10^{-4} joules of work is done against the electric forces in moving 2×10^{-5} coulombs of charge from one point to the other?

14.17 If there is no potential difference between any points in a region, what must be true of
  (a) the electric potential energy and
  (b) the electric field in that region?

14.18 Electric field intensity, $\vec{E}$ can be measured in either of two equivalent units: newtons-per-coulomb, and volts-per-meter. Using the definitions of volt and joule, show that newton/coulomb is actually the same as volt/meter. Can you give the reason for the equivalence in words?

14.19 By experiment, if the distance between the surfaces of two conducting spheres is about 1 cm, an electric potential difference of about 30,000 volts between them is required to produce a spark in ordinary air. (The higher the voltage above 30,000 V, the "fatter" the spark for this gap distance.) What is the minimum electric field strength (in the gap between the surfaces) necessary to cause sparking?

14.20 The gap between the two electrodes in an automobile sparkplug is about 1 mm (39 thousandths of an inch). If the voltage produced between them by the ignition coil is about 10,000 volts, what is the approximate electric field strength in the gap?

14.21 One can think of an electric battery as "pumping" charges into its terminals. This pumping continues until the electric potential difference between the terminals reaches a certain value, where those charges already there repel newcomers from inside the battery. Usually this value is very close to the voltage marked on the battery.

What would happen if we connected two or more batteries in a sequence? For example, the battery on the right, below, maintains terminal *C* at an electric potential 6 volts higher than

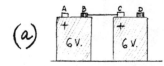

(a)

terminal *D*. This is what the + indicates under *C*: its electric potential is higher than the other terminal of the *same* battery. The battery on the left maintains terminal *A* at a potential 6 volts higher than terminal *B*. If we connect *B* to *C* with a good conductor, so that *B* and *C* are at the same potential level, what is the potential difference between *A* and *D*?

What would the potential difference be between the extreme left and right terminals in the following set-ups?

(b)

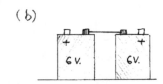

(c)

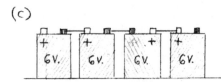

14.22 (a) What kinetic energy will an electron gain in an evacuated tube if it is accelerated through a potential difference of 100 volts? State your answer in electron volts and also in joules. (The magnitude of the charge on the electron is 1.6×10^{-19} coulomb.)

(b) What speed will it acquire due to the acceleration? (The mass of the electron is 10^{-30} kg.)

14.23 Suppose three resistors are each connected to a battery and to a current meter. The following table gives two of three quantities related by Ohm's law for three separate cases. Complete the table.

	Voltage	Current	Resistance
(a)	2 volts		0.5 ohms
(b)	10 volts	2 amps	
(c)		3 amps	5 ohms

14.24 The electric field at the earth's surface can increase to about 10^4 volts/meter under thunder clouds.

(a) About how large a potential difference between ground and cloud does that imply?

(b) A set of lightning strokes can transfer as much as 50 coulombs of charge. Roughly how much energy would be released in such a discharge?

14.25 International Physics Co.'s Pulsed Radiation Facility is now producing the world's most intense electron beams (40,000 amps/4 MeV) as a routine operation. This beam can precisely deposit upwards of 5,000 joules of energy in 30 nanoseconds." (From a recent advertisement in the journal *Physics Today*.)

The term "4MeV" means that the charges in the beam have an energy that would result from being accelerated across a potential difference of 4 million volts. A "nanosecond" is a billionth of a second. Are these published values consistent with one another? (Hint: calculate the power of the beam in two different ways.)

14.26 An electron "gun" includes several electrodes, kept at different voltages, to accelerate and focus the electron beam. But the energy of electrons in the beam that emerges from the gun depends only on the potential difference between their source (the hot wire) and the final accelerating electrode. In a color-TV picture tube, this potential difference is 20 to 30 kilovolts. A triple gun assembly (one each for red, blue, and green) from a color TV set is shown in the photograph below.

Suppose the beam in a TV tube is accelerated through 20,000 volts and forms an average current on the order of 10^{-3} amps. Roughly what is the power being dissipated against the screen of the tube?

14.27 Calculate the power dissipated in each of the three circuit elements of question 14.23.

14.28 A student trying to show the magnetic effect of a current on a pocket compass, slowly slid the compass along the tabletop toward a wire lying on the table and carrying a constant current. He was surprised by the lack of any observed turning effect on the compass needle. How would you explain his observations?

14.29 The sketch shows two long, parallel wires, lying in a vertical north-south plane (the view here is toward the west). A horizontal compass is located midway between the two wires. With no current in the wires, the needle points N. With 1 amp in the upper wire, the needle points NW.

(a) What is the direction of this one ampere current?

(b) What current (magnitude and direction) in the lower wire would restore the compass to its original position?

14.30 The deflecting force on a charged particle moving perpendicularly to a uniform magnetic field is always perpendicular to its velocity vector. Hence it is directed at every moment toward a single point—the center of the circular path the particle follows.

(a) The magnetic force (given by the expression qvB) therefore provides a centripetal force (which is always given by mv^2/R). Show that the radius of the circle R is directly proportional to the momentum of the particle mv.

(b) What information would you need to determine the ratio of the particle's charge to its mass?

14.31 By referring to the information given in the last problem:

(a) Find an equation for the period of the circular motion of a charged particle in a uniform magnetic field.

(b) Show mathematically that the radius of the helical path will be smaller where the magnetic field strength is greater. (See sketch below.)

(c) Using the right hand rule, show that the direction of the deflecting force on the particle *opposes* the movement of the particle into the region of stronger field.

14.32 If the energy of charged particles approaching the earth (say from the sun) is very great, they will not be trapped in the Van Allen belts. Rather, they will be somewhat deflected, continuing on past or into the earth. The direction of the lines of force of the earth's magnetic field is toward the earth's north end. If you set up a detector for positively charged particles on the earth, would you expect to detect more particles by directing it slightly toward the east or slightly toward the west?

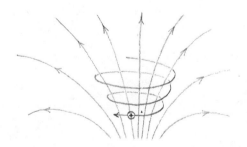

14.33 William Gilbert in *De Magnete* recorded that a piece of amber that had been rubbed attracted smoke rising from a recently extinguished candle. The smoke particles had been charged by passing through the ionized gases of the flame. After the development of electrostatic machines, experiments were done on the discharges (called *corona discharges*) from sharp or pointed electrodes like needles. As long ago as 1824 it was found that passing such a discharge through a jar filled with fog, cleared the fog from the jar. A similar experiment was performed using tobacco smoke. The corona discharge in these experiments ionized the gas, which in turn charged and precipitated the water droplets of the fog or the smoke particles.

However, no successful industrial precipitator came until Frederick Cottrell succeeded in using together the electric generator, high voltage transformer, and mechanical rectifier developed late in the nineteenth century. Cottrell achieved both a strong corona discharge and a high potential difference between the discharge electrode and the collecting electrode. Since that time many "electrostatic precipitators" have been built by electrical engineers to collect particulate matter. The most important such particles are fly ash from the burning of coal in the electrical power industry.

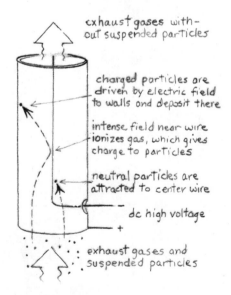

What is the significance of technological development in terms of pollution control? Are precipitators widely used by industry and utilities in your community? If not, why not?

CHAPTER FIFTEEN

Faraday and the Electrical Age

15.1 The problem: getting energy from one place to another

In Chapter 10 we discussed the development of steam engines in the eighteenth and nineteenth centuries. These engines enabled Europe and America to make use of the vast stores of energy contained in coal, wood, and oil. By burning fuel, chemical energy can be converted into heat energy, which in turn can be used to make steam. By letting the steam expand against a piston or a turbine blade, heat energy can be converted to mechanical energy. In this way a coal-fueled steam engine can power machinery.

SG 15.1

But steam engines had two major defects. First, the mechanical energy was available only at the place where the steam engine was located. Second, practical steam engines were big, hot, and dirty. As the use of machines run by steam engines increased, people were crowded together in factories, and their homes stood in the shadow of the smoke stacks. Even steam-powered locomotives, though useful for transportation, were limited by their size and weight. And they added further to polluting the air.

These defects could be partially overcome by using one central power plant for sending out energy for use at a distance. This energy could drive machines of any desired size and power at the most practical locations. After Volta's development of the battery, many scientists and inventors speculated that electricity might provide such a means of distributing energy and running machines. But the energy in batteries is quickly used up, unless it is delivered at a low rate. A better way of generating electric currents was needed. When such a way was found, it changed the whole shape of life in homes, factories, farms, and offices. And it changed the very appearance of cities and landscapes.

SG 15.2

In this chapter we will see another example of how discoveries in basic physics have given rise to new technologies. These technologies have revolutionized and benefited modern civilization. But they have brought some new problems in their turn.

SG 15.3

The first clue to the wide use of electricity came from Oersted's discovery that a magnetic needle is deflected by a current from a battery. Since an electric current can exert a force on a magnet, many physicists naturally speculated that a magnet could somehow produce a current in a wire. (Such reasoning from symmetry is common in physics—and often is useful.) Soon after the news of Oersted's discovery reached Paris, the French physicists Biot, Savart, and Ampère began research on the interactions of electricity and magnetism. (Some of their results were mentioned in Chapter 14.) A flood of other experiments and speculations on electromagnetism poured from all over the world into the scientific journals. Yet the one key discovery—how to generate an ample and continuous electric current—still eluded everyone.

Ampère also sensed that electricity might transmit not only energy but also *information* to distant places.

15.2 Faraday's first electric motor

Scientific journals regularly print brief announcements of the technical details of new discoveries. From time to time they also provide valuable in-depth surveys of recent broad advances in science. The need for such a review article is especially great after a burst of activity of the kind that followed Oersted's discovery of electromagnetism in 1820.

In 1821 the editor of the British journal *Annals of Philosophy* asked Michael Faraday to review the experiments and theories of electromagnetism which had appeared in the previous year. Faraday, who had once been apprenticed to a bookbinder, was an assistant to the well-known chemist Humphry Davy. Faraday came from a poor family, and had had no chance to receive formal training in science or mathematics. But he was eager to learn all he could, and quickly accepted the assignment. Soon, however, he found that he could not limit himself merely to reviewing what others had reported. He felt he had to repeat the experiments in his own laboratory. Also, not being satisfied with the theoretical explanations proposed by other physicists, he started to work out his own theories and plans for further experiments. Before long Faraday launched a series of researches in electricity that made him one of the most famous physicists of his time.

Faraday's first discovery in electromagnetism came on September 3, 1821. Repeating Oersted's experiment (described in Section 14.11), he put a compass needle at various places around a current-carrying wire. Faraday was particularly struck by one fact: the force exerted by the current on each pole of the magnet tended to carry the pole along a circular line around the wire. As he expressed it later, the wire is surrounded by *circular lines of force*—a circular magnetic field. Faraday then constructed an "electromagnetic rotator" based on this idea. It worked. Though very primitive, it was the first device for producing continuous motion by the action of a current—the first electric motor.

Faraday also designed an arrangement in which the magnet was fixed and the current-carrying wire rotated around it. (If a current exerts a force on a magnet, the magnet should exert an equal force on the current,

Two versions of Faraday's electro-magnetic rotator. In each, the cup was filled with mercury so that a large current can be passed between the base and overhead support.

according to Newton's third law.) As in many other cases, Faraday was guided by the idea that for every effect of electricity on magnetism, there must exist a corresponding effect of magnetism on electricity. Of course, it was not always so obvious what form the corresponding effect would take.

Q1 Why does the magnetic pole of Faraday's "electromagnetic rotator" move in a circle around a fixed wire?

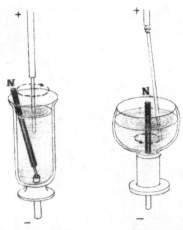

In one version (left) the north end of a bar magnet revolves along the circular electric lines of force surrounding the fixed current. In the other version (right), the rod carrying the current revolves around the fixed bar magnet —moving always perpendicular to the magnetic lines of force coming from the pole of the magnet.

15.3 The discovery of electromagnetic induction

Armed with his "lines of force" idea of electric and magnetic fields, Faraday joined the search for a way of producing currents by magnetism. Scattered through his diary in the years after 1824 are many descriptions of such experiments. Each report ended with a note: "exhibited no action" or "no effect."

Finally, in 1831, came the breakthrough. Like many discoveries which follow much research and discussion among scientists, this one was made almost at the same time by two scientists working independently in different countries. Faraday was not quite the first to produce electricity from magnetism. *Electromagnetic induction* (the production of a current by magnetism) was actually discovered first by the American scientist Joseph Henry. Henry was at the time teaching mathematics and philosophy at an academy in Albany, New York. Unfortunately for the reputation of American science, teachers at the Albany Academy were expected to spend all their time on teaching and related duties. There was little time left for research. Henry had hardly any opportunity to follow up his discovery, which he made during a one-month vacation. He was not able to publish his work until a year later. In the meantime, Faraday had made a similar discovery and published his results.

Faraday is known as the discoverer of electromagnetic induction not simply because he published his results first. More importantly, he conducted exhaustive investigations into all aspects of the subject. His earlier experiments and his ideas about lines of force had suggested that a current in one wire should somehow induce a current in a nearby wire. Oersted and Ampère had shown that a *steady* electric current produced a *steady* magnetic field around the circuit carrying the current. Perhaps a steady electric current could somehow be generated if a wire were placed near or around a very strong magnet. Or a steady current might be produced in one wire by a very large steady current in another wire nearby. Faraday tried all these possibilities, with no success.

The solution Faraday found in 1831 came partly by accident. He was experimenting with two wire coils that had been wound around an iron ring (see illustration in the margin). He noted that a current appeared in one coil while the current in the other coil was being switched on or off. When a current was turned on in coil A, a current was induced in coil B,

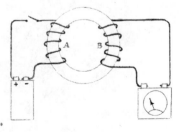

Michael Faraday (1791-1867) was the son of an English blacksmith. In his own words:

My education was of the most ordinary description, consisting of little more than the rudiments of reading, writing and arithmetic at a common day-school. My hours out of school were passed at home and in the streets.

At the age of twelve he went to work as an errand boy at a bookseller's store. Later he became a book-binder's assistant. When Faraday was about nineteen he was given a ticket to attend a series of lectures given by Sir Humphry Davy at the Royal Institution in London. The Royal Institution was an important center of research and education in science, and Davy was Superintendent of the Institution. Faraday became strongly interested in science and undertook the study of chemistry by himself. In 1813, he applied to Davy for a job at the Royal Institution and Davy hired him as a research assistant. Faraday soon showed his genius as an experimenter. He made important contributions to chemistry, magnetism, electricity and light, and eventually succeeded Davy as superintendent of the Royal Institution.

Because of his many discoveries, Faraday is generally regarded as one of the greatest of all experimental scientists. Faraday was also a fine lecturer and had an extraordinary gift for explaining the results of scientific research to non-scientists. His lectures to audiences of young people are still delightful to read. Two of them, "On the Various Forces of Nature" and "The Chemical History of a Candle," have been republished in paperback editions.

Faraday was a modest, gentle and deeply religious man. Although he received many international scientific honors, he had no wish to be knighted, preferring to remain without title.

Faraday's laboratory at the Royal Institution.

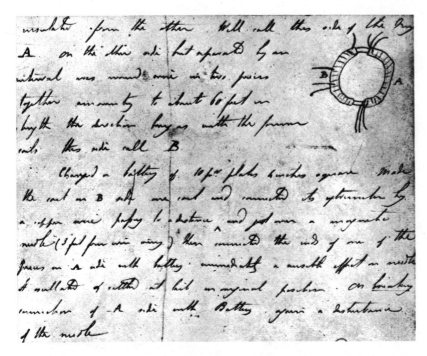

Part of a page in Faraday's diary where he recorded the first successful experiment in electromagnetic induction (about ½ actual size).

but it lasted only a moment. As soon as there was a steady current in coil A, the current in coil B disappeared. But when the current in coil A was turned off, a current again appeared briefly in coil B.

To summarize Faraday's result: a current in a stationary wire can induce a current in another stationary wire *only while the current is changing*. But a steady current in one wire cannot induce a current in another wire.

Faraday was not satisfied with merely observing and reporting his accidental arrangement and its important result. Guided by his concept of "lines of force," he tried to find out the basic principles involved in electromagnetic induction.

According to Faraday's theory, the changing current in coil A would change the lines of magnetic force in the whole iron ring. The change in lines of magnetic force in the part of the ring near coil B would then induce a current in B. But if this was really the correct explanation, Faraday asked himself, shouldn't it be possible to produce the same effect in another way? In particular:

1. Is the iron ring really necessary to produce the induction effect? Or does the presence of iron merely strengthen an effect that would also occur without it?

2. Is coil A really necessary? Or could current be induced simply by changing the magnetic lines of force through coil B in some other way, such as by moving a simple magnet relative to the wire?

Faraday answered these questions almost immediately by further experiments. First, he showed that the iron ring was not necessary. Starting or stopping a current in one coil of wire would induce a momentary current in a nearby coil, with only air (or vacuum) between the coils. (See top figure at the left. Note there is no battery in the circuit

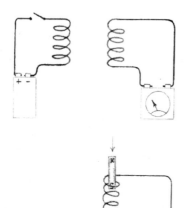

at the right—only a meter to measure the induced current.) Second, he studied what happened when a bar magnet was inserted into or removed from a coil of wire. He found that a current was induced at the instant of insertion or removal. (See second figure at the left.) In Faraday's words,

> A cylindrical bar magnet . . . had one end just inserted into the end of the helix cylinder; then it was quickly thrust in the whole length and the galvanometer needle moved; then pulled out again the needle moved, but in the opposite direction. The effect was repeated every time the magnet was put in or out . . . .

Note that this is a primitive *electric generator:* it provides electric current by having some mechanical agent move a magnet.

Having done these and many other experiments, Faraday stated his general principle of electromagnetic induction. Basically, it is that *changing lines of magnetic force can induce a current in a wire.* The needed "change" in lines of force can be produced either by a magnet moving relative to a wire, or by a changing current. In the case of the moving magnet, Faraday described the wire as "cutting across" lines of force. In the case of changing current, the lines of force "cut across" the wire. He later used the word *field* to refer to the arrangement and intensity of lines of force in space. We can say, then, that a current can be induced in a circuit by changes in a magnetic field around the circuit. Such changes may result either from relative motion of wire and field, or simply from a change in intensity of the field.

SG 15.4

SG 15.5

So far Faraday had produced only momentary surges of current by induction. This was hardly an improvement over batteries as a source of current. Was it possible to produce a continual current by electromagnetic induction? To do this would require a situation in which magnetic lines of force were *continually changing* relative to the conductor. Using a simple magnet, the relative change could be produced either by moving the magnet or by moving the conductor. This is just what Faraday did: he turned a copper disk between the poles of a magnet. (See illustration in margin.) A steady current was produced in a circuit connected to the disk through brass contacts or "brushes." His device, called the "Faraday disk dynamo," was the first constant-current electric generator. This particular arrangement did not turn out to be very practical. But it showed that continuous generation of electricity was possible.

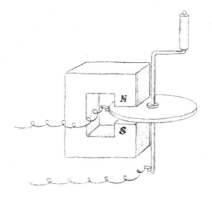

These first experimental means of producing a continuous current were important aids to understanding the connection between electricity and magnetism. Moreover, they suggested the possibility of eventually generating electricity on a large scale. The production of electrical current involves changing energy from one form to another. When electrical energy appears, it is at the cost of some other form of energy. In the electric battery, chemical energy—the energy of formation of chemical compounds—is converted to electrical energy. Batteries are useful for many portable applications (automobiles and flashlights, for example). But it is not practical to produce large amounts of electrical energy by this means. There is, however, a vast supply of mechanical energy available from many sources. Electrical energy could be produced on a large scale if some reasonably efficient means of converting mechanical energy to electrical energy were available. This mechanical energy might be in the form of wind, or falling water, or continuous mechanical motion produced by a steam engine. The discovery of electromagnetic induction showed that, at least in principle, it was possible to produce electricity by mechanical means. In this sense Faraday can rightly be regarded as the founder of the modern electrical age.

Faraday realized the practical importance of his discoveries. But his main interest was in basic science, the search for laws of nature for a deeper understanding of the relationship between separate experimental and theoretical findings. He appreciated the need for applied science, such as the eventual perfection of specific devices. But he left the development of the generator and the motor to others. In a way, this was unfortunate. In Faraday's time, the inventors and engineers who were interested in the practical and profitable applications of electricity did not know much about physics. As a result, most of the progress during the next fifty years was made by trial and error. In following the development of modern electrical technology, we will see several problems that could have been solved much earlier if a physicist with Faraday's knowledge had worked on them.

Q2 Why is Faraday considered the discoverer of electromagnetic induction?

Q3 What is the general definition of electromagnetic induction?

15.4 Generating electricity by the use of magnetic fields: the dynamo

Faraday had shown that when a conducting wire moves relative to a magnetic field, a current is produced. Whether it is the wire or the magnetic field that moves doesn't matter. What counts is the relative motion of one with respect to the other. Once the principle of electromagnetic induction had been discovered, experimenters tested many combinations of wires and magnets in relative motion. We will describe one basic type of generator (or "dynamo," as it was often called) which was widely used in the nineteenth century. In fact, it remains the basic model for many generators today.

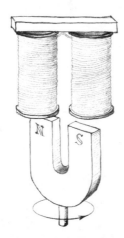

One generator of 1832 had a permanent horseshoe magnet rotated by hand beneath two stationary coils in which current was induced.

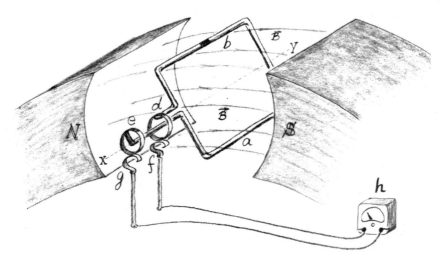

Alternating-current generator.

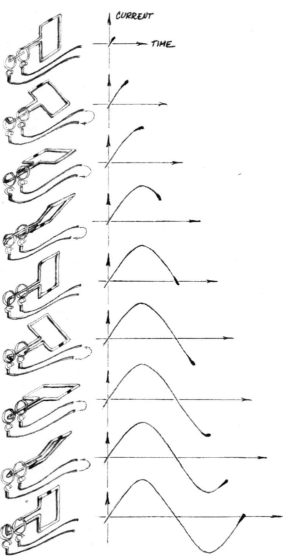

This form of generator is basically a coil of wire that can be rotated in a magnetic field. The coil is connected to an external circuit by sliding contacts. In the diagram above and on the left, the "coil" is shown for simplicity as a single rectangular loop of wire. This loop rotates around an axis XY between the north and south poles of a magnet. Two conducting rings d and e are permanently attached to the loop, and therefore also rotate around the axis. Conducting brushes f and g complete a circuit through a meter at h that indicates the current produced. The complete circuit is *abdfhgea*. (Note that one part of the wire goes through ring d without touching it, and connects to e.)

Initially the loop is at rest between the magnetic poles, and no charge flows through it. Now suppose we take hold of the loop and rotate it counterclockwise. The wire's long sides a and b now have a component of motion perpendicular to the direction of the magnetic lines of force. That is, the wire "cuts across" lines of force. This is the condition for inducing an electric current in the loop. The greater the rate at which the lines are cut, the greater the induced current.

Now, to understand better what is going on in the wire, we will describe its operation in terms of the force on the charges in the wire. It is the movement of these charges which forms the current. The charges in the part of the loop labeled b are being physically moved together with the loop across the magnetic field. Therefore, they experience a magnetic force given by qvB (as described in Section 14.13). This force pushes the charges in the wire "off to the side." In this situation, "off to the side" is *along the wire*.

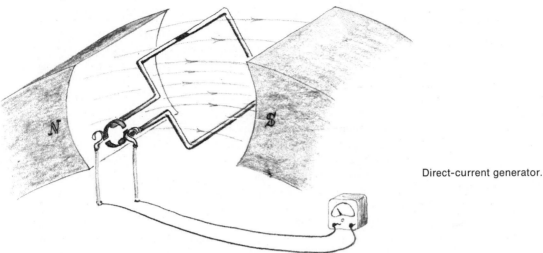

Direct-current generator.

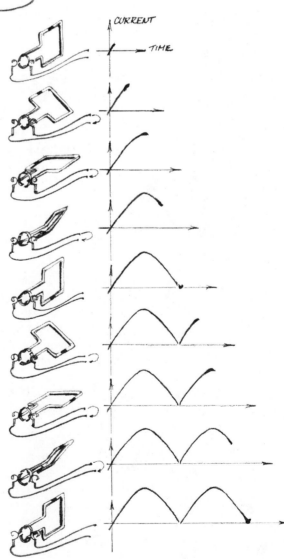

What about side *a*? It is also moving through the field and "cutting" lines of force, but in the opposite direction. So the charges in *a* experience a push along the wire in the direction opposite to those in *b*. This is just what is needed; the two effects reinforce each other in generating a current around the whole loop. The "push" that produces the current can also be regarded as resulting from a potential difference ("voltage") induced in the loop of wire. Hence a generator produces both "voltage" and current.

The generator we have just described produces *alternating current* (abbreviated ac). The current is called "alternating" because it regularly reverses (alternates) its direction. This is indicated in the margin on the left. At the time this kind of generator was first developed, in the 1830's, alternating current could not be used to run machines. Instead *direct current* (dc) was desired.

In 1832, Ampère announced that his instrument-maker, Hippolyte Pixii, had solved the problem of generating direct current. Pixii modified the ac generator by means of a device called the *commutator*. The name comes from the word *commute,* to interchange, or to go back and forth. The commutator is a split cylinder (see top of page) inserted in the circuit. In the ac generator (previous page) brushes *f* and *g* are always connected to the same part of the loop. But with the commutator, the brushes *reverse connections* each time the loop passes through the vertical position. Just as the direction of current induced in the loop is at the point of reversing, the contacts reverse. As a result, the current in the outside circuit is always in the same direction.

SG 15.6

Although the current in the outside circuit is always in the same direction, it is not constant. It rises and falls rapidly between zero and its maximum value, as shown in the drawings on page 79. In working generators many sets of loops and commutators are connected together on the same shaft. In this way their induced currents reach their maximum and zero values at different times. The *total* current from all of them together is then more uniform.

Whether a generator delivers alternating or direct current, the electric power (energy per unit time) produced at every instant is given by the same equation we developed in Section 14.10. For example, suppose that a wire (for example, the filament wire in a light bulb) with resistance R is substituted for the meter at h. If the current generated in the circuit at a given time is I, the electrical energy per unit time delivered to the wire is given by I^2R. For alternating current, the power output varies from instant to instant. But the *average* output power is simply $(I^2)_{av}R$. This electrical energy of course does not appear by itself, without any source. That would violate the laws of conservation of energy. In our generator, the "source" of energy is clearly the mechanical energy that keeps the coils rotating in the magnetic field. This mechanical energy is provided by a steam or gasoline engine, or by water power, wind power, etc. The generator is thus a device for converting mechanical to electrical energy.

The ac current continually reverses direction. So, in one sense, the average value for I is zero; charge is moved back and forth in the wire, but not transferred through it. The *magnitudes* of the average currents in the two halves of the cycle are equal, however. Therefore $(I^2)_{av}$ for the two halves of the cycle are equal and positive.

SG 15.7-15.9

Q4 What is the position of a rotating loop when it generates maximum current? minimum? Why?

Q5 What is the purpose of the commutator?

Q6 Where does the energy delivered by the generator come from?

15.5 The electric motor

The biggest obstacle to practical use of electric motors was the lack of cheap electric current to run them. The chemical energy in batteries was quickly exhausted. The dynamo, invented almost simultaneously by Faraday and Henry in 1832, was at first no more economical than the battery. What was needed were generators that used mechanical power efficiently to produce electrical power. But to design such generators required an understanding of the details of operation, and this took nearly 50 years. During that time, several inventions aroused great temporary enthusiasm and ambitious plans, followed by discouragement when unexpected practical difficulties arose. But the hope of making a fortune by providing cheap power to the world spurred on each new generation of inventors. Gradually, knowledge about the physics and technology of electromagnetic systems accumulated.

In fact, a chance event marks the effective start of the electric power age. This event was an accidental discovery at the Vienna Exhibition of 1873. In science it is never quite accurate to credit the beginning of an era to one person, performing one act, at one time. In reality, many scientists contribute their ideas and experiments in a particular scientific field. Eventually the situation becomes favorable for a breakthrough, and sometimes a seemingly chance event is all that is needed to get things going. In this case, as the story goes, an unknown workman at the exhibition just happened to connect two dynamos together. The current generated by the first dynamo, which was mechanically driven, went through the coils of the second dynamo. Amazingly, the second dynamo ran as an electric motor on the electricity generated by the first!

This accidental discovery, that a generator could function as a motor, was immediately utilized at the exhibition. A small artificial waterfall was used to drive the generator. Its current then drove the motor, which in turn operated a pump that sprayed water from a fountain. Thus

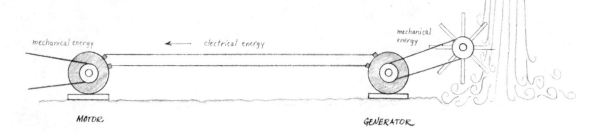

SG 15.10

SG 15.11

electromagnetic induction was first used to convert a substantial amount of mechanical energy to electrical energy by means of a generator. This electrical energy could be transmitted over a considerable distance to operate a motor, which in turn converted the energy back to mechanical energy. This is the basic operation of a modern electrical transmission system. A turbine driven by steam or falling water drives a generator which converts the mechanical energy to electrical energy. Conducting wires transmit the electricity over long distances to motors, toasters, electric lights, etc. These devices in turn convert the electrical energy to mechanical energy, heat, or light.

The development of electrical generators shows a different interaction of science and technology than did the development of steam engines. As was pointed out in Chapter 10, the early steam engines were developed by practical inventors. These inventors had no knowledge of what we now consider to be the correct theory of heat (thermodynamics). But their development of the steam engine, and attempts by Sadi Carnot and others to improve its efficiency through theoretical analysis, contributed greatly to the establishment of thermodynamics. In that case, the advance in technology came before the advance in science. In the case of electromagnetism, the reverse occurred. A large amount of scientific knowledge was built up by Ampère, Faraday, Kelvin, and Maxwell before any serious practical application succeeded. The scientists, who understood electricity better than anyone else were not especially interested in

Assembling a commercial generator. As in almost all large generators, the coils of wire in which current is induced are around the outside, and electromagnets are rotated on the inside.

Water-driven electric generators producing power at the Tennessee Valley Authority. The plant can generate electric energy at a rate of over 100,000,000 watts.

commercial applications. And the inventors, who hoped to make huge profits from electricity, knew very little theory. After Faraday announced his discovery of electromagnetic induction, people started making generators to produce electricity immediately. But it was not until 40 years later that inventors and engineers understood enough to work with such necessary concepts as lines of force and field vectors. With the introduction of the telegraph, telephone, radio, and alternating-current power systems, a much greater mathematical knowledge was needed to work with electricity. Universities and technical schools started to give courses in electrical engineering. Gradually a group of specialists developed who were familiar with the physics of electricity and who also knew how to apply it.

Q7 How would you make an electric motor out of a generator?

Q8 What prevented the electric motor from being an immediate economic success?

Q9 What chance event led to the beginning of the electric power age?

15.6 The electric light bulb

The growth of the electric industry has resulted largely from the great public demand for electrical products. One of the first commercially successful electrical products in the United States was the electric light bulb. Its success is an interesting case of the relationship between physics, industry, and society.

At the beginning of the nineteenth century, buildings and homes were lit by candles and oil lamps. There was almost no street lighting in cities except for a few lights hung outside houses at night. The natural gas industry was just starting to change this situation. London got its first street lighting system in 1813 when gas lights were installed on Westminster Bridge. However, the social effects of gas lighting were not all beneficial. For example, a gas lighting in factories enabled employers to extend an already long and difficult working day into one still longer.

In 1801, the British chemist Humphry Davy noted that a brilliant spark or arc appeared when he broke contact between carbon rods connected to the two terminals of a battery. This discovery led to the development of the "arc light."

The arc light was not practical for general use until steam-driven electrical generators replaced expensive batteries as a source of current. In the 1860's and 1870's, arc lights began to be used for street lighting and lighthouses. However, they were too glaring and too expensive for use in the home. Also, the carbon rods burned up in a few hours because of the high temeratures produced by the arc. This need for frequent service and replacement made the system inconvenient. (Arc lights are still used for some high-intensity purposes, such as spotlights in theaters.)

As Davy and other scientists showed, light can be produced simply by heating a wire to a high temperature by passing a current through it. This method is known as *incandescent* lighting. The major technical drawback was that the wire filament gradually burned up. The obvious solution was to enclose the filament in a glass container from which all the air had been removed. But this was easier said than done. The vacuum pumps available in the early nineteenth century could not produce a strong enough vacuum for this purpose. It was not until 1865, when Hermann Sprengel in Germany invented an improved vacuum pump, that the electric light bulb in its modern form could be developed. (Sprengel's pump also greatly aided Crookes and others in scientific experiments leading to important discoveries in atomic physics. We will discuss these discoveries in Chapter 18.)

Thomas Edison was not the first to invent an incandescent light, nor did he discover any essentially new scientific principles. What he did was develop a practical light bulb for use in homes. Even more important, he worked out a distribution system for electricity. His system not only made the light bulb practical, but opened the way for mass consumption of electrical energy in the United States.

Edison started by making an important assumption about *how* people would want to use their light bulbs. He decided that each customer must be able to turn on and off any single bulb without affecting the other

Davy's arc lamp

Demonstrations of the new electric light during a visit of Queen Victoria and Prince Albert to Dublin, Ireland. From *Illustrated London News*, August 11, 1849.

In the late 1800's, dynamo powered arc-lamps were used in some European cities.

Thomas Alva Edison (1847-1931) was born at Milan, Ohio, and spent most of his boyhood at Port Huron, Michigan. His first love was chemistry, and to earn money for his chemical experiments, he set up his own business enterprises. Before he was fifteen, he ran two stores in Port Huron, one for periodicals and the other for vegetables; hired a newsboy to sell papers on the Grand Trunk Railway running between Port Huron and Detroit; published a weekly newspaper; and ran a chemical laboratory in the baggage car of the train. His financial empire was growing rapidly when, in 1862, a stick of phosphorus in his laboratory caught fire and destroyed part of the baggage car. As a result, his laboratory and newspaper equipment were evicted from the train, and he had to look for another base of operations.

It was not long before his bad luck with the phosphorus was offset by a piece of good luck: he was able to save the life of the son of the station agent by pulling him out of the path of an oncoming train. In gratitude, the station agent taught Edison the art of telegraphy, and thus began Edison's career in electricity.

At the right are shown two portraits of Edison. On the opposite page is a copy of the drawing that accompanied his patent on the incandescent lamp. The labeled parts are the carbon filament (a), thickened ends of filament (c), platinum wires (d), clamp (h), leading wires (x), copper wires (e), tube to vacuum pump (m).

bulbs connected to the circuit. This meant that the bulbs must be connected "in parallel"—like the rungs of a ladder—rather than "in series."

The choice of parallel rather than series circuits had important technical consequences. In a series circuit, the same current would go through each bulb. In a parallel circuit, only part of the total current available from the source goes through any one bulb. To keep the total current needed from being too large, the current in each bulb would have to be small.

As we noted in Chapter 14, the heating effect of a current depends on both the resistance of the wire and the amount of current. The rate at which heat energy is produced is I^2R. That is, the rate goes up directly as the resistance, but increases as the *square* of the current. Therefore, most inventors used high-current, low-resistance bulbs, and assumed that parallel circuits would not be practical. But Edison realized that a small current can have a large heating effect if the resistance is high enough.

So Edison began a search for a suitable high-resistance, non-metallic substance for his filaments. To make such a filament, he first had to bake or "carbonise" a thin piece of a substance. Then he sealed it inside an evacuated glass bulb with wires leading out. His assistants tried more than 1,600 kinds of material: "paper and cloth, thread, fishline, fiber, celluloid, boxwood, coconut-shells, spruce, hickory, hay, maple shavings, rosewood, punk, cork, flax, bamboo, and the hair out of a redheaded Scotchman's beard." His first successful high-resistance lamp was made with

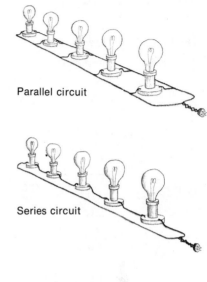

Parallel circuit

Series circuit

SG 15.12, 15.13

See the article "The Invention of the Electric Light" in *Reader 4.*

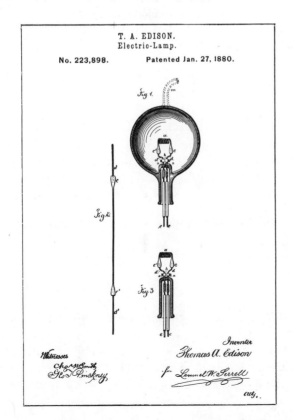

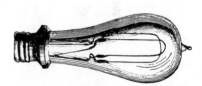

One type of Edison lamp. Note the familiar filament and screw-type base.

Drawing (about $\frac{1}{2}$ size) that accompanied Edison's patent application.

EDISON'S LIGHT.

The Great Inventor's Triumph in Electric Illumination.

A SCRAP OF PAPER.

It Makes a Light, Without Gas or Flame, Cheaper Than Oil.

TRANSFORMED IN THE FURNACE.

Complete Details of the Perfected Carbon Lamp.

FIFTEEN MONTHS OF TOIL.

Story of His Tireless Experiments with Lamps, Burners and Generators.

SUCCESS IN A COTTON THREAD.

The Wizard's Byplay, with Bodily Pain and Gold "Tailings."

HISTORY OF ELECTRIC LIGHTING.

The near approach of the first public exhibition of Edison's long looked for electric light, announced to take place on New Year's Eve at Menlo Park, on which occasion that place will be illuminated with the new light, has revived public interest in the great inventor's work, and throughout the civilized world scientists and people generally are anxiously awaiting the result. From the beginning of his experiments in electric lighting to the present time Mr. Edison has kept his laboratory guardedly closed, and no authoritative account (except that published in the HERALD some months ago relating to his first patent) of any of the important steps of his progress has been made public—a course of procedure the inventor found absolutely necessary for his own protection. The HERALD is now, however, enabled to present to its readers a full and accurate account of his work from its inception to its completion.

A LIGHTED PAPER.

Edison's electric light, incredible as it may appear, is produced from a little piece of paper—a tiny strip of paper that a breath would blow away. Through

First newspaper account of Edison's invention (New York Herald, December 21, 1879).

carbonized cotton thread in a high-vacuum sealed bulb. It burned continuously for two days before it fell apart. This was in October 1879. The following year, Edison produced lamps with filaments made from bamboo and paper.

The Edison Electric Light Company began to install lighting systems in 1882. After only three years of operation, the Edison company had sold 200,000 lamps. It had a virtual monopoly of the field, and paid big dividends to its stockholders.

The electric light bulb had changed somewhat since Edison's original invention. For example, the carbonized filaments of the older lamps had been replaced in newer bulbs by thin tungsten wires. Tungsten had the advantages of greater efficiency and longer life.

The widespread use of light bulbs confirmed the soundness of Edison's theory about what people would buy. It also led to the rapid development of systems of power generation and distribution. The need for more power for lighting spurred the invention of better generators, the harnessing of water power, and the invention of the steam turbine. Success in providing large quantities of cheap energy made other uses of electricity practical. Once homes were wired for electric lights, the current could be used to run sewing machines, vacuum cleaners, washing machines, toasters, and (later on) refrigerators, freezers, radios, and television sets. Once electric power was available for relatively clean public transportation, cities could grow rapidly in all dimensions. Electric elevators made high-rise buildings practical, while electric tramways and subways rapidly transported people from their homes to jobs and markets.

We are now so accustomed to more sophisticated applications of electricity that it is hard to realize the impact of something as simple as the light bulb. But most people who lived through the period of electrification—as late as the 1930's and 1940's in many rural areas of the United States—agreed that the electrical appliance that made the greatest difference in their daily lives was the electric light bulb.

Q10   Why were arc lights not used for illuminating homes?

Q11   What device was essential to the development of the incandescent lamp?

Q12   Why did Edison require a substance with a high resistance for his light bulb filaments?

Q13   What were some of the major effects the introduction of electric power had on everyday life?

15.7 Ac versus dc, and the Niagara Falls power plant

In Section 15.4 we stated that the earliest electric generators produced alternating current, which could be changed into direct current by the use of a commutator. Throughout most of the nineteenth century, most engineers believed that only dc was useful in practical applications of electricity. However, as the demand for electric power increased, some disadvantages of dc became evident. One problem was that the commutator complicated the mechanical design of generators—especially if the ring had to rotate at high speed. This difficulty became even more serious after the introduction of steam turbines in the 1890's, since turbines work most effectively at high speeds. Another disadvantage was that there was no convenient way of changing the generated voltage of a direct current supply.

Why should it be necessary to change the voltage with which current is driven through a transmission system? One reason involves the amount of power lost in heating the transmission wires. The power output of a generator depends (as indicated in Section 14.10) on the output *voltage* of the generator and the *amount of current:*

$$P_{total} = VI$$

The power made available by the generator is transmitted to the line and to the consumer. The *same* amount of power can be delivered at smaller I if V is somehow made larger. When there is a current I in a transmission wire of resistance R, the portion of the power lost as heat in transmission is proportional to the resistance and the square of the current:

$$P_{heat\ loss} = I^2R$$

SG 15.14

The power finally available to consumers is $P_{total} - P_{heat\ loss}$. For transmission lines of a given resistance R, the current I should be as small as possible in order to minimize the power loss. Obviously, therefore, electricity should be transmitted at low current and at high voltage.

However, most generators cannot produce electricity at very high voltages. To do so would require excessively high speeds of the moving parts. So we need some way of "stepping up" the generated electricity to a high voltage for transmission. But we also need some way of "stepping down" voltage again at the other end, where the consumer uses the power. For most applications of electricity, especially in homes, it is neither convenient nor safe to use high voltages. In short, we need *transformers* at both ends of the transmission line.

A transformer can easily be made by a simple change in Faraday's induction coil (Section 15.4). Recall that Faraday wound a coil of wire (which we will call the *secondary* coil) around one side of an iron ring. He then induced a current in this secondary coil by *changing* a current in another coil (the *primary* coil) wound around the other side of the ring. A current is induced in the secondary coil whenever the primary current changes. If the primary current is changing all the time, then a current is continually induced in the secondary. And an alternating current applied to the primary coil (for example, from a generator without a commutator) induces an alternating current in the secondary coil.

One more concept is important to understanding a simple electric

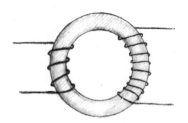

A steady current (dc) in the primary induces no current at all in the secondary; transformers work on ac.

By the law of conservation of
energy, the output power from a
transformer cannot exceed the input
power. So if the output voltage is
increased (by a greater coil ratio for
the secondary coil) the output
current will decrease proportionally.

SG 15.15–15.17

SG 15.18

transformer. If the secondary has *more* turns than the primary, the
alternating voltage produced across the secondary coil will be *greater* than
across the primary. If the secondary has *fewer* turns than the primary, the
alternating voltage produced across the secondary will be *lower* than the
voltage across the primary. This fact was discovered by Joseph Henry,
who built the first transformer in 1838.

The first ac system was demonstrated in Paris in 1883. An
experimental line which powered arc and incandescent lighting, through
transformers, was installed in a railway line in London in 1884. Another
one was exhibited shortly afterward in Italy. An American engineer,
George Westinghouse, saw the Italian system and bought the American
patent rights for it. Westinghouse had already gained a reputation by his
invention of the railway air brake. He also had set up a small electrical
engineering company in Pittsburgh. After improving the design and
construction of transformers, the Westinghouse Electric Company set up
its first commercial installation in 1886. Its purpose was to distribute
alternating current for incandescent lighting in Buffalo, New York.

When Westinghouse introduced its ac system in the United States,
the Edison Electric Light Company held an almost complete monopoly of
the incandescent lighting business. The Edison Company had invested a
lot of money in dc generating plants and distribution systems for most of
the large cities. Naturally Edison was alarmed by a new company which
claimed to produce electric power for illumination with a much cheaper
system. A bitter public controversy followed. Edison attempted to show
that ac was unsafe because of the high voltage used for transmission.
And, in the middle of the dispute, the New York State Legislature passed
a law establishing electrocution as a means of capital punishment. This
event seems to have added to the popular fear of high voltage.

Nevertheless, the Westinghouse system continued to grow. There
were no spectacular accidents, and the public began to accept ac as
reasonably safe. The invention of the "rotary converter" (essentially an ac
motor driving a dc generator) also helped to end the dispute. It could
change ac into dc for use in local systems already set up with dc
equipment, or it could power individual dc motors. So the Edison company
(later merged into General Electric) did not have to go out of business
when ac was generally adopted.

The final victory of the ac system was assured in 1893, when ac was
chosen for the new hydroelectric plant at Niagara Falls. In 1887,
businessmen in Buffalo had dangled a $100,000 prize before "the
Inventors of the World." The prize would go to the inventor who designed
a system for utilizing the power of the Niagara River "at or near Buffalo,
so that such power may be made practically available for various purposes
throughout the city." The contest attracted world-wide attention. Large
quantities of electrical power had never before been transmitted over such
a distance—it was 20 miles from Niagara Falls to Buffalo. The success or
failure of this venture would influence the future development of electrical
distribution systems for other large cities.

It was a close decision whether to use ac or dc for the Niagara Falls system. Ac could be generated and transmitted more efficiently. But the demand for electricity in 1890 was mainly for lighting. This meant that there would be a peak demand in the evening. The system would have to operate at less than full capacity during the day and late at night. Because of this variation in the demand for electricity some engineers believed that a dc system would be cheaper to operate. This was because *batteries* could be used to back up the generators in periods of peak demand. Thomas Edison was consulted, and without hesitation he recommended dc. But the Cataract Construction Company, which had been formed to administer the project, delayed making a decision.

The issue was still in doubt in 1891, when the International Electrical Exhibition opened in Frankfort, Germany. There, a fairly high-voltage ac line carrying sizable quantities of power 110 miles from Frankfort to Lauffen was demonstrated. Tests of the line showed an efficiency of transmission of 77%. That is, for every 100 watts fed in at one end of the line, only 23 were wasted by heating effects in the line. The other 77 were delivered as useful power. The success of this demonstration reinforced the gradual change in expert opinion in favor of ac over dc. Finally, the Cataract Company decided to construct an ac system.

After the ac system had been established, it turned out that the critics had been wrong about the variation of demand for electricity throughout the day. Electricity found many uses besides lighting. In the 1890's, electric motors were already being used in street railway cars, sewing machines, and elevators. Because of these diverse uses, the demand for electricity was spread out more evenly during each 24-hour period. In the particular case of the Niagara Falls power plant, the source of energy was the steady flow of water down the Niagara River. This made it possible to produce energy continuously without much extra cost. (The boiler for a steam turbine would either have to be kept supplied with fuel late at night, or shut down and started up again in the morning.) Since hydroelectric power was available at night at low cost, new uses for it became possible. The Niagara Falls plant attracted electric furnace industries, continually producing aluminum, abrasives, silicon, and graphite. Previously the electrochemical processes involved in these industries had been too expensive for large-scale use. Cheap power now made them practical. These new industries in turn provided a constant demand for power, making the Niagara project even more profitable than had been expected.

SG 15.19

The first transmission of power to Buffalo took place in November 1896. By 1899, there were eight 5,000 horsepower units in operation at Niagara. The stockholders of the Cataract Construction Company already had earned a profit of better than 50% on their investment. And the electrochemical industries, which had not figured in the original plans at all, were using more power than lighting and motors together.

As a postscript to the story of ac versus dc, we should mention that dc is now coming back into favor for long-distance transmission of electric

Wilson Dam (Tennessee Valley Authority), Alabama

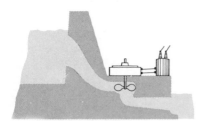

The general principle of hydroelectric power generation is shown in this sketch: water flowing from a higher to lower level turns turbine blades attached to a generator shaft. The details of construction vary widely.

Niagara Power Plant

power at very high voltages. The reasons for this turnabout are explained in an article, "The Future of Direct Current Power Transmission," reprinted in *Reader 4*.

Q14   Give one reason why it is more economical to transmit electric power at high voltage and low current than at low voltage and high current.
Q15   Why won't transformers operate if steady dc is furnished for the primary coil?

15.8 Electricity and society

An optimistic view. Many times during the last hundred years, enthusiastic promoters have predicted a marvelous future for us all, based on the application of electricity to all phases of life. First, machinery run by electricity will do all the backbreaking physical labor that has been the lot of 99% of the human race throughout the ages, and still is for most of humanity today. The average citizen will have nothing to do except supervise machinery for a few hours a day, and then go home to enjoy a life of leisure. Electric machines will also do all the household chores such as cleaning, laundering, ironing, cooking, and dishwashing.

A second social purpose of electrical technology was conceived by President Franklin D. Roosevelt and others who believed that country life is more natural and healthy than city life. In the nineteenth century, the steam engine had provided a source of power that could take over most work done by humans and animals. But to use this power people had had to crowd into the cities, close to the power generating plant. Now that electrical transmission of power at a distance was possible, people could go back to the countryside without sacrificing the comforts of city life. Heating, lighting, and refrigeration by electricity would make life easier and more sanitary in difficult climates. One of the major achievements of Roosevelt's administration in the 1930's was the rural electrification program. This program gave loans to rural cooperatives for installing electrical generating and distribution systems in areas where private power companies had found it unprofitable to operate. Federal power projects such as the Tennessee Valley Authority also assisted in the campaign to make electricity available to everyone. Electricity made country life a bit easier, reducing the physical labor involved in farming and lengthening the day for leisure and education. In this way, electrification should have helped to reverse the migration of people from rural to urban areas.

A third effect of electricity is its tendency to unite a large country into a single social unit by providing rapid transportation and even more rapid communication between the different parts. In transportation, electricity-operated devices play essential roles both in the mass manufacture and in the operation of cars, trucks, and buses. As to communication, we must remember that human society evolves much as do biological organisms: all parts develop in step and increase their interdependence. It follows that telecommunication and modern civilization *had* to develop together. The telephone is most valuable in a complicated, cosmopolitan society. In fact, many of the basic institutions of our society—for example, a free Press—could not operate today without rapid, two-way electronic communication.

SG 15.20

Optimists envision electricity doing more and more things for a larger and larger part of the population. Electric appliances such as refrigerators and air conditioners will contribute to healthier, more comfortable lives the world over. Electronic communications will continue to spread, allowing an ever-greater exchange of facts, opinions, and cultures. Electric machines will do more and more of our difficult work for us. Thanks to advances in science and related technology, many people no longer have to spend almost all of their time working for the bare necessities of life. Whatever it is that we really want to do, the optimists say, electricity can help us do it better.

See "The Electronic Revolution" in *Reader 4.*

A less optimistic opinion. Wonderful as all this seems, many people take a much dimmer view of the "progress" cited above. They point, for example, to our dwindling resources of fossil fuel (coal, oil, and gas). They argue that industries in the more advanced countries have used up in only 200 years most of the reserves of chemical energy accumulated over the

See the article on "High Fidelity" in *Reader 4.*

Commercial Distribution of Electric Power

The commercial distribution of ac electric power requires elaborate transmission facilities. Generator output voltages of about 10^4 volts are stepped up to about 10^5 volts for transmission, stepped down to about 10^4 volts for local distribution, and further stepped down to about 10^2 volts by neighborhood power-pole transformers. Within the home, it may be stepped down further (often to 6 volts for doorbells and electric trains) and stepped up by transformers in radio and TV sets for operating high-voltage tubes.

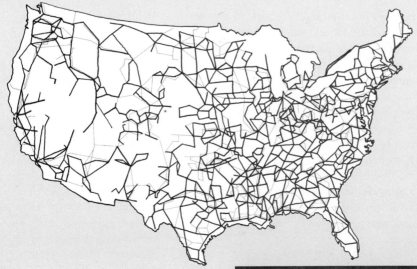

Major electric transmission lines in the United States. In many cases several lines are represented by a single line on the map. Not shown are the small-capacity lines serving widely scattered populations in the mountainous and desert areas. In the densely populated areas, only the high-voltage lines are shown.

The interdependence of our modern system of electrical power distribution was dramatically demonstrated at about 5 p.m. on November 9, 1965, when a faulty electrical relay in Canada caused a power failure and total blackout throughout most of the northeastern part of the United States.

last two hundred million years. Moreover, these industries have generally polluted the air and water, except when confronted by outraged public opinion. Other skeptics claim that a social system has been created in which the virtues of "honest toil and pride of workmanship" are endangered. Instead, most people work at dull, trivial jobs, while many others suffer chronic unemployment. And while it is true that many people in wealthy, industrial countries enjoy high standards of living and can purchase many gadgets and luxuries, these things have not fulfilled real human and social needs. Even the "demand" for them is not real, but is artificially created by advertising campaigns and planned obsolescence. Therefore, such items do not bring happiness and peace of mind, but only a growing, mindless clamor for more and more material possessions. Meanwhile, the materially less fortunate people are separated by a wider and wider gap from the richer ones, and look on in growing envy and anger.

And what about "labor-saving" household appliances? Do they really make life easier for the upper- and middle-income families who own them? Not much, say the critics, because the work done by such machines was previously done by servants, anyway. Of course, industrialization and electrification *have* created some jobs for people with little training. And these jobs may be more attractive than work as a servant. But they still do not pay very well. As a result, many low-income families cannot afford more than one major electrical appliance. And the one appliance usually purchased by such families is a television set—which, the skeptics say, isn't likely to contribute much to improving the quality of life.

The decentralization of population which electricity was supposed to help produce has come about, but in an unexpected way. The upper- and middle-income inhabitants of cities have indeed been able to escape to the suburbs where they can enjoy the convenience and pleasures of the electrical age. But they have left behind them urban ghettoes crowded with minority groups. These people are naturally angry at being deprived of the benefits of the "affluent society" and the suburban life presented to them on television. As for the farmer, modern technology has made agriculture into a giant industry with no place for the small landholder.

Electrical communications and rapid transportation are binding us more and more into a close-knit, interdependent social system. But this has its disadvantages, too. For example, an electronic computer may be used by an employer or a state to dredge up all a person's past mistakes. The threat of war has become ever more terrifying because of modern weapons. In the same way, the threat of an authoritarian state is much greater when government adopts the tools of rapid communication and information processing to its own purposes.

Electricity: good or bad? Such criticisms illustrate the other half of the total story: electrical devices, like all other technological improvements based on scientific discovery, are neither good nor bad by themselves. Electricity increases enormously the whole range of possibilities open to us. But choices among these possibilities still have to be made on the basis of value systems outside the framework of science or technology.

Important decisions lie ahead concerning electrification, the use of nuclear power, automation and other uses of computers, and many other applications of electricity. These decisions cannot be left to the experts in physics or engineering, or to the public or private utilities, or to government agencies. They must be made by citizens who have taken the trouble to learn something about the physical forces that play such an important role in modern civilization.

SG 15.21

Electric power lines in New York State

15.1 The Project Physics learning materials particularly appropriate for Chapter 15 include:

Activities

Faraday Disk Dynamo
Generator Jump Rope
Simple Meters and Motors
Simple Motor-generator Demonstration
Physics Collage
Bicycle Generator
Lapis Polaris, Magnes

Reader Articles

Systems, Feedback, Cybernetics
The Electronic Revolution
The Invention of the Electric Light
High Fidelity
The Future of Direct Power Transmission

15.2 What sources of energy were there for industry before the electrical age? How was the energy transported to where it was needed?

15.3 Oersted discovered that a magnetic needle was affected by a current. Would you expect a magnetic needle to exert a force on the current? Why? How would you detect this force?

15.4 In which of these cases will electromagnetic induction occur?

(a) A battery is connected to a loop of wire held near another loop of wire.
(b) A battery is disconnected from a loop of wire held near another loop of wire.
(c) A magnet is moved through a loop of wire.
(d) A loop of wire is held in a steady magnetic field.
(e) A loop of wire is moved across a magnetic field.

15.5 Describe a set-up for producing induced currents by means of a magnetic field, and spell out how the set-up differs from one for producing a field by means of a current.

15.6 It was stated on page 80 that the output of a dc generator can be made smoother by using multiple windings. If each of two loops were connected to commutators as shown what would the output current of the generator be like?

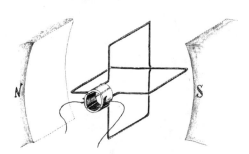

Multiple commutator segments of an electric generator for use in an automobile.

15.7 Refer to the simple ac generator shown on page 78. Suppose the loop is being rotated counter-clockwise by some externally applied mechanical force. Consider the segment *b* as it is pictured in the third drawing, moving *down* across the magnetic field. (Remember the useful rule: if your fingers point along $\vec{B}$, and your thumb along *v*, $\vec{F}$ will be in the direction your palm would push. For positive charges use the right hand, and for negative use the left hand.)

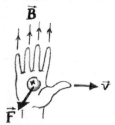

(a) Use the hand rule to determine the direction of the current induced in *b*.
(b) The induced current is an additional motion of charges, and they move also across the external magnetic field. Thus an additional magnetic force acts on segment *b*. Use the hand rule to determine the direction of the additional force—but *before* doing so try to guess the direction of the force.
(c) Determine the direction of the additional force on charges in the segment labeled *a*, which is moving upwards across the field.

15.8 Why is a generator coil harder to rotate when it is connected to an appliance to which it provides current, such as a lamp, than when it is disconnected from any load?

15.9 Suppose two bar magnets, each held by one end at the same level but a few feet apart, are dropped simultaneously. One of them passes through a closed loop of wire. Which magnet reaches the ground first? Why?

15.10 Sketch a situation in which a wire is perpendicular to a magnetic field, and use the hand rule to find the direction of the force on the current. Imagine the wire moves sideways in response to the force. This sideways motion is an additional motion across the field, and so each charge in the wire experiences an additional

force. In what direction is the additional force on the charges?

15.11 Connect a small dc motor to a battery through a current meter. By squeezing on the motor shaft, vary the speed of the motor. On the basis of your answer to question 15.10 can you explain the effect that the speed of the motor has on the current?

15.12 A dozen Christmas-tree lights are connected in series and plugged into a 120-volt wall outlet.

(a) If each lamp dissipates 10 watts of heat and light energy, what is the current in the circuit?
(b) What is the resistance of each lamp?
(c) What would happen to these lamps if they were connected in parallel across the 120-volt line? Why?

15.13 Suppose we wanted to connect a dozen lamps in *parallel* across a 120-volt line. What resistance must each lamp have in this case? To determine the resistance, proceed by answering the following questions:
(a) What current will there be in each lamp?
(b) What is the resistance of each lamp?

Compare the total current for this string of 10-watt lamps with the total current in the string of lamps in the previous question.

15.14 A man who built his own boat wanted to equip it with running lights and an interior light using a connecting wire with a resistance of $\frac{1}{5}$ ohm. But he was puzzled about whether a 6-volt system or a 12-volt system would have less heating loss in the connecting wires. Suppose that his interior lamp is to be a 6-watt lamp. (A

6-watt lamp designed for use in 6-volt systems has a resistance of 6 ohms.)
(a) If it were to operate at its full 6-volt, 6-watt rating, what current would the lamp require?
(b) If the current calculated in (a) were the actual current, what power loss would there be in the connecting wires?
(c) What would be the answers to (a) and (b) if he used a 12-volt battery and a 12 volt, 6 watt bulb?
(d) Because of the resistance of the connecting wires, the lamps described will not actually operate at full capacity. Recalculate parts (a) and (b) to determine what would be the actual currents, power losses, and power consumptions of the lamps.

15.15 A transformer for an electric toy train is used to "step down" the voltage from 120 volts to 6 volts. As in most transformers, the output power from the secondary coil is only a little less than the input power to the primary coil. If the current in the primary coil is $\frac{1}{4}$ amp, what is the current in the secondary coil?

15.16 For a transformer, the ratio of the secondary voltage to the primary voltage is the same as the ratio of the number of turns of wire on the secondary coil to the number of turns of wire on the primary coil. If a transformer were 100 percent efficient, the output power would equal the input power. Assume such is the case, and derive an expression for the ratio of the secondary current to the primary current in terms of the turn ratio.

15.17 On many transformers thicker wire (having lower resistance) is used for one of the coils than for the other. Which would you expect has the thicker wire, the low-voltage coil or the high-voltage coil?

15.18 Comment on the advisability and possible methods of getting out of a car over which a high-voltage power line has fallen.

15.19 What factors made Edison's recommendation for the use of dc for the Niagara Falls system in error?

15.20 Write a report comparing the earliest electric automobiles with those being developed now.

15.21 What were some of the major effects (both good and bad) of electricity on society?

Radio telescope in Alaska, framed by Northern Lights

CHAPTER SIXTEEN

Electromagnetic Radiation

16.1 Introduction

On April 11, 1846, the distinguished physicist Sir Charles Wheatstone was scheduled to give a lecture at the Royal Institution in London. Michael Faraday was to introduce Wheatstone to the audience. But at the last minute, just as Faraday and Wheatstone were about to enter the lecture hall, Wheatstone got stage fright, turned around and ran out into the street. Faraday had to give the lecture himself. Normally, Faraday discussed only his actual experiments in public. But on this occasion he revealed certain speculations which, as he later admitted, he would never had made public had he not suddenly been forced to speak for an hour.

Faraday's speculations dealt with the nature of light. Faraday, like Oersted before him, believed that all the forces of nature are somehow connected. Electricity and magnetism, for example, could not be separate things that just happen to exist in the same universe. Rather, they must be different forms of one basic phenomenon. This belief paralleled that of Schelling and other German nature philosophers at the beginning of the nineteenth century. It had inspired Oersted to search in the laboratory for a connection between electricity and magnetism. Eventually he found such a connection, in his discovery that an electric current in a conductor can turn a nearby magnet.

Faraday too, had been guided by a belief in the unity of natural forces. Could *light* also be another form of this basic "force"? Or rather, to use more modern terms, is light a form of *energy*? If so, scientists should be able to demonstrate experimentally its connection with other forms of energy such as electricity and magnetism. Faraday did succeed in doing just this. In 1845, he showed that light traveling through heavy glass had its plane of polarization rotated by a magnetic field applied to the glass.

This experiment convinced Faraday that there is a definite connection between light and magnetism. But he could not resist going one step

SG 16.1

Nature Philosophy was discussed in the Epilogue to Unit 2 *Text,* in Section 10.9, and its effect on Oersted in Section 14.11.

SG 16.2

further in his unrehearsed lecture the following year. Perhaps, he suggested, light itself is a vibration of magnetic lines of force. Suppose, for example, that two charged or magnetized objects are connected by an electric or magnetic line of force. If one of them moves, Faraday reasoned a disturbance would be transmitted along the line of force. Furthermore, if light waves were vibrations of lines of force, then we would not need to imagine an elastic substance such as "ether" in order to explain the propagation of light. We could replace the concept of the ether if we could show that lines of force themselves have the elastic properties needed for wave transmission.

Faraday could not make his idea more precise. He lacked the mathematical skill needed to prove that waves could propagate along lines of electric or magnetic force. Other physicists in Britain and Europe might have been able to develop a mathematical theory of electromagnetic waves. But at the time these scientists either did not understand Faraday's concept of lines of force, or did not consider them a good basis for a mathematical theory. Ten years passed before James Clerk Maxwell, a Scottish mathematical physicist, saw the value of the idea of lines of force and started using mathematics to express Faraday's concepts.

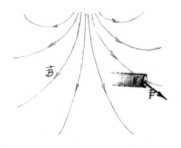

Magnetic lines of force indicate the direction of magnetic force on a north magnetic pole. (The force on a south pole is in the opposite direction.)

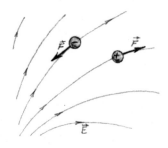

Electric lines of force indicate the direction of electric force on a positive test charge. (The force on a negative charge is in the opposite direction.)

16.2 Maxwell's formulation of the principles of electromagnetism

The work of Oersted, Ampère, Henry, and Faraday had established two basic principles of electromagnetism:

1. *An electric current in a conductor produces magnetic lines of force that circle the conductor.*

2. *When a conductor moves across externally set up magnetic lines of force, a current is induced in the conductor.*

In the 1860's, James Clerk Maxwell developed a mathematical theory of electromagnetism. In it, he added to and generalized these principles so that they applied to electric and magnetic fields in conductors, in insulators, even in space free of matter.

Maxwell began by putting Faraday's theory of electricity and magnetism into mathematical form. In 1855, less than two years after completing his undergraduate studies at Cambridge University, Maxwell presented to the Cambridge Philosophical Society a long paper. Entitled "On Faraday's Lines of Force," it described how these lines are constructed:

> . . . if we commence at any point and draw a line so that, as we go along it, its direction at any point shall always coincide with that of the resultant force at that point, this curve will indicate the direction of that force for every point through which it passes, and might be called on that account a *line of force*. We might in the same way draw other lines of force, till we had filled all space with curves indicating by their direction that of the force at any assigned point.

Maxwell stated that his paper was designed to "show how, by a strict application of the ideas and methods of Faraday, the connection of the very different orders of phenomena which he has discovered may be clearly placed before the mathematical mind." During the next ten years, Maxwell created his own models of electric and magnetic induction. In developing his theory, he first proposed a mechanical model for the electrical and magnetic quantities observed experimentally by Faraday and others. Maxwell then expressed the operation of the model in a group of equations which gave the relations between the electric and magnetic fields. He soon found these equations to be the most useful way to represent the theory. Their power allowed him eventually to discard the mechanical model altogether. Maxwell's mathematical view is still considered by physicists to be the proper approach to the theory of electromagnetic phenomena. If you go on to take another physics course after this introductory one, you will find that the development of Maxwell's mathematical model (Maxwell's equations) is one of the high points of the course. However, it will require vector calculus.

Maxwell's work contained an entirely new idea of far-reaching consequences: *an electric field that is changing with time generates a magnetic field.* Not only do *currents in conductors* produce fields around them, but *changing electric fields in insulators* such as glass or air or empty space also produce magnetic fields.

It is one thing to accept this newly stated connection between electric and magnetic fields. But it is harder—and more interesting—to *understand* the physical necessity for such a connection. The paragraphs below are intended to make it clearer.

An uncharged insulator (such as glass, wood, paper, rubber) contains equal amounts of negative and positive charge. In the normal state these charges are distributed evenly. Thus, the *net* charge is zero in every region of the material. But when the insulator is placed in an electric field, these charges are subjected to electrical forces. The positive charges are pushed in one direction, the negative in the opposite direction. Unlike the charges in a conductor, the charges in an insulating material are *not* free to move far through the material. The charges can be displaced only a small distance before restoring forces in the insulator balance the force of the electric field. If the strength of the field is increased, the charges will be displaced further. The changing displacement of charges that accompanies a changing electric field in an insulator forms a current. Maxwell called this current a *displacement current.* He assumed that this momentary displacement current in an insulator surrounds itself with a magnetic field just as a conduction current of the same magnitude does.

In an insulator, the displacement current is defined as *the rate at which the charge displacement changes.* This rate is directly proportional to the rate at which the electric field is changing in time. Thus, the magnetic field that circles the displacement current can be considered a consequence of the time-varying electric field. Maxwell assumed that this model, developed for matter, also applies to *space free of matter* (though at first glance this seems absurd). Therefore, under all circumstances, *an electric field that is changing with time surrounds itself with a magnetic*

See Maxwell's discussion "On the Induction of Electric Currents" in *Reader 4.*

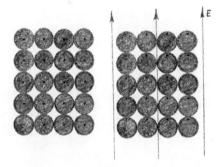

When an electric field is set up in an insulating material (as in the diagram at the right, above) the + and − charges, which are bound to one another by attraction, are displaced. This displacement forms a current. (The + charges are represented by dots, and − charges by shaded circles.)

SG 16.3

field. Previously it was thought that the only current that produced a magnetic field was the current in a conductor. Now Maxwell predicted that a magnetic field would also arise from a changing electric field, even in empty space. Unfortunately, this field was very small in comparison to the magnetic field produced by the current in the conductors of the apparatus. So it was not at that time possible to measure it directly. But, as we will see, Maxwell predicted consequences that soon *could* be tested.

According to Maxwell's theory, then, the two basic principles of electromagnetism should be expanded by adding a third:

3. *A changing electric field in space produces a magnetic field.* The induced magnetic field vector $\vec{B}$ is in a plane perpendicular to the changing electric field vector $\vec{E}$. The magnitude of $\vec{B}$ depends on the rate at which $\vec{E}$ is changing—not on $\vec{E}$ itself, but on $\Delta\vec{E}/\Delta t$. Hence, the higher the frequency of alteration of $\vec{E}$, the greater the field $\vec{B}$ so induced.

Consider a pair of conducting plates connected to a source of current, as shown at the left. Charges are moved onto or away from plates through the conductors connecting them to the source. Thus, the strength of the electric field $\vec{E}$ in the space between the plates changes with time. This changing electric field produces a magnetic field $\vec{B}$ as shown. (Of course, only a few of the infinitely many lines for $\vec{E}$ and $\vec{B}$ are shown.)

An additional principle, known before Maxwell, assumed new significance in Maxwell's work because it is so symmetrical to statement 3 above:

4. *A changing magnetic field in space produces an electric field.* The induced electric field vector $\vec{E}$ is in a plane perpendicular to the changing magnetic field vector $\vec{B}$. The magnitude of $\vec{E}$ depends on the *rate* at which $\vec{B}$ is changing—not on $\vec{B}$ itself, but on $\Delta\vec{B}/\Delta t$. Consider the changing magnetic field produced by, say, temporarily increasing the current in an electromagnet. (See the illustration in the right margin of this page.) This changing magnetic field induces an electric field in the region around the magnet. If a conductor happens to be lined up in the direction of the induced electric field, the free charges in the conductor will move under the field's influence. Thus, a current in the direction of the induced field will arise in the conductor. This electromagnetic induction had been

A changing electric field produces a magnetic field (See left margin): When the electric field $\vec{E}$ between a pair of charged plates starts to increase in intensity, a magnetic field $\vec{B}$ is induced. The faster $\vec{E}$ *changes,* the more intense $\vec{B}$ is. When $\vec{E}$ momentarily has reached its maximum value, $\vec{B}$ has decreased to zero momentarily. When $\vec{E}$ diminishes, a $\vec{B}$ field is again induced, in the opposite direction, falling to zero as $\vec{E}$ returns to its original strength.

A changing magnetic field produces an electric field (See right margin): When the magnetic field $\vec{B}$ between the poles of an electromagnet starts to increase, an electric field $\vec{E}$ is induced. The faster $\vec{B}$ *changes,* the more intense $\vec{E}$ is. When $\vec{B}$ momentarily has reached its maximum value, $\vec{E}$ has decreased to zero momentarily. When $\vec{B}$ diminishes, an $\vec{E}$ field is again induced, in the opposite direction, falling to zero as $\vec{B}$ returns to its original strength.

discovered experimentally by Faraday (Section 15.3).

Maxwell's ideas of the total set of relations between electric and magnetic fields were not at once directly testable. When the test finally came, it concerned his prediction of the existence of waves traveling as interrelating electric and magnetic fields—electromagnetic waves.

Q1   What did Maxwell propose is generated when there is a changing electric field?

Q2   What is a displacement current?

Q3   What are the four principles of electromagnetism?

16.3 The propagation of electromagnetic waves

Suppose we create, in a certain region of space, an electric field that changes with time. According to Maxwell's theory, an electric field $\vec{E}$ that varies in time simultaneously induces a magnetic field $\vec{B}$ that also varies with time. (The magnetic field also varies with the distance from the region where we created the changing electric field.) Similarly, a magnetic field that is changing with time simultaneously induces an electric field that changes with time. (Here, too, the electric field also changes with distance from the region where we created the changing magnetic field.)

As Maxwell realized and correctly predicted, mutual induction of time- and space-changing electric and magnetic fields should set up an unending sequence of events. First, a time-varying electric field in one region produces a time- and space-varying magnetic field at points near this region. But this *magnetic* field produces a time- and space-varying *electric* field in the space surrounding it. And *this* electric field produces time- and space-varying magnetic fields in *its* neighborhood, and so on. Thus, suppose that an electromagnetic disturbance is started at one location, say by vibrating charges in a hot gas or in the transmitter wire of a radio or television station. This disturbance can travel to distant points through the mutual generation of the electric and magnetic fields. The

See "The Relationship of Electricity and Magnetism" in *Reader 4.*

The electric and magnetic field changes occur together, much like the "action" and "reaction" of Newton's third law.

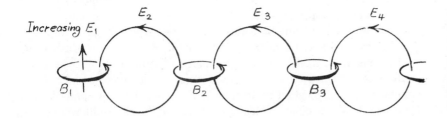

An *increasing* electric field E_1 at the left (or a current) surrounds itself with a magnetic field B_1. As B_1 changes, it induces an interlinking electric field E_2, etc. The chain-like process continues with finite velocity. This is only a rough description of the process, which propagates itself in all directions.

Electric and magnetic fields linked by induction, from Max Born, *Einstein's Theory of Special Relativity* (1924).

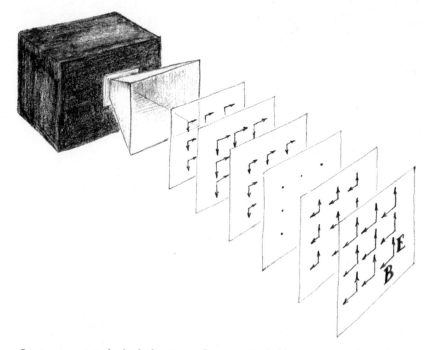

Electric oscillations in a vacuum-tube circuit are led onto a rod in a metal "horn." In the horn they generate a variation in electric and magnetic fields that radiates away into space. This drawing is an instantaneous "snapshot" of almost plane wavefronts directly in front of such a horn.

SG 16.4, 16.5

fluctuating, interlocked electric and magnetic fields propagate through space in the form of an "electromagnetic wave"—a disturbance in the electric and magnetic field intensities in space.

In Chapter 12 it was shown that waves occur when a disturbance created in one region produces at a later time a disturbance in adjacent regions. Snapping one end of a rope produces, through the action of one part of the rope on the other, a displacement at points farther along the rope and at a later time. Dropping a pebble into a pond produces a disturbance that moves away from the source as one part of the water acts on neighboring parts. Time-varying electric and magnetic fields produce a disturbance that moves away from the source as the varying fields in one region create varying fields in neighboring regions.

What determines the speed with which electromagnetic waves travel? Recall first that for mechanical waves the speed of propagation is determined by the stiffness and density of the medium. Speed increases with increasing stiffness, but decreases with increasing density. This relation between wave speed, stiffness, and density holds for mechanical wave motions and for many other types of waves. Here we can only sketch out in barest outline how Maxwell proceeded beyond this point. First, he assumed that a similar "stiffness and density" relation would hold for electromagnetic waves. Then he computed what he thought to be the "stiffness" and "density" of electric and magnetic fields propagating through the hypothetical ether. In finding values for these two properties of the electric and magnetic fields, he was guided by his mechanical model representing the ether. In this model, stiffness was related to the electric field, and density to the magnetic field. Next, he proved mathematically that the *ratio* of these two factors, which should determine the wave speed, is the same for all strengths of the fields. Finally, Maxwell demonstrated that the speed of the waves—if they exist!—is a

As was stated in Chapter 12, page 106, the speed of propagation depends on both the stiffness and density of the medium:

$$\text{speed} = \sqrt{\dfrac{\text{stiffness}}{\text{density}}}$$

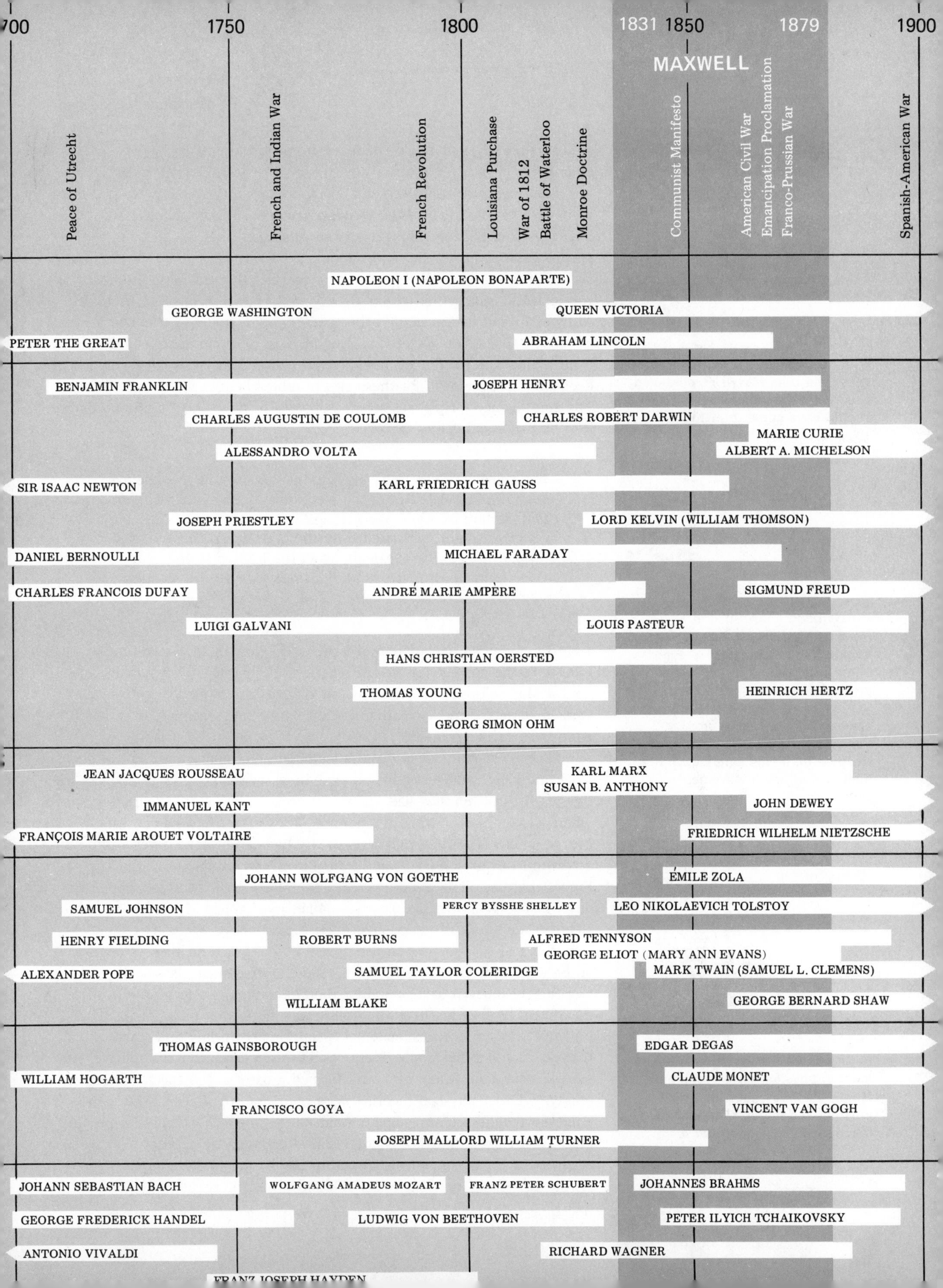

Timeline chart with top axis: 1700 | 1750 | 1800 | 1831 | 1850 | 1879 | 1900

MAXWELL (highlighted period, 1831–1879)

Historical events (vertical labels):
Peace of Utrecht · French and Indian War · French Revolution · Louisiana Purchase · War of 1812 · Battle of Waterloo · Monroe Doctrine · Communist Manifesto · American Civil War · Emancipation Proclamation · Franco-Prussian War · Spanish-American War

Statesmen / Rulers:
NAPOLEON I (NAPOLEON BONAPARTE)
GEORGE WASHINGTON
QUEEN VICTORIA
PETER THE GREAT
ABRAHAM LINCOLN

Scientists:
BENJAMIN FRANKLIN
JOSEPH HENRY
CHARLES AUGUSTIN DE COULOMB
CHARLES ROBERT DARWIN
ALESSANDRO VOLTA
MARIE CURIE
ALBERT A. MICHELSON
SIR ISAAC NEWTON
KARL FRIEDRICH GAUSS
JOSEPH PRIESTLEY
LORD KELVIN (WILLIAM THOMSON)
DANIEL BERNOULLI
MICHAEL FARADAY
CHARLES FRANCOIS DUFAY
ANDRÉ MARIE AMPÈRE
SIGMUND FREUD
LUIGI GALVANI
LOUIS PASTEUR
HANS CHRISTIAN OERSTED
THOMAS YOUNG
HEINRICH HERTZ
GEORG SIMON OHM

Philosophers / Reformers:
JEAN JACQUES ROUSSEAU
KARL MARX
SUSAN B. ANTHONY
IMMANUEL KANT
JOHN DEWEY
FRANÇOIS MARIE AROUET VOLTAIRE
FRIEDRICH WILHELM NIETZSCHE

Writers:
JOHANN WOLFGANG VON GOETHE
ÉMILE ZOLA
SAMUEL JOHNSON
PERCY BYSSHE SHELLEY
LEO NIKOLAEVICH TOLSTOY
HENRY FIELDING
ROBERT BURNS
ALFRED TENNYSON
GEORGE ELIOT (MARY ANN EVANS)
ALEXANDER POPE
SAMUEL TAYLOR COLERIDGE
MARK TWAIN (SAMUEL L. CLEMENS)
WILLIAM BLAKE
GEORGE BERNARD SHAW

Artists:
THOMAS GAINSBOROUGH
EDGAR DEGAS
WILLIAM HOGARTH
CLAUDE MONET
FRANCISCO GOYA
VINCENT VAN GOGH
JOSEPH MALLORD WILLIAM TURNER

Composers:
JOHANN SEBASTIAN BACH
WOLFGANG AMADEUS MOZART
FRANZ PETER SCHUBERT
JOHANNES BRAHMS
GEORGE FREDERICK HANDEL
LUDWIG VON BEETHOVEN
PETER ILYICH TCHAIKOVSKY
ANTONIO VIVALDI
RICHARD WAGNER
FRANZ JOSEPH HAYDEN

definite quantity that can be deduced from measurements in the laboratory.

The necessary measurements of the factors involved actually had been made five years earlier by the German scientists Weber and Kohlrausch. Using their published values, Maxwell calculated that the speed of the supposed electromagnetic waves should be about 311,000,000 meters per second. He was immediately struck by the fact that this large number was very close to a measured speed already well known in physics. In 1849 Armand Fizeau had measured the speed of *light,* and had obtained a value of about 315,000,000 meters per second. The close similarity could have been a chance occurrence. But Maxwell believed that there must be a deep underlying reason for these two numbers being so nearly the same. The significance for physics seemed obvious to him. Making an enormous leap of the imagination, he wrote:

> The velocity of the transverse undulations in our hypothetical medium, calculated from the electromagnetic experiments of MM. Kohlrausch and Weber, agrees so exactly with the velocity of light calculated from the optical experiments of M. Fizeau, that we can scarcely avoid the inference that *light consists in the transverse undulations of the same medium which is the cause of electric and magnetic phenomena.*

Here then was an explanation of light waves, and at the same time a joining of the previously separate sciences of electricity, magnetism, and optics. Maxwell realized the importance of his discovery. Now he set to work making the theory mathematically sound and freeing it from his admittedly artificial model.

Maxwell's synthesis of electromagnetism and optics, after it had been experimentally confirmed (see Section 16.4), was seen as a great event in physics. In fact, physics had known no greater time since the 1680's, when Newton was writing his monumental work on mechanics. Of course, Maxwell's electromagnetic theory had arisen in Maxwell's mind in a Newtonian, mechanical framework. But it had grown out of that framework, becoming another great general physical theory, independent of its mechanical origins. Like Newtonian mechanics, Maxwell's electromagnetic field theory succeeded spectacularly. We will see something of that success in the next few sections. The success occurred on two different levels: the practical and the theoretical. Practically, it led to a host of modern developments, such as radio and television. On the theoretical level, it led to a whole new way of viewing phenomena. The universe was not only a Newtonian machine of whirling and colliding parts; it included fields and energies that no machine could duplicate. As we will note later, Maxwell's work formed a basis of the special theory of relativity. Other physical theories were nourished by it also. Eventually, however, results accumulated that did not fit Maxwell's theory; something more was needed. Starting about 1925, after a quarter century of discovery, the development of quantum mechanics led to a larger synthesis, which included Maxwell's electromagnetism.

With better measurements we now know that both Maxwell's predicted speed and Fizeau's measured speed should have come to just under 3×10^8 m/sec, i.e., 2.99793×10^8 m/sec.

Maxwell had shown that in an electromagnetic disturbance $\vec{E}$ and $\vec{B}$ should be perpendicular to each other and to the direction of propagation of the wave. Hence, in the language of Chapter 12, electromagnetic waves are *transverse*. And as we noted in Chapter 13, it was long known that light waves are transverse.

For a general survey of the development of physical ideas leading up to Maxwell's theory, see the article by Einstein and Infeld, "The Electromagnetic Field," in *Reader 4.*

Q4 What discovery did Maxwell make upon calculating the speed with which electromagnetic disturbances should travel?

Q5 What is Maxwell's synthesis?

See also "James Clerk Maxwell, Part II" in *Reader 4.*

16.4 Hertz's experiments

Did Maxwell establish without doubt that light actually does consist of electromagnetic waves, or even that electromagnetic waves exist at all? No. Most physicists remained skeptical for several years. The fact that the ratio of two quantities determined by electrical experiments came out equal to the speed of light certainly suggested *some* connection between electricity and light. No one would seriously argue that this was only a coincidence. But stronger evidence was needed before the rest of Maxwell's theory, with its displacement current, could be accepted.

What further evidence was needed to persuade physicists that Maxwell's theory was correct? Maxwell showed that his theory could explain all the known facts about electricity, magnetism, and light. But so could other theories, although with less sweeping connection between their separate parts. To a modern physicist, the other theories proposed in the nineteenth century seem much more complicated and artificial than Maxwell's. But at the time, Maxwell's theory seemed strange to physicists who were not accustomed to thinking in terms of fields. It could be accepted over other theories only if it could be used to predict some *new* property of electromagnetism or light.

Maxwell himself made two such predictions from his theory. He did not live to see them verified experimentally in 1888, for he died in 1879 at the age of 48. Maxwell's most important prediction was that electromagnetic waves of many different frequencies could exist. All such waves would propagate through space at the speed of light. Light itself would correspond to waves of only a small range of high frequencies (from 4×10^{14} cycles/sec to 7×10^{14} cycles/sec). These are the frequencies detectable by the human eye.

To test this prediction required inventing apparatus that could both produce and detect electromagnetic waves—preferably of frequencies other than light frequencies. This was first done by the German physicist Heinrich Hertz, whose contribution was triggered by a chance observation. In 1886, Hertz noticed a peculiar effect produced during the sparking of an induction coil. As was well-known, sparks sometimes jump the air gap between the terminals of an induction coil (see drawing). You will recall (Chapter 15) that an induction coil can be used to produce high voltages if there are many more turns of wire on one side than the other. Ordinarily, air does not conduct electricity. But when there is a very large potential difference between two wires a short distance apart, a conducting pathway may form briefly as air molecules are ionized. A short burst of electricity then may pass through, attended by a visible spark. Each visible spark produced is actually a series of many small sparks, jumping rapidly back and forth (oscillating) between the terminals. Hertz found he could

Recall from page 102: The magnitude of *B* depends on the *rate* at which *E* changes (on $\Delta E / \Delta t$). Hence an electric field oscillating at a very high frequency induces magnetic fields that are large compared to the ordinary magnetic field surrounding the conductor for the current. But circuits to produce such high frequency oscillations were not available in Maxwell's time.

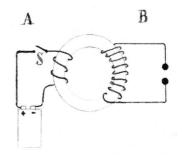

Operation of the induction coil: Starting and stopping the current in coil *A* with a vibrating switch *S* produces a rapidly changing magnetic field in the iron core. This rapidly changing field induces high voltage peaks in the many-turn coil *B*, and can cause a spark to jump across the air gap. Spark coils for use in car engines operate in this way.

Radio and television "static" is often produced by sparking in electrical appliances and in the ignition of passing cars. This fact shows that high-frequency oscillations occur in sparks.

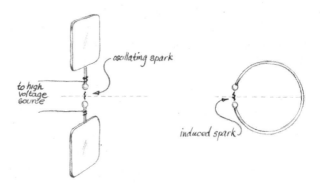

SG 16.6

Heinrich Hertz (1857-1894) was born in Hamburg, Germany. During his youth he was mainly interested in languages and the humanities, but was attracted to science after his grandfather gave him some apparatus. Hertz did simple experiments in a small laboratory which he had fitted out in his home. After completing secondary school (and a year of military service) he undertook the serious study of mathematics and physics at the University of Berlin in 1878. In 1882 he devoted himself to the study of electromagnetism, including the recent and still generally unappreciated work of Maxwell. Two years later he started his famous experiments on electromagnetic waves. During the course of this work, Hertz made another discovery—the photoelectric effect—which has had a profound influence on modern physics. We shall study this effect in Chapter 18 (Unit 5).

control the spark's frequency of oscillation by changing the size and shape of metal plates attached to the spark gap of the induction coil.

Now Hertz bent a simple piece of wire so that there was a short gap between its two ends. When it was held near an induction coil, *a spark jumped across the air gap in the wire just when a spark jumped across the terminals of the induction coil.* This was a surprising new phenomenon. Hertz reasoned that as the spark jumps back and forth across the gap of the induction coil, it must set up rapidly changing electric and magnetic fields. According to Maxwell's theory, these changes propagate through space as electromagnetic waves. (The frequency of the waves is the same as the frequency of oscillations of the sparks.) When the electromagnetic waves pass over the bent wire, they set up rapidly changing electric and magnetic fields there, too. A strong electric field produces a spark in the air gap, just as the transmitter field did between the terminals of the induction coil. Since the field is rapidly changing, sparks can jump back and forth between the two ends of the wire. This wire, therefore, serves as a detector of the electromagnetic waves generated by the induction coil. Hertz's observation of the induced spark was the first solid clue that electromagnetic waves do exist.

Let us assume that this interpretation is correct, and that waves travel through space from the induction coil. Then there must be a short delay between the appearance of the first (left) and second (right) spark. The spark in the detector cannot occur at exactly the same instant as the spark made by the induction coil. Even traveling at the speed of light the wave must take some finite time to go from one place to the other. In 1888 Hertz measured the speed of these electromagnetic waves. He found it to be, as Maxwell had predicted, the same as the speed of light.

In later experiments, Hertz showed that the electromagnetic radiation from his induction coil has all the usual properties of light waves. It can be reflected at the surface of solid bodies, including metallic conductors. Further, the angle of reflection is equal to the angle of incidence. The electromagnetic radiation can be focused by concave metallic mirrors. It shows diffraction effects when it passes through an opening in a screen. All interference phenomena can be shown, including standing waves. Also, electromagnetic waves are refracted by prisms made of glass, wood,

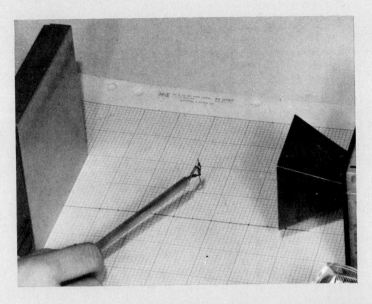

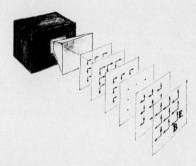

Electromagnetic radiation of a few centimeters wavelength is generated by oscillating electric fields inside the metal horn. Experiments with this radiation show phenomena similar to those observed for water waves and sound waves. Below is a record of measurements of the intensity of a standing interference pattern of electromagnetic waves in front of a flat reflecting surface. The intensity was measured by the current induced in a small detector on the end of a probe, as shown in the photograph.

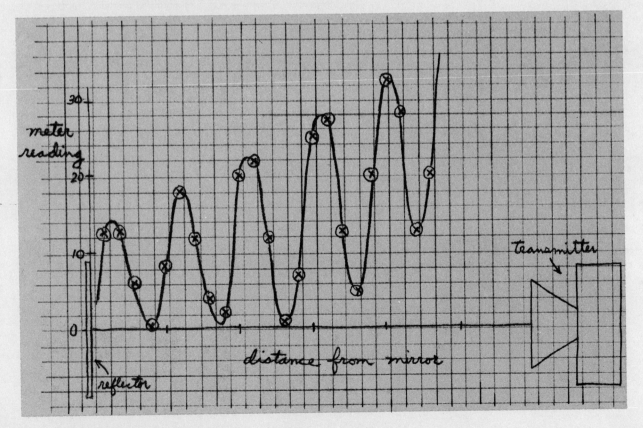

Instead of relying on oscillating sparks, modern electronic circuits use the wires of a transmitting antenna. Through the wires move the oscillating currents that radiate electromagnetic waves.

plastic, and other non-conducting material. All these experiments, with more modern apparatus, can be done in your laboratory.

Hertz's experiments dramatically confirmed Maxwell's electromagnetic theory. They showed that electromagnetic waves actually exist, that they travel with the speed of light, and that they have the familiar characteristics of light. Now mathematical physicists rapidly accepted Maxwell's theory and applied it with great success to the detailed analysis of a wide range of phenomena.

SG 16.7

Maxwell also predicted that electromagnetic waves will exert a pressure on any surface that reflects or absorbs them. This pressure is very small. Experimentally, it is extremely difficult to distinguish it from the pressure of air currents set up by heating of the surface that absorbs the waves. The technical difficulties involved in testing this prediction were not solved until 1899, by Lebedev in Russia. Two years later, Nichols and Hull in the United States also confirmed the existence of radiation pressure. It had exactly the value predicted by Maxwell's theory.

SG 16.8

Thus, at the end of the nineteenth century, Maxwell's electromagnetic theory stood with Newton's laws of mechanics as an established part of the foundations of physics.

Q6   What predictions of Maxwell's were verified by Hertz?

Q7   What did Hertz use as a detector of electromagnetic waves?

16.5 The electromagnetic spectrum

The frequency unit "cycles/sec" is now being given the name "hertz." You will sometimes see the forms 10^6 hertz, 10^6 cycles/sec, 10^3 kilocycles/sec, 1 megacycle/sec, or 1 megahertz. All signify the same frequency. Some radio stations now regularly announce their frequencies in megahertz (MHz).

Hertz's induction coil produced electromagnetic radiation with a wavelength of about 1 meter. This is about a million times the wavelength of visible light. Later experiments showed that a very wide and continuous range of electromagnetic wavelengths (and frequencies) is possible. The entire possible range is called the *electromagnetic spectrum*. A range of frequencies from about 1 cycle/sec to 10^{25} cycles/sec, corresponding to a wavelength range from 10^8 meters to 10^{-17} meters, has been studied. Many of these frequency regions have been put to practical use.

Light, heat, radio waves, and x rays are names given to radiations in certain regions of the electromagnetic spectrum. In each of these regions radiation is produced or observed in a particular way. For example, light may be perceived directly through its effect on the retina of the eye. But to detect radio waves we need electronic equipment. The named regions overlap. For example, some radiation is called "ultraviolet" or "x ray," depending on how it is produced.

All waves in the electromagnetic spectrum, although produced and detected in various ways, behave as predicted by Maxwell's theory. All electromagnetic waves travel through empty space at the same speed, the speed of light. They all carry energy; when they are absorbed, the absorber is heated. Electromagnetic radiation, whatever its frequency, can

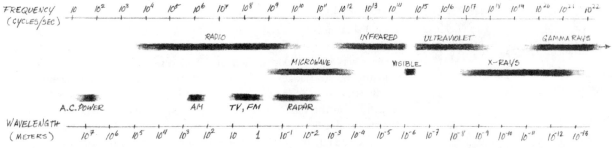

A chart of the electromagnetic spectrum.

SG 16.9

be emitted only if energy is supplied to the source of radiation. There is now overwhelming evidence that electromagnetic radiation originates from accelerated charges, as Faraday had speculated. This charge acceleration may be produced in many ways. For example, heating a material will increase the vibrational energy of charged particles. Also, one can vary the motion of charges on an electric conductor (an antenna), or cause a charged particle to change its direction. In these and other processes work is done by the force that is applied to accelerate the electric charge. Some of the energy supplied to the antenna in doing this work is "radiated" away. That is, it propagates away from the source as an electromagnetic wave.

The work of Maxwell and Hertz opened up a new scientific view of nature. It also prepared for a rapid blooming of new technologies, such as radio, TV, radar, etc. As we have done before—for example in the chapter on electric motors and generators—let us look briefly at these indirect consequences of a scientific advance.

Radio. Electromagnetic waves having frequencies of 10^4 to 10^7 cycles/sec are reflected quite well by electrically charged layers that exist in the upper atmosphere. This reflection makes it possible to detect radio waves at great distances from the source. Radio signals have wavelengths from tens to thousands of meters. Such waves can easily diffract around relatively small obstacles such as trees or buildings. But large hills and mountains may cast "dark" shadows.

See "The Electronic Revolution" in *Reader 4.*

SG 16.10
SG 16.11

In December 1901, Guglielmo Marconi successfully detected radio waves sent from Newfoundland to Ireland. Marconi's work showed that long distance radio communication is possible and revealed the previously unsuspected layers of electric charge in the upper atmosphere.

Radio waves that can cross large distances, either directly or by relay, are very useful for carrying information. Communication is accomplished by changing the signal according to an agreed code that can be deciphered at the receiving end. The first radio communication was achieved by turning the signal on and off in an agreed pattern, such as Morse code. Later, sounds were coded by continuous variations in the

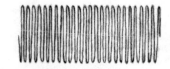

A "carrier" radio wave.

AM (amplitude modulation): information is coded as variations in the amplitude (or intensity) of the carrier.

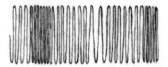

FM (frequency modulation): information is coded as variations in the frequency of the carrier.

amplitude (that is, the *intensity*) of the broadcast wave (AM). Later still, the information was coded as *frequency* variations in the broadcast wave (FM). In broadcast radio and television, the "decoding" is done in the receiver serving the loudspeaker or TV picture tube. The output message from the receiver takes the same form that it had at the transmitter.

Because signals from different stations should not be received at the same spot on the dial, it is necessary to restrict their transmission. The International Telecommunication Union (ITU) controls radio transmission and other means of international communication. Within the United States, the Federal Communications Commission (FCC) regulates radio transmission. In order to reduce the interference of one station's signal with another, the FCC assigns suitable frequencies to radio stations. It also limits their power or the power radiated in particular directions, and may restrict the hours of transmission.

Television and radar. Television and FM broadcasting stations operate at frequencies of about 10^8 cycles/sec. Waves at these frequencies are not reflected by the layers of electric charge in the upper atmosphere. Rather, the signals travel in nearly straight lines and pass into space instead of following the curvature of the earth. Thus, they can be used in communication between the earth and the moon, for example. But on earth, coaxial cables or relay stations are necessary to transmit signals between points more than about 50 miles apart, even if there are no mountains. Signals can be transmitted from one distant place to another, including from one continent to another, by relay satellites.

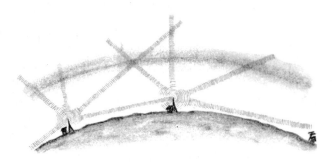

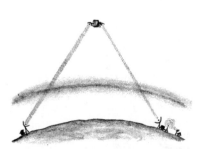

Satellites are used to relay microwaves all over the world. The microwaves can carry radio or TV information.

An important principle in radio transmission and detection is that of the resonant or "tuned" circuit. Reference to this can be found in the *Radio Amateur's Handbook*, or basic texts listed in most radio supply catalogues, e.g., Allied Radio.

SG 16.12—16.18

Since these signals have wavelengths of only about a meter, they are not diffracted much around objects which have dimensions of several meters, such as cars, ships, or aircraft. Thus, the reflected portion of signals of wavelengths from one meter down to one millimeter is used to detect such objects. The interference between the direct waves and reflection of these waves by passing airplanes can distort a television picture considerably. The signal also may be radiated in the form of pulses. If so, the time from the emission of a pulse to the reception of its echo measures the distance of the reflecting object. This technique is called *RA*dio *De*tection *A*nd *R*anging, or RADAR. By means of the reflection of a beam that is pulsed, both the direction and distance of an object can be measured.

Infrared radiation. Electromagnetic waves with wavelengths of 10^{-1} to 10^{-4} meters are often called microwaves. The shorter the wavelengths, the more difficult it becomes to construct circuits that oscillate and generate significant energy of radiation. However, in heated bodies, the atoms themselves give off electromagnetic waves shorter than about 10^{-4} meters. This "radiant heat" is usually called *infrared* rays, because most of the energy is of wavelengths slightly longer than the red end of the visible spectrum. While associated mainly with heat radiation, infrared rays do have some properties that are the same as those of visible light. The shorter infrared waves affect specially treated photographic film, and photographs taken with infrared radiation show some interesting effects. Also, scattering by small particles in the atmosphere is very much less for long wavelengths (Section 1.6). Thus, infrared rays can penetrate smoky haze dense enough to block visible light.

A photograph made with film sensitive only to infrared radiation.

Visible light. The visual receptors in the human eye are sensitive to electromagnetic radiation with wavelengths between about 7×10^{-7} and 4×10^{-7} meters. Radiation of these wavelengths is usually called light, or visible light. The eye is most sensitive to the green and yellow parts of the spectrum. This peak sensitivity corresponds roughly to the peak of solar radiation which reaches the earth's surface.

SG 16.19
SG 16.20

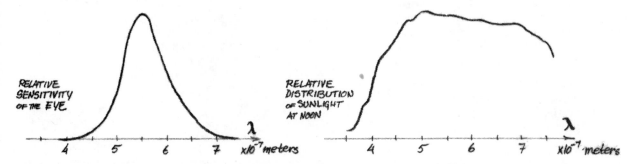

Ultraviolet light. Electromagnetic waves shorter than the visible violet are called *ultraviolet*. The ultraviolet region of the spectrum is of just as much interest in spectrum study as the visible and infrared. The atoms of many elements emit ultraviolet radiations that are characteristic of those elements. Ultraviolet light, like visible light, can cause photochemical reactions in which radiant energy is converted directly into chemical energy. Typical of these reactions are those which occur in silver bromide in the photographic process, in the production of ozone in the upper atmosphere, and in the production of a dark pigment, known as melanin, in the skin.

SG 16.21

X rays. This radiation involves wavelengths from about 10^{-8} meters to 10^{-17} meters. Usually, it is produced by the sudden deflection or stopping of electrons when they strike a metal target. The maximum frequency of the radiation generated is determined by the energy with which the electrons strike the target. In turn, this energy is determined by the voltage through which the electrons are accelerated (Section 14.8). So the

Electromagnetic waves generally are produced in the *acceleration* of charged particles.

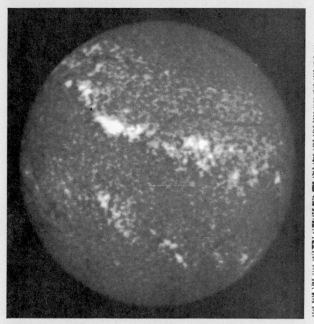

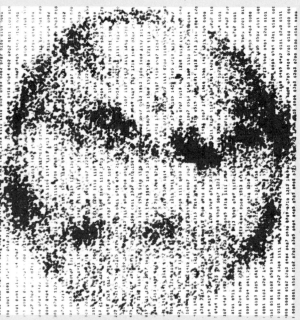

Astronomy Across the Spectrum

Electromagnetic radiation of different wavelengths brings us different kinds of information. Above are two views of the sun on Oct. 25, 1967. At the left is a photo taken in *violet* light. At the right is a computer plot of intensity of very short *ultraviolet* emission. The UV doesn't penetrate the earth's atmosphere; the information displayed here was collected by the Orbiting Solar Observatory satellite shown at the right. Below are three views of the sun on Mar. 17, 1965. At the left is a photograph in red light. At the right is an image formed by *x rays*, and on the next page is an intensity contour map made from this image. The x-ray tele-scope was raised above the earth's atmosphere by an Aerobee rocket. Longer-wavelength radiations such as

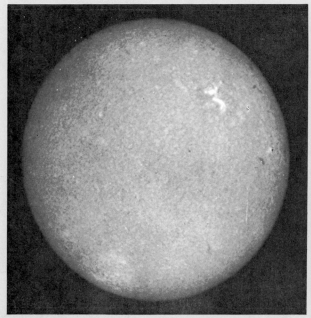

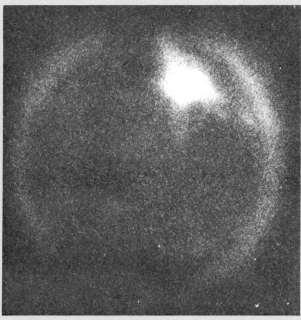

radio and infrared are able to penetrate interstellar dust. Radio telescopes come in a great variety of shapes and sizes. Above is shown the huge Arecibo telescope in Puerto Rico; it has a fixed reflector but a moveable detector unit. To the right are a photograph and a diagram of a precise steerable antenna, the Haystack antenna in Massachusetts. Information collected with this instrument at 3.7 cm wavelength led to the upper contour map at right. This map of radio brightness is of the portion of the sky around the center of our galaxy. The area covered is about that of the full moon. The *infrared* brightness of the same portion of sky is shown in the bottom contour map.

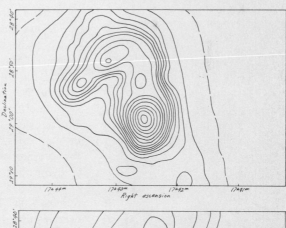

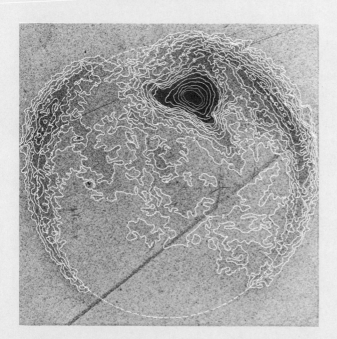

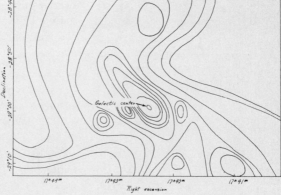

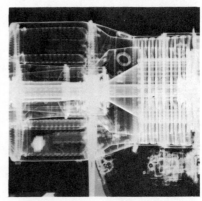

X-ray photos of (left) a Chambered Nautilus sea shell, and (right) a jet engine.

maximum frequency increases with the accelerating voltage. The higher the frequency of the x rays, the greater is their power to penetrate matter. But the distance of penetration also depends on the nature of the material being penetrated. X rays are readily absorbed by bone, which contains calcium; they pass much more easily through less dense organic matter (such as flesh) containing mainly the light atoms hydrogen, carbon, and oxygen. This fact, combined with the ability of x rays to affect a photographic plate, leads to some of the medical uses of x-ray photography. X rays can damage living cells, and should be used with great caution and only by trained technicians. But some kinds of diseased cells are injured more easily by x rays than are healthy cells. Thus, a carefully controlled x-ray beam is sometimes used to destroy cancerous growths or other harmful cells.

X rays produce interference effects when they fall on a crystal in which atoms and molecules are arranged in a regular pattern. Different portions of the incident beam of x rays are reflected from different planes of atoms in the crystal structure. These reflected rays can interfere constructively, and this fact can be used in either of two ways. If the spacing of the atoms in the crystal is known, the wavelength of the x rays can be calculated. If the x-ray wavelength is known, the distance between crystal planes, and thus the structure of the crystal, can be determined. X rays are now widely used by chemists, mineralogists, and biologists in studying the structure of crystals and complex molecules.

Gamma rays. The gamma-ray region of the electromagnetic spectrum overlaps the x-ray region (see page 111). Gamma radiation is emitted mainly by the unstable nuclei of natural or artificial radioactive materials. We will consider gamma rays further in the Supplemental Unit *The Nucleus.*

The glow in the photograph is caused when gamma rays emitted by radioactive cobalt cylinders interact with the surrounding pool of water.

Q8 Why do radio waves not cast noticeable "shadows" behind such obstacles as trees or small buildings?

Q9 Why are relay stations often needed in transmitting television signals?

Q10 How is the frequency of x rays related to their penetration of matter?

SG 16.22

Q11 How do the wavelengths used in radar compare with the wavelengths of visible light?

Q12 How does the production of x rays differ from that of gamma rays?

___

16.6 What about the ether now?

The "luminiferous ether" had been proposed specifically as a medium for the propagation of light waves. Maxwell found that the ether could also be thought of as a medium for transmitting electric and magnetic forces. Later, he realized that he could drop the concept entirely if he focused on the mathematical form of the theory. Yet, just before his death in 1879, Maxwell wrote an article in which he still supported the ether concept:

> Whatever difficulties we may have in forming a consistent idea of the constitution of the aether, there can be no doubt that the interplanetary and interstellar spaces are not empty, but are occupied by a material substance or body, which is certainly the largest, and probably the most uniform body of which we have any knowledge. . . .

Maxwell was aware of the failures of earlier ether theories. Near the beginning of the same article he said:

> Aethers were invented for the planets to swim in, to constitute electric atmospheres and magnetic effluvia, to convey sensations from one part of our bodies to another, and so on, till all space had been filled three or four times over with aethers. It is only when we remember the extensive and mischievous influence on science which hypotheses about aethers used formerly to exercise, that we can appreciate the horror of aethers which sober-minded men had during the 18th century. . . .

Maxwell had formulated his electromagnetic theory mathematically, independent of any detailed model of the ether. Why, then, did he continue to speak of the "great ocean of aether" filling all space? Like all of us, Maxwell could go only so far in changing his view of the world. It seemed unthinkable that there could be vibrations without something that vibrates, or waves without a medium. Also, to many nineteenth-century physicists the idea of "action at a distance" seemed absurd. How could one object exert a force on another body far away if something did not transmit the force? One body is said to act *on* another, and the word *on* gives the idea of contact. Thus, according to accepted ways of describing the world in common language, the ether seemed somehow necessary.

Yet twenty-five years after Maxwell's death the ether concept had lost much of its support. Within another decade, it had vanished from the

James Clerk Maxwell (1831-1879) was born in Edinburgh, Scotland in the same year Faraday discovered electromagnetic induction. Unlike Faraday, Maxwell came from a well-off family, and was educated at the Edinburgh Academy and the University of Edinburgh. He showed a lively interest in how things happened when he was scarcely three years old. As a child he constantly asked, "What's the go of that?" He studied mechanisms, from a toy top to a commercial steam engine, until he had satisfied his curiosity about how they worked. On the abstract side, his formal studies, begun at the Academy in Edinburgh and continued through his work as an undergraduate at Cambridge, gave Maxwell experience in using mathematics to develop useful parallels among apparently unrelated occurences. His first publication appeared in the proceedings of the Royal Society of Edinburgh when he was only fourteen years old. By the time he was seventeen he had published three papers on the results of his original research. In the 1870's he organized the Cavendish Laboratory at Cambridge University, which became a world center for physics research for the next several decades.

He was one of the main contributors to the kinetic theory of gases, to statistical mechanics and thermodynamics, and also to the theory of color vision. His greatest achievement was his electromagnetic theory. Maxwell is generally regarded as the most profound and productive physicist between the time of Newton and Einstein.

SG 16.23

A comparable effect *is* observed with sound waves: they go faster with respect to the ground when traveling *with* the wind than when traveling *against* the wind.

Michelson first tried the experiment in 1881, stimulated by speculations how to measure the effect of ether on light propagation, given in a letter of Maxwell's published just after Maxwell's death.

More on relativity theory appears in Chapter 20 and in *Reader 5*.

collection of useful concepts. In part, the success of Maxwell's theory itself helped to undermine the general belief in the existence of an ether. Maxwell's equations did not depend on details of the ether's structure. In fact, they could describe the relations between changes of electric and magnetic fields in space without any reference to the ether at all.

Another difficulty with belief in the ether was that all attempts to detect the motion of the earth relative to the ether failed. If light is a kind of vibration of an ether that fills all space, then light should travel at a definite speed relative to the ether. But the earth must also be moving through the ether in its annual orbit around the sun. Thus, the earth should be moving like a ship—against an "ether wind" at some times, and with it at other times. Under these conditions the apparent speed of light should be observed to differ. When the earth and a beam of light are moving in the same direction through the ether, the observed speed of light should not be the same as when the earth and light are moving in opposite directions.

Theorists computed the time required for light to make a round trip with and against the ether wind. They compared this interval with the time calculated for a round trip in the absence of an ether wind. The expected time difference was found to be very small: only 10^{-15} seconds for a round trip of 30 meters. This is too short a time difference to measure directly. But it is of the same order as the time for one vibration of visible light. Therefore, the difference might be detected from observations of a properly produced interference pattern. In 1887 the American scientists Albert A. Michelson and Edward Morley used a device sensitive enough to detect an effect only one percent as great as that predicted by the ether theory. Neither this experiment nor the many similar experiments done since then have revealed an ether wind.

Supporters of the ether concept offered various explanations for this unexpected result. For example, they suggested that objects moving at high speeds relative to the ether might change their size in just such a way as to make this relative speed undetectable. But even those who made such attempts to rescue the ether concept felt their proposals to be forced and artificial. Finally, a decisive development led scientists to abandon the ether concept. This breakthrough was not a specific experiment, but a brilliant proposal by a young man of 26 years. The man was Albert Einstein, who in 1905 suggested that a new and deep union of mechanics and electromagnetism could be achieved without the ether model. A few brief remarks here will provide a setting for your further study of relativity at a later time.

Einstein showed that the equations of electromagnetism can be written to fit the same principle of relativity that holds for mechanics. In Section 4.4 we discussed the Galilean principle of relativity. It states that *the same laws of mechanics apply in each of two frames of reference which have a constant velocity relative to each other*. Thus, it is impossible to tell by any mechanical experiment whether or not one's laboratory (reference frame) is at rest or is moving with constant velocity. The principle is illustrated by common experience within a ship, car, plane, or train moving at a constant speed in a straight line. The observer finds that objects move, remain at rest, fall, or respond to applied force in just the same way they do when the ship or whatever is at rest. Galileo, a convinced Copernican, applied this principle to the motion of objects with respect to the earth. You will recall the example of a stone falling straight down alongside a tower. Galileo argued that this event gives no indication whether the earth is fixed and the sun in motion, or the sun fixed and the earth moving.

Einstein extended this principle of relativity beyond mechanics. It applied, he proposed, to *all* of physics, including electromagnetism. A main reason for this assumption appears to have been his feeling that nature could not be lopsided: relativity could not apply only to *part of* physics. Einstein then added a second basic conjecture. He stated that *the speed of any light beam moving through free space is the same for all observers*—even when they are moving relative to each other or relative to the light source! This bold statement resolved the question of why the motion of observers with respect to the ether did not show up in experiments on the speed of light. In fact, Einstein rejected the ether and all other attempts to provide a "preferred frame of reference" for light propagation. The price of making these assumptions of his was, Einstein showed, the necessity of revising some common-sense notions of space and time. Einstein showed that Maxwell's equations are fully consistent with extending the principle of relativity to all physics. This was yet another great synthesis of previously separate ideas, like the syntheses forged by Copernicus, Newton, and Maxwell.

What then, was the role played by the elaborate theories of ether that underlay much of nineteenth-century physics? It would be unjust to call the ether concept useless. After all, it guided the work of Maxwell and others, and helped in developing an understanding of the elastic properties of matter. Perhaps we can best view the early mechanical models used for light and electricity as the scaffolding needed to erect a building. Once the building is completed, if the construction is sound, the scaffolding can be torn down and taken away.

Indeed, the whole concept of explanation by means of mechanism has been largely abandoned in modern physics. In Unit 5 and the Supplemental Unit *The Nucleus,* we will take up the important developments in twentieth-century physics that have demonstrated the shortcomings of mechanical explanation.

Einstein in 1912.

See Einstein's essay "On the Method of Theoretical Physics" in *Reader 4.*

Some of the other important consequences of Einstein's theory of relativity will be discussed in Unit 5.

SG 16.24–16.28

Q13 Why did Maxwell (and others) cling to the concept of an ether?

Q14 Whose argument finally showed that the ether was an unnecessary hypothesis?

EPILOGUE   In this unit we have followed the story of how light and electromagnetism became understandable, first separately and then together. The particle model of light explained the behavior of light in terms of moving particles. On experiencing strong forces at a boundary, these particles were thought of as bouncing back or swerving in just the direction that light is observed to be reflected and refracted. The wave model accounted for these and other effects by treating light as transverse waves in a continuous medium. These rival theories of light provided helpful mechanical models for light viewed either as particles or waves.

Mechanical models also worked, up to a point, in explaining electricity and magnetism. Both Faraday and Maxwell made use of mechanical models for electric and magnetic lines of force. Maxwell used these models as guides in developing a mathematical theory of electromagnetism that, when completed, went well beyond the models. This theory also explained light as an electromagnetic wave phenomenon.

The electric and magnetic fields of Maxwell's theory cannot be made to correspond to the parts of any mechanical model. Is there, then, any way we can picture in our minds what a field "looks like"? Here is the response of the Nobel Prize-winning American physicist Richard Feynman to this question:

> I have asked you to imagine these electric and magnetic fields. What do you do? Do you know how? How do I imagine the electric and magnetic field? What do I actually see? What are the demands of scientific imagination? Is it any different from trying to imagine that the room is full of invisible angels? No, it is not like imagining invisible angels. It requires a much higher degree of imagination to understand the electromagnetic field than to understand invisible angels. Why? Because to make invisible angels understandable, all I have to do is to alter their properties a *little bit*—I make them slightly visible, and then I can see the shapes of their wings and bodies, and halos. Once I succeed in imagining a visible angel, the abstraction required—which is to take almost invisible angels and imagine them completely invisible—is relatively easy. So you say, "Professor, please give me an approximate description of the electromagnetic waves, even though it may be slightly inaccurate, so that I too can see them as well as I can see almost-invisible angels. Then I will modify the picture to the necessary abstraction."
>
> I'm sorry that I can't do that for you. I don't know how. I have no picture of this electromagnetic field that is in any sense accurate. I have known about the electromagnetic field a long time—I was in the same position 25 years ago that you are now, and I have had 25 years of experience thinking about these wiggling waves. When I start describing the magnetic field moving through space, I speak of the *E*- and *B*-fields and wave my arms and you may imagine that I can see them. I'll tell you what I *can* see. I see some kind of vague shadowy wiggling lines—here and there is an *E* and *B* written on them somehow, and perhaps some of the lines have arrows on them—an arrow here or there which disappears when I look too closely at it.

When I talk about the fields swishing through space, I have a terrible confusion between the symbols I use to describe the objects and the objects themselves. I cannot really make a picture that is even nearly like the true waves. So if you have some difficulty in making such a picture, you should not be worried that your difficulty is unusual.

(A more extended excerpt of this discussion may be found in *Reader 4.*)

We can summarize the general trend in modern mechanics and electromagnetism by saying that physical theories have become increasingly abstract and mathematical. Newton replaced the celestial machinery of early theories with a mathematical theory using the laws of motion and the inverse-square law. Maxwell developed a mathematical theory of electromagnetism that, as Einstein showed, did not require any material medium such as "ether." We are seeing here a growing but quite natural gap between common-sense ideas developed from direct human experiences and the subtle mathematical abstractions describing effects that we cannot sense directly.

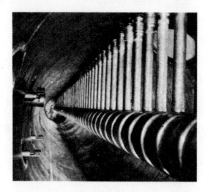

Yet, in the end, even these highly abstract theories must make sense when put into ordinary language. And they *do* tell us about the things we can see and touch and feel. They use abstract language, but have concrete tests and by-products. They have made it possible to devise the equipment that guides space probes to other planets and to design and operate the instruments that enable us to communicate with these probes. Not only are these theories at the base of all practical developments in electronics and optics, but they now also contribute to our understanding of vision and the nervous system.

Maxwell's electromagnetic theory and the interpretation given to electromagnetism and mechanics by Einstein in the special theory of relativity produced a profound change in the basic philosophical viewpoint of the Newtonian cosmology. (In this sense, Unit 4 marks a kind of watershed between the "old" and "new" ways of doing physics.) While it is too early to hope for a comprehensive statement of these changes, some aspects of a new cosmology can already be detected. For this purpose, we must now give further attention to the behavior of matter, and to the atomic theories developed to account for this behavior.

16.1 The Project Physics learning materials particularly appropriate for Chapter 16 include:

Activities
Microwave Transmission System
Science and the Artist – the Story Behind a
  Science Stamp
Bell Telephone Science Kits

Reader Articles
James Clerk Maxwell, Part II
On the Induction of Electric Current
The Relationship of Electricity and Magnetism
The Electromagnetic Field

Film Loop
Standing Electromagnetic Waves

Transparency
The Electromagnetic Spectrum

16.2 What inspired Oersted to look for a connection between electricity and magnetism?

16.3 A current in a conductor can be caused by a steady electric field. Can a *displacement* current in an insulator be similarly caused? Explain your answer briefly.

16.4 What causes an electromagnetic wave to be initiated? to be propagated?

16.5 What is the "disturbance" that travels in each of the following waves:
(a) water waves
(b) sound waves
(c) electromagnetic waves

16.6 In Hertz's detector, it is the electric field strength in the neighborhood of the wire that makes the sparks jump. How could Hertz show that the waves from the induction coil spark gap were polarized?

16.7 What evidence did Hertz obtain that his induction-coil-generated waves have many properties similar to visible light waves?

16.8 Give several factors that contributed to the twenty-five year delay in the general acceptance by scientists of Maxwell's electro-magnetic wave theory.

16.9 What evidence is there for believing that electromagnetic waves carry energy? Since the energy travels in the direction of wave propagation, how does this suggest why the early particle theory of light had some success?

16.10 What is the wavelength of an electromagnetic wave generated by the 60 cycles/sec alternating current in power lines? By radio broadcasts at the standard AM radio frequencies (between 500 and $1,500 \times 10^3$ cycles/sec)? By broadcasts on the AM "Citizen Band" (26.225×10^6 cycles/sec)?

16.11 How short are "short-wave" radio waves? (Look at the frequencies indicated on the dial of a short-wave radio.)

16.12 Electric discharges in sparks, neon signs, lighting, and some atmospheric disturbances produce radio waves. The result is "static" or noise in AM radio receivers. Give other likely sources of such static.

16.13 Why is there federal control on the broadcast power and direction of radio and TV stations, but no such controls on the distribution of newspapers and magazines?

16.14 If there are extraterrestial beings of advanced civilizations, what method for gathering information about earth-people might they have?

16.15 Why can radio waves be detected at greater distances than the waves used for television and FM broadcasting?

16.16 Some relay satellites have a 24-hour orbit. Thus they stay above the same point as the earth turns below them. What would the radius and location of the orbit of such a "synchronous" orbit be? (Refer to Unit 2 for whatever principles or constants you need.)

16.17 Explain why airplanes passing overhead cause "flutter" of a TV picture.

16.18 How much time would elapse between the sending of a radar signal to the moon and the return of the echo?

16.19 Refer to the black-and-white photograph on page 113, taken using film sensitive only to infrared. How do you explain the appearance of the trees, clouds, and sky?

16.20 Why do you think the eye is sensitive to the range of light wavelengths to which it *is* sensitive?

16.21 A sensitive thermometer placed in different parts of the visible light spectrum formed by a quartz prism will show a rise in temperature. This shows that all colors of light produce heat when absorbed. But the thermometer also shows an increase in temperature when its bulb is placed in either of the two dark regions to either side of the end of the visible spectrum. Why is this?

16.22 For each part of the electromagnetic spectrum discussed in Sec. 16.5, list the ways in which you have been affected by it. Give examples of things you have done with radiation in that frequency range, or of effects it has had on you.

16.23 What is the principal reason for the loss of support for the ether concept?

16.24 At many points in the history of science the "natural" or common sense way of looking at things has changed greatly. Our attitudes toward action-at-a-distance are a case in point. What are some other examples?

16.25 Can intuition be educated? That is, can our feelings about the fundamental aspects of reality be changed? Use attitudes taken toward action-at-a-distance of the ether as one example, and give others.

16.26 Explain the "cat-less" grin shown below.

16.27 Write a brief essay on any two of the five pictures on pages 120 and 121, explaining in some detail what principles of physics they illustrate. (Select first the main principle at work in each of the situations shown here. Also you need not limit yourself to the principles discussed in this unit.)

16.28 In a couple of pages, summarize how this unit built up the story (and physical details) of the theory of light and the particle model of light. Include the model of light as a material wave in a material ether. Go on to the joining of the initially separate disciplines of electricity and magnetism, first with each other and then with the theory of light in Maxwell's general electromagnetic theory.

In this chapter you have read about how mechanical models of light and electromagnetism faded away, leaving a model-less, *mathematical* (and therefore abstract) field theory. The situation might be likened to that of the Cheshire Cat, in a story written by the Reverend Charles Dodgson, a mathematics teacher at Oxford, in 1862. Some excerpts are reproduced below.

"I wish you wouldn't keep appearing and vanishing so suddenly," replied Alice, "you make one quite giddy." "All right," said the Cat; and this time it vanished quite slowly beginning with the end of the tail and ending with the grin, which remained some time after the rest of it had gone. "Well! I've often seen a cat without a grin," thought Alice, "but a grin without a cat! It's the most curious thing I ever saw in my life!"

[*Alice's Adventures in Wonderland*, Chapter VI]

PROJECT PHYSICS

5

Models of the Atom

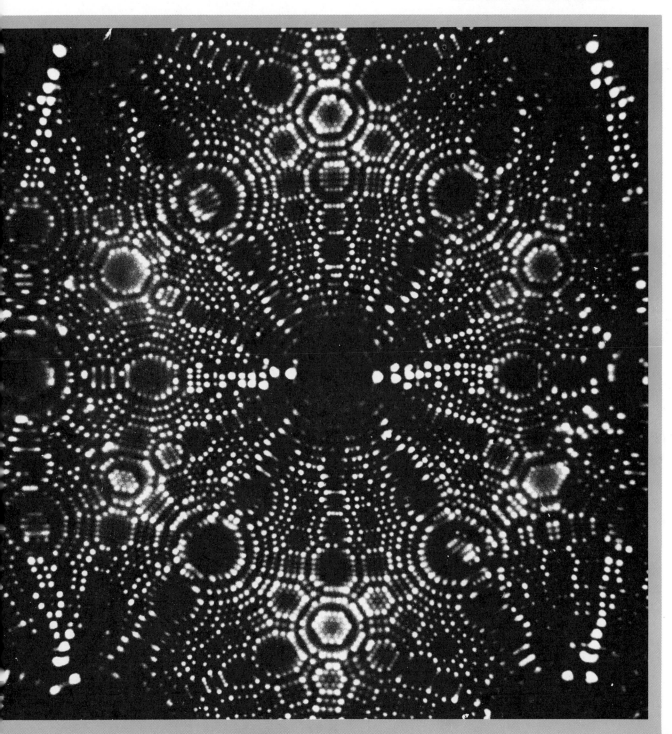

Experiments

5-1 Electrolysis
5-2 The Charge-to-Mass Ratio for an electron
5-3 The Measurement of Elementary Charge
5-4 The Photoelectric Effect
5-5 Spectroscopy

Activities

Dalton's Puzzle
Electrolysis of Water
Periodic Table
Single-Electrode Plating
Activities from *Scientific American*
Writings By or About Einstein
Measuring q/m for the Electron
Cathode Rays in a Crookes Tube
Lighting an Electric Lamp with a Match
X rays from a Crookes Tube
Scientists on Stamps
Measuring Ionization, a Quantum Effect
Modeling Atoms with Magnets
"Black Box" Atoms
Standing Waves on a Band-saw Blade
Turntable Oscillator Patterns Resembling deBroglie Waves
Standing Waves in a Wire Ring

Film Loops

L45 Production of Sodium by Electrolysis
L46 Thomson model of the Atom
L47 Rutherford Scattering

Transparencies

T35 Periodic Table
T36 Photoelectric Experiment
T37 Photoelectric Equation
T38 Alpha Scattering
T39 Energy Levels—Bohr Theory

Reader Articles

1 *Failure and Success*
by Charles Percy Snow
2 *The Clock Paradox in Relativity*
by C. G. Darwin
3 *The Island of Research*
by Ernest Harburg
4 *Ideas and Theories*
by V. Guillemin
5 *Einstein*
by Leopold Infeld
6 *Mr. Tompkins and Simultaneity*
by George Gamow
7 *Mathematics and Relativity*
by Eric M. Rogers
8 *Parable of the Surveyors*
by Edwin F. Taylor and John Archibald Wheeler
9 *Outside and Inside the Elevator*
by Albert Einstein and Leopold Infeld
10 *Einstein and Some Civilized Discontents*
by Martin Klein
11 *The Teacher and the Bohr Theory of the Atom*
by Charles Percy Snow
12 *The New Landscape of Science*
by Banesh Hoffmann
13 *The Evolution of the Physicist's Picture of Nature*
by Paul A. M. Dirac
14 *Dirac and Born*
by Leopold Infeld
15 *I am this Whole World: Erwin Schrödinger*
by Jeremy Bernstein
16 *The Fundamental Idea of Wave Mechanics*
by Erwin Schrödinger
17 *The Sentinel*
by Arthur C. Clarke
18 *The Sea-Captain's Box*
by John L. Synge
19 *Space Travel: Problems of Physics and Engineering*
by the Harvard Project Physics Staff
20 *Looking for a New Law*
by Richard P. Feynman
21 A Portfolio of Computer-made Drawings

Contents TEXT, Unit 5

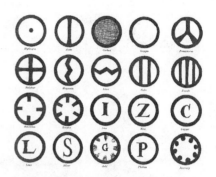

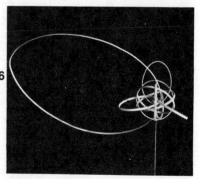

UNIT 5

Models of the Atom

PROLOGUE In the earlier units of this course we studied the motion of bodies: bodies of ordinary size, such as we deal with in everyday life, and very large bodies, such as planets. We saw how the laws of motion and gravitation were developed over many centuries and how they are used. We learned about conservation laws, waves, light, and electric and magnetic fields. All that we have learned so far can be used to study a problem which has intrigued people for many centuries: the problem of the nature of matter. The phrase "the nature of matter" may seem simple to us now. But its meaning has been changing and growing over the centuries. The kinds of questions asked about matter and the methods used to answer these questions are continually changing. For example, during the nineteenth century the study of the nature of matter consisted mainly of chemistry; in the twentieth century the study of matter has also moved into atomic and nuclear physics.

Since 1800 progress has been so rapid that it is easy to forget that people have theorized about matter for more than 2,500 years. In fact some questions which have been answered only during the last hundred years were first asked more than two thousand years ago. Some ideas which we consider new and exciting, such as the atomic structure of matter, were debated in Greece in the fifth and fourth centuries B.C. In this prologue we will review briefly the development of ideas concerning the nature of matter up to about 1800. This review will set the stage for the four chapters of Unit 5, which cover in greater detail the progress made since 1800. We will see that regardless of the form it takes—large or small, stable or shifting, solid, liquid, or gaseous—all matter is made up of separate particles that we call atoms. And we will find that the atoms themselves have structure.

Opposite: Monolith—The Face of Half Dome (Photo by Ansel Adams)

The photographs on these two pages illustrate some of the variety of forms of matter: large and small, stable and shifting.

microscopic crystals

condensed water vapor

Greek Ideas of Order

The Greek mind loved clarity and order, expressed in a way that still touches us deeply. In philosophy, literature, art, and architecture the Greeks sought to interpret things in terms of humane and lasting qualities. They tried to discover the forms and patterns thought to be essential to an understanding of things. They delighted in showing these forms and patterns when they found them. Their art and architecture express beauty and intellectual order by means of balance of form and simple dignity.

These aspects of Greek thought are beautifully expressed in the shrine of Delphi. The theater, which could seat 5,000 spectators, impresses us because of the size and depth of the tiered seating structure. But even more striking is the natural and orderly way in which the theater blends with its surroundings: the entire landscape takes on the aspect of a giant theater. The orderly proportions of

the Treasury building at Delphi integrate form and function into a logical, pleasing whole. The statue of the charioteer found at Delphi, with its balance and firmness, represents an ideal of male beauty at that time. After more than 2,000 years we are still struck by the elegance of Greek expression.

The Roman poet Lucretius based his ideas of physics on the tradition of atomism dating back to the Greek philosophers Democritus and Leucippus. The following passages are from his poem *De Rerum Natura (On the Nature of Things),* an effective statement of atomism:

> . . . If you think
> Atoms can stop their course, refrain from movement,
> And by cessation cause new kinds of motion,
> You are far astray indeed. Since there is void
> Through which they move, all fundamental motes
> Must be impelled, either by their own weight
> Or by some force outside them. When they strike
> Each other, they bounce off; no wonder, either,
> Since they are absolute solid, all compact,
> With nothing back of them to block their path.
>   . . . no atom ever rests
> Coming through void, but always drives, is driven
> In various ways, and their collisions cause,
> As the case may be, greater or less rebound.
> When they are held in thickest combination,
> At closer intervals, with the space between
> More hindered by their interlock of figure,
> These give us rock, or adamant, or iron,
> Things of that nature. (Not very many kinds
> Go wandering little and lonely through the void.)
> There are some whose alternate meetings, partings, are
> At greater intervals; from these we are given
> Thin air, the shining sunlight . . .
>   . . . It's no wonder
> That while the atoms are in constant motion,
> Their total seems to be at total rest,
> Save here and there some individual stir.
> Their nature lies beyond our range of sense,
> Far, far beyond. Since you can't get to see
> The things themselves, they're bound to hide their moves,
> Especially since things we can see, often
> Conceal their movements, too, when at a distance.
> Take grazing sheep on a hill, you know they move,
> The woolly creatures, to crop the lovely grass
> Wherever it may call each one, with dew
> Still sparkling it with jewels, and the lambs,
> Fed full, play little games, flash in the sunlight,
> Yet all this, far away, is just a blue,
> A whiteness resting on a hill of green.
> Or when great armies sweep across great plains
> In mimic warfare, and their shining goes
> Up to the sky, and all the world around
> Is brilliant with their bronze, and trampled earth
> Trembles under the cadence of their tread,
> White mountains echo the uproar to the stars,
> The horsemen gallop and shake the very ground,
> And yet high in the hills there is a place
> From which the watcher sees a host at rest,
> And only a brightness resting on the plain.
> *(Translated from the Latin by Rolfe Humphries)*

Early science had to develop out of ideas that were available before science started. These ideas came from experience with snow, wind, rain, mist, and clouds; heat and cold; salt and fresh water; wine, milk, blood, and honey; ripe and unripe fruit; fertile and infertile seeds. The most obvious and most puzzling facts were that plants, animals, and people were born, grew and matured, then aged and died. The world was continually changing and yet, on the whole, it seemed to remain much the same. The causes of these changes and of the apparent continuity of nature were unknown. Often they were assigned to the actions of gods and demons. Myths concerning the creation of the world and the changes of the seasons were among the earliest creative productions of primitive peoples everywhere. Such myths helped people to come to terms with events they could see happening but could not rationally understand.

Over a long period of time humans developed some control over nature and materials. They learned how to keep warm and dry, to smelt ores, to make weapons and tools, to produce gold ornaments, glass, perfumes, and medicines. Eventually, in Greece, by the year 600 B.C., philosophers—literally "lovers of wisdom"—had started to look for rational explanations of natural events. They wanted explanations that did not depend on the actions or the whims of gods or demons. They sought to discover the enduring, unchanging things out of which the world is made. How did these things give rise to the changes we perceive and to the great variety of material things that exists? This was the beginning of human attempts to understand the material world rationally, and it led to a theory of the nature of matter.

The earliest Greek philosophers thought that all the different things in the world were made out of a single basic substance. Some thought that water was the fundamental substance and that all other substances were derived from it. Others thought that air was the basic substance; still others favored fire. But neither water, nor air, nor fire was satisfactory. No one substance seemed to have enough different properties to give rise to the enormous variety of substances in the world. According to another view, introduced by Empedocles around 450 B.C., there were four basic types of matter—earth, air, fire, and water. All material things were made out of them. These four basic materials could mingle and separate and reunite in different proportions. In doing so, they could produce the variety of familiar objects around us as well as the changes in such objects. But the basic four materials, called *elements,* were supposed to persist through all these changes. This theory was the first appearance of a *model of matter* explaining all material things as just different arrangements of a few elements.

The first atomic theory of matter was introduced by the Greek philosopher Leucippus, born about 500 B.C., and his pupil Democritus (460-370 B.C.). Only scattered fragments of the writings of these philosophers remain. But their ideas were discussed in considerable detail by the Greek philosophers Aristotle (389-321 B.C.) and Epicurus (341-270 B.C.), and by the Latin poet Lucretius (100-55 B.C.). To these men we owe most of our knowledge of ancient atomism.

This gold earring, made in Greece about 600 B.C., shows the great skill with which ancient artisans worked metals. [Museum of Fine Arts, Boston]

The theory of the atomists was based on a number of assumptions:

(1) Matter is eternal—no material thing can come from nothing, nor can any material thing pass into nothing.

(2) Material things consist of very small indivisible particles. The word "atom" meant "uncuttable" in Greek. In discussing the ideas of the early atomists, we could use the word "indivisibles" instead of the word "atoms."

(3) Atoms differ chiefly in their sizes and shapes.

(4) Atoms exist in otherwise empty space (the void) which separates them, and this space allows them to move from one place to another.

(5) Atoms are continually in motion, although the nature and cause of the motion are not clear.

(6) In the course of their motions atoms come together and form combinations which are the material substances we know. When the atoms forming these combinations separate, the substances decay or break up. Thus, the combinations and separations of atoms give rise to the changes which take place in the world.

(7) The combinations and separations take place according to natural laws which are not yet clear, but do not require the action of gods or demons or other supernatural powers. In fact, one of the chief aims of the atomists was to liberate people from superstition and fear. As Lucretius put it, "fear in sooth takes hold of all mortals because they see many operations go on in earth and heaven, the causes of which they can in no way understand, believing them therefore to be done by divine power." By explaining natural events by the motion of atoms, he hoped to show "the manner in which all things are done without the hand of the gods."

With the above assumptions, the ancient atomists worked out a consistent story of change, which they sometimes called "coming-to-be" and "passing away." They could not demonstrate experimentally that their theory was correct—it was simply an explanation derived from assumptions that seemed reasonable to them. The theory was a "likely story." It was not useful for predicting new phenomena; but prediction became an important value for a theory only later. To the atomists, it was more significant that the theory also helped to allay an unreasonable belief in capricious supernatural beings.

The atomic theory was criticized severely by Aristotle. He argued logically—from his own assumptions—that no vacuum or void could exist. Therefore, the idea of atoms in continual motion must be rejected. (Aristotle was also probably sensitive to the fact that in his time belief in atomism was identified with atheism.) For a long time Aristotle's argument against the void was widely held to be convincing. One must here recall that not until the seventeenth century did Torricelli's experiments (described in Chapter 11) show that a vacuum could indeed exist. Furthermore, Aristotle argued that matter is continuous and infinitely divisible, so that there can be no atoms.

Aristotle developed a theory of matter as part of his grand scheme of the universe. This theory, with some modifications, was considered satisfactory by most philosophers of nature for nearly two thousand years.

According to Aristotle in his *Metaphysics,* "There is no consensus concerning the number or nature of these fundamental substances. Thales, the first to think about such matters, held that the elementary substance is clear liquid. . . . He may have gotten this idea from the observation that only moist matter can be wholly integrated into an object—so that all growth depends on moisture. . . .

"Anaximenes and Diogenes held that colorless gas is more elementary than clear liquid, and that indeed, it is the most elementary of all simple substances. On the other hand, Hippasus of Metpontum and Heraclitus of Ephesus said that the most elementary substance is heat. Empedocles spoke of four elementary substances, adding dry dust to the three already mentioned . . . Anaxagoras of Clazomenae said that there are an infinite number of elementary constituents of matter. . . ." [From a translation by D. E. Gershenson and D. A. Greenberg.]

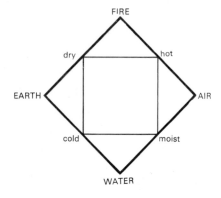

It was based on the four basic elements, Earth, Air, Fire, and Water, and four "qualities," Cold, Hot, Moist, and Dry. Each element was characterized by two qualities (the nearer two to each side, as shown in the diagram at the left). Thus the element

Earth is Dry and Cold,
Water is Cold and Moist,
Air is Moist and Hot,
Fire is Hot and Dry.

According to Aristotle, it is always the first of the two qualities which dominates. In his version the elements are not unchangeable. Any one of them may be transformed into any other if one or both of its qualities change to their opposites. The transformation takes place most easily between two elements having one quality in common. Thus Earth is transformed into Water when dryness changes into moistness. Earth can be transformed into Air only if both of the qualities of earth (dry and cold) are changed into their opposites (moist and hot).

As we mentioned in Chapter 2, Aristotle was able to explain many natural phenomena by means of his ideas. Like the atomic theory, Aristotle's theory of coming-to-be and passing-away was a consistent model of the nature of matter. And it had certain advantages over the atomic theory. For example, it was based on elements and qualities that were familiar to people; it did not involve atoms, which couldn't be seen or otherwise perceived, or a void, which was difficult to imagine. In addition, Aristotle's theory provided some basis for further experimentation: it supplied what seemed like a rational basis for the fascinating possibility of changing any material into any other.

Although the atomistic view was not completely abandoned, it found few supporters between 300 B.C. and about 1600 B.C. The atoms of Leucippus and Democritus moved through empty space, which contained no "spirit" and had no definite plan or purpose. Such an idea remained contrary to the beliefs of the major religions. Like the Athenians in the time of Plato and Aristotle, the later Christian, Hebrew, and Moslem theologians considered atomists atheistic and "materialistic" for claiming that everything in the universe could be explained in terms of matter and motion.

About 300 or 400 years after Aristotle, a kind of research called *alchemy* appeared in the Near and Far East. Alchemy in the Near East combined Aristotle's ideas about matter with methods of treating ores and metals. One aim of the alchemists was to change or "transmute" ordinary metals into precious metals. Although they failed to do this, the alchemists found and studied many properties that are now classified as chemical properties. They invented some pieces of chemical apparatus, such as reaction vessels and distillation flasks, that (in modern form) are still common in chemical laboratories. They studied such processes as calcination, distillation, fermentation, and sublimation. In this sense alchemy may be regarded as the chemistry of the Middle Ages. But alchemy left unsolved the fundamental questions. At the opening of the eighteenth century the most important of these questions were: (1) What is a chemical element? (2) What is the nature of chemical composition and chemical change, especially burning? (3) What is the chemical nature of the so-called elements, Earth, Air, Fire and Water? Until these questions were

Laboratory of a 16th-century alchemist.

answered, it was impossible to make real progress in finding out the structure of matter. Real progress was delayed until about a century after the "scientific revolution" of the seventeenth century, which clarified the chief problems of astronomy and mechanics, but not of chemistry.

During the seventeenth century, however, some forward steps were made, supplying a basis for future progress on the problem of matter. The Copernican and Newtonian revolutions greatly undermined the authority of Aristotle. Now his ideas about matter were also more easily questioned. Atomic concepts were revived, offering a way of looking at things that was very different from Aristotle's ideas. As a result, theories involving atoms (or "particles" or "corpuscles") were again considered seriously. Boyle based his models on the idea of "gas particles." Newton also discussed the behavior of a gas (and even of light) by supposing it to consist of particles. In addition, there was now a successful science of mechanics. Through it, scientists could hope to describe how the atoms interacted with each other. Thus the stage was set for a general revival of atomic theory.

In the eighteenth century, chemistry became more quantitative. Weighing, in particular, was done more frequently and more carefully. New substances were isolated and their properties examined. The attitude that grew up in the second half of the century was apparent in the work of Henry Cavendish (1731-1810). According to a biographer, Cavendish regarded the universe as consisting

> . . . solely of a multitude of objects which could be weighed, numbered, and measured; and the vocation to which he considered himself called was to weigh, number, and measure as many of those objects as his alloted threescore years and ten would permit. . . . He weighed the Earth; he analysed the Air; he discovered the compound nature of Water; he noted with numerical precision the obscure actions of the ancient element Fire.

Eighteenth-century chemistry reached its peak in the work of Antoine Lavoisier (1743-1794). Lavoisier worked out the modern views of combustion, established the law of conservation of mass, and explained the elementary nature of hydrogen and oxygen and the composition of water. Above all, he emphasized the quantitative aspects of chemistry. His famous book, *Traité Elémentaire de Chimie* (or *Elements of Chemistry*), published in 1789, established chemistry as a modern science. In it, he analyzed the idea of an element in a way which is very close to modern views:

> . . . if, by the term *elements* we mean to express those simple and indivisible atoms of which matter is composed, it is extremely probable that we know nothing at all about them; but if we apply the term *elements,* or *principles of bodies,* to express our idea of the last point which analysis is capable of reaching, we must admit as elements all the substances into which we are capable, by any means, to reduce bodies by decomposition. Not that we are entitled to affirm that these substances we consider as simple may not be compounded of two, or even of a greater number of principles; but since these principles cannot be separated, or rather since we have not

One of those who contributed greatly to the revival of atomism was Pierre Gassendi (1592-1655), a French priest and philosopher. He avoided the criticism of atomism as atheistic by saying that God created the atoms and bestowed motion upon them. Gassendi accepted the physical explanations of the atomists, but rejected their disbelief in the immortality of the soul and in Divine Providence. He was thus able to provide a philosophical justification of atomism which met some of the serious religious objections.

It was Cavendish, remember, who designed the sensitive torsional balance that made it possible to find a value for the gravitational constant G. (*Text* Sec. 8.8.)

Lavoisier's work on the conservation of mass was described in *Text* Chapter 9.

TRAITE
ELEMENTAIRE
DE CHIMIE,

PRÉSENTÉ DANS UN ORDRE NOUVEAU

ET D'APRÈS LES DÉCOUVERTES MODERNES;

Avec Figures :

Par M. *LAVOISIER*, de l'Académie des
Sciences, de la Société Royale de Médecine, des
Sociétés d'Agriculture de Paris & d'Orléans, de
la Société Royale de Londres, de l'Inſtitut de
Bologne, de la Société Helvétique de Baſle, de
celles de Philadelphie, Harlem, Mancheſter,
Padoue, &c.

TOME PREMIER.

A PARIS,

Chez CUCHET, Libraire, rue & hôtel Serpente.

M. DCC. LXXXIX.

Sous le Privilége de l'Académie des Sciences & de la
Société Royale de Médecine

Title page of Lavoisier's *Traité Ele-
méntaire de Chimie* (1789)

hitherto discovered the means of separating them, they act with
regard to us as simple substances, and we ought never to
suppose them compounded until experiment and observation
have proved them to be so.

During the second half of the eighteenth century and the early years of the
nineteenth century great progress was made in chemistry. This progress
resulted largely from the increasing use of quantitative methods. Chemists
found out more and more about the composition of substances. They
separated many elements and showed that nearly all substances are
compounds—combinations of a fairly small number of chemical elements.
They learned a great deal about how elements combine and form
compounds, and how compounds can be broken down into the elements of
which they consist. This information allowed chemists to establish many
empirical laws of chemical combination. Then chemists sought an
explanation for these laws.

During the first ten years of the nineteenth century, the English chemist
John Dalton introduced a modified form of the old Greek atomic theory.
Dalton's theory was an attempt to account for the laws of chemical
combination. It is here that the modern story of the atom begins. Dalton's
atomic theory was an improvement over that of the Greeks because it
opened the way for quantitative study of the atom. Today the existence of
the atom is no longer a topic of speculation. There are many kinds of
experimental evidence, not only for the existence of atoms but also for their
inner structure. In this unit we will trace the discoveries and ideas that
provided this evidence.

The first convincing modern idea of the atom came from chemistry. We
will, therefore, start with chemistry in the early years of the nineteenth
century; this is the subject of Chapter 17. Then we will see that chemistry
raised certain questions about atoms which could only be answered by
physics. Physical evidence, accumulated in the nineteenth century and the
early years of the twentieth century, made it possible to propose models for
the structure of atoms. This evidence will be discussed in Chapters 18 and
19. Some of the latest ideas about atomic theory will then be discussed in
Chapter 20.

Chemical laboratory of the 18th century

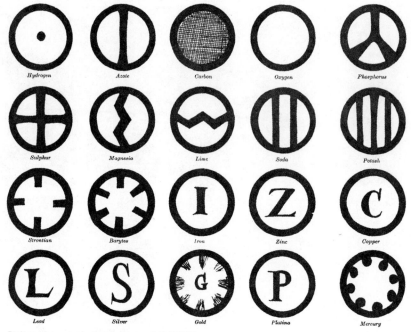

Dalton's symbols for ''elements'' (1808)

CHAPTER SEVENTEEN

The Chemical Basis of Atomic Theory

17.1 Dalton's atomic theory and the laws of chemical combination

The atomic theory of John Dalton appeared in his treatise, *A New System of Chemical Philosophy*, published in two parts, in 1808 and 1810. The main postulates of his theory were:

(1) Matter consists of indivisible atoms.

SG 17.1

> . . . matter, though divisible in an *extreme degree,* is nevertheless not *infinitely* divisible. That is, there must be some point beyond which we cannot go in the division of matter. The existence of these ultimate particles of matter can scarcely be doubted, though they are probably much too small ever to be exhibited by microscopic improvements. I have chosen the word *atom* to signify these ultimate particles. . . .

(2) Each element consists of a characteristic kind of identical atoms. Consequently there are as many different kinds of atoms as there are elements. The atoms of an element "are perfectly alike in weight and figure, etc."

(3) Atoms are unchangeable.

(4) When different elements combine and form a compound, the smallest possible portion of the compound is a group containing a definite number of atoms of each element.

(5) In chemical reactions, atoms are neither created nor destroyed, but only rearranged.

Dalton's theory really grew out of his interest in meteorology and his research on the composition of the atmosphere. He tried to explain many of the physical properties of gases in terms of atoms (for example, the fact that gases readily mix, and the fact that the pressures of two gases add simply when both are combined in a closed container). He thought of the atoms of different elements as being different in size and in mass. In keeping with the quantitative spirit of the time, he tried to determine numerical values for their relative masses. This was a crucial step forward. Shortly we will consider how to determine the relative masses of atoms of the different elements. But first let us see how Dalton's postulates make it possible to account for the experimentally known laws of chemical combination.

Meteorology is a science that deals with the atmosphere and its phenomena—weather forecasting is one branch of meteorology.

Dalton's atomic theory explains the law of conservation of mass in a simple and direct way. According to Dalton's theory (postulates 4 and 5), chemical changes are only rearrangements of unions of atoms. Since atoms are unchangeable (according to postulate 3), rearranging them cannot change their masses. Hence, the total mass of all the atoms before the reaction must equal the total mass of all the atoms after the reaction.

Another well known empirical law which Dalton's theory easily explains is the *law of definite proportions*. This law states that any particular chemical compound always contains the same elements, united in the same proportions of weight. For example, the ratio of the masses of oxygen and hydrogen which combine and form water is always 7.94 to 1:

$$\frac{\text{mass of oxygen}}{\text{mass of hydrogen}} = \frac{7.94}{1}$$

This law holds even if more of one element is present than is needed for full combination in a chemical reaction. If 10 grams of oxygen and one gram of hydrogen are present, only 7.94 grams of oxygen combine with the hydrogen. The rest of the oxygen, 2.06 grams, remains uncombined.

The fact that elements combine in fixed proportions suggests that each chemical compound will also decompose into definite proportions of elements. For example, the decomposition of sodium chloride (common salt) always gives 39 percent sodium and 61 percent chlorine by weight.

Now let us see how Dalton's model applies to a chemical reaction, such as the formation of water from oxygen and hydrogen. According to Dalton's second postulate, all the atoms of oxygen have the same mass. Further, all the atoms of hydrogen have the same mass, which is different from the mass of the oxygen atoms. To express the total mass of oxygen entering into the reaction, we multiply the mass of a single oxygen atom by the number of oxygen atoms:

$$\text{mass of oxygen} = \left(\begin{array}{c}\text{mass of}\\ \text{oxygen atom}\end{array}\right) \times \left(\begin{array}{c}\text{number of}\\ \text{oxygen atoms}\end{array}\right)$$

Similarly, for the total mass of hydrogen entering into the reaction:

$$\text{mass of hydrogen} = \left(\begin{array}{c}\text{mass of}\\ \text{hydrogen atom}\end{array}\right) \times \left(\begin{array}{c}\text{number of}\\ \text{hydrogen atoms}\end{array}\right)$$

We can find the ratio of the mass of oxygen to the mass of hydrogen by dividing the first equation by the second equation in the following equation

$$\frac{\text{mass of oxygen}}{\text{mass of hydrogen}} = \frac{\begin{array}{c}\text{mass of}\\ \text{oxygen atom}\end{array}}{\begin{array}{c}\text{mass of}\\ \text{hydrogen atom}\end{array}} \times \frac{\begin{array}{c}\text{number of}\\ \text{oxygen atoms}\end{array}}{\begin{array}{c}\text{number of}\\ \text{hydrogen atoms}\end{array}}$$

Recall that empirical laws (such as these, or Kepler's laws of planetary motion) are just summaries of experimentally observed facts. They cry out for some theoretical base from which they can be shown to follow as necessary consequences. Physical science looks for these deeper necessities that describe nature, and is not satisfied with mere summaries of observation, useful though these may be initially.

SG 17.2, 17.3

SG 17.4

If the masses of the atoms do not change (postulate 3), the first ratio on the right side of the equation has a certain unchangeable value. If the smallest portion of the compound water consists of a definite number of atoms of each element (postulate 4), the second ratio on the right side of the equation has a certain unchangeable value also. So the product of the two ratios on the right side will always have the same value. This equation then, based on an atomic theory, tells us that the ratio of the masses of oxygen and hydrogen combined as water will always have the same definite value. And this is just what the experimental law of definite proportions says. Dalton's theory accounts for this law of chemical combination, and this success tends to confirm Dalton's concept.

Dalton's theory was also consistent with another empirical law of chemical combination, the *law of multiple proportion*. For some combinations of elements there is a *set* of possible values for their proportions, corresponding to a set of possible compounds. Dalton showed that these cases could all be accounted for by different combinations of

A page from Dalton's notebook, showing his representation of two adjacent atoms (top) and of a molecule or "compound atom" (bottom)

John Dalton (1766-1844). His first love was meteorology, and he kept careful daily weather records for 46 years—a total of 200,000 observations. He was the first to describe color blindness in a publication and was color-blind himself, not exactly an advantage for a chemist who had to see color changes in chemicals. (His color blindness may help to explain why Dalton is said to have been a rather clumsy experimenter.) However, his accomplishments rest not on successful experiments, but on his ingenious interpretation of the known results of others. Dalton's notion that all elements were composed of extremely tiny, indivisible and indestructible atoms, and that all substances are composed of combinations of these atoms was accepted soon by most chemists with surprisingly little opposition. There were many attempts to honor him, but being a Quaker he shunned any form of glory. When he received a doctor's degree from Oxford, his colleagues wanted to present him to King William IV. He had always resisted such a presentation because he would not wear court dress. He agreed to the presentation only when he found that his Oxford robes satisfied the protocol.

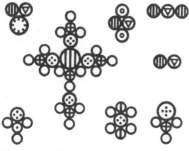

Dalton's visualization of the composition of various compounds.

whole numbers of atoms.

There are other laws of chemical combination which are explained by Dalton's theory. Because discussion of these laws would be lengthy and would add relatively little that is new, we will not go into it here.

Dalton's interpretation of the experimental facts of chemical combination made possible several important conclusions: (1) The difference between one chemical element and another must be described in terms of the differences between the atoms of which these elements are made up. (2) There are, therefore, as many different types of atoms as there are chemical elements. (3) Chemical combination is the union of atoms of different elements into molecules of compounds. Dalton's theory also implied that analysis of a large number of chemical compounds could establish relative mass values for the atoms of different elements. This possibility will be discussed in the next section.

Q1 What did Dalton *assume* about the atoms of an element?

Q2 What two *experimental* laws did Dalton's theory explain? What follows from these successes?

17.2 The atomic masses of the elements

The first good estimates of molecular size came from the kinetic theory of gases and indicated that atoms (or molecules) had diameters of the order of 10^{-10} meter. Atoms are thus much too small for ordinary mass measurements to be made on single atoms.

One of the most important concepts to come from Dalton's work is that of atomic mass and the possibility of determining numerical values for the masses of the atoms of different elements. Dalton had no idea of the actual absolute mass of individual atoms. Reasonably good estimates of the size of atoms did not appear until about 50 years after Dalton published his theory. Nevertheless, Dalton showed that *relative* values of atomic masses could be found by using the law of definite proportions and experimental data on chemical reactions.

To see how this could be done we return to the case of water. The ratio of the mass of oxygen to the mass of hydrogen is found by experiment to be 7.94:1. If we knew how many atoms of oxygen and hydrogen a molecule of water contains, we could calculate the ratio of the mass of the oxygen atom to the mass of the hydrogen atom. But Dalton didn't know the numbers of oxygen and hydrogen atoms in a molecule of water. So he made an assumption. As is done often, Dalton made the *simplest* possible assumption: that a molecule of water consists of *one* atom of oxygen combined with *one* atom of hydrogen. By this reasoning Dalton concluded that the oxygen atom is 7.94 times more massive than the hydrogen atom. (As we will see, the simplest assumption proved in this case to be incorrect. Actually, *two* atoms of hydrogen combine with one atom of oxygen in a molecule of water. The oxygen atom has 7.94 times the mass of the two hydrogen atoms. Therefore, it has 15.88 times the mass of a single hydrogen atom.)

SG 17.5
SG 17.6

More generally, Dalton assumed that when only one compound of any two elements is known to exist, molecules of the compound always consist of one atom of each. With this assumption he could find values for the

relative masses of different atoms. (However, later work showed that
Dalton's assumption of one-to-one ratios was often as incorrect as it was
for water.) Dalton studied the composition of water as well as many other
chemical compounds. He found that the hydrogen atom appeared to have
a smaller mass than the atoms of any other element. Therefore, he
proposed to express the masses of atoms of all other elements relative to
the mass of the hydrogen atom. Dalton defined the *atomic mass* of an
element as the mass of an atom of that element compared to the mass of
a hydrogen atom. For example, the masses of chlorine and hydrogen gas
that react and form hydrogen chloride (the only hydrogen and chlorine
compound) are in the ratio of about 35½ to 1. Therefore the chlorine
atom should have an atomic mass of 35½ atomic mass units. Chemists in
the nineteenth century could use this definition even before the actual
values of the masses of individual atoms (say in kilograms) were measured
directly.

SG 17.7
SG 17.8

During the nineteenth century chemists extended and improved
Dalton's ideas. They studied many chemical reactions quantitatively. They
developed highly accurate methods for determining relative atomic and
molecular masses. Because oxygen combined readily with many other
elements, chemists decided to use oxygen rather than hydrogen as the
standard for atomic masses. Oxygen was assigned an atomic mass of 16 so
that hydrogen would have an atomic mass close to one. The atomic
masses of other elements could be obtained by applying the laws of
chemical combination to the compounds of the elements with oxygen.
Throughout the nineteenth century more and more elements were
identified and their atomic masses determined. For example, the table on
the next page lists 63 elements found by 1872, with the modern values for
the atomic masses. This table contains much valuable information. We
will consider it at greater length in Section 17.4. (The special marks on
the table—circles and rectangles—will be useful then.)

The system of atomic masses used
in modern physical science is based
on this principle, although it differs
in details. (Also, the standard for
comparison by international
agreement is now carbon instead of
hydrogen or oxygen.)

Q3 Was the simplest chemical formula for the composition of a
molecule necessarily the correct one?

Q4 Why did Dalton choose hydrogen as the unit of atomic mass?

The progress made in identifying
elements in the 19th century may be
seen in the following table.

Year	Total number of elements identified
1720	14
1740	15
1760	17
1780	21
1800	31
1820	49
1840	56
1860	60
1880	69
1900	83

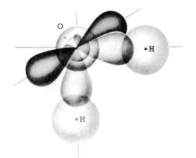

Some of the current representations
of a water molecule.

Elements known by 1872, in order of increasing relative atomic mass.

Elements known by 1872

Name	Symbol	Atomic Mass*	Name	Symbol	Atomic Mass*
hydrogen	H	1.0	cadmium	Cd	112.4
☐ lithium	Li	6.9	indium	In	114.8(113)
beryllium	Be	9.0	tin	Sn	118.7
boron	B	10.8	antimony	Sb	121.7
carbon	C	12.0	tellurium	Te	127.6(125)
nitrogen	N	14.0	○ iodine	I	126.9
oxygen	O	16.0	☐ cesium	Cs	132.9
○ fluorine	F	19.0	barium	Ba	137.3
☐ sodium	Na	23.0	didymium(**)	Di	—— (138)
magnesium	Mg	24.3	cerium	Ce	140.1
aluminum	Al	27.0	erbium	Er	167.3(178)
silicon	Si	28.1	lanthanum	La	138.9(180)
phosphorus	P	31.0	tantalum	Ta	180.9(182)
sulfur	S	32.1	tungsten	W	183.9
○ chlorine	Cl	35.5	osmium	Os	190.2(195)
☐ potassium	K	39.1	iridium	Ir	192.2(197)
calcium	Ca	40.1	platinum	Pt	195.1(198)
titanium	Ti	47.9	gold	Au	197.0(199)
vanadium	V	50.9	mercury	Hg	200.6
chromium	Cr	52.0	thallium	Tl	204.4
manganese	Mn	54.9	lead	Pb	207.2
iron	Fe	55.8	bismuth	Bi	209.0
cobalt	Co	58.9	thorium	Th	232.0
nickel	Ni	58.7	uranium	U	238.0(240)
copper	Cu	63.5			
zinc	Zn	65.4			
arsenic	As	74.9			
selenium	Se	79 0	☐ alkaline metals		
○ bromine	Br	79.9			
☐ rubidium	Rb	85.5	○ halogens		
strontium	Sr	87.6			
yttrium	Yt	88.9	*Atomic masses given are modern values. Where these differ greatly from those accepted in 1872, the old values are given in parentheses.		
zirconium	Zr	91.2			
niobium	Nb	92.9			
molybdenum	Mo	95.9			
ruthenium	Ru	101.1(104)	**Didymium (Di) was later shown to be a mixture of two different elements, namely praseodymium (Pr; atomic mass 140.9) and neodymium (Nd; atomic mass 144.2).		
rhodium	Rh	102.9(104)			
palladium	Pd	106.4			
silver	Ag	107.9			

17.3 Other properties of the elements: combining capacity

The standard international chemical symbols are derived from languages other than English. The Latin name for sodium is *natrium,* hence the symbol is Na.

As a result of studies of chemical compounds, chemists were able to design chemical *formulas.* By a kind of symbolic shorthand, such formulas indicate the number of atoms in each molecule of a compound. For example, water has the familiar formula H_2O, which indicates that a molecule of water contains two atoms of hydrogen (H) and one atom of oxygen (O). (Dalton thought it was HO.) Hydrogen chloride (hydrochloric acid when dissolved in water) has the formula HCl, signifying that one atom of hydrogen combines with one atom of chlorine (Cl). Common salt has the formula NaCl; this indicates that one atom of sodium (Na) combines with one atom of chlorine and forms one molecule of sodium chloride—table salt. Another salt, calcium chloride (often used to melt ice on roads), has the formula $CaCl_2$; one atom of calcium (Ca) and two atoms of chlorine form this compound. Carbon tetrachloride is a common compound of chlorine used for dry cleaning. In its formula, CCl_4, the C stands for a carbon atom that combines with four chlorine atoms. Another common substance, ammonia, has the formula NH_3; in this case one atom of nitrogen (N) combines with three atoms of hydrogen.

There are especially important examples of *combining capacity* among the gaseous elements. For example, the gas hydrogen occurs in nature in the form of molecules, each of which contains two hydrogen atoms. Since the hydrogen molecule consists of two atoms, it has the formula H_2. Similarly, chlorine has the molecular formula Cl_2. Chemical analysis always gives these results. It would contradict experiment to assign the formula H_3 or H_4 to a molecule of hydrogen, or Cl, Cl_3, or Cl_4 to a molecule of chlorine. Moreover, each element shows great consistency in its combining proportions with other elements. For example, calcium and oxygen seem to have twice the combining capacity of hydrogen and chlorine. One atom of hydrogen is enough for one atom of chlorine, but two hydrogens are needed to combine with oxygen and two chlorines are required to combine with calcium.

The above examples indicate that different elements have different capacities for chemical combination. It appears that each kind of atom has some definite combining capacity (which is sometimes called *valence*). At one time combining capacity was considered as though a given atom had a certain number of "hooks." These "hooks" represented the number of links that an atom could form with others of the same or different species. For example, hydrogen and chlorine atoms each would have just one hook—that is, a combining capacity of 1. Thus, one could easily see why molecules like H_2, Cl_2, and HCl are stable, while certain other species like H_3, H_2Cl, HCl_2, and Cl_3 don't exist at all. And if the hydrogen atom is assigned a combining capacity of 1, the formula of water (H_2O) requires that the oxygen atom have two hooks (a combining capacity of 2). The formula NH_3 for ammonia leads us to assign a combining capacity of three to nitrogen; the formula CH_4 for methane indicates a capacity of 4 for carbon; and so on. Proceeding in this manner, we can assign a combining capacity number to each of the known elements. Sometimes complications arise as, for example, in the case of sulfur. In H_2S the sulfur atom seems to have a combining capacity of 2. But in sulfur trioxide (SO_3), sulfur seems to have a combining capacity of 6. In this case and others, we may have to assign two (or even more) different possible capacities to an element. At the other extreme are elements like helium and neon, which have not been found as parts of compounds. To these elements we may assign a combining capacity of zero.

For future reference we should also define one other term. Since oxygen combines with a greater variety of elements, the combining capacity of an element can often be determined by its combination with oxygen. For example, an element X that is found to have an *oxide formula* XO would have a combining capacity equal to oxygen's, namely 2.

The atomic mass and combining capacities are numbers that can be assigned to an element; they are "numerical characterizations" of the atoms of the element. There are other numbers which also represent properties of the atoms of the elements. But atomic mass and combining capacity were the two most important to nineteenth-century chemists. These numbers were used in attempts to find order and regularity among the elements—a problem which we will discuss in the next section.

In the thirteenth century the theologian and philosopher Albert Magnus (Albert the Great) introduced the idea of *affinity*. By this he meant an attractive force between substances that causes them to enter into chemical combination. It was not until 600 years later that it became possible to replace this qualitative notion by *quantitative* concepts. Combining capacity is one of these concepts.

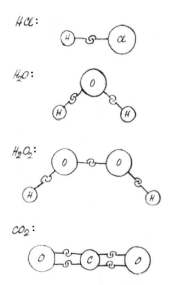

Representations of molecules formed from "atoms with hooks." Of course this conception is just a guide to the imagination. There are no such mechanical linkages among atoms.

SG 17.9

Q5 At this point we have two numbers which are characteristic of the atoms of an element. What are they?

Q6 Assume the combining capacity of oxygen is 2. In each of the following molecules, give the combining capacity of the atoms other than oxygen: CO, CO_2, N_2O_5, Na_2O and MnO.

17.4 The search for order and regularity among the elements

By 1872 sixty-three elements were known; they are listed in the table on page 16 with their atomic masses and chemical symbols. Sixty-three elements are many more than Aristotle's four. Chemists tried to make things simpler by looking for ways of organizing what they had learned about the elements. They tried to find relationships among the elements—much as Kepler had earlier searched for rules that would relate the motions of the planets of the solar system.

In addition to relative atomic masses, many other properties of the elements and their compounds were determined. Among these properties were: melting point, boiling point, density, electrical conductivity, heat conductivity, heat capacity (the amount of heat needed to change the temperature of a sample of a substance by 1°C), hardness, and refractive index. By 1870 an enormous amount of information was available about a large number of elements and their compounds.

In 1865, the English chemist J. A. R. Newlands pointed out that the elements could usefully be listed simply in the order of increasing atomic mass. When this was done, a surprising fact became evident: similar chemical and physical properties appeared over and over again in the list. Newlands believed that, in the whole list, elements with similar properties *recurred periodically* (appeared at regular intervals): ". . . the eighth element, starting from a given one, is a kind of repetition of the first, like the eighth note in an octave of music." Newlands' proposal was met with skepticism. One chemist even suggested that Newlands might look for a similar pattern in an alphabetical list of elements.

Yet relationships did indeed appear. There seemed to be families of elements with similar properties. One such family consists of the so-called *alkali metals*—lithium, sodium, potassium, rubidium, and cesium. We have identified these elements by a □ in the table on page 16. All these metals are similar physically. They are soft and have low melting points. Their densities are very low; in fact, lithium, sodium, and potassium are less dense than water. The alkali metals are also similar chemically. They all have combining capacity 1. They all combine with the same other elements and form similar compounds. They form compounds readily with other elements, and so are said to be highly "reactive." Consequently, they do not occur free in nature, but are always found in combination with other elements.

There were also many false trails. Thus in 1829 the German chemist Johann Wolfgang Döbereiner noticed that elements often formed groups of three members with similar chemical properties. He identified the "triads": chlorine, bromine, and iodine; calcium, strontium, and barium; sulfur, selenium, and tellurium; iron, cobalt, and manganese. In each "triad," the atomic mass of the middle member was approximately the arithmetical average of the masses of the other two elements. But all this turned out to be of little significance.

Another family of elements, called the *halogens,* includes fluorine, chlorine, bromine, and iodine. The halogens are identified in the table on page 16 by small circles.

These four halogen elements exhibit some marked differences. For example, at 25°C the first two are gases, the third a liquid, the last a volatile solid. But they also have much in common. They all combine violently with many metals and form white, crystalline salts (*halogen* means "salt-former"). These salts have similar formulas, such as NaF, NaCl, NaBr, and NaI, or MgF_2, $MgCl_2$, $MgBr_2$, and MgI_2. Much similar evidence indicates that all four members of the family seem to have the same valence with respect to any other particular element. All four elements form simple compounds with hydrogen (HF, HCl, HBr, HI) which dissolve in water and form acids. All four, under ordinary conditions, exist as *diatomic* molecules; that is, each molecule contains two atoms. But notice: each halogen precedes an alkali metal in the list, although the list is ordered simply by increasing atomic mass. It is as if some new pattern is coming out of a jig-saw puzzle.

The elements that follow the alkali metals in the list also form a family. Called the *alkaline earth family,* this family includes beryllium, magnesium, calcium, strontium, and barium. Their melting points and densities are higher than those of the alkali metals. The alkaline earths all have a valence of two. They react easily with many elements, but not as easily as do the alkali metals.

When chemists recognized the existence of these families of elements, they began to look for a systematic way of arranging the elements so that the members of a family would group together. Many schemes were suggested; the most successful and far reaching was that of the Russian chemist D. I. Mendeleev.

Modern chemists use the word "valence" less and less in the sense we use it here. They are more likely to discuss "combining number" or "oxidation number." Even the idea of a definite valence number for an element has changed, since combining properties can be different under different conditions.

Q7   What are those properties of elements which recur systematically with increasing atomic mass?

17.5 Mendeleev's periodic table of the elements

Mendeleev, examining the properties of the elements, concluded that the atomic mass was the fundamental "numerical characterization" of each element. He discovered a new way to arrange the elements in a table. He still placed them in the order of their atomic masses—but in a special way, a bit like cards laid out in the game of solitaire. Now the different chemical families turned out to fall into the different vertical columns of the table. There was no evident physical reason why this should be so, but it hinted at some remarkable connection among all elements.

Although the properties of elements do recure periodically with increasing atomic weight, Newlands had not realized that the separation of similar elements in the list becomes greater for the heavier elements.

In this table, hydrogen was omitted because of its unique properties. Helium and other elements of the family of "noble gases" had not yet been discovered.

Li 7	Be 9.4	B 11	C 12	N 14	O 16	F 19
Na 23	Mg 24	Al 27.4	Si 28	P 31	S 32	Cl 35.3
K 39	Ca 40	.. ..	Ti 50	V 51		...etc.

Dmitri Ivanovich Mendeleev (men-deh-lay'-ef) (1834-1907). Unable to get into college in Moscow, he was accepted in St. Petersburg, where a friend of his father had some influence. In 1866 he became a professor of chemistry there; in 1869 he published his first table of the sixty-three then known elements arranged according to increasing atomic mass. His paper was translated into German at once and so became known to scientists everywhere. Mendeleev came to the United States, where he studied the oil fields of Pennsylvania in order to advise his country on the development of the Caucasian resources. His liberal political views caused him often to be in trouble with the oppressive regime of the Czars.

As in the table on the preceding page, Mendeleev set down seven elements, from lithium to fluorine, in order of increasing atomic masses. He put the next seven, from sodium to chlorine, in the second row. The periodic nature of chemical behavior is already evident before we go on to the third row. In the first column on the left are the first two alkali metals. In the seventh column are the first two members of the family of halogens. Indeed, within *each* vertical column the elements are chemically similar, having, for example, the same characteristic combining capacity.

When Mendeleev added a third row of elements, potassium (K) came below elements Li and Na. These three are members of the same family and have the same oxide formula, X_2O, and the same combining capacity 1. Next in the horizontal row is Ca, oxide formula XO as with Mg and Be above it. In the next space to the right, the element of next higher atomic mass should appear. Of the elements known at the time, the next heavier was titanium (Ti). Various workers had developed tables which placed titanium right below aluminum (Al) and boron (B). Mendeleev, however, recognized that titanium (Ti) has chemical properties similar to those of carbon (C) and silicon (Si). For example, the pigment titanium white, TiO_2, has a formula comparable to CO_2 and SiO_2. Therefore he concluded that titanium should be put in the *fourth* column. Then, if all this was not just a game but had deeper meaning, Mendeleev thought, there should exist a hitherto unsuspected element. It should have an atomic mass between that of calcium (40) and titanium (48), and an oxide X_2O_3. Here was a definite prediction. Mendeleev also found other cases of this sort among the remaining elements when the family properties of elements in each column were taken properly into account.

The table below is Mendeleev's periodic system, or "periodic table" of the elements, as proposed by him in 1872. He distributed the 63 elements then known (with 5 in doubt) in 12 horizontal rows or *series*. Hydrogen had a unique separated position at the top left. The table ended with uranium at the bottom right. All elements were listed in order of increasing atomic mass (Mendeleev's values given in parentheses). But

Periodic classification of the elements as proposed by Mendeleev, 1872. The numbers in parentheses are relative atomic masses assigned at that time. (See page 16 for names of elements.)

GROUP→	I	II	III	IV	V	VI	VII	VIII
Higher oxides and hydrides	R_2O ———	RO ———	R_2O_3 ———	RO_2 H_4R	R_2O_5 H_3R	RO_3 H_2R	R_2O_7 HR	RO_4 ———
1	H(1)							
2	Li(7)	Be(9.4)	B(11)	C(12)	N(14)	O(16)	F(19)	
3	Na(23)	Mg(24)	Al(27.3)	Si(28)	P(31)	S(32)	Cl(35.5)	
4	K(39)	Ca(40)	—(44)	Ti(48)	V(51)	Cr(52)	Mn(55)	Fe(56), Co(59), Ni(59), Cu(63)
5	[Cu(63)]	Zn(65)	—(68)	—(72)	As(75)	Se(78)	Br(80)	
6	Rb(85)	Sr(87)	?Yt(88)	Zr(90)	Nb(94)	Mo(96)	—(100)	Ru(104),Rh(104), Pd(106), Ag(108)
7	[Ag(108)]	Cd(112)	In(113)	Sn(118)	Sb(122)	Te(125)	I(127)	
8	Cs(133)	Ba(137)	?Di(138)	?Ce(140)	——	——	——	
9	——	——	——	——	——	——	——	
10	——	——	?Er(178)	?La(180)	Ta(182)	W(184)	——	Os(195), Ir(197), Pt(198), Au(199)
11	[Au(199)]	Hg(200)	Tl(204)	Pb(207)	Bi(208)	——	——	
12	——	——	——	Th(231)	——	U(240)		

they were so placed that elements with similar chemical properties are in the same vertical column or *group*. Thus in Group VII are all the halogens; in Group VIII, only ductile metals—metals that can easily be drawn into wires; in Groups I and II, metals of low densities and melting points; and in I, the family of alkali metals.

The table at the bottom of the previous page shows many gaps. Also, not all horizontal rows (series) have equally many elements. Nonetheless, the table revealed an important generalization: according to Mendeleev,

> For a true comprehension of the matter it is very important to see that all aspects of the distribution of the elements according to the order of their atomic weights express essentially one and the same fundamental dependence— *periodic properties.*

There is gradual change in physical and chemical properties within each vertical group, and a more striking periodic change of properties in the horizontal sequence.

This *periodic law* is the heart of the matter, and a real novelty. Perhaps we can best illustrate it as Lothar Meyer did, by graphing the value of some measurable physical quantity as a function of atomic mass. Below is a plot of the relative *atomic volumes* of the elements, the space taken up by an atom in the liquid or solid state. Each circled point on this graph represents an element; a few of the points are labeled with the identifying chemical symbols. Viewed as a whole, the graph demonstrates a striking periodicity. As the mass increases starting with Li, the atomic volume first drops, then increases to a sharp maximum, drops off again, increases to another sharp maximum, and so on. At the successive peaks we find Li, Na, K, Rb, and Cs. All of these are members of the family of alkali metals, and all lie in the same vertical column in Mendeleev's table.

Mendeleev's periodic table of the elements related the elements and their properties in a remarkable way. It also enabled him to predict certain

The "atomic volume" is thus defined as the atomic mass divided by the density of the element in its liquid or solid state.

In 1864, the German chemist Lothar Meyer wrote a chemistry textbook. There he considered how the properties of the chemical elements might depend on their atomic masses. He later found that if he plotted atomic volume against the atomic mass, the line drawn through the plotted points rose and fell periodically. This was exactly what Mendeleev had discovered in connection with valence. Mendeleev published his first result in 1869. Meyer, as he himself later admitted, lacked the courage to include empty spaces that would amount to the prediction of unknown elements. Nevertheless, Meyer should be given credit for an early form of the idea of the periodic table.

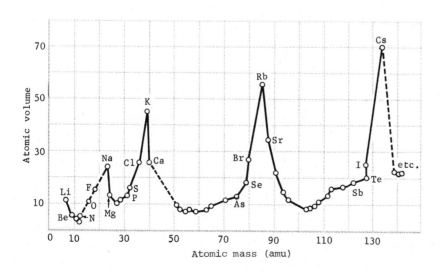

The relative atomic volumes of elements graphed against their relative atomic masses.

unknown elements and many of their properties. To estimate physical properties of a missing element, Mendeleev averaged the properties of its nearest neighbors in the table: right and left, above and below. A striking example of his success in this is his set of predictions concerning the gap in Series 5, Group IV. Group IV contains silicon and elements resembling it. Mendeleev assigned the name "eka-silicon" (Es) to the unknown element. His predictions of the properties of this element are listed in the left-hand column below. In 1887, this element was isolated and identified. It is now called "germanium," Ge. Its properties are listed in the right-hand column. Notice how remarkably close Mendeleev's predictions are to the properties actually found.

"The following are the properties which this element should have on the basis of the known properties of silicon, tin, zinc, and arsenic.

Its atomic mass is nearly 72, it forms a higher oxide EsO_2, . . . Es gives volatile organometallic compounds; for instance . . .Es $(C_2H_5)_4$, which boils at about 160°, etc.; also a volatile and liquid chloride, $EsCl_4$, boiling at about 90° and of specific gravity about 1.9. . . . the specific gravity of Es will be about 5.5, and EsO_2 will have a specific gravity of about 4.7, ..."

The predictions in the left column were made by Mendeleev in 1871. In 1887 an element (germanium) was discovered which was found to have the following properties:

Its atomic mass is 72.5. It forms an oxide GeO_2, and an organometallic compound $Ge(C_2H_5)_4$ which boils at 160° and forms a liquid chloride $GeCl_4$ which boils at 83° C and has a specific gravity of 1.9. The specific gravity of germanium is 5.5 and the specific gravity of GeO_2 is 4.7.

The daring of Mendeleev is shown in his willingness to offer detailed numerical predictions. The sweep and power of his system is shown above in the amazing accuracy of those predictions. Mendeleev also described the properties to be expected for then unknown elements in gaps in Group III, period 4, and in Group III, period 5. These elements are now called gallium and scandium. Again, his predictions turned out to be remarkably accurate.

Not every aspect of Mendeleev's work yielded such successes. But these were indeed impressive results, rather like the successful use of Newtonian laws to find an unknown planet. Successful numerical predictions like these are among the most desired results in physical science—even if in Mendeleev's case no one yet understood why the table worked as it did.

The discovery of Uranus and Neptune is described in *Text* Chapter 8.

Q8	Why is Mendeleev's table called "periodic table"?
Q9	What was the basic ordering principle in Mendeleev's table?
Q10	What reasons led Mendeleev to leave gaps in the table?
Q11	What success did Mendeleev have in the use of the table?

17.6 The modern periodic table

The periodic table has had an important place in chemistry and physics for a century. It presented a serious challenge to any theory of the atom proposed after 1880. Any such theory had to offer an explanation for the wonderful order among the elements as expressed by the table. Any successful model of the atom had to provide a physical reason why the table works as it does. In Chapter 19 we will see how one model of the atom—the Bohr model—met this challenge.

Since 1872 many changes have had to be made in the periodic table, but they have involved details rather than general ideas. None of these changes has affected the basic periodic feature among the properties of the elements. A modern form of the table with present values is shown in the table below.

One difference between the modern and older tables results from new elements having been found since 1872. The table now contains over 100 elements. Some of these are especially interesting, as shown in the Supplemental Unit *The Nucleus*.

A modern form of the periodic table of the chemical elements. The number above the symbol is the atomic mass, the number below the symbol is the atomic number (the place number of the element in this chart). Numbers above the symbols are the average atomic masses (relative to Carbon 12). The names of the elements and their symbols are listed on the following pages. Parentheses enclose the mass number of the longest-lived isotope of a radioactive element when there are no stable isotopes.

Group→ Period ↓	I	II												III	IV	V	VI	VII	0
1	1.0080 H *1*																		4.0026 He *2*
2	6.939 Li *3*	9.012 Be *4*												10.811 B *5*	12.011 C *6*	14.007 N *7*	15.999 O *8*	18.998 F *9*	20.183 Ne *10*
3	22.990 Na *11*	24.312 Mg *12*												26.982 Al *13*	28.086 Si *14*	30.974 P *15*	32.04 S *16*	35.453 Cl *17*	39.984 Ar *18*
4	39.10 K *19*	40.08 Ca *20*	44.96 Sc *21*	47.90 Ti *22*	50.94 V *23*	52.00 Cr *24*	54.94 M *25*	55.85 Fe *26*	58.93 Co *27*	58.71 Ni *28*	63.54 Cu *29*	65.37 Zn *30*		69.72 Ga *31*	72.59 Ge *32*	74.92 As *33*	78.96 Se *34*	79.91 Br *35*	83.80 Kr *36*
5	85.47 Rb *37*	87.62 Sr *38*	88.91 Y *39*	91.22 Zr *40*	92.91 Nb *41*	95.94 Mo *42*	(99) Tc *43*	101.07 Ru *44*	102.91 Rh *45*	106.4 Pd *46*	107.87 Ag *47*	112.40 Cd *48*		114.82 In *49*	118.69 Sn *50*	121.75 Sb *51*	127.60 Te *52*	126.90 I *53*	131.30 Xe *54*
6	132.91 Cs *55*	137.34 Ba *56*	* *57–71*	178.49 Hf *72*	180.95 Ta *73*	183.85 W *74*	186.2 Re *75*	190.2 Os *76*	192.2 Ir *77*	195.09 Pt *78*	196.97 Au *79*	200.59 Hg *80*		204.37 Tl *81*	207.19 Pb *82*	208.98 Bi *83*	(210) Po *84*	(210) At *85*	222 Rn *86*
7	(223) Fr *87*	226.05 Ra *88*	† *89–103*																

*Rare- earth metals	138.91 La *57*	140.12 Ce *58*	140.91 Pr *59*	144.27 Nd *60*	(147) Pm *61*	150.35 Sm *62*	151.96 Eu *63*	157.25 Gd *64*	158.92 Tb *65*	162.50 Dy *66*	164.93 Ho *67*	167.26 Er *68*	168.93 Tm *69*	173.04 Yb *70*	174.97 Lu *71*
† Actinide metals	(227) Ac *89*	232.04 Th *90*	(231) Pa *91*	238.03 U *92*	(237) Np *93*	(242) Pu *94*	(243) Am *95*	(245) Cm *96*	(249) Bk *97*	(249) Cf *98*	(253) Es *99*	(255) Fm *100*	(256) Md *101*	(253) No *102*	(257) Lw *103*

List of the Elements

Element	Symbol	Atomic Number	Year of Isolation or Discovery and Origin of Name*
Actinium	Ac	89	1900 Greek *aktis*, ray
Aluminum	Al	13	1825 Latin *alumen*, substance with astringent taste
Americium	Am	95	1944 America
Antimony	Sb	51	15th century, Greek *antimonos*, opposite to solitude
Argon	Ar	18	1894 Greek *argos*, inactive
Arsenic	As	33	13th century, Greek *arsenikon*, valiant
Astatine	At	85	1940 Greek *astatos*, unstable
Barium	Ba	56	1808 Greek *barys*, heavy
Berkelium	Bk	97	1949 Berkeley, California
Beryllium	Be	4	1797 mineral, beryl
Bismuth	Bi	83	15th century, German *Weisse Masse*, white mass
Boron	B	5	1808 Arabic *bawraq*, white
Bromine	Br	35	1826 Greek *bromos*, a stench
Cadmium	Cd	48	1817 Latin *cadmia*, calamine, a zinc ore
Calcium	Ca	20	1808 Latin *calcis*, lime
Californium	Cf	98	1950 State and University of California
Carbon	C	6	prehistoric, Latin *carbo*, coal
Cerium	Ce	58	1804 the asteroid Ceres, discovered 1803
Cesium	Cs	55	1860 Latin *caesius*, sky blue
Chlorine	Cl	17	1808 Greek *chloros*, grass green
Chromium	Cr	24	1797 Greek *chroma*, color
Cobalt	Co	27	1735 Greek *kobolos*, a goblin
Copper	Cu	29	prehistoric, Latin *cuprum*, copper
Curium	Cm	96	1944 Marie and Pierre Curie
Dysprosium	Dy	66	1886 Greek *dysprositos*, hard to get at
Einsteinium	Es	99	1952 Albert Einstein
Erbium	Er	68	1843 Ytterby, a mining town in Sweden where first sample found
Europium	Eu	63	1900 Europe
Fermium	Fm	100	1953 Enrico Fermi
Fluorine	F	9	1886 Latin *fluere*, to flow
Francium	Fr	87	1939 France
Gadolinium	Gd	64	1886 Johan Gadolin, Finnish chemist
Gallium	Ga	31	1875 Gaul, or France
Germanium	Ge	32	1886 Germany
Gold	Au	79	prehistoric, Anglo-Saxon gold, symbol from Latin *aurum*
Hafnium	Hf	72	1922 *Hafnia*, Latin for Copenhagen
Helium	He	2	1895 Greek *helios*, the sun
Holmium	Ho	67	1879 *Holmia*, Latin for Stockholm
Hydrogen	H	1	1766 Greek *hydro genes*, water former
Indium	In	49	1863 indigo-blue spectrum line
Iodine	I	53	1811 Greek *iodes*, violet-like
Iridium	Ir	77	1804 Latin *iridis*, rainbow
Iron	Fe	26	prehistoric, Anglo-Saxon *iren* or *isen*, symbol from Latin *ferrum*
Krypton	Kr	36	1898 Greek *kryptos*, hidden
Lanthanum	La	57	1839 Greek *lanthanien*, to be concealed
Lawrencium	Lw	103	1961 Ernest O. Lawrence, inventor of cyclotron
Lead	Pb	82	Prehistoric, middle English *led*, symbol from Latin *plumbum*
Lithium	Li	3	1817 Greek *lithos*, stone
Lutetium	Lu	71	1905 *Lutetia*, ancient name of Paris
Magnesium	Mg	12	1774 Latin *magnes*, magnet
Mendelevium	Md	101	1955 Dmitri Mendeleev, who devised first Periodic Table

List of the Elements (cont.)

Element	Symbol	Atomic Number	Year of Isolation or Discovery and Origin of Name*
Mercury	Hg	80	prehistoric, Latin *Mercurius*, the gold and planet
Molybdenum	Mo	42	1782 Greek *molybdos*, lead
Neodymium	Nd	60	1885 Greek *neos*, new, and *didymos*, twin
Neon	Ne	10	1898 Greek *neos*, new
Neptunium	Np	93	1940 planet Neptune
Nickel	Ni	28	1750 German *Nickel*, a goblin or devil
Niobium	Nb	41	1801 Niobe, daughter of Tantalus
Nitrogen	N	7	1772 Latin *nitro*, native soda, and *gen*, born
Nobelium	No	102	1957 Alfred Nobel
Osmium	Os	76	1804 Greek *osme*, a smell, from the odor of its volatile tetroxide
Oxygen	O	8	1774 Greek *oxys*, sharp, and *gen*, born
Palladium	Pd	46	1803 planetoid Pallas, discovered 1801
Phosphorus	P	15	1669 Greek *phosphoros*, light bringer
Platinum	Pt	78	1735 Spanish *plata*, silver
Plutonium	Pu	94	1940 Pluto, the second planet beyond Uranus
Polonium	Po	84	1898 Poland, native country of co-discoverer Marie Curie
Potassium	K	19	1807 English *potash*, symbol Latin *kalium*
Praseodymium	Pr	59	1885 Greek *praseos*, leek green and *didymos*, a twin
Promethium	Pm	61	1947 Prometheus, fire bringer of Greek mythology
Protactinium	Pa	91	1917 Greek *protos* first, and actinium because it disintegrates into it
Radium	Ra	88	1898 Latin *radius*, ray
Radon	Rn	86	1900 because it comes from radium
Rhenium	Re	75	1924 Latin *Rhenus*, Rhine province of Germany
Rhodium	Rh	45	1804 Greek *rhodon*, a rose
Rubidium	Rb	37	1860 Latin *rubidus*, red
Ruthenium	Ru	44	1845 Latin *Ruthenia*, Russia
Samarium	Sm	62	1879 Samarski, a Russian engineer
Scandium	Sc	21	1879 Scandinavian peninsula
Selenium	Se	34	1817 Greek selene, moon
Silicon	Si	14	1823 Latin *silex*, flint
Silver	Ag	47	prehistoric, Anglo-Saxon *seolfor*, symbol from Latin *argentum*
Sodium	Na	11	1807 Medieval Latin *soda*, symbol from Latin *natrium*
Strontium	Sr	38	1808 town of Strontian, Scotland
Sulfur	S	16	prehistoric, Latin *sulphur*
Tantalum	Ta	73	1802 Tantalus of Greek mythology
Technetium	Tc	43	1937 Greek *technetos*, artificial
Tellurium	Te	52	1782 Latin *tellus*, the earth
Terbium	Tb	65	1843 Ytterby, town in Sweden
Thallium	Tl	81	1862 Greek *thallos*, a young shoot
Thorium	Th	90	1819 Scandinavian mythology, *Thor*
Thulium	Tm	69	1879 Latin Thule, most northerly part of the habitable world
Tin	Sn	50	prehistoric, origin of name unknown, symbol Latin *stannum*
Titanium	Ti	22	1791 Greek mythology, Titans, first sons of the earth
Tungsten	W	74	1783 Swedish *tung sten*, heavy stone, symbol from the mineral wolframite
Uranium	U	92	1789 Planet Uranus
Vanadium	V	23	1830 goddess *Vanadis* of Scandinavian mythology
Xenon	Xe	54	1898 Greek *xenos*, strange
Ytterbium	Yb	70	1905 Ytterby, a town in Sweden
Yttrium	Y	39	1843 Ytterby, a town in Sweden
Zinc	Zn	30	prehistoric, German *Zink*, akin to *Zinn*, tin
Zirconium	Zr	40	1824 Arabian *Zerk*, a precious stone

*adapted from Alfred Romer, *The Restless Atom*, Science Study Series, Doubleday Co., N.Y.

Although Mendeleev's table had eight columns, the column labeled VIII did not contain a family of elements. It contained the "transition" elements which are now placed in the long series (periods) labelled 4, 5 and 6 in the table on page 23. The group labelled "0" in that table does consist of a family of elements, the noble gases, which do have similar properties in common.

Helium was first detected in the spectrum of the sun (Chapter 20). Its name comes from *helios*, the Greek word for the sun.

In chemistry, elements such as gold and silver that react only rarely with other elements were called "noble."

Compared with Mendeleev's table, the modern table contains eight groups, or families, instead of seven. The additional group is labeled "zero." In 1894, the British scientists Lord Rayleigh and William Ramsay discovered that about 1 percent of our atmosphere consists of a gas that had previously escaped detection. It was given the name argon (Ar). Argon does not seem to enter into chemical combination with any other element, and is not similar to any of the groups of elements in Mendeleev's original table. Later, other elements similar to argon were also discovered: helium (He), neon (Ne), krypton (Kr), xenon (Xe), and radon (Rn). These elements are considered to form a new group or family of elements called the "noble gases." The molecules of the noble gases contain only one atom. Until recent years no compound of any noble gas was known. The group number zero was thought to correspond to the chemical inertness (zero combining capacity) of the members of the group. In 1963, some compounds of xenon and krypton were produced, so we now know that these elements are not really inert. These compounds are not found in nature, however, and some react very easily, and therefore are difficult to keep. The noble gases as a group are certainly less able to react chemically than any other elements.

In addition to the noble gases, two other sets of elements had to be included in the table. After the fifty-seventh element, lanthanum, room had to be made for a whole set of 14 elements that are chemically almost exactly alike. Known as the *rare earths* or lanthanide series, most of these elements were unknown in Mendeleev's time. There is also a set of 14 very similar elements after actinium at the eighty-ninth place, forming what is called the *actinide* series. These elements are shown in two rows below the main table. No more additions are expected except, possibly, at the end of the table. There are no known gaps, and according to the best theory of the atom now available no new gaps are expected within the table.

Besides the addition of new elements to the periodic table, there have also been some changes of a more general type. As we have seen, Mendeleev arranged most of the elements in order of increasing atomic mass. In the late nineteenth century, however, this basic scheme was found to break down in a few places. For example, the chemical properties of argon (Ar) and potassium (K) demand that they be placed in the eighteenth and nineteenth positions in order to fall into the columns characteristic of their families. But on the basis of their atomic masses alone (39.948 for argon, 39.102 for potassium), their positions should be reversed. Other reversals of this kind are also necessary, for example for the fifty-second element, tellurium (atomic mass = 127.60) and the fifty-third, iodine (atomic mass = 126.90).

The numbers that place elements in the table with the greatest consistency in periodic properties are called the *atomic numbers* of the elements. The table on page 23 gives the atomic numbers of all the elements. The atomic number usually is represented by the symbol Z. Thus for hydrogen, Z = 1, for chlorine, Z = 17, for uranium, Z = 92. In Chapter 19 we will see that the atomic number has a fundamental physical meaning related to atomic structure. This relationship is the key to both the many successes and the few puzzling failures of Mendeleev's scheme.

The need for some reversals in mass order in the periodic table of the elements was apparent to Mendeleev. He attributed this—wrongly, as it turned out—to faulty atomic mass data. He confidently expected, for example, that the atomic mass of tellurium (which he placed fifty-second), when more accurately determined would be lower than that of iodine (which he placed fifty-third). In fact, in 1872 (see Table page 20) he had convinced himself that the correct atomic mass of tellurium was 125! As the figures in the modern tables show, however, tellurium does have a greater atomic mass than iodine. The reversal is real. Mendeleev overestimated the ability of the periodic law to account for every detail—especially since the law itself had not yet received a physical explanation. He did not realize that atomic mass was not the underlying ordering principle for atomic numbers. Rather, it was only one physical property (with slightly imperfect periodicity). Satisfactory explanations for these reversals have been found in modern atomic physics, and will be explained in the Supplemental Unit *The Nucleus*.

SG 17.10
SG 17.11
SG 17.12

Q12 What is the "atomic number" of an element? Give examples of the atomic number of several elements.

17.7 Electricity and matter: qualitative studies

While chemists were applying Dalton's atomic theory in the first decade of the nineteenth century, another development was opening an important new path to understanding the atom. Humphry Davy and Michael Faraday made discoveries which showed that electricity and matter are closely related. Their discoveries in "electrochemistry" had to do with decomposing chemical compounds by passing an electric current through them. This process is called *electrolysis*.

The study of electrolysis was made possible by the invention of the electric cell in 1800 by the Italian scientist Alessandro Volta. As we saw in Unit 4, Volta's cell consisted of disks of different metals. The disks were separated from each other by paper moistened with a weak solution of salt. Chemical changes occurring in such a cell establish an electric potential difference between the metals. A *battery* is a set of several similar cells connected together. A battery usually has two terminals, one charged positively and the other charged negatively. When the terminals are connected to each other by wires or other conducting materials, there is an electric current in the battery and the materials. Thus, the battery can produce and maintain an electric current. It is not the only device that can do so, but it was the first source of steady currents.

Within a few weeks after Volta announced his discovery, it was found that an electric current could decompose water into oxygen and hydrogen. On page 28 is a diagram of an electrolysis apparatus. The two terminals of the battery are connected, by conducting wires, to two thin sheets of platinum ("electrodes"). When these platinum sheets are placed in

Some liquids conduct electricity. Pure distilled water is a poor conductor. But when certain substances such as acids or salts are dissolved in water, the resulting solutions are good electrical conductors. Gases are not conductors under normal conditions, but can be made electrically conducting in the presence of strong electric fields, or by other methods. The conduction of electricity in gases, vital to the story of the atom, will be discussed in Chapter 18.

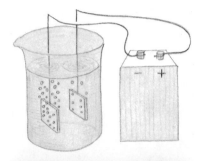

Humphry Davy (1778–1829) was the son of a farmer. In his youth he worked as an assistant to a physician, but was discharged because of his liking for explosive chemical experiments. He became a chemist, discovered nitrous oxide (laughing gas), which was later used as an anaesthetic, and developed a safety lamp for miners as well as an arc light. His work in electrochemistry and his discovery of several elements made him world-famous; he was knighted in 1812. In 1813 Sir Humphry Davy hired a young man, Michael Faraday, as his assistant and took him along on an extensive trip through France and Italy. It became evident to Davy that young Faraday was a man of scientific genius. Davy is said to have been envious, at first, of Faraday's great gifts. He later said that he believed his greatest discovery was Faraday.

By chemical change we mean here the breaking up of molecules during electrolysis, as by forming gas bubbles at the electrodes, or by metal deposited on it.

ordinary water, bubbles of oxygen appear at one sheet and bubbles of hydrogen at the other. Adding a certain amount of certain acids speeds up the reaction without changing the products. Hydrogen and oxygen gases form in the proportion of 7.94 grams of oxygen to 1 gram of hydrogen—exactly the proportion in which these elements combine and form water. Water had previously been impossible to decompose, and had long been regarded as an element. The ease with which electrolysis now separated water into its elements dramatized the chemical use of electricity, and stimulated many other investigations of electrolysis.

Among these investigations, some of the most successful were those of the young English chemist Humphry Davy. Perhaps the most striking of Davy's successes came in 1807 when he studied the effect of current from a large electric battery upon soda and potash. Soda and potash were materials of commercial importance (for example, in the manufacture of glass, soap, and gunpowder). They had completely resisted every earlier attempt to decompose them. Soda and potash were thus regarded as true chemical elements—up to the time of Davy's work. (See Dalton's symbols for the elements on page 10.) When electrodes connected to a large battery were touched to a solid lump of soda or potash, part of the solid was heated to its melting point. At one electrode small globules of molten metal appeared which burned brightly and almost explosively in air. When the electrolysis was done in the absence of air, the metallic material could be collected and studied. The metallic elements discovered in this way were called sodium and potassium. Sodium was obtained from soda (now called sodium bicarbonate). Potassium was obtained from potash (now called potassium carbonate). Within a few years, electrolysis experiments made on several previously undecomposed "earths" yielded the first samples ever obtained of such metallic elements as magnesium, strontium, and barium. There were also many other demonstrations of the striking changes produced by the chemical activity of electricity.

Q13 Why was the first electrolysis of water such a surprising achievement?

Q14 What were some other unexpected results of electrolysis?

17.8 Electricity and matter: quantitative studies

Davy's work on electrolysis was mainly qualitative. But quantitative questions were also asked. How much chemical change can be produced when a certain amount of electric charge is passed through a solution? If the same amount of charge is passed through different solutions, how do the amounts of chemical change compare? Will doubling the amount of electricity double the chemical change effected?

The first answers to these questions were given by Michael Faraday, who discovered two fundamental and simple empirical laws of electrolysis.

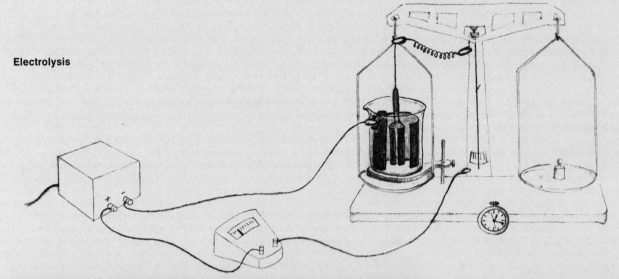

Student laboratory apparatus like that shown in the sketch above can be used for experiments in electrolysis (as described in the Handbook). This setup allows measurement of the amount of electric charge passing through the solution in the beaker, and of the mass of metal deposited on the suspended electrode.

The separation of elements by electrolysis is important in industry, particularly in the production of aluminum. These photographs show the large scale of a plant where aluminum is obtained from aluminum ore in electrolytic tanks.

(a) A row of tanks where aluminum is separated out of aluminum ore.

(b) A closer view of the front of some tanks, showing the thick copper straps that carry the current for electrolysis.

(c) A huge vat of molten aluminum that has been siphoned out of the tanks is poured into molds.

(a)

(b)

(c)

He studied the electrolysis of a solution of the blue salt copper sulfate in water. The electric current between electrodes placed in the solution caused copper from the solution to be deposited on the negative electrode. Meanwhile, oxygen was given off at the positive electrode. Faraday determined the amount of copper deposited on one electrode by weighing the electrode before the electrolysis started and again after a known amount of current had passed through the solution. He found that the mass of copper deposited depends on only two things: the magnitude of the electric current (measured, say, in amperes), and the length of time that the current was maintained. In fact, the mass of copper deposited is directly proportional to both the current and the time. When either is doubled, the mass of copper deposited is doubled. When both are doubled, four times as much copper is deposited. Similar results were found in experiments on the electrolysis of many different substances.

Faraday's results may be described very simply: the amount of chemical change produced in electrolysis is proportional to the product of the current and the time. Now, the current (in amperes) is the quantity of charge (in coulombs) transferred per unit time (in seconds). The product of current and time therefore gives the *total charge* in coulombs that has moved through the cell during the given experiment. We then have Faraday's first law of electrolysis:

Mass $\propto$ current $\times$ time
$\propto \dfrac{\text{charge}}{\text{time}} \times$ time
$\propto$ total charge transferred

> The mass of an element released at an electrode during electrolysis is proportional to the amount of charge which has passed through the electrode.

Next Faraday measured the mass of different elements released from chemical compounds by an equal amount of electric charge. He found that the amount of an element liberated from the electrolyte by a given amount of electricity depends on the element's *atomic mass* and on its combining capacity (valence). His second law of electrolysis states:

> If A is the atomic mass of an element, and if v is its valence, a transfer of 96,540 coulombs of electric charge releases A/v grams of the element.

This experimentally determined amount of electric charge, 96,540 coulombs, is now called a *faraday*.

SG 17.13–17.16

For hydrogen, for example, where $v = 1$, the charge needed is about 9.6×10^4 coul per gram, or 9.6×10^7 coul per kilogram.

The table on the next page gives examples of Faraday's second law of electrolysis. In each case the mass of the element produced by electrolysis is equal to its atomic mass divided by its combining capacity.

The quantity A/v has significance beyond electrolysis experiments. For example, the values for A/v are 8.00 for oxygen and 1.008 for hydrogen. The ratio is $8.00/1.008 = 7.94$. But this is just the ratio of masses of oxygen and hydrogen that combine and produce water. In general, when two elements combine, the ratio of their combining masses is equal to the ratio of their values for A/v.

Faraday's second law of electrolysis has an important implication. It shows that a given amount of electric charge is somehow closely connected with the atomic mass and valence of an element. The atoms of

Masses of elements that would be electrolyzed from compounds by 96,540 coulombs of electric charge.

ELEMENT	ATOMIC MASS A	COMBINING CAPACITY v	MASS OF ELEMENT LIBERATED (grams)
Hydrogen	1.008	1	1.008
Chlorine	35.45	1	35.45
Oxygen	16.00	2	8.00
Copper	63.54	2	31.77
Zinc	65.37	2	32.69
Aluminum	26.98	3	8.99

The values of atomic mass in this table are based on a value of exactly 16 for oxygen.

any given element have a characteristic mass and valence. Perhaps, then, a certain amount of electricity is somehow connected with an *atom* of the element. In other words, electricity may also be atomic in character. (For example, the current during electrolysis of water might consist of the motion of charged atoms [*ions*] of hydrogen, each carrying about 9.6×10^7 coulombs per kilogram of atomic mass.) The possibility of this general picture was considered by Faraday, who wrote cautiously:

> . . . if we adopt the atomic theory or phraseology, then the atoms of bodies which are equivalents to each other in their ordinary chemical action have equal quantities of electricity naturally associated with them. But I must confess that I am jealous of the term *atom;* for though it is very easy to talk of atoms, it is very difficult to form a clear idea of their nature, especially when compound bodies are under consideration.

Research eventually did establish the fact that electricity itself is atomic in character, and that the "atoms" of electricity are part of the atoms of matter. This research, for which Faraday's work and his cautious guess prepared, helped make possible the exploration of the structure of the atom. Chapter 18 will deal with the details of this research.

SG 17.17–17.20

Q15 The amount of an element deposited in electrolysis depends on three factors. What are they?

Q16 What are the significances of the quantity A/v for an element?

17.1 The Project Physics learning materials particularly appropriate for Chapter 17 include the following:

> **Experiment**
>> Electrolysis
>
> **Activities**
>> Dalton's Puzzle
>> Electrolysis of Water
>> Periodic Table
>> Single-electrode Plating
>> Activities from the *Scientific American*
>
> **Film Loops**
>> Production of Sodium by Electrolysis
>
> **Reader**
>> Articles of general interest in *Reader 5* are:
>> The Island of Research
>> The Sentinel

Although most of the articles in *Reader 5* are related to ideas presented in Chapter 20, you may prefer to read some of them earlier.

17.2 The chemical compound zinc oxide (molecular formula ZnO) contains equal numbers of atoms of zinc and oxygen. Using values of atomic masses from the modern version of the periodic table (on page 23), find the percentage by mass of zinc in zinc oxide. What is the percentage of oxygen in zinc oxide?

17.3 The chemical compound zinc chloride (molecular formula $ZnCl_2$) contains two atoms of chlorine for each atom of zinc. Using values of atomic masses from the modern version of the periodic table, find the percentage by mass of zinc in zinc chloride.

17.4 A 5.00-gram sample of ammonia gas is completely decomposed into its elements, nitrogen and hydrogen. 4.11 grams of nitrogen are obtained. The molecular formula of ammonia is NH_3. Find the mass of a nitrogen atom relative to that of a hydrogen atom. Compare your result with the one you would get by using the values of the atomic masses in the modern version of the periodic table. If your result is different from the latter result, how do you account for the difference?

17.5 From the information in Problem 17.4, calculate how much nitrogen and hydrogen are needed to make 1.2 kg of ammonia.

17.6 *If* the molecular formula of ammonia were falsely thought to be NH_2, and you used the result of the experiment in Problem 17.4, what value would you get for the ratio of the mass of a nitrogen atom relative to that of a hydrogen atom?

17.7 A sample of nitric oxide gas, weighing 1.00 g, after separation into its components, is found to have contained 0.47 g of nitrogen. Taking the atomic mass of oxygen to be 16.00, find the corresponding numbers that express the atomic mass of nitrogen relative to oxygen if

the molecular formula of nitric oxide is (a) NO; (b) NO_2; (c) N_2O.

17.8 Early and crude data yielded 9.2/8.0 for the mass ratio of nitrogen and oxygen atoms, and 1/7 for the mass ratio of hydrogen and oxygen atoms. Show that these results lead to a value of 8 for the relative atomic mass of nitrogen, provided that the value 1 is assigned to hydrogen.

17.9 Given the molecular formulas HCl, NaCl, $CaCl_2$, $AlCl_3$, $SnCl_4$, PCl_5, find possible combining capacities of sodium, calcium, aluminum, tin, and phosphorus.

17.10 (a) Examine the modern periodic table of elements and cite all reversals in the order of increasing atomic mass.

(b) Restate the periodic law in your own words, not forgetting about these reversals.

17.11 On the next page is a table of the melting and boiling temperatures of the elements.
(a) Plot these quantities against atomic number in two separate graphs. Comment on any periodicity you observe in the plots.
(b) Predict the values for melting and boiling points of the noble gases, which were unknown in 1872. Compare your predictions with the modern values given in, say, the *Handbook of Chemistry and Physics*.

17.12 In recent editions of the *Handbook of Chemistry and Physics* the valence numbers of the elements are printed in or below one of the periodic tables. Ignore the negative valence numbers and plot (to element 65) a graph of maximum valences observed vs. atomic mass. What periodicity is found? Is there any physical or chemical significance to this periodicity?

17.13 According to the table on page 31, when about 96,500 coulombs of charge pass through a water solution, how much of oxygen will be released at the same time when (on the other electrode) 1.008 g of hydrogen are released? How much oxygen will be produced when a current of 3 amperes is passed through water for 60 minutes (3,600 seconds)?

17.14 If a current of 0.5 amperes is passed through molten zinc chloride in an electrolytic apparatus, what mass of zinc will be deposited in

(a) 5 minutes (300 seconds);

(b) 30 minutes;

(c) 120 minutes?

17.15 (a) For 20 minutes (1200 seconds), a current of 2.0 amperes is passed through molten zinc chloride in an electrolytic apparatus. What mass of chlorine will be released at the anode?

(b) If the current is passed through molten zinc iodide rather than molten zinc chloride, what mass of iodine will be released at the anode?

(c) Would the quantity of zinc deposited in part (b) differ from what it was in part (a)? Why?

(d) How would you set up a device for plating a copper spoon with silver?

17.16 What may be the relation of Faraday's speculation about an "atom of electricity" to the presumed atomic composition of chemical elements?

17.17 96,540 coulombs in electrolysis frees A grams of a monovalent element ($v = 1$) of atomic mass A, such as hydrogen when hydrochloric acid is used as electrolyte. How much chlorine will be released on the other electrode?

17.18 96,540 coulombs in electrolysis always frees A grams of a monovalent element, $A/2$ grams of a divalent element ($v = 2$), etc. What relation does this suggest between valence and "atoms" of electricity?

17.19 The idea of chemical elements composed of identical atoms makes it easier to understand the phenomena discussed in this chapter. Could the phenomena be explained without using the idea of atoms? Chemical phenomena usually involve a fairly large quantity of material (in terms of the number of "atoms"). Do such phenomena provide sufficient evidence for Dalton's belief that an element consists of atoms, all of which are exactly identical with each other?

17.20 A sociologist recently wrote a book about the place of man in modern society, called *Multivalent Man*. In general, what validity is there for using such terms from physics or chemistry for sociological or other descriptions?

17.21 Which of Dalton's main postulates (page 11) were similar to those in Greek atomism (page 5)? Which are quite different?

Melting and Boiling Temperatures of the Elements Known by 1872

ATOMIC NUMBER	NAME	MELTING POINT	BOILING POINT
1	hydrogen	−259°C	−253°C
3	lithium	186	1340
4	beryllium	1280	2970
5	boron	2300	2550
6	carbon	>3350	4200
7	nitrogen	−210	−196
8	oxygen	−218	−183
9	fluorine	−223	−188
11	sodium	98	880

Melting and Boiling Temperatures of the Elements Known by 1872 (cont.)

ATOMIC NUMBER	NAME	MELTING POINT	BOILING POINT
12	magnesium	651	1107
13	aluminum	660	2057
14	silicon	1420	2355
15	phosphorus	44	280
16	sulfur	113	445
17	chlorine	−103	−35
19	potassium	62	760
20	calcium	842	1240
22	titanium	1800	>3000
23	vanadium	1710	3000
24	chromium	1890	2480
25	manganese	1260	1900
26	iron	1535	3000
27	cobalt	1495	2900
28	nickel	1455	2900
29	copper	1083	2336
30	zinc	419	907
33	arsenic	814	615
34	selenium	217	688
35	bromine	−7	59
37	rubidium	39	700
38	strontium	774	1150
39	yttrium	1490	2500
40	zirconium	1857	>2900
41	niobium	2500	3700
42	molybdenum	2620	4800
44	ruthenium	2450	2700
45	rhodium	1966	2500
46	palladium	1549	2200
47	silver	961	1950
48	cadmium	321	767
49	indium	156	2000
50	tin	232	2270
51	antimony	631	1380
52	tellurium	452	1390
53	iodine	114	184
55	cesium	29	670
56	barium	725	1140
57	lanthanum	826	......
58	cerium	804	1400
68	erbium	......	......
73	tantalum	3000	4100
74	tungsten	3370	5900
76	osmium	2700	>5300
77	iridium	2454	>4800
78	platinum	1774	4300
79	gold	1063	2600
80	mercury	−39	357
81	thallium	302	1460
82	lead	327	1620
83	bismuth	271	1560
90	thorium	1845	4500
92	uranium	1133	ignites

The tube used by J. J. Thomson to determine the charge-to-mass ratio of electrons.

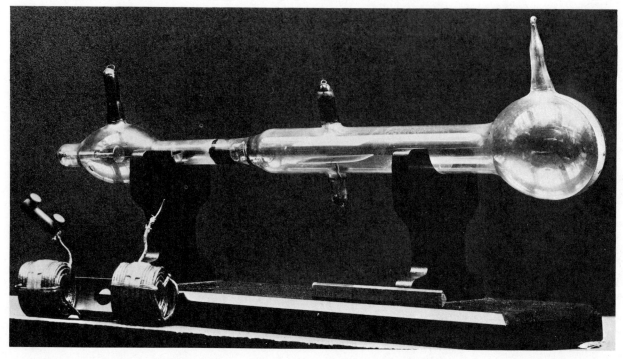

CHAPTER EIGHTEEN

Electrons and Quanta

18.1 The idea of atomic structure

SG 18.1

Chemistry in the nineteenth century had succeeded remarkably in accounting for combining proportions and in predicting chemical reactions. This success had convinced most scientists that matter is indeed composed of atoms. But there remained a related question: are atoms really indivisible, or do they consist of still smaller particles?

We can see how this question arose by thinking a little more about the periodic table. Mendeleev had arranged the elements in the order of increasing atomic mass. But the atomic masses of the elements cannot explain the *periodic* features of Mendeleev's table. Why, for example, do the 3rd, 11th, 19th, 37th, 55th, and 87th elements, with quite different atomic masses, have similar chemical properties? Why are these properties somewhat different from those of the 4th, 12th, 20th, 38th, 56th, and 88th elements in the list, but greatly different from the properties of the 2nd, 10th, 18th, 36th, 54th, and 86th elements?

The periodicity in the properties of the elements led to speculation that atoms might have structure, that they might be made up of smaller pieces. The properties changed gradually from group to group. This fact suggested that some unit of atomic structure might be added from one element to the next, until a certain portion of the structure is completed. The completed condition would occur in the atom of a noble gas. In an atom of the next heavier element, a new portion of the structure would be started, and so on. The methods and techniques of classical chemistry could not supply experimental evidence for such structure. In the nineteenth century, however, discoveries and new techniques in physics opened the way to proof that atoms actually do consist of smaller pieces. Evidence piled up that the atoms of different elements differ in the number and arrangement of these pieces.

In this chapter, we will discuss the discovery of one structural unit which all atoms contain: the electron. Then we will see how experiments with light and electrons led to a revolutionary idea—that *light* energy is

These elements burn when exposed to air; they decompose water, often explosively.

These elements react slowly with air or water.

These elements rarely combine with any others.

transmitted in separate "chunks." In Chapter 19, we will describe the discovery of another part of the atom, the nucleus. Finally we will show how Niels Bohr combined these pieces to create a workable model of the atom. The story starts with the discovery of cathode rays.

18.2 Cathode rays

In 1855 the German physicist Heinrich Geissler invented a powerful vacuum pump. This pump could remove enough gas from a strong glass tube to reduce the pressure to 0.01 percent of normal air pressure. It was the first major improvement in vacuum pumps after Guericke's invention of the air pump, two centuries earlier. And it opened new fields to pure scientific research. Geissler's friend Julius Plücker connected one of Geissler's evacuated tubes to a battery. He was surprised to find that, at the very low pressure obtained with Geissler's pump, electricity flowed through the tube. Plücker used apparatus similar to that sketched in the margin. He sealed a wire into each end of a strong glass tube. Inside the tube, each wire ended in a metal plate, called an electrode. Outside the tube, each wire ran to a source of high voltage. (The negative plate is called the *cathode,* and the positive plate is called *anode.*) A meter indicated the current going through the tube.

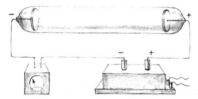

Cathode ray apparatus

Substances which glow when exposed to light are called fluorescent. Fluorescent lights are essentially Geissler tubes with an inner coating of fluorescent powder.

Plücker and his student, Johann Hittorf, noticed that when an electric current passes through the low-pressure gas in a tube, the tube itself glows with a pale green color. Several other scientists observed this effect, but two decades passed before anyone undertook a thorough study of the glowing tubes. By 1875, Sir William Crookes had designed new tubes for studying the glow. When he used a bent tube (see figure at the left) the most intense green glow appeared on the part of the tube which was directly opposite the cathode (at g). This suggested that the green glow is produced by something which comes out of the cathode and travels down the tube until it hits the glass. Another physicist, Eugen Goldstein, was also studying the effects of passing an electric current through a gas at low pressure. Goldstein coined a name for whatever it was that appeared to be coming from the cathode: *cathode rays.* For the time being, it was quite mysterious just what these cathode rays were.

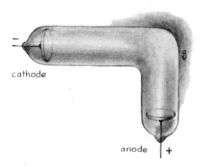

cathode

anode +

Bent Geissler tube. The most intense green glow appeared at g.

To study the nature of the rays, Crookes did some clever experiments. He reasoned that if cathode rays could be stopped before they reached the end of the tube, the intense green glow would disappear. He therefore introduced barriers like the Maltese cross in the sketch in the margin. A shadow of the barrier appeared in the midst of the green glow at the end of the tube. The cathode seemed to act like a source which radiates a kind of light; the cross acted like a barrier blocking the light. The shadow, cross, and cathode appeared along one straight line. Therefore, Crookes concluded, cathode rays, like light rays, travel in straight lines. Next, Crookes moved a magnet near the tube, and the shadow moved. Thus he found that magnetic fields deflect cathode rays (which does not happen with light).

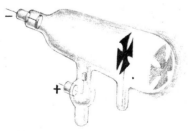

A Crookes tube

In the course of many experiments, Crookes found the following properties of cathode rays:

(a) No matter what material the cathode is made of, it produces rays with the same properties.

(b) In the absence of a magnetic field, the rays travel in straight lines perpendicular to the surface that emits them.

(c) A magnetic field deflects the path of the cathode rays.

(d) The rays can produce some chemical reactions similar to the reactions produced by light. For example, certain silver salts change color when hit by the rays.

In addition, Crookes suspected (but did not succeed in showing) that (e) charged objects deflect the path of cathode rays.

Physicists were fascinated by the cathode rays. Some thought that the rays must be a form of light. After all, they have many of the properties of light: they travel in straight lines, and produce chemical changes and fluorescent glows just as light does. According to Maxwell's theory of electricity and magnetism, light consists of electromagnetic waves. So the cathode rays might, for example, be electromagnetic waves of frequency much higher than that of visible light.

However, magnetic fields do not bend light; they do bend the path of cathode rays. In Chapter 14 we described how magnetic fields exert forces on currents—that is, on moving electric charges. A magnetic field deflects cathode rays in the same way that it deflects negative charges. Therefore, some physicists believed that cathode rays consisted of negatively charged particles.

The debate over whether cathode rays are a form of electromagnetic waves or a stream of charged particles continued for 25 years. Finally, in 1897, J. J. Thomson made a series of experiments which convinced physicists that cathode rays are negatively charged particles. A brief summary of Thomson's experiment and calculations appears on page 38. A detailed account of the discovery of the electron is given in Chapter 2 of the Supplemental Unit B, *Discoveries in Physics.*

It was then well-known that the paths of charged particles are affected by both magnetic and electric fields. By assuming that cathode rays were negatively charged particles, Thomson could predict what should happen when they passed through such fields. For example, an electric field of just the right magnitude and direction should exactly balance the deflection of a beam of cathode rays by a magnetic field. As page 38 indicates, the predictions were verified. Thomson could therefore conclude that cathode rays were indeed made up of negatively charged particles. He was then able to calculate, from the experimental data, the ratio of the charge of a particle to its mass. This ratio is represented by q/m, where q is the charge and m is the mass of the particle.

Thomson found that the rays coming from cathodes made of different materials all had the same value of q/m, namely 1.76×10^{11} coulombs per kilogram.

Thus, it was clear that cathode rays must be made of something all materials have in common. Thomson's negatively charged particles were later called *electrons.* The value of q/m for the cathode ray particles was

J. J. Thomson later observed this to be possible.

Sir Joseph John Thomson (1856-1940), one of the greatest British physicists, attended Owens College in Manchester, England and then Cambridge University. He worked on the conduction of electricity through gases, on the relation between electricity and matter, and on atomic models. His greatest single contribution was the discovery of the electron. He was the head of the famous Cavendish Laboratory at Cambridge University, where one of his students was Ernest Rutherford.

Thomson's *q/m* Experiment

J. J. Thomson measured the ratio of charge q to mass m for cathode-ray particles by means of the evacuated tube shown in the photograph on page 34. A high voltage applied between two electrodes in the left end of the tube produced cathode rays. Those rays that passed through both slotted cylinders in the narrow neck of the tube formed a nearly parallel beam. The beam produced a spot of light on a fluorescent coating inside the large end of the tube at the right.

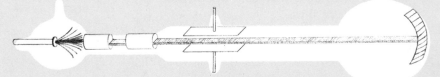

The path of the beam was deflected by an electric field applied between two horizontal plates in the mid-section of the tube (note that direction of electric field $\vec{E}$ is upward along the plane of the page):

The beam was also deflected when there was no electric field but when a magnetic field was set up by a pair of current-carrying wire coils placed around the midsection of the tube. (The direction of the magnetic field $\vec{B}$ is perpendicular to and down into the plane of the page):

When only the magnetic field $\vec{B}$ is turned on, particles in the beam, having charge q and speed v, would experience a force Bqv. This force is always perpendicular to the direction of the velocity vector, therefore the beam is deflected in a nearly circular arc of radius R as long as it is in the nearly uniform magnetic field. If the particles in the beam have mass m, they must be experiencing a centripetal force mv^2/R while moving in a circular arc. Since the centripetal force is provided by the magnetic force Bqv, we can write $Bqv = mv^2R$. Rearranging terms: $q/m = v/BR$.

B can be calculated from the geometry of the coils and the electric current in them. R can be found geometrically from the displacement of the beam spot on the end of the tube. To determine v, Thomson applied the electric field and the magnetic field at the same time. He then arranged the directions and strengths of the two fields so that the electric field $\vec{E}$ exerted a downward force Eq on the beam particles exactly equal to the upward force Bqv due to the magnetic field. This condition is evidenced by the fact that the beam, acted on by both fields in opposing ways, goes along a straight line.

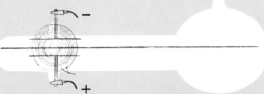

If the magnitudes of the forces due to the electric and magnetic fields are equal, then $Eq = Bqv$. Solving for v we have: $v = E/B$. E can be calculated from the separation of the two plates and the voltage between them; so the speed of the particles v can be determined. Now all the terms on the right of the earlier equation for q/m are known, and q/m can be computed. The experimental value is 1.76×10^{11} coul/kg.

about 1800 times larger than the values of q/m for charged hydrogen atoms (ions), which we found to be 9.6×10^7 coulombs per kilogram as measured in electrolysis experiments of the kind we discussed in Section 17.8 (See table on page 31.) Thomson concluded from these results that either the *charge* of the cathode ray particles is much *greater* than that of the hydrogen ion, or the *mass* of the cathode ray particles is much *less* than the mass of the hydrogen ion.

Thomson also measured the charge q on these negatively charged particles with methods other than deflection by electric and magnetic fields. His experiments were not very accurate. But they were good enough to indicate that the charge of a cathode ray particle was the same or not much different from that of the hydrogen ion in electrolysis. In view of the small value of q/m, Thomson concluded that the mass of cathode ray particles is much less than the mass of hydrogen ions.

In short, the cathode ray particles, or electrons, were found to have two important properties: (1) they were emitted by a wide variety of cathode materials, and (2) they were much smaller in mass than the hydrogen atom, which has the smallest known mass. Thomson therefore concluded that the cathode ray particles form a part of all kinds of matter. He suggested that the atom is not the ultimate limit to the subdivision of matter; rather, the electron is part of an atom, and is perhaps even a basic building block of atoms. We now know that this is correct. The electron—whose existence Thomson had first proved by quantitative experiment—is one of the fundamental or "elementary" particles of which matter is made.

In the article in which he published his discovery, Thomson also speculated about how electrons might be arranged in atoms of different elements. He thought that such arrangements might account for the periodicity of the chemical properties of the elements. As we will see in the next chapter, Thomson did not say the *last* word about the arrangement and number of electrons in the atom. But he did say the *first* word about it.

SG 18.2

The data in the table on page 31 show that 1.008 g of hydrogen is freed when 96,540 coul of electric charge are transferred: this implies $q/m = 96,540$ coul/1.008 g, or about 9.6×10^7 coul/kg.

Q1 What was the most convincing evidence that cathode rays were not electromagnetic radiation?

Q2 What was the reason given for the ratio q/m for electrons being 1800 times larger than q/m for hydrogen ions?

Q3 What were two main reasons for Thomson's belief that electrons may be "building blocks" from which all atoms are made?

18.3 The measurement of the charge of the electron: Millikan's experiment

After the ratio of charge to the mass (q/m) of the electron had been determined, physicists tried to measure the value of the charge q itself. If

From now on we represent the magnitude of the charge of the electron by q_e.

$q_e = 1.6 \times 10^{-19}$ coul.

The sign of the charge is negative for the electron.

SG 18.3

In 1964, an American physicist, Murray Gell-Mann, suggested that particles with charge equal to 1/3 or 2/3 of q might exist. He named these particles "quarks"—the word comes from James Joyce's novel *Finnegan's Wake*. Quarks are now being looked for in cosmic-ray and bubble-chamber experiments.

Thomson found that

$q_e/m = 1.76 \times 10^{11}$ coul/kg.

According to Millikan's experiment the magnitude of q_e is 1.6×10^{-19} coul.

Therefore, the mass of an electron is:

$$m = \frac{1.6 \times 10^{-19} \text{ coul}}{1.76 \times 10^{11} \text{ coul/kg}}$$

$$= 0.91 \times 10^{-30} \text{ kg}$$

(Mass of a hydrogen ion is 1.66×10^{-27} kg. This is approximately the value of one "atomic mass unit.")

the charge could be determined, the mass of the electron could be found from the known value of q/m. In the years between 1909 and 1916, the American physicist Robert A. Millikan succeeded in measuring the charge of the electron. This quantity is one of the fundamental constants of physics; it comes up again and again in atomic and nuclear physics as well as in electricity and electromagnetism.

Millikan's "oil-drop experiment" is still one of the best experiments that students can do. It is described in general outline on page 41. He found that the electric charge that a small object such as an oil drop can pick up is always a simple multiple of a certain *minimum value*. For example, the charge may have the value -4.8×10^{-19} coulombs, or -1.6×10^{-19} coulombs, or -6.4×10^{-19} coulombs, or -1.6×10^{-18} coulombs. But it never has a charge of, say, -2.4×10^{-19} coulombs. And it never has a value smaller than -1.6×10^{-19} coulombs. In other words, electric charges always come in multiples (1, 2, 3...) of 1.6×10^{-19} coulombs, a quantity often symbolized by q_e. Millikan correctly took this minimum charge to be the amount of charge of a single electron.

The magnitude of the charges of nuclei or atomic and molecular ions is also always a multiple of the electron charge q_e. For example, a chemist may refer to a "doubly charged oxygen ion." This means that the magnitude of the charge of the ion is $2q_e$, or 3.2×10^{-19} coulombs.

Note that Millikan's experiments did not prove that no charges smaller than q_e can exist. All we can say is that no experiment has yet proved the existence of smaller charges. Recent theoretical advances suggest that in some very high-energy experiments, an elementary particle of charge $1/3\ q_e$ may eventually be discovered. But no such "fractional" charge is expected to be found on nuclei, ions, or droplets.

In everyday life, the electric charges we meet are huge compared to that on one electron. Thus, we usually think of such charges or currents as being continuous, just as we think of the flow of water in a river as continuous rather than as a flow of individual molecules. A current of one ampere, for example, is equivalent to the flow of 6.25×10^{18} electrons per second. The "static" electric charge one accumulates by shuffling over a rug on a dry day consists of something like 10^{12} electron charges.

Since the work of Millikan, other experiments involving many different fields within physics have all pointed to the charge q_e as being fundamental in the structure and behavior of atoms, nuclei, and smaller particles. For example, it has been shown directly that cathode ray particles carry this basic unit of charge—that they are, in other words, electrons.

By combining Millikan's value for the electron charge q_e with Thomson's value for the ratio of charge to mass (q_e/m), we can calculate the mass of a single electron (see margin). The mass found for the electron is about 10^{-30} kilograms. From electrolysis experiments (see Section 17.8) we know that the charge-to-mass ratio of a hydrogen ion is 1836 times smaller than the charge-to-mass ratio of an electron. But an electron and a hydrogen ion form a neutral hydrogen atom when they combine. Therefore, it is reasonable to expect that they have equal and opposite charges. If so, we may conclude that the *mass* of the hydrogen ion is 1836 times as great as the mass of the electron: that is, the mass of

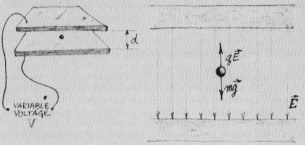

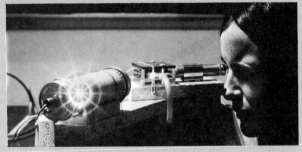

Millikan's Oil-drop Experiment

R. A. Millikan's own apparatus (about 1910) for measuring the charge of the electron is seen in the photograph above. A student version of Millikan's apparatus is shown in the lower photograph.

In principle Millikan's experiment is simple; the essential part of the apparatus is sketched above. When oil is sprayed into the chamber containing two horizontal plates, the tiny droplets formed are electrically charged as they emerge from the spray nozzle. The charge of a droplet is what must be measured. Consider a small oil drop of mass m carrying an electric charge q. It is situated between the two horizontal plates that are separated by a distance d and at an electrical potential difference V. There will be a uniform electric field $\vec{E}$ between the plates, of strength V/d (see Section 14.8). This field can be adjusted so that the electrical force $q\vec{E}$ exerted upward on the drop's charge will balance the force ma_g exerted downward by gravity. In this balanced situation,

$$F_{el} = F_{grav}$$

therefore

$$qE = ma_g$$

or

$$q = ma_g/E$$

The mass of the drop can, in principle, be determined from its radius and the density of the oil from which it was made. Millikan had to measure these quantities by an indirect method. (Today it is possible to do the experiment with small manufactured polystyrene spheres instead of oil drops. Their mass is known, so that some of the complications of the original experiment can be avoided.) Millikan's remarkable result was that the charge q on objects such as an oil drop is always a multiple (1, 2, 3 ...) of a smallest charge, which he identified with the magnitude of the charge of one electron (q_e).

the hydrogen ion is $1836 \times 0.91 \times 10^{-30}$ kg $= 1.66 \times 10^{-7}$ kg. This is approximately the value of one *atomic mass unit*.

Q4 Oil drops pick up different amounts of electric charge. On what basis did Millikan decide that the lowest charge he found was actually just one electron charge?

18.4 The photoelectric effect

In 1887 the German physicist Heinrich Hertz was testing Maxwell's theory of electromagnetic waves. He noticed that a metallic surface can emit electric charges when light of very short wavelength falls on it. Because light and electricity are both involved, the name *photoelectric effect* was given to this phenomenon. When the electric charges so produced passed through electric and magnetic fields, their paths were changed in the same ways as the paths of cathode rays. It was therefore deduced that the electric charges consist of negatively charged particles. In 1898, J. J. Thomson measured the value of the ratio q/m for these photoelectrically emitted particles. Using the same method that he had used for cathode ray particles, he got the same value for the photoelectric particles as he had for the cathode-ray particles. These experiments (and others) demonstrated that photoelectric particles had the same properties as electrons. In fact, we consider them to be ordinary electrons, although they are often referred to as *photoelectrons* to indicate their origin. Later work showed that all substances—solids, liquids and gases—exhibit the photoelectric effect under appropriate conditions. However, it is convenient to study the effect with metallic surfaces.

The photoelectric effect, which we will be studying in greater detail, has had an important place in the development of atomic physics. The effect could not be explained in terms of the ideas of physics we have studied so far. New ideas had to be introduced to account for the experimental results. In particular, a revolutionary concept was introduced—that of *quanta*. A new branch of physics—*quantum theory*—developed at least in part because of the explanation provided for the photoelectric effect.

The basic information for studying the photoelectric effect comes from two kinds of measurements: (1) measurements of the *photoelectric current* (the number of photoelectrons emitted per unit time); and (2) measurements of the *kinetic energies* with which the photoelectrons are emitted.

The *photoelectric current* can be studied with an apparatus like that sketched in Fig. (a) below. Two metal plates, C and A, are sealed inside a well-evacuated quartz tube. (Quartz glass is transparent to ultraviolet light as well as visible light.) The two plates are connected to a source of potential difference (for example, a battery). In the circuit is also an ammeter. As long as light strikes plate C, as in Fig. (b), electrons are emitted from it. If the potential of plate A is positive relative to plate C, these emitted photoelectrons will accelerate to plate A. (Some emitted electrons will reach plate A even if it is not positive relative to C.) The resulting "photoelectric" current is indicated by the ammeter. The result of the experiment is that the stronger the beam of light of a given color (frequency), the greater the photoelectric current.

The best way to study this part—as most other parts—of physics is by actually doing the experiments discussed!

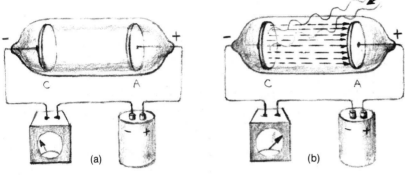

(a)   (b)

Schematic diagram of apparatus for photoelectric experiments.

Any metal used as plate C shows a photoelectric effect, but only if the light has a frequency *greater* than a certain value. This value of the frequency is called the *threshold frequency* for that metal. Different metals have different threshold frequencies. If the incident light has a frequency lower than the threshold frequency, *no* photoelectrons are emitted, no matter how great the intensity of the light or how long the light is left on! This is the first of a set of surprising discoveries.

The *kinetic energies of the electrons* can be measured in a slightly modified version of the apparatus, sketched in Fig. (c) below. The battery is reversed so that the plate A now tends to repel the photoelectrons. The voltage can be changed from zero to a value just large enough to keep any electrons from reaching the plate A, as indicated in Fig. (d).

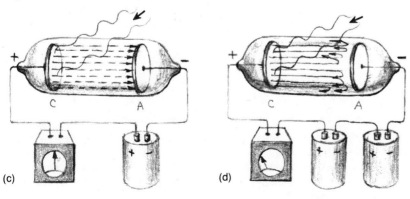

(c)   (d)

SG 18.4

When the voltage across the plates is zero, the meter will indicate a current. This reading shows that the photoelectrons, emerging with kinetic energy from the metallic surface, can reach plate A. As the repelling voltage is increased, the photoelectric current decreases. Eventually a certain voltage is reached at which the current becomes zero, as indicated in Fig. (d) on page 43. This voltage, which is called the *stopping voltage,* is a measure of the maximum kinetic energy of the emitted photoelectrons (KE_{max}). If we call the stopping voltage V_{stop}, this maximum kinetic energy is given by the relation:

$$KE_{max} = V_{stop} \, q_e$$

The results can be stated more precisely. Let us list the important experimental results here so that we can more accurately discuss their theoretical interpretation later.

(1) A substance shows a photoelectric effect only if the incident light has a frequency above a certain threshold frequency (symbol f_o).

(2) If light of a given frequency does produce a photoelectric effect, the photoelectric current from the surface is proportional to the intensity of the light falling on it.

(3) If light of a given frequency releases photoelectrons, the emission of these electrons is *immediate.* The time interval between the instant the light strikes the metallic surface and the appearance of electrons is at most 3×10^{-9} sec, and probably much less. In some experiments, the light intensity used was extremely low. According to the classical theory, it should take several hundred seconds for an electron to accumulate enough energy from such light to be emitted. But even in these cases electrons are sometimes emitted about a billionth of a second after the light strikes the surface.

(4) The maximum kinetic energy of the photoelectrons increases in direct proportion to the *frequency* of the light which causes their emission. (Maximum *KE* is *not* dependent on the *intensity* of the incident light.) The way in which the maximum kinetic energy of the electrons varies with the frequency of the incident light is shown in the margin. The symbols $(f_o)_1$, $(f_o)_2$ and $(f_o)_3$ stand for the different threshold frequencies of three different substances. For each substance, the experimental data points fall on a straight line. All the lines have the same slope.

What is most astonishing about the results is that photoelectrons are emitted if the light frequencies are *a little above* the threshold frequency, no matter how weak the beam of light. But if the light frequencies are just *a bit below* the threshold frequency, no electrons are emitted *no matter how great the intensity of the light beam is.*

Findings (1), (3) and (4) could not be explained on the basis of the classical electromagnetic theory of light. How could a low-intensity train of light waves spread out over a large number of atoms, in a very short time interval, concentrate enough energy on one electron to knock the electron out of the metal?

In Section 14.8, we saw that the change in potential energy of a charge is given by *Vq*. In Unit 3 we saw that (in the absence of friction) the decrease in kinetic energy in a system is equal to the increase in its potential energy.

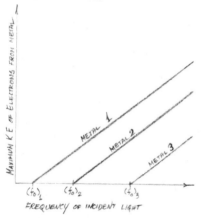

Photoelectric effect: maximum kinetic energy of the electrons as a function of the frequency of the incident light; different metals yield lines that are parallel, but have different threshold frequencies.

Furthermore, the classical wave theory could not account for the existence of a threshold frequency. There seemed to be no reason why a sufficiently intense beam of low-frequency radiation should not produce photoelectricity, if low-intensity radiation of higher frequency could produce it. Neither could classical theory explain why the maximum kinetic energy of the photoelectrons increases directly with the frequency of the light but is independent of the intensity. Thus, the photoelectric effect posed a challenge which the classical wave theory of light could not meet.

Q5 Light falling on a certain metal surface causes electrons to be emitted. What happens to the photoelectric current as the intensity of the light is decreased?

Q6 What happens as the frequency of the light is decreased?

Q7 Sketch a rough diagram of the equipment and circuit used to demonstrate the main facts of photoelectricity.

18.5 Einstein's theory of the photoelectric effect

The explanation of the photoelectric effect was the major work cited in the award to Albert Einstein of the Nobel Prize in physics for the year 1921. Einstein's theory, proposed in 1905, played a major role in the development of atomic physics. The theory was based on a daring proposal, for few of the experimental details were known in 1905. Moreover, the key point of Einstein's explanation contradicted the classical ideas of the time.

Einstein assumed that energy of light is not distributed evenly over the whole expanding wave front (as the classical theory assumed). Instead, the light energy is concentrated in separate "lumps." Further, the amount of energy in each of these regions is not just any amount, but a definite amount of energy which is proportional to the frequency f of the wave. The proportionality factor is a constant (symbol h); it is called Planck's constant, for reasons which we will discuss later. Thus, in this model, the light energy in a beam of frequency f comes in pieces, each of amount hf. The amount of radiant energy in each piece is called a *quantum* of energy. It represents the smallest possible quantity of energy for light of that frequency. The quantum of light energy was later called a *photon*.

There is no explanation clearer or more direct than Einstein's. We quote below from his first paper (1905) on this subject. Only the notation is changed, in order to agree with modern practice (including our own notation):

> . . . According to the idea that the incident light consists of quanta with energy hf, the ejection of cathode rays by light can be understood in the following way. Energy quanta penetrate the surface layer of the body, and their energy is converted, at least in part, into kinetic energy of electrons. The

See the articles "Einstein" and "Einstein and some Civilized Discontents" in *Reader 5.*

$h = 6.6 \times 10^{-34}$ joule-sec

SG 18.5

simplest picture is that a light quantum gives up all its energy to a single electron; we shall assume that this happens. The possibility is not to be excluded, however, that electrons receive their energy only in part from the light quantum. An electron provided with kinetic energy inside the body may have lost part of its kinetic energy by the time it reaches the surface. In addition, it is to be assumed that each electron, in leaving the body, has to do an amount of work W (which is characteristic of the body). The electrons ejected directly from the surface and at right angles to it will have the greatest velocities perpendicular to the surface. The maximum kinetic energy of such an electron is

$$KF_{max} = hf - W$$

If the body plate C is charged to a positive potential, V_{stop} just large enough to keep the body from losing electric charge, we must have

$$KE_{max} = hf - W = V_{stop}\, q_e$$

where q_e is the magnitude of the electronic charge . . .

If the derived formula is correct, then V_{stop}, when plotted as a function of the frequency of the incident light, should yield a straight line whose slope should be independent of the nature of the substance illuminated.

We can now compare Einstein's photoelectric equation with the experimental results to test whether or not his theory accounts for those results. According to the equation, the kinetic energy is greater than zero only when hf is greater than W. Hence, an electron can be emitted only when the frequency of the incident light is greater than a certain lowest value f_0 (where $hf_0 = W$.)

Next, according to Einstein's photon model, it is an individual photon that ejects an electron. Now, the intensity of the light is proportional to the number of the photons in the light beam. Further, the number of photoelectrons ejected is proportional to the number of photons incident on the surface. Hence, the number of electrons ejected (and with it the photoelectric current) is proportional to the intensity of the incident light.

According to Einstein's model, the light energy is concentrated in the quanta (photons). So no time is needed for collecting light energy. Instead, the quanta transfer their energy immediately to the photoelectrons, which emerge after the very short time required for them to escape from the surface.

Each electron must be given a minimum energy to emerge from the surface because it must do work against the forces of attraction as it leaves the rest of the atoms.

This equation is usually called Einstein's photoelectric equation.

SG 18.6-18.8

How Einstein's theory explains the photoelectric effect:
(1) No photoelectric emission below threshold frequency. Reason: low-frequency photons don't have enough energy to provide electrons with *KE* sufficient to leave the metal.
(2) Current ∝ light intensity. Reason: one photon ejects one electron.

SG 18.9, 18.10

Student apparatus for photoelectric experiments often includes a vacuum phototube, like the one shown at the left. The collecting wire corresponds to A in Fig. (a) on page 43, and is at the center of a cylindrical photosensitive surface that corresponds to C. The frequency of the light entering the tube is selected by placing colored filters between the tube and a white light source, as shown at the right.

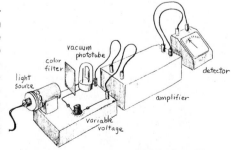

Albert Einstein (1879-1955) was born in the city of Ulm, in Germany. Like Newton he showed no particular intellectual promise as a youngster. He received his early education in Germany, but at the age of 15, dissatisfied with the discipline in school and militarism in the nation, he left and went to Switzerland. After graduation from the Polytechnic Institute in Zurich, Einstein (in 1902) found work in the Swiss Patent Office in Berne. This job gave Einstein a salary to live on and an opportunity to use his spare time for working in physics on his own. In 1905 he published three papers of immense importance. One dealt with quantum theory and included his theory of the photoelectric effect. Another treated the problem of molecular motions and sizes, and worked out a mathematical analysis of the phenomenon of "Brownian motion." Einstein's analysis and experimental work by Jean Perrin, a French physicist, provided a strong argument for the molecular motions assumed in the kinetic theory. Einstein's third 1905 paper provided the theory of special relativity which revolutionized modern thought about the nature of space and time, and of physical theory itself.

In 1915, Einstein published a paper on the theory of general relativity. In it he provided a new theory of gravitation which included Newton's theory as a special case.

When Hitler and the Nazis came to power in Germany, in 1933, Einstein came to the United States and became a member of the Institute for Advanced Study at Princeton. He spent the rest of his working life seeking a unified theory which would include gravitation and electromagnetism. Near the beginning of World War II, Einstein wrote a letter to President Roosevelt, warning of the war potential of an "atomic bomb," for which the Germans had all necessary knowledge and motivation to work. After World War II, Einstein devoted much of his time to organizations advocating world agreements to end the threat of atomic warfare.

(3) Immediate emission. Reason: a single photon provides the energy concentrated in one place.

(4) KE_{max} Increases directly with frequency above F_0. Reason: the work needed to remove the electron is $W = hf_0$; any energy left over from the original photon is now available for kinetic energy of the electron.

The equation $KE_{max} = hf - W$ can be said to have led to two Nobel prizes: one to Einstein, who derived it theoretically, and one to Millikan, who verified it experimentally. This equation is the subject of a Project Physics laboratory experiment.

SG 18.11

Finally, the photoelectric equation predicts that the greater the frequency of the incident light, the greater is the maximum kinetic energy of the ejected electrons. According to the photon model, the photon's energy is directly proportional to the light frequency. The minimum energy needed to eject an electron is the energy required for the electron to escape from the metal surface. This explains why light of frequency less than some frequency f_o cannot eject any electrons. The kinetic energy of the escaping electron is the difference between the energy of the absorbed photon and the energy lost by the electron in escaping the surface.

Thus, Einstein's photoelectric equation agreed qualitatively with the experimental results. There remained two quantitative tests to be made: (1) does the maximum energy vary in direct proportion to the light frequency? (2) is the proportionality factor h really the same for all substances? For some 10 years, experimental physicists attempted these quantitative tests. One experimental difficulty was that the value of W for a metal changes greatly if there are impurities (for example, a layer of oxidized metal) on the surface. Finally, in 1916, Robert A. Millikan established that there is indeed a straight-line relationship between the frequency of the absorbed light and the maximum kinetic energy of the photoelectrons. (See the graph on page 44.) To obtain his data Millikan designed an apparatus in which the metal photoelectric surface was cut clean while in a vacuum. A knife inside the evacuated volume was manipulated by an electromagnet outside the vacuum to make the cuts. This rather intricate arrangement was required to achieve a pure metal surface.

The straight-line graphs Millikan obtained for different metals all had the same slope, even though the threshold frequencies were different. The value of h could be obtained from Millikan's measurements, and it was the same for each metal surface. Also, it agreed very well with a value obtained by means of other, independent methods. So Einstein's theory of the photoelectric effect was verified quantitatively.

Actually, the first suggestion that the energy in electromagnetic radiation is "quantized" (comes in definite quanta) did not come from the photoelectric effect. Rather, it came from studies of the heat and light radiated by hot solids. The concept of *quanta of energy* was introduced by Max Planck, a German physicist, in 1900, five years before Einstein's theory. (Thus the constant h is known as *Planck's constant.*) Planck was trying to explain how the heat (and light) energy radiated by a hot body is related to the frequency of the radiation. Classical physics (nineteenth-century thermodynamics and electromagnetism) could not account for the experimental facts. Planck found that the facts could be interpreted only by assuming that atoms, on radiating, change their energy in separate, quantized amounts. Einstein's theory of the photoelectric effect was actually an extension and application of Planck's quantum theory of thermal radiation. Einstein postulated that the change in the atom's energy is carried off as a distinct photon rather than being spread continuously over the light wave.

The experiments and the theory on radiation are much harder to

Robert Andrews Millikan (1868-1953), an American physicist, attended Oberlin College where his interest in physics was only mild. After his graduation he became more interested in physics, taught at Oberlin while taking his master's degree, and then obtained his doctor's degree from Columbia University in 1895. After more study in Germany he went to the University of Chicago, where he became a professor of physics in 1910. His work on the determination of the electronic charge took place from 1906 to 1913. He was awarded the Nobel Prize in physics in 1923 for this research, and for the very careful experiments which resulted in the verification of the Einstein photoelectric equation (Section 18.4). In 1921, Millikan moved to the California Institute of Technology, eventually to become its president.

describe than the experiments and theory of the photoelectric effect. That is why we have chosen to introduce the concept of quanta of energy by means of the photoelectric effect. By now, many tests have been made of both Planck's and Einstein's conceptions. In all cases, Planck's constant h is found to have the same basic position in quantum physics that Newton's universal constant G has in the physics of gravitation.

The photoelectric effect presented physicists with a real dilemma. According to the classical wave theory, light consists of electromagnetic waves extending continuously throughout space. This theory was highly successful in explaining optical phenomena (reflection, refraction, polarization, interference). But it could not account for the photoelectric effect. Einstein's theory, which postulated the existence of separate lumps of light energy, accounted for the photoelectric effect. But it could not account for the other properties of light. The result was that there were two models whose basic concepts seemed to contradict each other. According to one, light is a wave phenomenon; according to the other, light has particle-like properties. Each model had its limits, successes, and failures. What, if anything, could be done about the contradictions between the two models? We will see later that this problem and its treatment have a central position in modern physics.

Max Planck (1858-1947), a German physicist, was the originator of the quantum theory, one of the two great revolutionary physical theories of the 20th century. (The other is Einstein's relativity theory.) Planck won the Nobel Prize in 1918 for his quantum theory. He tried for many years to show that this theory could be understood in terms of the classical physics of Newton and Maxwell, but this attempt did not succeed. Quantum physics is fundamentally different, through its postulate that energy in light and matter is not continuously divisible, but exists in quanta of definite amount.

Q8   Einstein's idea of a quantum of light had a definite relation to the wave model of light. What was it?

Q9   Why does the photoelectron not have as much energy as the quantum of light which causes it to be ejected?

Q10   What does a "stopping voltage" of, say, 2.0 volts indicate about the photoelectrons emerging from a metal surface?

Wilhelm Konrad Röntgen (1845-1923)

18.6 X rays

In 1895, a surprising discovery was made. Like the photoelectric effect, it did not fit in with accepted ideas about electromagnetic waves and eventually needed quanta for its explanation. The discovery was that of x rays by the German physicist Wilhelm Röntgen. Its consequences for atomic physics and technology are dramatic and important.

On November 8, 1895, Röntgen was experimenting with the newly found cathode rays, as were many physicists all over the world. According to a biographer,

> . . . he had covered the all-glass pear-shaped tube [Crookes tube—see Section 18.2] with pieces of black cardboard, and had darkened the room in order to test the opacity of the black paper cover. Suddenly, about a yard from the tube, he saw a weak light that shimmered on a little bench he knew was nearby. Highly excited, Röntgen lit a match and, to his great surprise, discovered that the source of the mysterious light was a little barium platinocyanide screen lying on the bench.

Barium platinocyanide, a mineral, is one of the many chemicals known to *fluoresce* (emit visible light when illuminated with ultraviolet light). But no source of ultraviolet light was present in Röntgen's experiment. Cathode rays had not been observed to travel more than a few centimeters in air. So, neither ultraviolet light nor the cathode rays themselves could have caused the fluorescence. Röntgen therefore deduced that the fluorescence involved rays of a new kind. He named them *x rays*—that is, rays of an unknown nature. In an intensive series of experiments over the next seven weeks, he determined the properties of this new radiation. He reported his results on December 28, 1895, in a paper whose title (translated) is "On a New Kind of Rays."

Röntgen's paper described nearly all of the properties of x rays that are known even now. It described the method of producing the rays, and proved that they originated in the glass wall of the tube, where the cathode rays struck it. Röntgen showed that x rays travel in straight lines from their place of origin and that they darken a photographic plate. He reported in detail the ability of x rays to penetrate various substances—paper, wood, aluminum, platinum, and lead. Their penetrating power was greater through light materials (paper, wood, flesh) than through dense materials (platinum, lead, bone). He described photographs showing "the shadows of bones of the hand, of a set of weights inside a small box, and of a piece of metal whose inhomogeneity becomes apparent with x rays." He gave a clear description of the shadows cast by the bones of the hand on the fluorescent screen. Röntgen also reported that the x rays were not deflected by a magnetic field. Nor did they show reflection, refraction, or interference effects in ordinary optical apparatus.

Opposite: One of the earliest x-ray photographs made in the United States (1896). The man x-rayed had been hit by a shotgun blast.

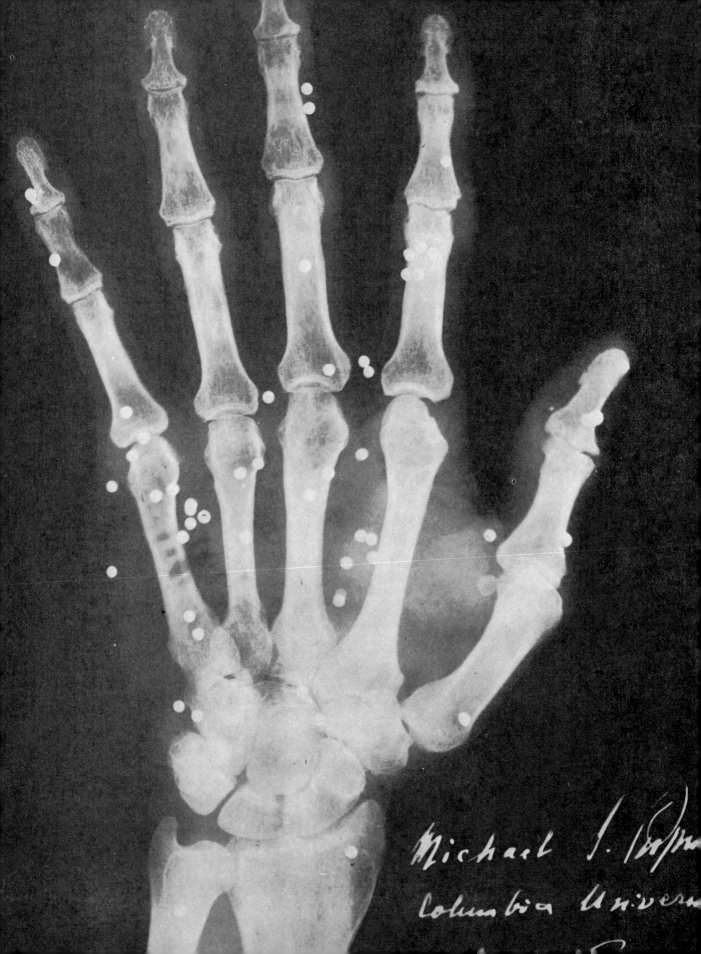

Michael I. *Pupin*

Columbia Universi...

X rays were often referred to as
Röntgen rays, after their discoverer.

It is easy to see why a charged
electroscope will be discharged
when the air around it is ionized: It
attracts the ions of the opposite
charge from the air.

Such a particle—the neutron—was
discovered in 1932. But the neutron
has nothing to do with x rays.

SG 18.12

SG 18.13

J. J. Thomson discovered one of the most important properties of x rays a month or two after the rays themselves had become known. He found that when the rays pass through a gas they make it a conductor of electricity. He attributed this effect to "a kind of electrolysis, the molecule being split up, or nearly split up by the Röntgen rays." The x rays, in passing through the gas, knock electrons loose from some of the atoms or molecules of the gas. The atoms or molecules that lose these electrons become positively charged. They are called ions because they resemble the positive ions in electrolysis, and the gas is said to be *ionized*. Also, the freed electrons may attach themselves to previously neutral atoms or molecules, giving them negative charges.

Röntgen and Thomson found, independently, that electrified bodies lose their charges when the air around them is ionized by x rays. The rate of discharge depends on the intensity of the rays. This property was therefore used as a convenient quantitative means of measuring the intensity of an x-ray beam. As a result, careful quantitative measurements of the properties and effects of x rays could be made.

One problem that aroused keen interest following the discovery of x rays concerned the nature of the mysterious rays. Unlike charged particles—electrons, for example—they were not deflected by magnetic or electric fields. Therefore it seemed that they had to be either neutral particles or electromagnetic waves. It was difficult to choose between these two possibilities. On the one hand, no neutral particles of atomic size (or smaller) were then known which had the penetrating power of x rays. And the existence of such particles would be extremely hard to prove, because there was no way of getting at them. On the other hand, if the x rays were electromagnetic waves, they would have to have *extremely short wavelengths*. Only in this case, according to theory, could they have high penetrating power and show no refraction or interference effects with ordinary optical apparatus.

As we discussed in Chapters 12 and 13, distinctly wavelike properties become apparent only when waves interact with objects (like slits in a barrier) that are smaller than several wavelengths across. The wavelength hypothesized for x rays would be on the order of 10^{-10} meter. So a demonstration of their wave behavior would require, say, a diffraction grating with slits spaced about 10^{-10} meter apart. Evidence from kinetic theory and from chemistry indicated that atoms were about 10^{-10} meter in diameter. It was suggested, therefore, that x rays might be diffracted measurably by crystals, in which the atoms form orderly layers about 10^{-10} meter apart.

In 1912, such experiments succeeded. The layers of atoms did act like diffraction gratings, and x rays did, indeed, act like electromagnetic radiations of very short wavelength—like *ultra*-ultraviolet light. These experiments are more complicated to interpret than diffraction of a beam of light by a single, two-dimensional optical grating. The diffraction effect occurs in three dimensions instead of two. Hence the diffraction patterns are far more elaborate (see the illustration on page 53).

In addition to wave properties, x rays were found to have quantum properties. For example, they can cause the emission of electrons from

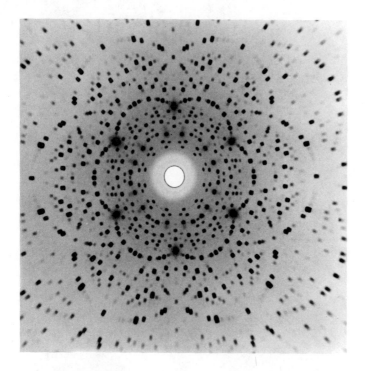

X-ray diffraction patterns from a metal crystal. The black spots are produced by constructive interference of x rays.

metals. These electrons have greater kinetic energies than those produced by ultraviolet light. (The ionization of gases by x rays is also an example of the photoelectric effect. In this case the electrons are freed from the atoms and molecules of the gas.) Thus, x rays also require quantum theory for the explanation of some of their behavior. So, like light, x rays were shown to have both wave and particle properties.

SG 18.14

SG 18.15

SG 18.16

Röntgen's discovery of x rays excited scientists throughout the world. His experiments were immediately repeated and extended in many laboratories in both Europe and America. Scientific journals during the year 1896 were filled with letters and articles describing new experiments or confirming the results of earlier experiments. This widespread experimentation was made easier since, during the years before Röntgen's discovery, the passage of electricity through gases had been a popular topic for study by physicists. So many physics laboratories had cathode-ray tubes and could produce x rays easily.

Intense interest in x rays was generated by the spectacular use of these rays in medicine. Within three months of Röntgen's discovery, x rays were put to practical use in surgical operations in a hospital in Vienna. The use of this new aid to surgery spread rapidly. Since Röntgen's time, x rays have revolutionized some phases of medical practice, especially the diagnosis of some diseases and treatment of some forms of cancer. Extremely important uses of x rays also occur in other fields of applied science, both physical and biological. Among these are the study of the crystal structure of materials; "industrial diagnosis," such as the search for possible defects in materials and engineering structures; the study of old paintings and sculptures; and many others.

Originally, x rays were produced in Röntgen's laboratory when cathode rays (electrons) struck a target (the glass wall of the tube). Nowadays x rays usually are produced by directing a beam of high-energy electrons onto a metal target. As the electrons are deflected and stopped, x rays of various energies are produced. The maximum energy a single ray can have is the total kinetic energy the incident electron gives up on being stopped. So the greater the voltage across which the electron beam is accelerated, the more energetic—and penetrating—are the x rays. One type of x ray tube is shown in the sketch below. A stream of electrons is emitted from a cathode C and accelerated to a tungsten target T by a strong electric field (high potential difference).

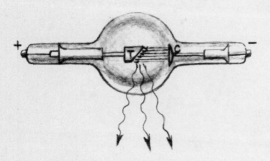

The photograph at the right is an x ray of a jet engine. X-ray photographs are often used to discover internal structural damage and flaws in pieces of complex machinery like this engine and nuclear reactor components, as well as in more mundane objects such as bowling pins and golf balls.

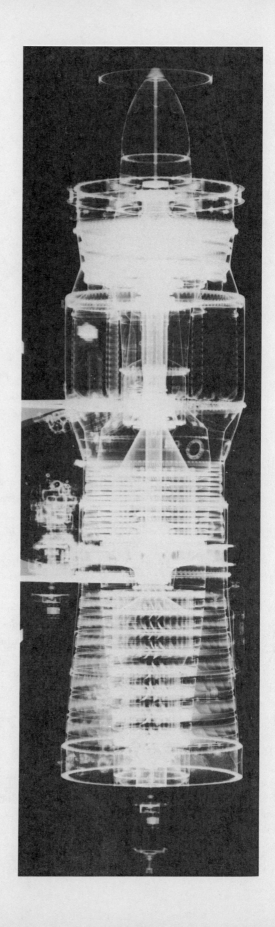

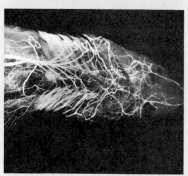

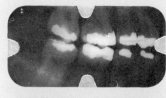

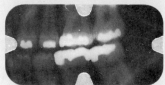

Above left is a rose, photographed with x rays. The potential difference between the electron-emitting cathode and the target in the x-ray tube was 30,000 volts.

Below the rose is the head of a dogfish shark. The blood vessels have been injected with a fluid that absorbs x rays so that the vessels can be studied.

The photograph at the bottom of the page illustrates another use of x rays to discover internal damage, this time in a piece of art. Here, a technician is preparing to take x-ray photographs of. Michelangelo's "Pieta."

Immediately above is illustrated the familiar use of x rays in dentistry and the resulting records. Because x rays can injure tissues, a great deal of caution is required in using them. The shortest possible pulse of x rays is used, lead shielding is provided for the body, and the technician stands behind a wall of lead and lead glass.

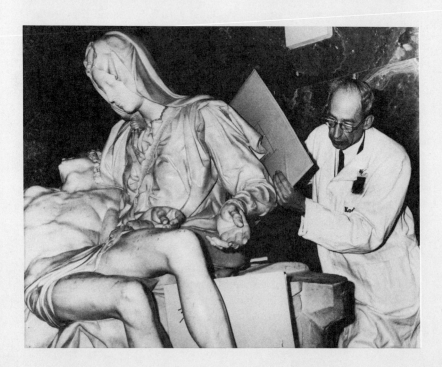

Q11   X rays were the first "ionizing" radiation discovered. What does "ionizing" mean?

Q12   What were three properties of x rays that led to the conclusion that x rays were electromagnetic waves?

Q13   What was the evidence that x rays had a very short wavelength?

18.7 Electrons, quanta and the atom

By the beginning of the twentieth century enough chemical and physical information was available that many physicists devised models of atoms. It was known that negative particles with identical properties—electrons—could be obtained from many different substances and in different ways. This suggested that electrons are parts of all atoms. Electrons are negatively charged. But samples of an element are ordinarily electrically *neutral*. Therefore the atoms making up such samples are also presumably neutral. If so, the presence of negative electrons in an atom would seem to require the presence of an equal amount of positive charge.

In Section 18.2, we discussed comparison of the values of q/m for the electron and for charged hydrogen atoms. As we mentioned, hydrogen atoms are nearly two thousand times more massive than electrons. Experiments (which will be discussed in some detail in Chapter 2 of the Supplemental Unit *The Nucleus*) showed that electrons make up only a very small part of the atomic mass in any atom. Consequently any model of an atom must take into account the following information: (a) an electrically neutral atom contains equal amounts of positive and negative charge; (b) the negative charge is associated with only a small part of the mass of the atom. Further, any atomic model should answer at least two questions: (1) How *many* electrons are there in an atom? (2) How are the electrons and the positive charge *arranged* in an atom?

During the first ten years of the twentieth century, several atomic models were proposed, but none was satisfactory. The early models were all based entirely upon classical physics—that is, upon the physics of Newton and Maxwell. No one knew how to invent a model that took account of Planck's theory of quantization of energy. More detailed experimental facts were also needed. For example, this was the period during which the charge on the electron and the main facts of photoelectricity were still being found. Nevertheless, scientists cannot and should not wait until every last fact is in, for that will never happen. And you can't even know what the missing facts *are* unless you have some sort of model. Even an incomplete or a partly wrong model will provide clues on which to build a better one.

Until 1911 the most popular model for the atom was one proposed by J. J. Thomson in 1904. Thomson suggested that an atom consisted of a sphere of positive electricity in which an equal amount of negative charge was distributed in the form of electrons. Under this assumption, the atom was like a pudding of positive electricity, with the negative electricity scattered in it like raisins. The positive "fluid" was assumed to act on the negative charges, holding them in the atom by electric forces only. Thomson did not specify how the positive "fluid" was held together. The radius of the atom was taken to be of the order of 10^{-10} m. This value was based on information from the kinetic theory of gases and other considerations (see SG 18.13). With this model Thomson was able to calculate that certain arrangements of electrons would be stable. This was the first requirement for explaining the existence of stable atoms. Thomson's theory also suggested that chemical properties might be associated with particular groupings of electrons. A systematic repetition of chemical properties might then occur among groups of elements. But it was not possible to deduce the detailed structure of the atoms of particular elements. Nor could any detailed comparison with the actual periodic table be made.

See the Project Physics film loop
Thomson Model of the Atom.

   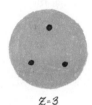

Z=1   Z=2   Z=3   Z=4

 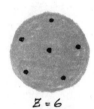

Z=5   Z=6

Some stable (hypothetical) arrangements of electrons in Thomson atoms. The atomic number Z is interpreted as equal to the number of electrons.

In Chapter 19 we will discuss some additional experimental information that provided valuable clues to improved models of the structure of atoms. We will also see how one of the greatest physicists of our time, Niels Bohr, combined the experimental evidence then available with the new concept of quanta into a successful theory of atomic structure. Bohr's model was eventually replaced by more sophisticated ones. But it led to the presently accepted theory of the atom, and to this day is quite adequate for explaining most of the main facts which concern us in this course.

Q14   Why was most of the mass of an atom believed to be associated with positive electric charge?

Q15   Why don't physicists wait until "all the facts are in" before they begin to theorize or make models?

18.1 The Project Physics learning materials particularly appropriate for Chapter 18 include the following:

Experiments
>The charge-to-mass ratio for an electron
>The measurement of elementary charge
>The photoelectric effect

Activities
>Measuring q/m for the electron
>Cathode rays in a Crookes tube
>X rays from a Crookes tube
>Lighting a bulb photoelectrically

Reader Articles
>Failure and Success
>Einstein
>Einstein and Some Civilized Discontents

Transparencies
>Photoelectric experiment
>Photoelectric equation

18.2 In Thomson's experiment on the ratio of charge to mass of cathode ray particles (page 38), the following might have been typical values for B, V and d: with a magnetic field B alone, the deflection of the beam indicated a radius of curvature of the beam within the field of 0.114 meters for $B = 1.0 \times 10^{-3}$ tesla.* With the same magnetic field, the addition of an electric field in the same region ($V = 200$ volts, plate separation $d = 0.01$ meter) made the beam go on straight through.
>(a) Find the speed of the cathode ray particles in the beam.
>(b) Find q/m for the cathode ray particles.

18.3 Given the value for the charge on the electron, show that 'a current of one ampere is equivalent to the movement of 6.25×10^{18} electrons per second past a given point.

18.4 In the apparatus of Fig. (d) in Section 18.4, an electron is turned back before reaching plate A and eventually arrives at electrode C from which it was ejected. It arrives with some kinetic energy. How does this final energy of the electron compare with the energy it had as it left the electrode C?

18.5 At light frequencies below the threshold frequency no photoelectrons are emitted. What happens to the light energy?

18.6 For most metals, the work function W is about 10^{-18} joules. Light of what frequency will cause photoelectrons to leave the metal with virtually no kinetic energy? In what region of the spectrum is this frequency?

18.7 What is the energy of a light photon which

*The MKSA unit for B is N/amp·m and is now called the *tesla*, (after the electrical engineer Nikola Tesla).

corresponds to a wavelength of 5×10^{-7} m? 5×10^{-8} m?

18.8 The minimum or threshold frequency of light from emission of photoelectrons for copper is 1.1×10^{15} cycles/sec. When ultraviolet light of frequency 1.5×10^{15} cycles/sec shines on a copper surface, what is the maximum energy of the photoelectrons emitted, in joules? In electron volts?

18.9 What is the lowest-frequency light that will cause the emission of photoelectrons from a surface whose work function is 2.0 eV (that is, an energy of at least 2.0 eV is needed to eject an electron)?

18.10 Monochromatic light of wavelength 5000 Å falls on a metal cathode to produce photo-electrons. ($1\text{Å} = 10^{-10}$ meter) The light intensity at the surface of the metal is 10^2 joules/m² per sec.
>(a) What is the frequency of the light?
>(b) What is the energy (in joules) of a single photon of the light?
>(c) How many photons fall on 1 m² in one sec?
>(d) If the diameter of an atom is about 1 Å, how many photons fall on one atom in one second, on the average?
>(e) How often would one photon fall on one atom, on the average?
>(f) How many photons fall on one atom in 10^{-10} sec, on the average?
>(g) Suppose the cathode is a square 0.05 m on a side. How many electrons are released per second, assuming every photon releases a photoelectron? How big a current would this be in amperes?

18.11 Roughly how many photons of visible light are given off per second by a 1-watt flashlight? (Only about 5 percent of the electric energy input to a tungsten-filament bulb is given off as visible light.)
Hint: first find the energy, in joules, of an average photon of visible light.

18.12 Recall from Sec. 17.8 that 96,540 coulombs of charge will deposit 31.77 grams of copper in the electrolysis of copper sulfate. In Sec. 18.3, the charge of a single electron was reported to be 1.6×10^{-19} coulomb.
>(a) How many electrons must be transferred to deposit 31.77 grams of copper?
>(b) The density of copper is 8.92 grams per cm³. How many copper atoms would there be in the 1 cm³? (Actually copper has a combining number of 2, which suggests that 2 electrons are required to deposit a single copper atom.)
>(c) What is the approximate volume of each copper atom?
>(d) What is the approximate diameter of a copper atom? (For this rough approximation, assume that the atoms are cubes.)

18.13 The approximate size of atoms can be calculated in a simple way from x-ray scattering experiments. The diagram below represents the paths of two portions of an x-ray wavefront. Part of the front is scattered from the first layer of atoms in a crystal, and part is scattered from the second layer. The part reflected from the second layer travels a distance $2x$ further before it emerges from the crystal.

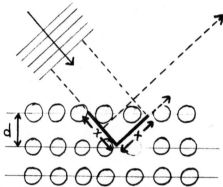

(a) At which angle of incidence for the original beam will the scattered wavefronts reinforce one another (that is, be in phase)?
(b) At which angle of incidence will the scattered wavefronts cancel one another?
(c) Use trigonometry to express the relationship among wavelength λ, the distance d between layers, and the angle of reflection θ_{max} that will have maximum intensity.

18.14 The highest frequency, f_{max} of the x rays produced by an x ray tube is given by the relation

$$hf_{max} = q_e V$$

where h is Planck's constant, q_e is the charge of an electron, and V is the potential difference at which the tube operates. If V is 50,000 volts, what is f_{max}?

18.15 The equation giving the maximum energy of the x rays in the preceding problem looks like one of the equations in Einstein's theory of the photoelectric effect. How would you account for this similarity? For the difference?

18.16 What potential difference must be applied across an x-ray tube for it to emit x rays with a minimum wavelength of 10^{-11} m? What is the energy of these x rays in joules? In electron volts?

18.17 A *glossary* is a collection of terms applicable to a special field of knowledge. Make a glossary of terms that appeared for the first time in this course in Chapter 18. Make an informative statement or definition for each term.

18.18 In his *Opticks,* Newton proposed a set of hypotheses about light which, taken together, formed a fairly successful model of light. The hypotheses were stated as questions. Three of the hypotheses are given below:

> Are not all hypotheses erroneous, in which light is supposed to consist in pression or motion waves . . . ? [Quest. 28]

> Are not the rays of light very small bodies emitted from shining substances? [Quest. 29]

> Are not gross bodies and light convertible into one another, and may not bodies receive much of their activity from the particles of light which enter their composition? [Quest. 30]

(a) In what respect is Newton's model similar to and different from the photon model of light?
(b) Why would Newton's model be insufficient to explain the photoelectric effect? What predictions can we make with the photon model that we cannot with Newton's?´

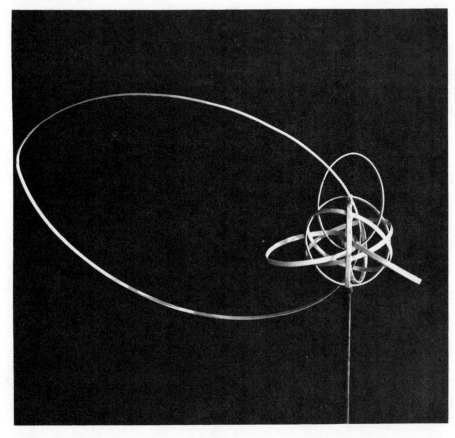

A sculptor's construction representing the Bohr model of a sodium atom.

CHAPTER NINETEEN

The Rutherford-Bohr Model of the Atom

19.1 Spectra of gases

One of the first real clues to understanding atomic structure appeared in the study of emission and absorption of light by different elements. The results of this study are so important to our story that we will review their development in some detail.

SG 19.1

It had long been known that light is emitted by gases or vapors when they are excited in any one of several ways: (1) by heating the gas to a high temperature, as when a volatile substance is put into a flame; (2) by an electric discharge through gas in the space between the terminals of an electric arc; (3) by a continuous electric current in a gas at low pressure (as in the now familiar "neon sign").

The pioneer experiments on light emitted by various excited gases were made in 1752 by the Scottish physicist Thomas Melvill. He put one substance after another in a flame; and "having placed a pasteboard with a circular hole in it between my eye and the flame. . ., I examined the constitution of these different lights with a prism." Melvill found that the spectrum of light from a hot gas was different from the well-known rainbow-colored spectrum of a glowing solid or liquid. Melvill's spectrum was not an unbroken stretch of color continuously graded from violet to red. Rather, it consisted of individual patches, each having the color of that part of the spectrum in which it was located. There were dark gaps (missing colors) between the patches. Later, more general use was made of a narrow slit through which to pass the light. Now the emission spectrum of a gas was seen as a set of bright lines (see the figure in the margin on page 63). The bright lines are in fact colored images of the slit. Such spectra show that light from a gas is a mixture of only a few definite colors or narrow wavelength regions of light.

Melvill also noted that the colors and locations of the bright spots were different when different substances were put in the flame. For example, with ordinary table salt in the flame, the dominant color was "bright yellow" (now known to be characteristic of the element sodium).

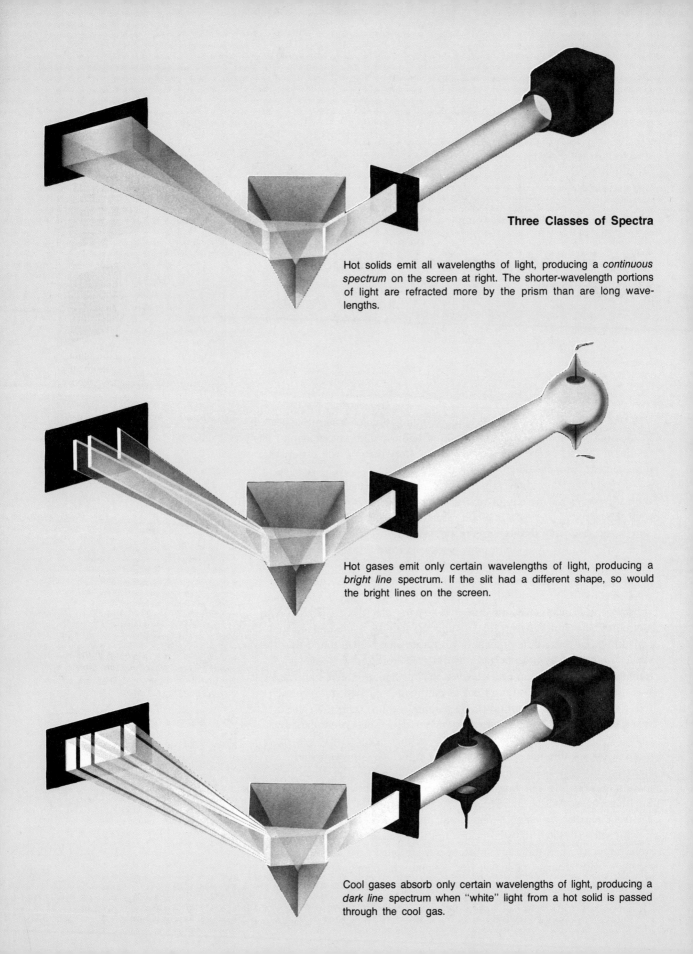

Three Classes of Spectra

Hot solids emit all wavelengths of light, producing a *continuous spectrum* on the screen at right. The shorter-wavelength portions of light are refracted more by the prism than are long wavelengths.

Hot gases emit only certain wavelengths of light, producing a *bright line* spectrum. If the slit had a different shape, so would the bright lines on the screen.

Cool gases absorb only certain wavelengths of light, producing a *dark line* spectrum when "white" light from a hot solid is passed through the cool gas.

In fact, the line emission spectrum is markedly different for each
chemically different gas because each chemical element emits its own
characteristic set of wavelengths. (See the figure in the margin.) In
looking at a gaseous source without the aid of a prism or a grating, the
eye combines the separate colors. It perceives the mixture as reddish for
glowing neon, pale blue for nitrogen, yellow for sodium vapor, and so on.

Some gases have relatively simple spectra. Thus the most prominent
part of the visible spectrum of sodium vapor is a pair of bright yellow
lines. Some gases or vapors have very complex spectra. Iron vapor, for
example, has some 6000 bright lines in the visible range alone.

In 1823 the British astronomer John Herschel suggested that each
gas could be identified from its unique line spectrum. By the early 1860's
the physicist Gustav R. Kirchhoff and the chemist Robert W. Bunsen, in
Germany, had jointly discovered two new elements (rubidium and cesium)
by noting previously unreported emission lines in the spectrum of the
vapor of a mineral water. This was the first of a series of such discoveries.
And it started the development of a technique for speedy chemical analysis
of small amounts of materials by *spectrum analysis*.

In 1802 the English scientist William Wollaston saw in the spectrum
of sunlight something that had been overlooked before. Wollaston noticed
a set of seven sharp, irregularly spaced *dark* lines across the continuous
solar spectrum. He did not understand why they were there, and did not
investigate further. A dozen years later, the German physicist Joseph von
Fraunhofer used better instruments and detected many hundreds of such
dark lines. To the most prominent dark lines, Fraunhofer assigned the
letters A, B, C, etc. These dark lines can be easily seen in the sun's
spectrum with even quite simple modern spectroscopes. The letters A, B,
C, . . . are still used to identify them.

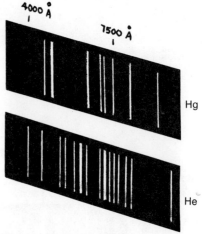

Parts of the line emission spectra
of mercury (Hg) and helium (He),
redrawn from photographic records.

Spectroscope: A device for
examining the spectrum by eye.

Spectrometer or spectrograph: A
device for measuring the wave
length of the spectrum and for
recording the spectra (for example
on film).

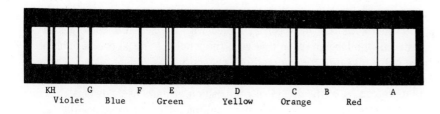

KH	G	F	E	D	C	B	A
Violet	Blue	Green	Yellow	Orange	Red		

The Fraunhofer dark lines in the visible
part of the solar spectrum. Only a few
of the most prominent lines are represented.

In the spectra of several other bright stars, Fraunhofer found similar
dark lines. Many, but not all, of these lines were in the same positions as
those in the solar spectrum.

In 1859, Kirchhoff made some key observations that led to better
understanding of both dark-line and bright-line spectra of gases. It was
already known that the two prominent yellow lines in the emission
spectrum of heated sodium vapor had the same wavelengths as two
neighboring prominent dark lines in the solar spectrum. (The solar
spectrum lines were the ones to which Fraunhofer had assigned the letter
D.) It was also known that the light emitted by a glowing solid forms a

perfectly continuous spectrum that shows no dark lines. Kirchhoff now experimented with light from a glowing solid, as shown on page 62. The light was first passed through cooler sodium vapor and then dispersed by a prism. The spectrum produced had two prominent dark lines at the same place in the spectrum as the D-lines of the sun's spectrum. It was therefore reasonable to conclude that the light from the sun, too, was passing through a mass of sodium gas. This was the first evidence of the chemical composition of the gas envelope around the sun.

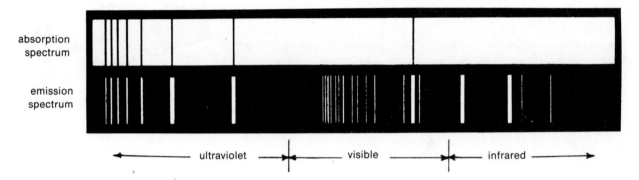

absorption spectrum

emission spectrum

← ———— ultraviolet ———— →|← ———— visible ———— →|← ———— infrared ————→

Comparison of the line absorption spectrum and line emission spectrum of sodium vapor.

Kirchhoff's experiment was repeated with various other relatively cool gases placed between a glowing solid and the prism. Each gas produced its own characteristic set of dark lines. Evidently each gas in some way absorbs light of certain wavelengths from the passing "white" light. Further, Kirchhoff showed that the wavelength of each absorption line matches the wavelength of a bright line in the emission spectrum of the same gas. The conclusion is that a gas can absorb *only* light of those wavelengths which, when excited, it can emit. (But note that not *every* emission line is represented in the absorption spectrum. Soon you will see why.)

Each of the various Fraunhofer lines across the spectra of the sun and other stars has now been identified with the action of some gas as tested in the laboratory. In this way, the whole chemical composition of the outer region of the sun and other stars has been determined. This is really quite breathtaking from several points of view. First, it is surprising that we can learn the chemical composition of immensely distant objects. It is even more surprising that chemical materials out there are the same as those in our own surroundings on earth. (That this is true is clearly shown by the fact that even very complex absorption spectra are reproduced exactly in star spectra.) Finally, we can draw a striking conclusion: the physical processes that cause light absorption in the atom must be the same among the distant stars as on earth.

In these facts we have a hint of how *universal* physical law really is. Even at the farthest edges of the cosmos from which we receive light, the laws of physics appear to be the same as for common materials close at hand in our laboratory! This is just what Galileo and Newton had intuited when they proposed that there is no difference between terrestrial and celestial physics.

SG 19.2

Q1   What can you conclude about a source if its light gives a bright line spectrum?

Q2   What can you conclude about the source if its light gives a dark line spectrum?

Q3   What evidence is there that the physics and chemistry of materials at great distances from us is the same as of matter close at hand?

19.2 Regularities in the hydrogen spectrum

Of all the spectra, the line emission spectrum of hydrogen is especially interesting for both historical and theoretical reasons. In the visible and near-ultraviolet regions, the emission spectrum consists of an apparently systematic series of lines. (See the illustration at the right.) In 1885, Johann Jakob Balmer found a simple formula—an empirical relation—which gave the wavelengths of the lines known at the time. The formula is:

$$\lambda = b \left(\frac{n^2}{n^2 - 2^2} \right)$$

The quantity b is a constant which Balmer determined empirically and found to be equal to 3645.6 Å (or 3645.6×10^{-10} m); n is a whole number, different for each line. Specifically, to give the observed value for the wavelength, n must be 3 for the first (red) line of the hydrogen emission spectrum (named H_α); $n = 4$ for the second (green) line (H_β); $n = 5$ for the third (blue) line (H_γ); and $n = 6$ for the fourth (violet) line (H_δ). The table below shows excellent agreement (within 0.02%) between Balmer's calculations from his empirical formula and previously measured values.

Johann Jakob Balmer (1825-1898) was a teacher at a girl's school in Switzerland. His interest in mathematical puzzles and numerology led him to study wavelengths of spectra listed in tables.

The Balmer lines of hydrogen, redrawn from a photograph made with a film sensitive to ultraviolet light as well as visible. The lines get more crowded as they approach the series limit in the ultraviolet.

Wavelength λ (in Å) for Hydrogen Emission Spectrum

NAME OF LINE	n	FROM BALMER'S FORMULA	BY ANGSTROM'S MEASUREMENT	DIFFERENCE
H_α	3	6562.08	6562.10	+0.02
H_β	4	4860.8	4860.74	−0.06
H_γ	5	4340	4340.1	+0.1
H_δ	6	4101.3	4101.2	−0.1

Data on hydrogen spectrum (as given in Balmer's paper of 1885).

It took nearly 30 years before anyone understood why Balmer's empirical formula worked so well—why the hydrogen atom emitted light whose wavelength made such a simple sequence. But this did not keep Balmer from speculating that there might be other series of unsuspected lines in the hydrogen spectrum. Their wavelengths, he suggested, could be found by replacing the 2^2 in his equation with numbers such as 1^2, 3^2, 4^2, and so on. This suggestion stimulated many workers to search for such additional spectral series. The search turned out to be fruitful, as we will see shortly.

To use modern notation, we first rewrite Balmer's formula in a form that will be more useful:

$$\frac{1}{\lambda} = R_H \left(\frac{1}{2^2} - \frac{1}{n^2} \right)$$

In this equation, which can be derived from the first one, R_H is a constant, equal to $4/b$. (It is called the *Rydberg constant for hydrogen,* in honor of the Swedish spectroscopist J. R. Rydberg. Following Balmer, Rydberg made great progress in the search for various spectral series.) The series of lines described by Balmer's formula are called the *Balmer series.* Balmer constructed his formula from known λ of only four lines. But the formula predicted that there should be many more lines in the same series (indeed, infinitely many such lines as n takes on values such as $n = 3, 4, 5, 6, 7, 8, \ldots \infty$). The figure in the margin indicates that this has indeed been observed. Moreover, every one of the lines is correctly predicted by Balmer's formula with considerable accuracy.

If we follow Balmer's speculative suggestion of replacing 2^2 by other numbers, we obtain the possibilities:

$$\frac{1}{\lambda} = R_H \left(\frac{1}{1^2} - \frac{1}{n^2} \right), \frac{1}{\lambda} = R_H \left(\frac{1}{3^2} - \frac{1}{n^2} \right), \frac{1}{\lambda} = R_H \left(\frac{1}{4^2} - \frac{1}{n^2} \right)$$

and so on. Each of these equations describes a possible series. All these hypothetical series of lines can then be summarized in one overall formula:

$$\frac{1}{\lambda} = R_H \left(\frac{1}{n_f^2} - \frac{1}{n_i^2} \right)$$

where n_f is a whole number that is fixed for any one series for which wavelengths are to be found. (For example, it is 2 for all lines in the Balmer series.) The letter n_i stands for integers that take on the values $n_f + 1, n_f + 2, n_f + 3, \ldots$ for the successive individual lines in a given series. (Thus, for the first two lines of the Balmer series, n_i is 3 and 4.) The constant R_H should have the same value for all of these hydrogen series.

So far, our discussion has been merely speculation. No series, no single line fitting the general formula, *need* exist (except for the observed Balmer series, where $n_f = 2$). But when physicists began to look for these hypothetical lines with good spectrometers, they found that they do exist!

In 1908, F. Paschen in Germany found two hydrogen lines in the infrared. Their wavelengths were correctly given by setting $n_f = 3$ and $n_i = 4$ and 5 in the general formula. Many other lines in this "Paschen series" have since been identified. With improved experimental apparatus and techniques, new regions of the spectrum could be explored. Thus,

H_{10}

H_{20}

Part of the absorption spectrum observed in the light from the star Rigel (β Orion). The dark lines are at the same location as lines due to absorption by hydrogen gas in the ultraviolet region as produced in a laboratory; they match the lines of the Balmer series as indicated by the H numbers (where H_1 would be H_α, H_2 would be H_β, etc.). This photograph thus indicates the presence of hydrogen in the star.

other series gradually were added to the Balmer and Paschen series. In the table below, the name of each series listed is that of the discoverer.

Series of lines in the hydrogen spectrum

NAME OF SERIES	DATE OF DISCOVERY	REGION OF SPECTRUM	VALUES IN BALMER EQUATION
Lyman	1906-1914	ultraviolet	$n_f = 1$, $n_i = 2, 3, 4, \ldots$
Balmer	1885	ultraviolet-visible	$n_f = 2$, $n_i = 3, 4, 5, \ldots$
Paschen	1908	infrared	$n_f = 3$, $n_i = 4, 5, 6, \ldots$
Brackett	1922	infrared	$n_f = 4$, $n_i = 5, 6, 7, \ldots$
Pfund	1924	infrared	$n_f = 5$, $n_i = 6, 7, 8, \ldots$

Balmer hoped that his formula for hydrogen spectra might be a pattern for finding series relationships in the spectra of other gases. This suggestion bore fruit also. Balmer's formula itself did not work directly in describing spectra of gases other than hydrogen. But it did inspire formulas of similar mathematical form that successfully described order in portions of many complex spectra. The Rydberg constant R_H also reappeared in such empirical formulas.

For three decades after Balmer's success, physicists tried to account for spectra by constructing atomic models that would radiate light of the right wavelengths. But it was difficult to find a successful model. Even the simplest atom, hydrogen, emitted a great number and variety of spectral lines. Eventually models were made that succeeded in revealing the origin of spectra. In this chapter and the next one, we will see how it was done.

What you have already learned in Chapter 18 about quantum theory suggests one line of attack. Obviously, the emission and absorption of light from an atom must correspond to a decrease and an increase of the atom's energy. If atoms of an element emit light of only certain frequencies, then the energy of the atoms must be able to change only by certain amounts. These changes of energy must involve some rearrangement of the parts of the atom.

SG 19.3

SG 19.4

SG 19.5

Q4 What evidence did Balmer have that there were other series of lines in the hydrogen spectrum, with terms 3^2, 4^2, etc. instead of 2^2?

Q5 Often discoveries result from grand theories (like Newton's) or from a good intuitive grasp of phenomena (like Faraday's). What led Balmer to his relation for spectra?

Q6 What accounts for the success of Balmer's overall formula in predicting new series of the emission spectrum of hydrogen?

19.3 Rutherford's nuclear model of the atom

A new basis for atomic models was provided during the period 1909 to 1911 by Ernest Rutherford. Rutherford was interested in the rays emitted

SG 19.6

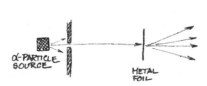

In somewhat the same way, you could, in principle, use a scattering experiment to discover the size and shape of an object hidden in a cloud or fog. You could do so by directing a series of projectiles at the unseen object and tracing their paths back after deflection.

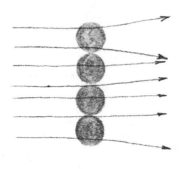

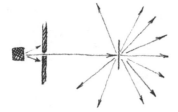

by radioactive substances, especially in α (alpha) rays. As we will see in Chapter 1 of the Supplemental Unit, *The Nucleus,* α rays consist of positively charged particles. These particles are positively charged helium atoms with masses about 7500 times greater than the electron mass. Some radioactive substances emit α particles at very high rates and energies. Such particles are often used as projectiles in bombarding samples of elements. The experiments that Rutherford and his colleagues did with α particles are examples of a highly important kind of experiment in atomic and nuclear physics—the scattering experiment.

In a scattering experiment, a narrow, parallel beam of projectiles (for example, α particles, electrons, x rays) is aimed at a target. The target is usually a thin foil or film of some material. As the beam strikes the target, some of the projectiles are deflected, or scattered, from their original direction. The scattering is the result of the interaction between the particles in the beam and the atoms of the material. A careful study of the projectiles after scattering can yield information about the projectiles, the atoms, and the interaction between them. If we know the mass, energy, and direction of the projectiles, and see how they are scattered, we can deduce properties of the atoms that scattered the projectiles.

Rutherford noticed that when a beam of α particles passed through a thin metal foil, the beam spread out. This scattering may be thought of as caused by electrostatic forces between the positively charged α particles and the charges that make up atoms. Atoms contain both positive and negative charges. Therefore, an α particle undergoes both repelling and attracting forces as it passes through matter. The magnitude and direction of these forces depend on how closely the particle approaches the centers of the atoms among which it moves. When a particular atomic model is proposed, the extent of the expected scattering can be calculated and compared with experiment. The Thomson model of the atom predicted almost no chance that an α particle would be deflected by an angle of more than a few degrees.

The breakthrough to the modern model of the atom followed a discovery by one of Rutherford's assistants, Hans Geiger. Geiger found that the number of particles scattered through angles of 10° or more was much greater than the number predicted by the Thomson model. In fact, one out of about every 8000 α particles was scattered through an angle greater than 90°. Thus, a significant number of α particles virtually bounced right back from the foil. This result was entirely unexpected. According to Thomson's model, the atom should have acted only slightly on the projectile—rather like a cloud in which fine dust is suspended. Some years later, Rutherford wrote:

> . . . I had observed the scattering of α-particles, and Dr. Geiger in my laboratory had examined it in detail. He found, in thin pieces of heavy metal, that the scattering was usually small, of the order of one degree. One day Geiger came to me and said, "Don't you think that young Marsden, whom I am training in radioactive methods, ought to begin a small research?" Now I had thought that, too, so I said, "Why not let him see if any α-

Ernest Rutherford (1871-1937) was born, grew up, and received most of his education in New Zealand. At age 24 he went to Cambridge, England to work at the Cavendish Laboratory under J. J. Thomson. From there he went to McGill University in Canada, then home to be married and back to England again, now to Manchester University. At these universities, and later at the Cavendish Laboratory where he succeeded J. J. Thomson as director, Rutherford performed important experiments on radioactivity, the nuclear nature of the atom, and the structure of the nucleus. Rutherford introduced the concepts "alpha," "beta" and "gamma" rays, "protons," and "half-life." His contributions will be further discussed in the Supplemental Unit *The Nucleus.* For his scientific work, Rutherford was knighted and received a Nobel Prize.

particles can be scattered through a large angle?" I may tell you in confidence that I did not believe that they would be, since we knew that the α-particle was a very fast, massive particle, with a great deal of [kinetic] energy, and you could show that if the scattering was due to the accumulated effect of a number of small scatterings, the chance of an α-particle's being scattered backward was very small. Then I remember two or three days later Geiger coming to me in great excitement and saying, "We have been able to get some of the α-particles coming backward . . ." It was quite the most incredible event that has ever happened to me in my life. It was almost as incredible as if you fired a 15-inch shell at a piece of tissue paper and it came back and hit you. On consideration, I realized that this scattering backward must be the result of a single collision, and when I made calculations I saw that it was impossible to get anything of that order of magnitude unless you took a system in which the greater part of the mass of the atom was concentrated in a minute nucleus. It was then that I had the idea of an atom with a minute massive centre, carrying a charge.

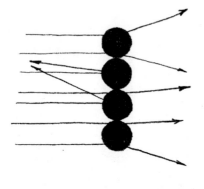

SG 19.6

SG 19.7

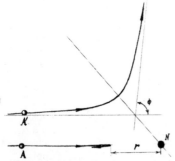

Paths of two α particles A and A' approaching a nucleus N. (Based on Rutherford, *Philosophical Magazine*, vol. 21 (1911), p. 669.)

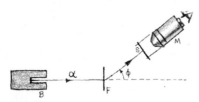

Rutherford's scintillation apparatus was placed in an evacuated chamber so that the α particles would not be slowed down by collisions with air molecules.

SG 19.8

These experiments and Rutherford's interpretation marked the origin of the modern concept of the *nuclear atom.* Let us look at the experiments and Rutherford's conclusion more closely. Why must the atom have its mass and positive charge concentrated in a tiny nucleus at the center about which the electrons are clustered?

A possible explanation of the observed scattering is that the foil contains concentrations of mass and charge—positively charged nuclei. These nuclei are much more dense than in Thomson's atoms. An α particle heading directly toward one of them is stopped and turned back. In the same way, a ball would bounce back from a rock—but not from a cloud of dust particles. The figure in the margin is based on one of Rutherford's diagrams in his paper of 1911, which laid the foundation for the modern theory of atomic structure. It shows two positively charged α particles, A and A'. The α particle A is heading directly toward a massive nucleus N. If the nucleus has a positive electric charge, it will repel the positive α particle. Because of this electrical repulsive force, A will slow to a stop at some distance r from N, and then move directly back. A' is an α particle that is *not* headed directly toward the nucleus N. It is repelled by N along a path which calculation shows must be an hyperbola. The deflection of A' from its original path is indicated by the angle ϕ.

Rutherford considered the effects on the α particle's path of the important variables: the particle's speed, the foil thickness, and the quantity of charge Q on each nucleus. According to the model, *most* of the α particles should be scattered through small angles, because the chance of approaching a very small nucleus nearly head-on is so small. But a significant number of α particles should be scattered through large angles.

Geiger and Marsden tested these predictions with the apparatus sketched in the margin. The lead box B contains a radioactive substance (radon) which emits α particles. The particles emerging from the small hole in the box are deflected through various angles ϕ in passing through the thin metal foil F. The number of particles deflected through each angle ϕ is found by letting the particles strike a zinc sulfide screen S. Each α particle that strikes the screen produces a scintillation (a momentary pinpoint of fluorescence). These scintillations can be observed and counted by looking through the microscope M. The microscope and screen can be moved together along the arc of a circle. In later experiments, the number of α particles at any angle ϕ was counted more conveniently by a counter invented by Geiger (see sketch in the margin of page 71). The Geiger Counter, in its more recent versions, is now a standard laboratory item.

Geiger and Marsden found that the number of α particles counted depended on the scattering angle, the speed of the particles, and the thickness of the foil. These findings agreed with Rutherford's predictions and supported an atomic model in which most of the mass and all positive charge occupy a very small region at the center of the atom.

Q7 Why are α particles scattered by atoms? Why is the angle of scattering mostly small but sometimes large?

Q8 What was the basic difference between the Rutherford and the Thomson models of the atom?

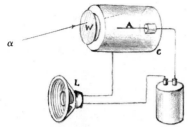

19.4 Nuclear charge and size

Despite the success of Rutherford's model, a problem remained: there still was no way to measure independently the nucleus charge Q which he had to assume. However, the scattering experiments had confirmed Rutherford's predictions about the effect of the speed of the α particle and the thickness of the foil on the angle of scattering. And, as often happens when part of a theory is confirmed, it is reasonable to proceed temporarily as if the whole theory were justified. That is, pending further proof, one could assume that the value of Q needed to explain the observed scattering data was the correct value of Q for the actual nucleus. On this basis, scattering data was compiled for several different elements—among them carbon, aluminum and gold. The following nuclear charges were obtained: for carbon, $Q = 6q_e$, for aluminum, $Q = 13$ or $14q_e$, and for gold, $Q = 78$ or $79q_e$. Similarly, values were found for other elements.

The magnitude of the positive charge of the nucleus was an important and welcome piece of information about the atom. The atom as a whole is of course electrically neutral. So if the nucleus has a positive charge of $6q_e$, 13 or $14q_e$, etc., the number of electrons surrounding the nucleus must be 6 for carbon, 13 or 14 for aluminum, etc. Thus, for the first time, scientists had a good idea of just how many electrons an atom may have. But an even more important fact was soon noticed. For each element, the value for the nuclear charge—in multiples of q_e—was close to the atomic number Z, the place number of that element in the periodic table! The results of scattering experiments with α particles were not yet precise enough to make this conclusion with certainty. But the data indicated that *each nucleus has a positive charge Q numerically equal to Zq_e.*

This suggestion made the picture of the nuclear atom much clearer and simpler. On this basis, the hydrogen atom (Z = 1) has one electron outside the nucleus. A helium atom (Z = 2) has in its neutral state two electrons outside the nucleus. A uranium atom (Z = 92) has 92 electrons. Additional experiments further supported this simple scheme. The experiments showed that it was possible to produce singly ionized hydrogen atoms, H^+, and doubly ionized helium atoms, He^{++}, but not H^{++} or He^{+++}. Evidently, a hydrogen atom has only one electron to lose, and a helium atom only two. Unexpectedly, the concept of the nuclear atom thus provided new insight into the periodic table of the elements. The nuclear concept suggested that the periodic table is really a listing of the elements according to *the number of electrons around the nucleus, or according to the number of positive units of charge on the nucleus.*

A Geiger counter (1928). It consists of a metal cylinder C containing a gas and a thin wire A that is insulated from the cylinder. A potential difference slightly less than that needed to produce a discharge through the gas is maintained between the wire (anode A) and cylinder (cathode C). When an α particle enters through the thin mica window (W), it frees a few electrons from the gas molecules. The electrons are accelerated toward the anode, freeing more electrons along the way by collisions with gas molecules. The avalanche of electrons constitutes a sudden surge of current which can be amplified to produce a click in the loudspeaker (L) or to operate a register (as in the Project Physics scaler, used in experiments in the Supplemental Unit *The Nucleus*).

q_e = numerical value of charge of one electron.

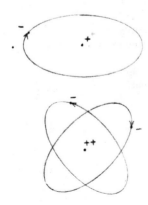

These results cleared up some of the difficulties in Mendeleev's periodic table. For example, the elements tellurium and iodine had been assigned positions $Z = 52$ and $Z = 53$ on the basis of their chemical properties. This positioning contradicted the order of their atomic weights. But now Z was seen to correspond to a fundamental fact about the nucleus. Thus, the reversed order of atomic weights was understood to be only an accident rather than a basic fault in the scheme.

As an important additional result of these scattering experiments, the size of the nucleus could be estimated. Suppose an α particle is moving directly toward a nucleus. Its kinetic energy on approach is transformed to electrical potential energy. It slows down and eventually stops. The distance of closest approach can be computed from the original kinetic energy of the α particle and the charges of α particle and nucleus. (See SG 19.8.) The value calculated for the closest approach is approximately 3×10^{-14}m. If the α particle does not penetrate the nucleus, this distance must be at least as great as the sum of the radii of α particles and nucleus; thus, the radius of the nucleus could not be larger than about 10^{-14}m. But 10^{-14}m is only about 1/1000 of the known radius of an atom. Further, the total volume of the atoms is proportional to the cube of its radius. So it is clear that the atom is mostly empty, with the nucleus occupying only one billionth of the space! This explains how α particles or electrons can penetrate thousands of layers of atoms in metal foils or in gases, with only occasional large deflection backward.

Successful as this model of the nuclear atom was in explaining scattering phenomena, it raised many new questions: What is the arrangement of electrons about the nucleus? What keeps the negative electron from falling into a positive nucleus by electrical attraction? Of what is the nucleus composed? What keeps it from exploding on account of the repulsion of its positive charges? Rutherford realized the problems raised by these questions, and the failure of his model to answer them. But he rightly said that one should not expect one model, made on the basis of one set of puzzling results which it handled well, also to handle all other puzzles. Additional assumptions were needed to complete the model and answer the additional questions about the details of atomic structure. The remainder of this chapter will deal with the theory proposed by Niels Bohr, a young Danish physicist who joined Rutherford's group just as the nuclear model was being announced. Occasionally the algebra may seem a bit lengthy, but it is not complicated—and it will help to explain why Bohr's work is generally regarded as a prime example of scientific method at its best.

The central dot representing the nucleus in relation to the size of the atom as a whole is about 100 times too large. Popular diagrams of atoms often greatly exaggerate the relative size of the nucleus, (perhaps in order to suggest the greater mass).

SG 19.9

Q9 What does the "atomic number" of an element refer to, according to the Rutherford model of the atom?

Q10 What is the greatest positive charge that an ion of lithium (the next heaviest element after helium) could have?

19.5 The Bohr theory: the postulates

We assume that an atom consists of a positively charged nucleus surrounded by a number of negatively charged electrons. What, then, keeps the electrons from falling into the nucleus, pulled in by the electric force of attraction? One possible answer is that an atom may be like a planetary system with the electrons revolving in orbits around the nucleus. Instead of the gravitational force, the electric attractive force between the nucleus and an electron would supply a centripetal force. This centripetal force would tend to keep the moving electron in orbit.

This idea seems to be a good start toward a theory of atomic structure. But a serious problem arises concerning the stability of a "planetary" atom. According to Maxwell's theory of electromagnetism, a charged particle radiates energy when it is accelerated. Now, an electron moving in an orbit around a nucleus continually changes its velocity vector. In other words, it is *always being accelerated* by the centripetal electric force. The electron, therefore, should lose energy by emitting radiation. A detailed analysis of the electron's motion shows that the electron should be drawn steadily closer to the nucleus. (Somewhat similarly, an artificial satellite loses energy due to friction in the upper atmosphere and gradually spirals toward the earth.) Within a very short time, the energy-radiating electron should actually be pulled into the nucleus. According to classical physics—mechanics and electromagnetism—a planetary atom would not be stable for more than a very small fraction of a second.

The idea of a planetary atom was nevertheless appealing. Physicists continued to look for a theory that would include a stable planetary structure and predict separate line spectra for the elements. Niels Bohr, then an unknown young physicist who had just received his PhD degree, succeeded in constructing such a theory in 1912-1913. This theory was widely recognized as a major victory. Although it had to be modified later to account for many more phenomena, it showed how to attack atomic problems by using quantum theory. Today, it seems a rather naive way of thinking about the atom, compared with more recent quantum-mechanical theories. But in fact, considering what it was designed to do, Bohr's theory is a beautiful example of a successful physical model.

Bohr introduced two new postulates specifically to account for the existence of stable electron orbits and separate emission spectra. These postulates may be stated as follows:

Since Bohr incorporated Rutherford's idea of the nucleus, the model which Bohr's theory discusses is often called the Rutherford-Bohr model.

(1) Contrary to expectations based on classical physics, an atomic system can exist in any one of several states which involve no emission of radiation. Such states may occur even when the particles (electrons and nucleus) are called *stationary states* of the atom.

(2) Any emission or absorption of radiation, either as visible light or other electromagnetic radiation, corresponds to a sudden transition between two such stationary states. The radiation emitted or absorbed has a frequency f determined by the relation $hf = E_i - E_f$. (In this equation, h is Planck's constant and E_i and E_f are the energies of the atom in the initial and final stationary states, respectively.)

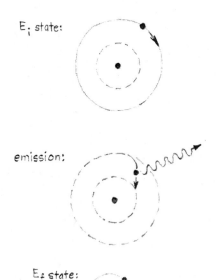

E_i state:

emission:

E_f state:

Quantum theory had begun with Planck's idea that *atoms emit light* only in definite amounts of energy. This concept was extended by Einstein's idea that *light travels* only as definite parcels of energy. Now it was extended further by Bohr's idea that *atoms exist* only in definite energy states. But Bohr also used the quantum concept in deciding which of all the *conceivable* stationary states were actually *possible*. An example of how Bohr did this is given in the next section.

For simplicity we consider the hydrogen atom, with a single electron revolving around the nucleus. Following Bohr, we assume that the possible electron orbits are simply circular. The details of some additional assumptions and calculations are worked out on page 75. Bohr's result for the possible stable orbit radii r_n was $r_n = an^2$ where a is a constant $(h^2/4\pi^2 mkq_e^2)$ which can be calculated from known physical values, and n stands for any whole number, 1, 2, 3. . . .

Q11 What was the main evidence that an atom could exist only in certain energy states?

Q12 What reason did Bohr give for the atom existing only in certain energy states?

19.6 The size of the hydrogen atom

Bohr's result is remarkable: in hydrogen atoms the possible orbital radii of the electrons are whole multiples of a constant which we can at once evaluate. That is n^2 takes on values of 1^2, 2^2, 3^2, . . . , and all factors to the left of n^2 are quantities known previously by independent measurement! Calculating the value $(h^2/4\pi^2 mkq_e^2)$ gives us 5.3×10^{-11}m. Hence, *according to Bohr's model* the radii of stable electron orbits should be $r_n = 5.3 \times 10^{-11}$m $\times n^2$. That is, 5.3×10^{-11}m when $n = 1$ (first allowed orbit), $4 \times 5.3 \times 10^{-11}$m when $n = 2$ (second allowed orbit), $9 \times 5.3 \times 10^{-11}$m when $n = 3$, etc. In between these values, there are no allowed radii. In short, the separate allowed electron orbits are spaced around the nucleus in a regular way, with the allowed radii quantized in a regular manner. (See the drawing at the top of page 80.) Emission and absorption of light should therefore correspond to the transition of the electron from one allowed orbit to another.

SG 19.10

This is just the kind of result we had hoped for. It tells us which radii are possible, and where they lie. But so far, it has all been model building. Do the orbits in a real hydrogen atom actually correspond to this model? In his first paper of 1913, Bohr could give at least a partial yes as an answer. It had long been known that the normal "unexcited" hydrogen atom has a radius of about 5×10^{-11}m. (That is, the size of the atom obtained, for example, by interpreting measured characteristics of gases in light of the kinetic theory.) This known value of about 5×10^{-11}m corresponds excellently to the prediction from the equation for orbital radius r if n has the lowest value, namely 1. Now there was a way to

Bohr's Quantization Rule and the Size of Orbits

The magnitude of the charge on the electron is q_e; the charge on a nucleus is Zq_e, and for hydrogen ($Z = 1$) is just q_e. The electric force with which the hydrogen nucleus attracts its electron is therefore

$$F_{el} = k\,\frac{q_e q_e}{r^2}$$

where k is the coulomb constant, and r is the center-to-center distance. If the electron is in a stable circular orbit of radius r around the nucleus, moving at a constant speed v, then the centripetal force is equal to mv^2/r. Since the centripetal force is provided by the electric attraction, we can write

$$\frac{mv^2}{r} = k\,\frac{q^2_e}{r^2}$$

In the last equation, m, q_e and k are constants; r and v are variables, whose values are related by the equation. What are the possible values of v and r for stationary states of the atom?

We can begin to get an answer if we write the last equation in slightly different form. Multiplying both sides by r^2 and dividing both sides by v, we get

$$mvr = \frac{kq^2_e}{v}$$

The quantity on the left side of this equation is the product of the momentum of the electron and the radius of the orbit. We can use this quantity to characterize the stable orbits. According to classical mechanics, the radius of the orbit could have any value, so the quantity mvr could also have any value. Of course, classical physics also seemed to deny that there could be *any* stable orbits in the hydrogen atom. But Bohr's first postulate implies that certain stable orbits (and only those) are permitted. So Bohr needed to find the rule that decides *which* stable orbits are possible. Here Bohr appears to have been largely guided by his intuition. He found that what was needed was the recognition that the quantity mvr does not take on just any value, but only certain *allowed values*. These values are defined by the relation

$$mvr = n\,\frac{h}{2\pi}$$

where h is Planck's constant, and n is a positive integer; that is, $n = 1, 2, 3, 4, \ldots$ (but not zero). When the possible values of the mvr are restricted in this way, the quantity mvr is said to be *quantized*. The integer n which appears in the formula is called the *quantum number*. The main point is that each quantum number ($n = 1$ or 2 or 3 . . .) corresponds to one allowed, stable orbit of the electron.

If we accept this rule, we can at once describe the "allowed" states of the atom, say in terms of the radii r of the possible orbits. We can combine the last expression above with the classical centripetal force relation as follows: the quantization rule is

$$mvr = n\,\frac{h}{2\pi}$$

so

$$r = \frac{nh}{2\pi m v}$$

and

$$r^2 = \frac{n^2 h^2}{4\pi^2 m^2 v^2}$$

From classical mechanics, we had

$$\frac{mv^2}{r} = k\,\frac{q^2_e}{r^2}$$

so

$$v^2 = \frac{kq^2_e}{mr}$$

Substituting this "classical" value for v^2 into the quantization expression for r^2 gives

$$r^2 = \frac{n^2 h^2}{4\pi^2 m^2 \left(\dfrac{kq^2_e}{mr}\right)}$$

Simplifying, we get the expression for the allowed radii, r_n:

$$r_n = \frac{n^2 h^2}{4\pi^2 kmq^2_e} = \left(\frac{h^2}{4\pi^2 kmq^2_e}\right) n^2$$

understand the size of the neutral, unexcited hydrogen atom. For every such atom, the size corresponds to the size of the innermost allowed electron orbit. And that orbit, fixed by nature, is described by the quantization rule.

Q13   Why do all unexcited hydrogen atoms have the same size?
Q14   Why does the hydrogen atom have just the size it has?

19.7 Other consequences of the Bohr model

With his two postulates, Bohr could calculate the radius of each permitted orbit. Further, he could calculate the total energy of the electron in each orbit—the energy of the stationary state.

The results that Bohr obtained may be summarized in two simple formulas. As we saw, the radius of an orbit with quantum number n is given by the expression

$$r_n = n^2 r_1$$

where r_1 is the radius of the first orbit (the orbit for $n = 1$) and has the value 5.3×10^{-9}cm or 5.3×10^{-11}m.

The energy (the sum of kinetic and electric potential energy) of the electron in the orbit with quantum number n can also be computed from Bohr's postulate (see SG 19.11). As we pointed out in Chapter 10, it makes no sense to assign an absolute value to potential energy. Only *changes* in energy have physical meaning. Hence, we can pick any convenient zero level. For an electron orbiting in an electric field, the mathematics is particularly simple if we choose as a zero level for energy the state $n = \infty$. At this level, the electron would be infinitely far from the nucleus (and therefore free of it). We can consider the energy for any other state E_n to be the *difference* from this free state. If so, we can write the possible energy states for the hydrogen atom as

$$E_n = \frac{1}{n^2} E_1$$

where E_1 is the total energy of the atom when the electron is in the first orbit. E_1 is the lowest energy possible for an electron in a hydrogen atom. Its value is -13.6 eV (the negative value means only that the energy is 13.6 eV *less* than the free state value E_∞). This is called the *ground state*. In that state, the electron is most tightly "bound" to the nucleus. The value of E_2, the first "excited" state above the ground state, is $1/2^2 \times -13.6$ eV $= -3.4$ eV (only 3.4 eV less than in the free state).

According to the formula for r_n, the first Bohr orbit has the smallest radius, with $n = 1$. Higher values of n correspond to orbits that have larger radii. Although the higher orbits are spaced further and further apart, the force field of the nucleus falls off rapidly. So the work required to move out to the next larger orbit actually becomes smaller and smaller.

Also, the jumps in energy from one level of allowed energy E to the next become smaller and smaller.

19.8 The Bohr theory: the spectral series of hydrogen

The most spectacular success of Bohr's model was that it could be used to explain all emission (and absorption) lines in the hydrogen spectrum. That is, Bohr could use his model to derive, and so to explain, the Balmer formula! By his second postulate, the radiation emitted or absorbed in a transition in Bohr's atom should have a frequency f determined by

See the radius and energy diagrams on page 80.

$$hf = E_i - E_f$$

If n_f is the quantum number of the final state, and n_i is the quantum number of the initial state, then according to the result for E_n we know that

$$E_f = \frac{1}{n_f^2} E_1 \qquad \text{and} \qquad E_i = \frac{1}{n_i^2} E_1$$

The frequency of radiation emitted or absorbed when the atom goes from the initial state to the final state is therefore determined by the equation

$$hf = \frac{E_1}{n_i^2} - \frac{E_1}{n_f^2} \qquad \text{or} \qquad hf = E_1 \left(\frac{1}{n_i^2} - \frac{1}{n_f^2} \right)$$

To deal with wavelength λ (as in Balmer's original formula, page 65) rather than frequency f, we use the relation between frequency and wavelength given in Unit 3. The frequency is equal to the speed of the light wave divided by its wavelength: $f = c/\lambda$. Substituting c/λ for f in this equation, and then dividing both sides by the constant hc (Planck's constant times the speed of light), we obtain

$$\frac{1}{\lambda} = \frac{E_1}{hc} \left(\frac{1}{n_i^2} - \frac{1}{n_f^2} \right)$$

According to Bohr's model, then, this equation gives the wavelength λ of the radiation emitted or absorbed when a hydrogen atom changes from one stationary state with quantum number n_i to another with n_f.

How does this prediction from Bohr's model compare with the long established *empirical* Balmer formula for the Balmer series? That, of course, is the crucial question. The Balmer formula was given on page 65:

$$\frac{1}{\lambda} = R_H \left(\frac{1}{2^2} - \frac{1}{n^2} \right)$$

Niels Bohr (1885–1962) was born in Copenhagen, Denmark and was educated there, receiving his doctor's degree in physics in 1911. In 1912 he was at work in Rutherford's laboratory in Manchester, England, which was a center of research on radioactivity and atomic structure. There he developed his theory of atomic structure to explain chemical properties and atomic spectra. Bohr later played an important part in the development of quantum mechanics, in the advancement of nuclear physics, and in the study of the philosophical aspects of modern physics. In his later years he devoted much time to promoting plans for international cooperation and the peaceful uses of nuclear physics. (The photograph at the right shows Niels Bohr with his fiancee Margrethe Norlund shortly after the announcement of their engagement.)

We see at once that the equation for λ of emitted (or absorbed) light derived from the Bohr model is exactly the same as Balmer's formula, if $R_H = -E_1/hc$ and $n_f = 2$.

The Rydberg constant R_H was long known from spectroscopic measurements to have the value of $1.097 \times 10^7 m^{-1}$. Now it could be compared with the value for $-(E_1/hc)$. Remarkably, there was fine agreement, as one can show without much difficulty (see SG 19.11). R_H, previously regarded as just an experimentally determined constant, was now shown not to be accidental. Rather, it depended on the mass and charge of the electron, on Planck's constant, and on the speed of light.

SG 19.11

More important, we can now see the *meaning*, in physical terms, of the old empirical formula for the lines (H_α, H_β . . .) in the Balmer series. All the lines in the Balmer series simply correspond to transitions from various initial states (various values of n_i) to the same final state, for which $n_f = 2$. Thus photons having the frequency or wavelength of the line H_α are emitted when electrons in a gas of hydrogen atoms "jump" from their $n = 3$-state to their $n = 2$-state (see diagram, page 80). The H_β line corresponds to "jumps" from $n = 4$ to $n = 2$; and so forth.

When the Bohr theory was proposed in 1913, emission lines in only the Balmer and Paschen series for hydrogen were known definitely. Balmer had suggested, and the Bohr model agreed, that additional series should exist. Further experiments revealed the Lyman series in the ultraviolet portion of the spectrum (1916), the Brackett series (1922), and the Pfund series (1924). In each series, the measured frequencies of the lines were found to be those predicted by Bohr's theory. Similarly, the general formula that Balmer guessed might apply for all spectral lines of hydrogen is explained. We find that the lines of the Lyman series correspond to transitions from various initial states to the final state $n_f = 1$; the lines of the Paschen series correspond to transitions from various initial states to the final state $n_f = 3$; etc. (See table on page 67.) The general scheme of possible transitions among the first six stable orbits is shown in the figure on page 80. Thus the theory not only related known information about the hydrogen spectrum, but also predicted correctly the wavelengths of previously unknown series of lines in the spectrum. Moreover, it provided a reasonable physical model; Balmer's general formula had offered no physical reason. The schematic diagram shown at the left is useful as an aid for the imagination. But it has the danger of being too specific. For instance, it leads us to think of the emission of radiation in terms of "jumps" of electrons between orbits. This is a useful idea. But one must not forget that we cannot actually detect an electron moving in an orbit. Nor can we watch an electron "jump" from one orbit to another. A second way of presenting the results of Bohr's theory yields the same facts but does not commit us too closely to a picture of orbits. This scheme is shown in the bottom figure. It focuses not on orbits but on the corresponding possible energy states. These energy states are all given by the formula $E_n = 1/n^2 \times E_1$. In terms of this *mathematical model*, the atom is normally unexcited, with an *energy E_1* about -22×10^{-19} joules (-13.6 eV). Absorption of energy can place the atoms in an excited state, with a correspondingly higher energy. The excited atom is then ready to

SG 19.12
SG 19.13

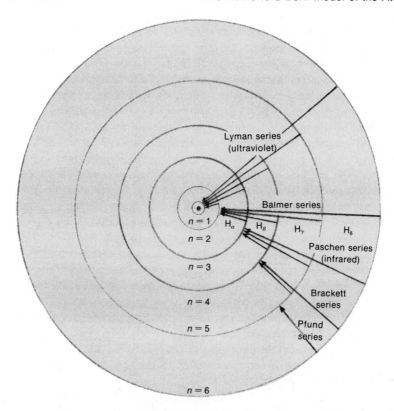

A schematic diagram of relative energy levels of electron states in atoms. Each circle represents a state which can be occupied by 2 electrons.

Energy-level diagram for the hydrogen atom. Possible transitions between energy states are shown for the first six levels. The dotted arrow for each series indicates the *series limit,* a transition from the state where the electron is completely free (infinitely far) from the nucleus.

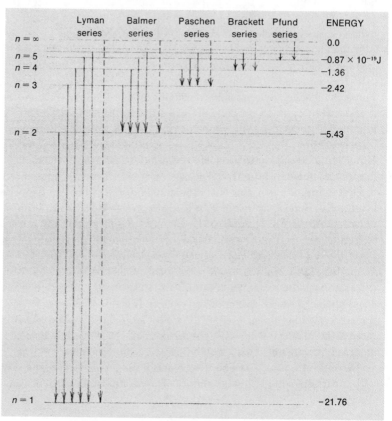

emit light, with a consequent reduction in energy. The energy absorbed or emitted always shifts the total energy of the atom to one of the values specified by the formula for E_n. We may thus, if we prefer, represent the hydrogen atom by means of the energy level diagram.

Q15 Balmer had predicted accurately the other spectral series of hydrogen thirty years before Bohr did. Why is Bohr's prediction considered more significant?

Q16 How does Bohr's model explain line absorption spectra?

19.9 Stationary states of atoms: the Franck-Hertz experiment

The success of the Bohr theory in accounting for the spectrum of hydrogen left this question: could experiments show directly that atoms have only certain, separate energy states? In other words, were there really gaps between the energies that an atom can have? A famous experiment in 1914, by the German physicists James Franck and Gustav Hertz, showed that these separate energy states do indeed exist.

Franck and Hertz bombarded atoms with electrons from an electron gun. They were able to measure the energy lost by electrons in collisions with atoms. They could also determine the energy gained by atoms in these collisions. In their first experiment, Franck and Hertz bombarded mercury vapor contained in a chamber at very low pressure. The procedure was equivalent to measuring the kinetic energy of electrons on leaving the electron gun, and again after they had passed through the mercury vapor. The only way electrons could lose energy was in collisions with mercury atoms. Franck and Hertz found that when the kinetic energy of the electrons leaving the gun was small (up to several eV) the electrons still had almost exactly the same energy after passage through the mercury vapor as they had on leaving the gun. This result could be explained in the following way. A mercury atom is several hundred thousand times more massive than an electron. When it has low kinetic energy, the electron just bounces off a mercury atom, much as a golf ball thrown at a bowling ball would bounce off. A collision of this kind is called an "elastic" collision. (We discussed it in Section 9.7.) In an elastic collision, the mercury atom (bowling ball) takes up only a very small part of the kinetic energy of the electron (golf ball). The electron loses practically none of its kinetic energy.

But when the kinetic energy of the electrons was raised to 5 electron-volts, the experimental results changed dramatically. When an electron collided with a mercury atom, the electron lost almost exactly 4.9 eV of energy. But when the energy was increased to 6 eV, the electron still lost just 4.9 eV of energy in collision, being left with 1.1 eV of energy. These results indicated that a mercury atom cannot accept less than 4.9 eV of

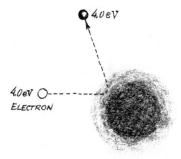

MERCURY ATOM

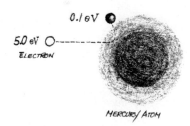

MERCURY ATOM

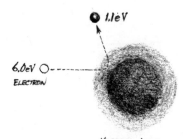

MERCURY ATOM

energy. Further, when the mercury atom is offered somewhat more energy, for example, 5 or 6 eV, it still can accept only 4.9 eV. The accepted amount of energy cannot go into kinetic energy of the mercury because the atom is so much more massive than the electron. Hence, Franck and Hertz concluded that the 4.9 eV is added to the internal energy of the mercury atom. That is, the mercury atom enters a stationary state with energy 4.9 eV greater than that of the lowest energy state, with no allowed energy level in between.

What happens to this extra 4.9 eV of internal energy? According to the Bohr model, this amount of energy should be emitted as electromagnetic radiation when the atom returns to its lowest state. Franck and Hertz looked for this radiation, and found it. They observed that the mercury vapor emitted light at a wavelength of 2535 Å. This wavelength was known to exist in the emission spectrum of hot mercury vapor. The wavelength corresponds to a frequency f for which the photon's energy, hf, is just 4.9 eV (as you can calculate). This result showed that mercury atoms had indeed gained (and then radiated away) 4.9 eV of energy in collisions with electrons.

SG 19.14, 19.15

Later experiments showed that mercury atoms bombarded by electrons could also gain other sharply defined amounts of energy—for example, 6.7 eV and 10.4 eV. In each case, the radiation emitted corresponded to known lines in the emission spectrum of mercury. And in each case, similar results were obtained: the electrons always lost energy, and the atoms always gained energy, both in sharply defined amounts. Each type of atom studied was found to have separate energy states. The amounts of energy gained by the atoms in collisions with electrons always corresponded to known spectrum lines. Thus, direct experiment confirmed the existence of separate stationary states of atoms predicted by the Bohr theory of atomic spectra. This result was considered to provide strong evidence for the validity of the Bohr theory.

SG 19.16

Q17 How much kinetic energy will an electron have after a collision with a mercury atom if its kinetic energy before collision is (a) 4.0 eV? (b) 5.0 eV? (c) 7.0 eV?

19.10 The periodic table of the elements

In the Rutherford-Bohr model, atoms of the different elements differ in the charge and mass of their nuclei, and in the number and arrangement of the electrons. Bohr came to picture the electronic orbits as shown on the next page. However, Bohr envisioned not a series of concentric rings in one plane, but patterns in three dimensions. For example, the orbits of the two electrons of helium in the normal state are indicated as circles in planes inclined at about 60° to each other. For each circular orbit, elliptical orbits with the nucleus at one focus are also possible. These would have the same (or nearly the same) total energy as the circular orbit.

　　Bohr found a way of using his model to understand better the periodic table of the elements. In fact, the periodic table, rather than the explanation of Balmer spectra, was Bohr's main concern when he began his study. He suggested that the chemical and physical properties of an element depend on how the electrons are arranged around the nucleus. He also indicated how this might come about. He regarded the electrons in an atom as grouped together in layers or shells around the nucleus. Each shell can contain not more than a certain number of electrons. Chemical properties are related to how nearly full or empty a shell is. For example, full shells are associated with chemical stability, and in the inert gases the electron shells are completely filled.

　　Let us see how the Bohr model of atoms helps to understand chemical properties. We may begin with the observation that the elements hydrogen (Z = 1) and lithium (Z = 3) are somewhat alike chemically. Both have valences of 1. Both enter into compounds of similar types, for example hydrogen chloride, HCl, and lithium chloride, LiCl. There are also some similarities in their spectra. All this suggests that the lithium atom resembles the hydrogen atom in some important respects. Bohr speculated that two of the three electrons of the lithium atom are relatively close to the nucleus, in orbits resembling those of the helium atom. But the third electron is in a circular or elliptical orbit outside the inner system. Since this inner system consists of a nucleus of charge (+) $3q_e$ and two electrons each of the charge (−) q_e, its *net* charge is (+) q_e. Thus the lithium atom may be roughly pictured as having a central core of charge (+) q_e. Around this core one electron revolves, somewhat as for a hydrogen atom. This similar physical structure, then, is the reason for the similar chemical behavior.

　　Helium (Z = 2) is a chemically inert noble gas. So far no one has been able to form compounds from it. These properties indicate that the helium atom is highly stable, having both of its electrons closely bound to the nucleus. It seems sensible, then, to regard both electrons as moving in the same *innermost shell* around the nucleus when the atom is unexcited. Moreover, because the helium atom is so stable and chemically inert, we may reasonably assume that this shell cannot hold more than two electrons. This shell is called the K-shell. The single electron of hydrogen is also said to be in the K-shell when the atom is unexcited. Lithium has two electrons in the K-shell, filling it to capacity; the third electron starts a new shell, called the L-shell. This single outlying and loosely bound electron is the reason why lithium combines so readily with oxygen, chlorine, and many other elements.

　　Sodium (Z = 11) is the next element in the periodic table that has chemical properties similar to those of hydrogen and lithium. This similarity suggests that the sodium atom also is hydrogen-like in having a central core about which one electron revolves. Moreover, just as lithium follows helium in the periodic table, sodium follows the noble gas neon (Z = 10). We may assume that two of neon's 10 electrons are in the first (K) shell, while the remaining 8 electrons are in the second (L) shell.

The sketches below are based on diagrams Bohr used in his lectures.

HYDROGEN (Z = 1)

HELIUM (Z = 2)

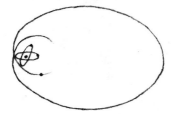

LITHIUM (Z = 3)

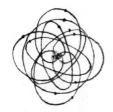

NEON (Z = 10)

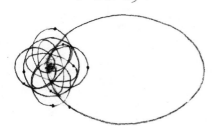

SODIUM (Z = 11)

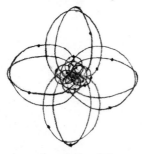

ARGON (Z = 18)

These two pages will be easier to follow if you refer to the table of the elements and the periodic table in Chapter 17 page 23.

Because of the chemical inertness and stability of neon, we may further assume that these 8 electrons fill the L-shell to capacity. For sodium, then, the eleventh electron must be in a third shell, called the M-shell. Passing on to potassium (Z = 19), the next alkali metal in the periodic table, we again picture an inner core and a single electron outside it. The core consists of a nucleus with charge (+) $19q_e$. There are 2, 8, and 8 electrons occupying the K-, L-, and M-shells, respectively. The 19th electron revolves around the core in a fourth shell, called the N-shell. The atom of the noble gas argon, with Z = 18, comes just before potassium in the periodic table. Argon again represents a tight and stable electron pattern, with 2 in the K-, 8 in the L-, and 8 in the M-shell.

These qualitative considerations have led us to a consistent picture of electrons distributed in groups, or shells, around the nucleus. The arrangement of electrons in the noble gases may be considered particularly stable. Each time we encounter a new alkali metal in Group I of the periodic table, a new shell is started. Each alkali metal atom has a single electron around a core which resembles the pattern for the preceding noble gas. We may expect this outlying electron to be easily "loosened" by the action of neighboring atoms, and this agrees with the facts. The elements lithium, sodium, and potassium are alkali metals. In compounds or in solution (as in electrolysis) they may be considered to be in the form of ions such as Li^+, Na^+ and K^+. Each ion lacks one electron and so has one positive net charge (+) q_e. In the neutral atoms of these elements, the outer electron is relatively free to move about. This property has been used as the basis of a theory of electrical conductivity. According to this theory, a good conductor has many "free" electrons which can form a current under appropriate conditions. A poor conductor has relatively few "free" electrons. The alkali metals are all good conductors. Elements whose electron shells are filled are very poor conductors; they have no "free" electrons.

We turn now to Group II of the periodic table. We would expect those elements that follow immediately after the alkali metals to have atoms with two outlying electrons. For example, beryllium (Z = 4) should have 2 electrons in the K-shell, thus filling it, and 2 in the L-shell. If the atoms of all these elements have two outlying electrons, they should be chemically similar, as indeed they are. Thus, calcium and magnesium, which belong to this group, should easily form ions such as Ca^{++} and Mg^{++}, each with a positive net charge of (+) $2q_e$. This is also found to be true.

As a final example, consider those elements that immediately *precede* the noble gases in the periodic table. For example, fluorine atoms (Z = 9) should have 2 electrons filling the K-shell but only 7 electrons in the L-shell—one less than enough to fill it. If a fluorine atom captures an additional electron, it should become an ion F^- with one negative net charge. The L-shell would then be filled, as it is for neutral neon (Z = 10), and we would expect the F^- ion to be relatively stable. This prediction agrees with observation. Indeed, all the elements immediately preceding the inert gases tend to form stable singly-charged negative ions in solution. In the solid state, we would expect these elements to lack free

Shell name	Number of electrons in filled shell
K	2
L	8
M	18

electrons. And in fact all of them are poor conductors of electricity.

Altogether there are seven main shells, K, L, M, . . . Q, and further analysis shows that all but the first are divided into *subshells*. The second (L) shell consists of two subshells, the third (M) shell consists of three subshells, and so on. The first subshell in any shell can always hold up to 2 electrons, the second up to 6, the third up to 10, the fourth up to 14, and so on. For all the elements up to and including argon (Z = 18), the buildup of electrons proceeds quite simply. Thus the argon atom has 2 electrons in the K-shell, 8 in the L-shell, then 2 in the first M-subshell and 6 in the second M-subshell. But the first subshell of the N-shell is lower in energy than the third subshell of the M-shell. Since atoms are most likely to be in the lowest energy state available, the N-shell will begin to fill before the M-shell is completed. Therefore, after argon, there may be electrons in an "outer" shell before an "inner" one is filled. This complicates the scheme somewhat, but still allows it to be consistent. The electron arrangement in any unexcited atom is always the one that provides greatest stability for the whole atom. According to this model, chemical phenomena generally involve only the outermost electrons of the atoms.

Bohr carried through a complete analysis along these lines. Finally, in 1921, he proposed the form of the periodic table shown below. The periodicity results from the completion of subshells. This phenomenon is complicated even beyond the shell overlap in the figure on page 86 by the interaction of electrons in the same subshell. Bohr's table, still useful, was

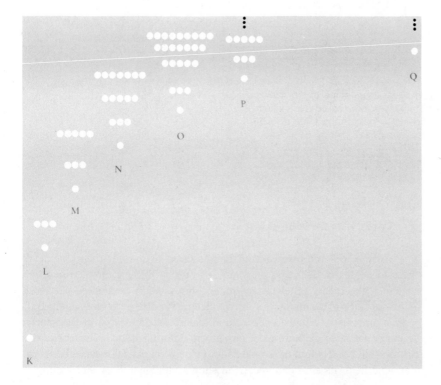

SG 19.17
SG 19.18

Relative energy levels of electron states in atoms. Each circle represents a state which can be occupied by 2 electrons.

the result of *physical* theory and offered a fundamental *physical* basis for understanding chemistry. For example, it showed how the structure of the periodic table follows from the shell structure of atoms. This was another triumph of the Bohr theory.

Q18 Why do the next heavier elements after the noble gases easily become positively charged?

Q19 Why are there only 2 elements in Period I, 8 in Period II, 8 in Period III, etc?

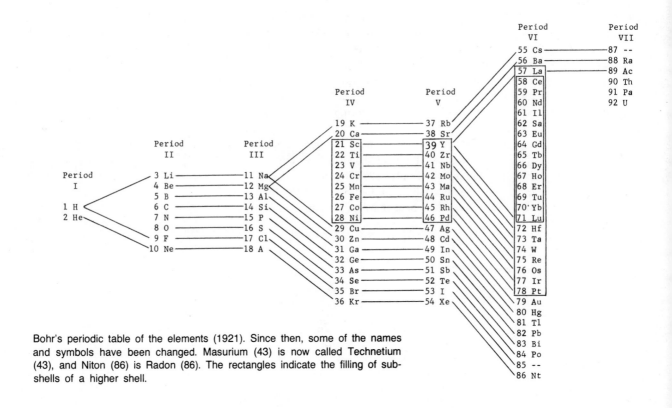

Bohr's periodic table of the elements (1921). Since then, some of the names and symbols have been changed. Masurium (43) is now called Technetium (43), and Niton (86) is Radon (86). The rectangles indicate the filling of sub-shells of a higher shell.

19.11 The inadequacy of the Bohr theory, and the state of atomic theory in the early 1920's

Every model and every theory has its limits. The Bohr theory achieved great successes in the years between 1913 and 1924. But problems arose for which the theory proved inadequate. Bohr's theory accounted very well for the spectra of atoms with a single electron in the outermost shell. But serious differences between theory and experiment appeared in the spectra of atoms with two or more electrons in the outermost shell. Experiments also revealed that when a sample of an element is placed in an electric or magnetic field, its emission spectrum shows additional lines. For example,

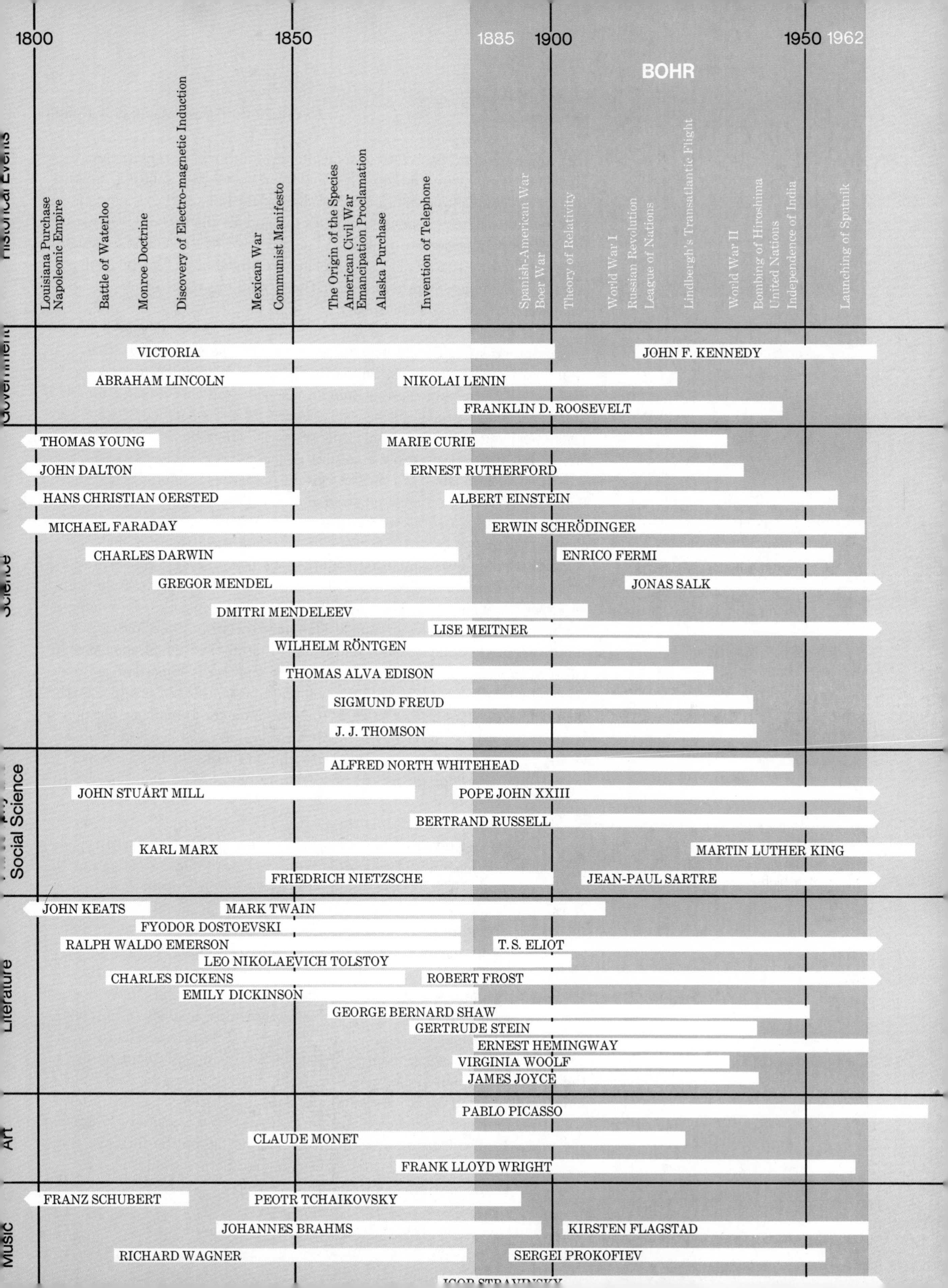

1800 | **1850** | **1885** | **1900** | **1950** | **1962**

BOHR

Historical Events

Louisiana Purchase
Napoleonic Empire
Battle of Waterloo
Monroe Doctrine
Discovery of Electro-magnetic Induction
Mexican War
Communist Manifesto
The Origin of the Species
American Civil War
Emancipation Proclamation
Alaska Purchase
Invention of Telephone
Spanish-American War
Boer War
Theory of Relativity
World War I
Russian Revolution
League of Nations
Lindbergh's Transatlantic Flight
World War II
Bombing of Hiroshima
United Nations
Independence of India
Launching of Sputnik

Government

VICTORIA
JOHN F. KENNEDY
ABRAHAM LINCOLN
NIKOLAI LENIN
FRANKLIN D. ROOSEVELT

Science

THOMAS YOUNG
MARIE CURIE
JOHN DALTON
ERNEST RUTHERFORD
HANS CHRISTIAN OERSTED
ALBERT EINSTEIN
MICHAEL FARADAY
ERWIN SCHRÖDINGER
CHARLES DARWIN
ENRICO FERMI
GREGOR MENDEL
JONAS SALK
DMITRI MENDELEEV
LISE MEITNER
WILHELM RÖNTGEN
THOMAS ALVA EDISON
SIGMUND FREUD
J. J. THOMSON

Social Science

ALFRED NORTH WHITEHEAD
JOHN STUART MILL
POPE JOHN XXIII
BERTRAND RUSSELL
KARL MARX
MARTIN LUTHER KING
FRIEDRICH NIETZSCHE
JEAN-PAUL SARTRE

Literature

JOHN KEATS
MARK TWAIN
FYODOR DOSTOEVSKI
RALPH WALDO EMERSON
T. S. ELIOT
LEO NIKOLAEVICH TOLSTOY
CHARLES DICKENS
ROBERT FROST
EMILY DICKINSON
GEORGE BERNARD SHAW
GERTRUDE STEIN
ERNEST HEMINGWAY
VIRGINIA WOOLF
JAMES JOYCE

Art

PABLO PICASSO
CLAUDE MONET
FRANK LLOYD WRIGHT

Music

FRANZ SCHUBERT
PEOTR TCHAIKOVSKY
JOHANNES BRAHMS
KIRSTEN FLAGSTAD
RICHARD WAGNER
SERGEI PROKOFIEV
IGOR STRAVINSKY

In March 1913, Bohr wrote to Rutherford enclosing a draft of his first paper on the quantum theory of atomic constitution. On March 20, 1913, Rutherford replied in a letter, the first part of which we quote, "Dear Dr. Bohr:

I have received your paper and read it with great interest, but I want to look it over again carefully when I have more leisure. Your ideas as to the mode of origin of spectra in hydrogen are very ingenious and seem to work out well: but the mixture of Planck's ideas with the old mechanics make it very difficult to form a physical idea of what is the basis of it. There appears to me one grave difficulty in your hypothesis, which I have no doubt you fully realize, namely, how does an electron decide what frequency it is going to vibrate at when it passes from one stationary state to the other. It seems to me that you would have to assume that the electron knows before hand where it is going to stop...."

in a magnetic field each line is split into several lines. The Bohr theory could not account in a quantitative way for the observed splitting. Further, the theory supplied no method for predicting the relative brightness of spectral lines. These relative intensities depend on the probabilities with which atoms in a sample undergo transitions among the stationary states. Physicists wanted to be able to calculate the probability of a transition from one stationary state to another. They could not make such calculations with the Bohr theory.

By the early 1920's it was clear that the Bohr theory, despite its great successes, was inadequate beyond certain limits. To get a theory that would solve more problems, Bohr's theory would have to be revised or replaced. But the successes of Bohr's theory showed that a better theory of atomic structure would still have to account for the existence of stationary states—separate, distinct atomic energy levels. Therefore, such a theory would have to be based on quantum concepts.

Besides the inability to predict certain properties of atoms at all, the Bohr theory had two additional shortcomings. First, it predicted some results that did not agree with experiment (such as the spectra of elements with two or three electrons in the outermost electron shells). Second, it predicted results that could not be tested in any known way (such as the details of electron orbits). Although orbits were easy to draw on paper, they could not be observed directly. Nor could they be related to any observable properties of atoms. Planetary theory has very different significance when applied to a real planet in orbit than when applied to an electron in an atom. The precise position of a planet is important, especially in experiments such as photographing an eclipse or a portion of the surface of Mars from a satellite. But the moment-to-moment position of an electron in an orbit has no such meaning because it has no relation to any experiment physicists have been able to devise. It thus became evident that the Bohr theory led to some questions which could not be answered experimentally.

In the early 1920's, physicists—above all, Bohr himself—began to work seriously on revising the basic ideas of the theory. One fact that stood out was that the theory started with a *mixture* of classical and quantum ideas. An atom was assumed to act according to the laws of classical physics up to the point where these laws did not work. Beyond this point, quantum ideas were introduced. The picture of the atom that emerged was an inconsistent mixture. It combined ideas from classical physics with concepts for which there was no place in classical physics. The orbits of the electrons were determined by the classical, Newtonian laws of motion. But of the many possible orbits, only a small portion were regarded as possible. And even these few orbits were selected by rules that contradicted classical mechanics. Or again, the frequency calculated for the orbital revolution of electrons was quite different from the frequency of light emitted or absorbed when the electron moved from or to this orbit. Or again, the decision that n could never be zero was necessary to prevent the model from collapsing by letting the electron fall on the nucleus. It became evident that a better theory of atomic structure would need a more consistent foundation in quantum concepts.

The contribution of the Bohr theory may be summarized as follows. It provided some excellent answers to the questions raised about atomic structure in Chapters 17 and 18. Although the theory turned out to be inadequate, it drew attention to how quantum concepts can be used. It indicated the path that a new theory would have to take. A new theory would have to supply the right answers that the Bohr theory gave. But it would also have to supply the right answers for the problems the Bohr theory could not solve. One of the most fascinating aspects of Bohr's work was the proof that physical and chemical properties of matter can be traced back to the fundamental role of *integers*—(quantum numbers such as $n = 1, 2, 3 \ldots$). As Bohr said, "The solution of one of the boldest dreams of natural science is to build up an understanding of the regularities of nature upon the consideration of pure number." We catch here an echo of the hope of Pythagoras and Plato, of Kepler and Galileo.

Since the 1920's, a successful theory of atomic structure has been developed and generally accepted by physicists. It is part of "quantum mechanics," so called because it is built directly on quantum concepts. It goes far beyond understanding atomic structure. In fact, it is the basis of our modern conception of events on a submicroscopic scale. Some aspects will be discussed in the next chapter. Significantly, Bohr himself was again a leading contributor.

Remember, for example, (in Unit 1) how proudly Galileo pointed out, when announcing that all falling bodies are equally and constantly accelerated: "So far as I know, no one has yet pointed out that the distances traversed, during equal intervals of time, by a body falling from rest, stand to one another in the same ratio as the odd numbers beginning with unity [namely 1:3:5:7:...]."

SG 19.19–19.23

Q20 The Bohr model of atoms is widely given in science books. What is wrong with it? What is good about it?

19.1 The Project Physics materials particularly appropriate for Chapter 19 include:

Experiment
Spectroscopy

Activities
Measuring ionization, a quantum effect
"Black box" atoms

Reader Article
The Teacher and the Bohr Theory of the Atom

Film Loop
Rutherford Scattering

Transparencies
Alpha Scattering
Energy Levels – Bohr Theory

19.2 (a) Suggest experiments to show which of the Fraunhofer lines in the spectrum of sunlight result from absorption in the sun's atmosphere rather than from absorption by gases in the earth's atmosphere.

(b) How might one decide from spectroscopic observations whether the moon and the planets shine by their own light or by reflected light from the sun?

19.3 Theoretically, how many series of lines are there in the emission spectrum of hydrogen? In all these series, how many lines are in the visible region?

19.4 The Rydberg constant for hydrogen, R_H, has the value 1.097×10^7/m. Calculate the wavelengths of the lines in the Balmer series corresponding to $n = 8$, $n = 10$, $n = 12$. Compare the values you get with the wavelengths listed in the table on page 65. Do you see any pattern in the values?

19.5 (a) As indicated in the figure on page 65 the lines in one of hydrogen's spectral series are bunched very closely at one end. Does the formula

$$\frac{1}{\lambda} = R_H \left(\frac{1}{n^2_f} - \frac{1}{n^2_i} \right)$$

suggest that such bunching will occur?

(b) The "series limit" corresponds to the last possible line(s) of the series. What value should be taken for n_i in the above equation to compute the wavelength of the series limit?

(c) Compute the series limit for the Lyman, Balmer, or Paschen series of hydrogen.

(d) Consider a photon with a wavelength corresponding to the series limit of the Lyman series. What energy could it carry? Express the answer in joules and in electron volts (1 eV = 1.6×10^{-19} J).

19.6 In what ways do Thomson's and Rutherford's atomic models agree? In what ways do they disagree?

19.7 In 1903, the German physicist Philipp Lenard (1864-1947) proposed an atomic model different from those of Thomson and Rutherford. He observed that, since cathode-ray particles can penetrate matter, most of the atomic volume must offer no obstacle to their penetration. In Lenard's model there were no electrons and no positive charges separate from the electrons. His atom was made up of particles called *dynamides*, each of which was an electric doublet possessing mass. (An electric doublet is a combination of a positive charge and a negative charge very close together.) All dynamides were identical, and an atom contained as many of them as were needed to make up its mass. They were distributed throughout the volume of the atom. But their radius was so small compared with that of the atom that most of the atom was empty.

(a) In what ways does Lenard's model agree with those of Thomson and Rutherford? In what ways does it disagree with those models?

(b) Why would you not expect α particles to be scattered through large angles if Lenard's model were valid?

(c) In view of the scattering of α particles that is observed, is Lenard's model valid?

19.8 Determine a likely upper limit for the effective size of a gold nucleus from the following facts and hypotheses:

i. A beam of α-particles of known velocity $v = 2 \times 10^7$ m/sec is scattered from a gold foil. The manner of this scattering makes sense only if the α particles are repelled by nuclear charges that exert a Coulomb's law repulsion on the α particles.

ii. Some of these α particles come straight back after scattering. They therefore approached the nuclei up to a distance r from the nucleus' center. At this point the initial kinetic energy $\frac{1}{2}m_\alpha v_\alpha^2$ has been completely changed to the potential energy of the system.

iii. The potential energy of a system made up of an α particle of charge $2q_e$ at a distance r from a nucleus of charge Zq_e is given by the product of the "potential" (Zq_e/r) set up by the nucleus at distance r, and the charge ($2q_e$) of the α particle.

iv. The distance r can now be computed. We know v_α, m_α (7×10^{-27} kg, from other evidence), Z for gold atoms (see periodic table), and q_e (see Section 14.5).

v. The nuclear radius must be equal to or less than r. Thus we have a reasonable upper limit for the size of this nucleus.

19.9 We generally suppose that the atom and the nucleus are each spherical. We assume that the diameter of the atom is of the order of 1 Å (Ångstrom unit = 10^{-10} m) and that the diameter of the nucleus is of the order of 10^{-12} cm.

(a) What are the evidences that these are reasonable suppositions?

(b) What is the ratio of the diameter of the nucleus to that of the atom?

19.10 The nucleus of the hydrogen atom is thought to have a radius of about 1.5×10^{-13} cm. Imagine this atom magnified so that the nucleus is 0.1 mm across (the size of a grain of dust). How far away from it would the electron be in the Bohr orbit closest to it?

19.11 Show that the total energy of a neutral hydrogen atom made up of a positively charged nucleus and an electron is given by

$$E_n = \frac{1}{n^2} E_1$$

where E_1 is the energy when the electron is in the first orbit ($n = 1$), and where the value of $E_1 = -13.6$ electron-volts. (You may consult other texts, for example *Foundation of Modern Physical Science* by Holton and Roller, sections 34.4 and 34.7.) Program and hints:

i. The total energy E of the system is the kinetic and potential energy $KE + PE$ of the electron in its orbit. Since $mv^2/r = kq_e^2/r^2$ (see page 73), $KE = \frac{1}{2}mv^2$ can be quickly calculated.

ii. The electrical potential energy PE of a charged point object (electron) is given by the electrical potential V of the region in which it finds itself, times its own charge. The value of V set up by the (positive) nucleus at distance r is given by Kq_e/r. The charge on the electron is $-q_e$. Hence $PE = -kq^2_e/r$. The meaning of the negative sign is simply that PE is taken to be zero if the electron is infinitely distant. The system radiates energy as the electron is placed closer to the nucleus. On the other hand energy must be supplied to move the electron away from the nucleus.

iii. Now you can show that the total energy E is

$$E = KE + PE = -k\frac{q_e^{2}}{2r}$$

iv. Using the equation derived on page 73, namely $r = \dfrac{n^2h^2}{4\pi^2mq^2_e}$, show that

$$E_n = -\frac{k^2 2\pi^2 m q_e^2}{n^2 h^2} = \frac{1}{n^2} E_1$$

where $E_1 = k^2 2\pi^2 m q_e^2 / h^2$.

The numerical value for this can be computed by using the known values (in consistent units) for k, m, q_e and h.

v. Find the numerical value of the energy of the hydrogen atom for each of the first 4 allowed orbits ($n = 1, 2, 3, 4$).

vi. As a final point, show that the quantity $-E_1/hc$ has the same value as the constant R_H, as claimed in Sec. 19.8.

19.12 Using the Bohr theory, how would you account for the existence of the dark lines in the absorption spectrum of hydrogen?

19.13 A group of hydrogen atoms is excited (by collision, or by absorption of a photon of proper frequency). They all reach the stationary state for which $n = 5$. Refer to the top figure in the margin on page 80 and list all possible lines emitted by this sample sample of hydrogen gas.

19.14 Make an energy level diagram to represent the results of the Franck-Hertz experiment.

19.15 Many substances emit visible radiation when illuminated with ultraviolet light. This phenomenon is an example of fluorescence. Stokes, a British physicist of the nineteenth century, found that in fluorescence the wavelength of the emitted light usually was the same or longer than the illuminating light. How would you account for this phenomenon on the basis of the Bohr theory?

19.16 In Query 31 of his Opticks, Newton wrote:

> All these things being consider'd, it seems probable to me that God in the beginning formed matter in solid, massy, hard, impenetrable, moveable particles, of such sizes and figures, and with such other properties, and in such proportion to the end for which He formed them; and that these primitive particles being solids, are incomparably harder than any porous bodies compounded of them, even so very hard, as never to wear or break in pieces; no ordinary power being able to divide what God Himself made one in the first creation. While the particles continue entire, they may compose bodies of one and the same nature texture and in all ages: But should they wear away, or break in pieces, the nature of things depending on them would be changed. Water and earth, composed of old worn particles and fragments of particles, would not be of the same nature and texture now, with water and earth composed of entire particles in the beginning. And therefore that nature may be lasting, the changes of corporeal things are to be placed only in the various separations and new associations and motions of these permanent particles; compound bodies being apt to break, not in the midst of solid particles, but where those particles are laid together, and only touch in a few points.

Compare what Newton says here about atoms with

(a) the views attributed to Leucippus and Democritus concerning atoms (see the Prologue to this unit);

(b) Dalton's assumptions about atoms (see the end of the Prologue to this unit);

(c) the Rutherford-Bohr model of the atom

19.17 Use the chart on page 85 to explain why atoms of potassium ($Z = 19$) have electrons in the N shell even though the M shell is not filled.

19.18 Use the chart on page 85 to predict the atomic number of the next inert gas after argon. That is, imagine filling the electron levels with pairs of electrons until you reach an apparently stable, or complete, pattern. Do the same for the next inert gas following.

19.19 Make up a glossary, with definitions, of terms which appeared for the first time in this chapter.

19.20 The philosopher John Locke (1632-1704) proposed a science of human nature which was strongly influenced by Newton's physics. In Locke's atomistic view, elementary ideas ("atoms") are produced by elementary sensory experiences and then drift, collide, and interact in the mind. Thus the formation of ideas was only a special case of the universal interactions of particles.

Does such an approach to the subject of human nature seem reasonable to you? What argument for and against this sort of theory can you think of?

19.21 In a recently published textbook of physics, the following statement is made:

Arbitrary though Bohr's new postulate may seem, it was just one more step in the process by which the apparently continuous macroscopic world was being analyzed in terms of a discontinuous, quantized, microscopic world. Although the Greeks had speculated about quantized matter (atoms), it remained for the chemists and physicists of the nineteenth century to give them reality. In 1900 Planck found it necessary to quantize the energy of electromagnetic waves. Also, in the early 1900's a series of experiments culminating in Millikan's oil-drop experiment conclusively showed that electric charge was quantized. To this list of quantized entities, Bohr added angular momentum (the product mvr).

(a) What other properties or things in physics can you think of that are "quantized?"

(b) What properties or things can you think of outside physics that might be said to be "quantized?"

19.22 Write an essay on the successes and failures of the Bohr model. Can it be called a good model? A simple model? A beautiful model?

19.23 In 1903 a philosopher wrote:
The propounders of the atomic view of electricity disagree with theories which would restrict the method of science to the use of only such quantities and data as can be actually seen and directly measured, and which condemn the introduction of such useful conceptions as the atom and the electron, which cannot be directly seen and can only be measured by indirect processes.

On the basis of the information now available to you, with which view do you tend to agree: the view of those who think in terms of atoms and electrons, or the view that we must use only such things as can be actually seen and measured?

This construction is meant to represent the arrangement of mutually attracting sodium and chlorine ions (the smaller structures and the larger ones, respectively) in a crystal of common salt. The outermost electrons of the sodium atoms have been lost to the chlorine atoms. This leaves positively charged sodium ions with completed K and L shells, and negatively charged chlorine ions with completed K, L and M shells.

The diffraction pattern on the left was made by a beam of x rays passing through thin aluminum foil. The diffraction pattern on the right was made by a beam of electrons passing through the same foil.

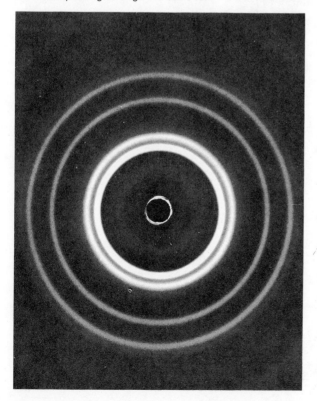 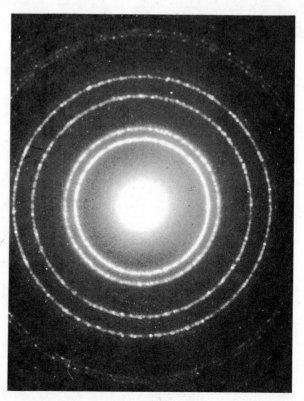

CHAPTER TWENTY

Some Ideas from Modern Physical Theories

20.1 Some results of relativity theory

Progress in atomic and nuclear physics has been based on two great advances in physical thought: quantum theory and relativity. In a single chapter we could not even begin to give a full account of the actual development of physical and mathematical ideas in these fields. But we can offer you some idea of what kind of problems led to the development, suggest some of the unexpected conclusions, and prepare for material in later chapters. And—very important!—we can introduce you to the beautiful ideas on relativity theory and quantum mechanics, offered in articles in *Reader 5,* and to nuclear physics, offered in the Supplemental Unit *The Nucleus* and in other supplemental units.

SG 20.1

In Chapters 18 and 19 we saw how quantum theory entered into atomic physics. To follow its further development into *quantum mechanics,* we need to learn some of the results of the relativity theory. These results will also be essential to our treatment of nuclear physics. Therefore, we will devote this section to a brief discussion of one essential result of the theory of relativity introduced by Einstein in 1905—the same year in which he published the theory of the photoelectric effect.

In Unit 1 we discussed the basic idea of relativity. We stated that certain aspects of physical events appear the same from different frames of reference, even if the reference frames are moving with respect to one another. We said that mass, acceleration, and force seem to be such *invariant* quantities. Thus, Newton's laws relating these quantities should be equally valid in all reference frames.

By 1905 it had become clear that this is true enough for all ordinary cases of motion. But problems arise if the bodies involved move with respect to the observer at a speed more than a few percent of that of light. Einstein wondered whether the relativity principle could be extended to the mechanics of rapidly moving bodies, and even to the description of electromagnetic waves. He found that this could be done by replacing Newton's definitions of length and time with definitions that produce a

Topics in relativity theory are developed further in *Reader 5*. See the articles:
"The Clock Paradox"
"Mr. Tompkins and Simultaneity"
"Mathematics and Relativity"
"Parable of the Surveyors"
"Outside and Inside the Elevator"
"Space Travel: Problems of Physics and Engineering"

more consistent physics. His work resulted in a new viewpoint, and this viewpoint is the most interesting part of Einstein's thinking. Parts of it are discussed in articles in *Reader 5* and *Reader 6*. But here we will deal with high-speed phenomena from an essentially Newtonian viewpoint. We will focus on the *corrections* required to make Newtonian mechanics better fit a new range of phenomena.

For bodies moving at speeds that are small compared to the speed of light, measurements predicted by relativity theory differ only very slightly from measurements predicted by Newtonian mechanics. We know that this is true because Newton's laws account very well for the motion of bodies with which we are familiar in ordinary life. But differences between relativistic mechanics and Newtonian mechanics become apparent in experiments involving high-speed particles.

We saw in Section 18.2 that J. J. Thomson devised a method for determining the speed v and the ratio of charge to mass q_e/m for electrons. Not long after Thomson discovered the electron, it was found that the value of q_e/m seemed to vary with the speed of the electrons. Between 1900 and 1910, several physicists found that electrons have the value $q_e/m = 1.76 \times 10^{11}$ coul/kg only for speeds that are very small compared to the speed of light. As electrons were given greater speeds, the ratio became smaller. Relativity theory offered an explanation: the electron charge is invariant—it does not depend on the speed of the electrons. But the *mass* of an electron, as measured by an observer in a laboratory, should vary with speed. The mass should *increase*, according to the formula:

$$m = \frac{m_0}{\sqrt{1 - v^2/c^2}}$$

In this formula, v is the speed the electron has relative to the observer, while c is the speed of light in a vacuum. The quantity m_0 is the *rest mass*—the electron's mass measured by an observer when the electron is at rest with respect to the observer; m is the mass of an electron measured while it moves with speed v relative to the observer. We may call m the *relativistic* mass. It is the mass determined, for example, by J. J. Thomson's method.

The ratio of relativistic mass to rest mass, m/m_0, is equal to $1/\sqrt{1-v^2/c^2}$. The table in the margin shows how this ratio varies as values of v/c approach 1. The value of m/m_0 becomes very large as v approaches c.

The formula for the relativistic mass was derived by Einstein from fundamental ideas of space and time. It has been tested experimentally. Some of the results, for electrons with speeds so high that the value of v reaches about 0.8 c, are graphed on the next page. At $v = 0.8 c$ the relativistic mass m is about 1.7 times the rest mass m_0. The curve shows the theoretical variation of m as the value of v increases. The agreement of experiment and theory is excellent. The increase in mass with speed fully accounts for the shrinking of the ratio q_e/m with speed, which was mentioned earlier.

The Relativistic Increase of Mass with Speed

v/c	m/m$_0$	v/c	m/m$_0$
0.0	1.000	0.95	3.203
0.01	1.000	0.98	5.025
0.10	1.005	0.99	7.089
0.50	1.155	0.998	15.82
0.75	1.538	0.999	22.37
0.80	1.667	0.9999	70.72
0.90	2.294	0.99999	223.6

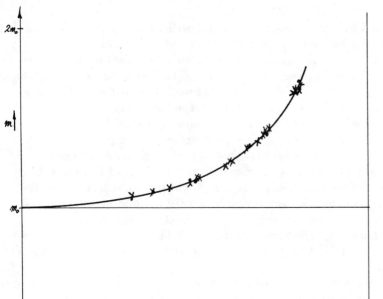

Variation of relativistic mass with speed (expressed as a fraction of the speed of light). The dots and crosses indicate the results of two different experiments.

The formula for variation of mass with speed is valid for *all* moving bodies, not just for electrons and other atomic particles. But the large bodies which we encounter in everyday life move at very small speeds compared to the speed of light. Thus, for such bodies, the value of v/c is very small. The value of v^2/c^2 in the denominator is also very small, and the values of m and m_0 are so nearly the same that we cannot tell the difference. In other words, the relativistic increase in mass can be detected in practice only for particles of atomic or sub-atomic size. For it is only these particles to which we can give speeds higher than a small fraction of c.

SG 20.2
SG 20.3
SG 20.4

The effects discussed so far are mainly of historical interest because they eventually helped to convince physicists of the correctness of relativity theory. More recent experiments provide more striking evidence of the inadequacy of Newtonian physics for particles with very high speeds. Electrons can be given very high energies by accelerating them in a vacuum by means of a high voltage V. Since the electron charge q_e is known, the energy increase, q_eV, is known. The rest mass m_0 of an electron is also known (see Section 18.3), and the speed v can be measured by timing the travel over a known distance. It is therefore possible to compare the value of the energy supplies, q_eV, with the expression for kinetic energy in classical mechanics, $\frac{1}{2}m_0v^2$. Experiments of this kind have shown that when electrons have speeds that are small compared to the speed of light, it is correct to write $\frac{1}{2}m_0v^2 = q_eV$. We used this relation in Section 18.5 in discussing the photoelectric effect. We could do so correctly because photoelectrons do

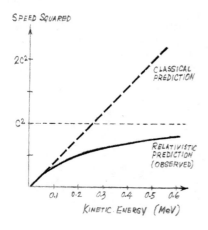

SPEED SQUARED

$2c^2$

CLASSICAL
PREDICTION

c^2

RELATIVISTIC
PREDICTION
(OBSERVED)

0.1   0.2   0.3   0.4   0.5   0.6

KINETIC ENERGY (MeV)

The Supplemental Unit *The Nucleus*
deals further with accelerators. The
operation of one of these, the Cambridge Electron Accelerator (CEA)
apparatus is also the subject of the
Project Physics film *Synchrotron*.

To increase the mass of a body by 1
gram, it would have to be given a kinetic energy of 10^{14} joules (about 6
million mile-tons).

The rest energy m_0c^2 includes the
potential energy, if there is any. Thus
a compressed spring has a somewhat
larger rest mass and rest energy than
the same spring when relaxed.

indeed have small speeds, and m and m_0 have nearly the same value. But
when the speed of the electron becomes so large that v/c is no longer a
small fraction, the quantity $\frac{1}{2}m_0v^2$ no longer increases in proportion to
q_eV. This disagreement increases as q_eV increases. The increase in kinetic
energy still is equal to the amount of work done by the electrical field,
q_eV. But the mass is no longer m_0 and so kinetic energy can't be
measured by $\frac{1}{2}m_0v^2$. The value of v^2, instead of steadily increasing
with energy supplied, approaches a limiting value: c^2.

One of several accelerators of its kind is the Stanford Linear
Accelerator (SLAC) operated in California by Stanford University. In it
electrons are accelerated to an energy which is equivalent to what they
would gain in being accelerated by a potential difference of 10^{10} volts.
This is an enormous energy for electrons. The speed attained by the
electrons is 0.999999999 c. At this speed the relativistic mass m (both by
calculation and by experiment) is over 10,000 times greater than the rest
mass m_0!

Another way of saying mass increases with speed is this: *any increase
in kinetic energy is accompanied by an increase in mass.* If the kinetic
energy measured from a given frame of reference is *KE*, the increase in
mass Δm (above the rest mass) measured in that frame is proportional to
KE:

$$\Delta m \propto KE$$

But it takes a great deal of kinetic energy to give a measurable increase in
mass. The proportionality constant is very small. In fact, Einstein showed
that the constant would be $1/c^2$, where c is the speed of light in a
vacuum:

$$\Delta m = \frac{KE}{c^2}$$

Thus the total mass m of a body is its rest mass, m_0, plus KE/c^2:

$$m = m_0 + \frac{KE}{c^2}$$

Einstein proposed that the "mass equivalent" of kinetic energy is only
a special case. In general, there should be a precise equivalence between
mass and energy. Thus, the rest mass m_0 should correspond to an
equivalent amount of "rest energy" E_0 such that $m_0 = E_0/c^2$. That is,

$$m = \frac{E_0}{c^2} + \frac{KE}{c^2}$$

If we use the symbol E for the *total* energy of a body, $E = E_0 + KE$, we
can write

$$m = \frac{E}{c^2}$$

This is just what Einstein concluded in 1905: "The mass of a body is a measure of its energy content." We can write this in a more familiar form, as what is probably the most famous equation in physics:

Do not confuse *E* with symbol for electric field.

$$E = mc^2$$

The last four equations all represent the same idea—that mass and energy are different expressions for the *same* characteristic of a system. You should not think of mass as being "converted" to energy, or energy to mass. Rather, a body with a measured mass *m has* an energy *E* equal to mc^2. And a body of total energy *E has* a mass equal to E/c^2.

SG 20.5, 20.6

   This equivalence has exciting significance. First, two great conservation laws become alternate statements of a single law: In any system whose total mass is conserved, the total energy is conserved also. Second, the idea arises that some of the rest energy might be transformed into a more familiar form of energy. Since the energy equivalent of mass is so great, a very small reduction in rest mass would release a tremendous amount of energy—for example, kinetic energy or electromagnetic radiation.

   In the Supplemental Unit *The Nucleus,* we will see how such changes come about experimentally. And we will discuss additional experimental evidence that supports this relationship.

   Q1   What happens to the measurable mass of a particle as its kinetic energy is increased?

   Q2   What happens to the speed of a particle as its kinetic energy is increased?

20.2 Particle-like behavior of radiation

   We can now use one of these mass-energy relations to further study light quanta and their interaction with atoms. Study of the photoelectric effect taught us that a light quantum has energy *hf,* where *h* is Planck's constant and *f* is the frequency of the light. This concept also applies to x rays which, like visible light, are electromagnetic radiation, but of higher frequency than visible light. The photoelectric effect, however, did not tell us anything about the *momentum* of a quantum. If a light quantum has energy, does it also have momentum?

   The magnitude of the momentum $\vec{p}$ of a body is defined as the product of its mass m_0 and speed *v:* $p = mv$. If we replace *m* with its energy equivalent E/c^2 we can write

SG 20.7

$$p = \frac{Ev}{c^2}$$

Note that this equation is an expression for momentum, but that it contains no direct reference to mass. Now suppose we apply this same equation to the momentum of a photon of energy *E*. Since a photon moves at the speed of light, v would be replaced by the speed of light c and we would get

$$p = \frac{Ec}{c^2} = \frac{E}{c}$$

Now, $E = hf$ for a light quantum. If we substitute this expression for E in $p = E/c$, we get the momentum of a light quantum:

$$p = \frac{hf}{c}$$

Or, using the wave relation that the speed equals the frequency times the wavelength, $c = f\lambda$, we can express the momentum as

$$p = \frac{h}{\lambda}$$

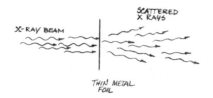

X-RAY BEAM

SCATTERED X RAYS

THIN METAL FOIL

SG 20.8

Arthur H. Compton (1892-1962) was born in Wooster, Ohio and graduated from the College of Wooster. After receiving his doctor's degree in physics from Princeton University in 1916, he taught physics and then worked in industry. In 1919-1920 he did research under Rutherford at the Cavendish Laboratory of the University of Cambridge. In 1923, while studying the scattering of x rays, he discovered and interpreted the changes in the wavelengths of x rays when the rays are scattered. He received the Nobel Prize in 1927 for this work.

Does it make sense to define the momentum of a photon in this way? It does, if the definition helps in understanding experimental results. The first successful use of this definition was in the analysis of an effect discovered by Arthur H. Compton. Let us take a look at Compton's work.

Consider a beam of light (or x rays) striking the atoms in a target (such as a thin sheet of metal). According to classical electromagnetic theory, the light will be scattered in various directions, but its frequency will not change. The absorption of light of a certain frequency by an atom may be followed by re-emission of light of a different frequency. But if the light wave is simply *scattered,* then according to classical theory the frequency should not change.

According to quantum theory, however, light is made up of photons. And, according to relativity theory, photons have momentum. Therefore, Compton reasoned, in a collision between a photon and an atom the law of conservation of momentum should apply. According to this law (see Chapter 9), when a body of small mass collides with a massive object at rest, it simply bounces back or glances off. It experiences very little loss in speed, and so very little change in energy. But if the masses of the two colliding objects are not very different, a significant amount of energy can be transferred in the collision. Compton calculated how much energy a photon should lose in a collision with an atom, if the photon's momentum is hf/c. He concluded that the change in energy is too small to observe if a photon simply bounces off an entire atom. But if a photon strikes an *electron,* which has a small mass, the photon should transfer a significant amount of energy to the electron.

Experiments up to 1923 revealed no difference between the frequencies of the incident and scattered light (or x rays) when electromagnetic radiation was scattered by matter. But in 1923 Compton showed that when a beam of x rays is scattered, the scattered beam consists of two parts. One part has the same frequency as the incident x rays; the other part has *slightly lower* frequency. The reduction in frequency of some of the scattered x rays is called the Compton effect.

The scattered x rays of unchanged frequency have been scattered by whole atoms. But the existence of x rays with changed frequency indicates a transfer of energy from some photons to electrons. Further, this transfer agrees with the laws of conservation of momentum and energy. The observed change in frequency is just what would be predicted if the photons were particle-like projectiles having momentum $p = hf/c$.

The electrons that were struck by photons could also be detected, because they were knocked out of the target. Compton found that the momentum of these electrons was related to their direction just as if they had been struck by particles with momentum equal to hf/c.

Compton's experiment showed that a photon can be regarded as a particle with a definite momentum as well as energy. It also showed that collisions between photons and electrons obey the laws of conservation of momentum and energy.

As we noted in Section 18.5 in discussing the photoelectric effect, light has particle-like properties. The Compton effect gave additional evidence for this fact. To be sure, photons are not like ordinary particles—if only because photons do not exist at speeds other than that of light. (There can be no resting photons, and therefore no rest mass for photons.) But in other ways, as in their scattering behavior, photons act much like particles of matter. For example, they have momentum as well as energy. And yet, they also act like waves, having frequency and wavelength. In other words, electromagnetic radiation in some experiments exhibits behavior similar to what we think of as particle behavior. In other experiments, its behavior is similar to what we think of as wave behavior. This pattern of behavior is often referred to as the *wave-particle dualism of radiation*. Is a photon a wave or a particle? We can only answer: it can *act* like either, depending on what we are doing with it. (This fascinating topic is explored in several of the *Reader 5* articles.)

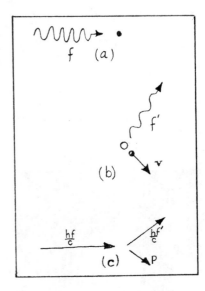

SG 20.9

SG 20.10

Q3 How does the momentum of a photon depend on the frequency of the light?

Q4 What is the Compton effect, and what did it prove?

20.3 Wave-like behavior of particles

In 1923, the French physicist Louis de Broglie suggested that the wave-particle dualism which applies to radiation might also apply to electrons and other atomic particles. Perhaps, he said, the wave-particle dualism is a fundamental property of all quantum processes. If so, particles that we have always thought of as material particles can, in some circumstances, act like waves. De Broglie sought an expression for the wavelength that might be associated with wave-like behavior of an electron. He found such an expression by means of a simple argument.

The momentum of a photon of wavelength λ is $p = h/\lambda$. De Broglie thought that this relation might also apply to electrons with the momentum $p = mv$. He therefore boldly suggested that the wavelength of an electron is

$$\lambda = \frac{h}{mv}$$

The "de Broglie wavelength" of a material particle does not refer to anything having to do with light, but to some new wave property associated with the motion of matter itself.

where m is the electron's mass and v its speed.

What does it mean to say that an electron has a wavelength equal to Planck's constant divided by its momentum? If this statement is to have any physical meaning, it must be possible to test it by some kind of experiment. Some wave property of the electron must be measured. The first such property to be measured was *diffraction*.

The relationship $\lambda = h/mv$ indicates that the wavelengths associated with electrons will be very short, even for fairly slow electrons. An electron accelerated across a potential difference of only 100V would have a wavelength of only 10^{-10} meter. So small a wavelength would not give measurable diffraction effects on encountering even a microscopically small object (say, 10^{-5} meter).

By 1920 it was known that crystals have a regular lattice structure. The distance between rows of planes of atoms in a crystal is about 10^{-10} m. After de Broglie proposed that electrons have wave properties, several physicists suggested that the existence of electron waves might be shown by using crystals as diffraction gratings. Experiments begun in 1923 by C. J. Davisson and L. H. Germer in the United States, yielded diffraction patterns similar to those obtained for x rays (see Section 18.6). Their method is illustrated in the drawing at the top of page 103. The experiment showed two things. First, electrons *do* have wave properties. One may say that an electron moves along the path taken by the de Broglie wave that is associated with the electron. Second, electron wavelengths are correctly given by de Broglie's relation, $\lambda = h/mv$. These results were confirmed in 1927 when G. P. Thomson directed an electron beam through thin gold foil. Thomson found a pattern like the one in the margin. It resembles diffraction patterns produced by light beams going through thin slices of materials. By 1930, diffraction from crystals had

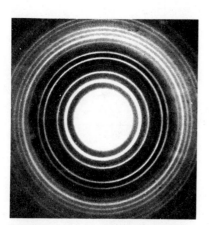

Diffraction pattern produced by directing a beam of electrons through polycrystalline aluminum. With a similar pattern, G. P. Thomson demonstrated the *wave* properties of electrons—28 years after their *particle* properties were first demonstrated by J. J. Thomson, his father.

The de Broglie wavelength: examples.

A body of mass 1 kg moves with a speed of 1 m/sec. What is its de Broglie wavelength?

$$\lambda = \frac{h}{mv}$$

$$h = 6.6 \times 10^{-34} \text{ joule} \cdot \text{sec}$$

$$mv = 1 \text{ kg} \cdot \text{m/sec}$$

$$\lambda = \frac{6.6 \times 10^{-34} \text{ joule} \cdot \text{sec}}{1 \text{ kg} \cdot \text{m/sec}}$$

so

$$\lambda = 6.6 \times 10^{-34} \text{ m}$$

The de Broglie wavelength is many orders of magnitude smaller than an atom. Thus, it is much too small to be detected. There are, for example, no slits or obstacles small enough to show diffraction effects. We would expect to detect no wave aspects in the motion of this body.

An electron of mass 9.1×10^{-31} kg moves with a speed of 2×10^6 m/sec. What is its de Broglie wavelength?

$$\lambda = \frac{h}{mv}$$

$$h = 6.6 \times 10^{-34} \text{ joule} \cdot \text{sec}$$

$$mv = 1.82 \times 10^{-24} \text{ kg} \cdot \text{m/sec}$$

$$\lambda = \frac{6.6 \times 10^{-34} \text{ joule} \cdot \text{sec}}{1.82 \times 10^{-24} \text{ kg} \cdot \text{m/sec}}$$

so

$$\lambda = 3.6 \times 10^{-10} \text{ m}$$

The de Broglie wavelength is of atomic dimensions. For example, it is of the same order of magnitude as the distances between atoms in a crystal. So we expect to see wave aspects in the interaction of electrons with crystals.

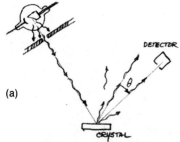

(a)

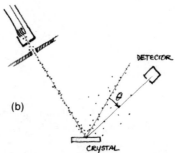

(b)

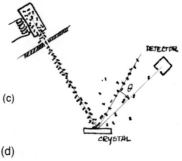

(c)

a. One way to demonstrate the wave behavior of x rays is to direct a beam at the surface of a crystal. The reflections from different planes of atoms in the crystal interfere to produce reflected beams at angles other than the ordinary angle of reflection.

b. A very similar effect can be demonstrated for a beam of electrons. The electrons must be accelerated to an energy that corresponds to a de Broglie wavelength of about 10^{-10}m. This would require an accelerating voltage of only about 100 volts.

c. Like any other beam of particles, a beam of molecules directed at a crystal will show a diffraction pattern. Diagram (c) shows how a beam of hydrogen molecules (H_2) can be formed by slits at the opening of a heated chamber. The average energy of the molecules is controlled by adjusting the temperature of the oven.

d. The graph, reproduced from *Zeitschrift für Physik*, 1930, shows results obtained by I. Estermann and O. Stern in Germany. The detector reading is plotted against the deviation to either side of the angle of ordinary reflection. A low but distinct peak owing to diffraction is seen to each side of the ordinary reflection beams.

(d)

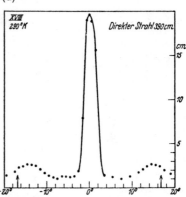

Diffraction pattern for H_2 molecules glancing off a crystal of lithium fluoride.

SG 20.11
SG 20.12
SG 20.13

been used to demonstrate the wave-like behavior of helium *atoms* and hydrogen *molecules*. (See the drawings above.)

According to de Broglie's hypothesis, wave-particle dualism is a general property not only of radiation but also of matter. This has been confirmed by all experiments. Scientists now customarily refer to electrons and photons as "particles" while recognizing that both have properties of waves as well. (Of course, there are also important differences between them.)

You will recall Bohr's postulate that the quantity mvr (called the angular momentum) of the electron in the hydrogen atom can have only certain values. De Broglie's relation, $\lambda = h/mv$, has an interesting yet simple application which supports this postulate. Bohr assumed that mvr can have only the values:

$$mvr = n\frac{h}{2\pi} \qquad \text{where } n = 1, 2, 3, \ldots$$

Now, suppose that an electron wave is somehow spread over an orbit of radius r so that, in some sense, it "occupies" the orbit. We may ask if *standing waves* can be set up as indicated, for example, in the sketch in the margin. If so, the circumference of the orbit must be equal in length to a whole number of wavelengths—that is, to $n\lambda$. The mathematical expression for this condition of "fit" is:

$$2\pi r = n\lambda$$

If we now replace λ by h/mv according to de Broglie's relation, we get

Only certain wavelengths will "fit" around a circle.

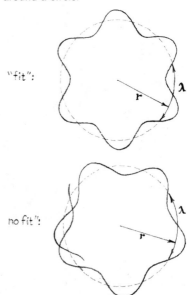

"fit":

no "fit":

$$2\pi r = n\,\frac{h}{mv}$$

or

$$mvr = n\,\frac{h}{2\pi}$$

But, this is just Bohr's quantization condition! The de Broglie relation for electron waves—and the idea that electrons have orbits that allow standing waves—allows us to *derive* the quantization that Bohr had to *assume*.

The result obtained indicates that we may picture the electron in the hydrogen atom in two ways. We may think of it as a particle moving in an orbit with a certain quantized value of *mvr*. Or we may picture it as a standing de Broglie-type wave occupying a certain region around the nucleus.

SG 20.14

Either way is incomplete by itself.

Q5   Where did de Broglie get the relation $\lambda = h/mv$ for electrons?

Q6   Why were crystals used to get diffraction patterns of electrons?

20.4 Mathematical vs. visualizable atoms

It was now clear that "things" (electrons, atoms, molecules), long regarded as particles, also show properties of waves. This fact is the basis for the presently accepted theory of atomic structure. This theory, *quantum mechanics*, was introduced in 1925. Its foundations were developed very rapidly during the next few years, primarily by Heisenberg, Born, Schrödinger, Bohr, and Dirac. At first, the theory appeared in two different mathematical forms, proposed independently by Heisenberg and Schrödinger. A few months later, these two forms were shown by Schrödinger to be equivalent, different ways of expressing the same relationships. Schrödinger's form of the theory is closer to the ideas of de Broglie (discussed in the last section). It is often referred to as *wave mechanics*.

Schrödinger sought to express the dual wave-particle nature of matter mathematically. Maxwell had formulated the electromagnetic theory of light in terms of a wave equation. Physicists were familiar with this theory and its applications. Schrödinger reasoned that the de Broglie waves associated with electrons would resemble the classical waves of light. Thus, there should be a wave equation that holds for matter waves, just as there is a wave equation for electromagnetic waves. We cannot discuss this mathematical part of wave mechanics even adequately without using advanced mathematics. But the physical ideas involved require only a little mathematics and are essential to understanding modern physics. So, in the rest of this chapter, we will discuss some of the physical ideas of the theory. We will try to make them seem reasonable, and we will consider some of the results of the theory and some of the significance of these results. But, again, our aim is not (and cannot honestly be in the available time and space) a full presentation. We want only to prepare for the use of specific results, and for readings in *Reader 5* and *Reader 6*.

Schrödinger successfully derived an equation for the "matter waves" that are associated with moving electrons. This equation, which has been named after him, defines the wave properties of electrons and also predicts particle-like behavior. The Schrödinger equation for an electron bound in an atom has a solution only when a constant in the equation has the whole-number values 1, 2, 3. . . . It turns out that these numbers correspond to different energies. Thus, the Schrödinger equation predicts that only certain electron energies are possible in an atom. In the hydrogen atom, for example, the single electron can be in *only* those states for which the energy of the electron has the numerical values:

$$E_n = \frac{k^2 2\pi^2 m q_e^2}{n^2 h^2}$$

with n having only whole number values. But these are just the energy values that are found experimentally—and just the ones given by the Bohr theory! In Schrödinger's theory, this result follows directly from the mathematical formulation of the wave and particle nature of the electron. The existence of these stationary states is not assumed, and no assumptions are made about orbits. The new theory yields all the results of the Bohr theory, with none of the Bohr theory's inconsistent hypotheses. The new theory also accounts for the experimental information for which the Bohr theory failed to account. For instance, it deals with the probability of an electron changing from one energy state to another.

On the other hand, quantum mechanics does not supply a physical model or visualizable "picture" of the atom. The planetary model of the atom has been given up, but has not been replaced by another simple picture. There is now a highly successful *mathematical* model, but no easily visualized *physical* model. The concepts used to build quantum mechanics are more abstract than those of the Bohr theory. Thus, it is hard to get a "feeling" for atomic structure without training in the field. But the mathematical theory of quantum mechanics is much more powerful than the Bohr theory in predicting and explaining phenomena. Many problems that were previously unsolvable have been solved with quantum mechanics. Physicists have learned that the world of atoms, electrons, and photons cannot be thought of in the same mechanical terms as the world of everyday experience. Instead, the study of atoms presents us with some fascinating new concepts, which will be discussed in the next two sections. What has been lost in easy visualizability is made up for by an increase in fundamental understanding.

Topics in quantum physics are developed further in *Reader 5*. See the articles:
"Ideas and Theories"
"The New Landscape of Science"
"The Evolution of the Physicist's Picture of Nature"
"Dirac and Born"
"I am the Whole World: Erwin Schrödinger"
"The Fundamental Idea of Wave Mechanics"
"The Sea-Captains' Box"

Visualizability is an unnecessary luxury when it clouds our understanding. For the same reason we learned to do without visualizability in many other fields. For example, we no longer think of the action of an ether to explain light propagation.

Q7 The set of energy states of hydrogen could be derived from Bohr's postulate that $mvr = nh/2\pi$. In what respect was the derivation from Schrödinger's equation better?

Q8 Quantum (or wave) mechanics has had great success. What is its drawback for those trained on physical models?

P. A. M. Dirac (1902-), an English physicist, was one of the developers of modern quantum mechanics. In 1932, at the age of 30, Dirac was appointed Lucasian Professor of Mathematics at Cambridge University, the post held by Newton.

Max Born (1882-1969) was born in Germany, but left that country for England in 1933 when Hitler and the Nazis gained control. Born was largely responsible for introducing the statistical interpretation of wave mechanics.

Prince Louis Victor de Broglie (1892–), whose ancestors served the French kings as far back as the time of Louis XIV, was educated at the Sorbonne in Paris. He proposed the idea of wave properties of electrons in his PhD thesis.

Erwin Schrödinger (1887-1961) was born in Austria. He developed wave mechanics in 1926, fled from Germany in 1933 when Hitler and the Nazis came to power. From 1940 to 1956, when he retired, he was professor of physics at the Dublin Institute for Advanced Studies.

Werner Heisenberg (1901–), a German physicist, was one of the developers of modern quantum mechanics (at the age of 23). He was the first to state the uncertainty principle. After the discovery of the neutron in 1932, he proposed the proton-neutron theory of nuclear structure.

20.5 The uncertainty principle

Up to this point we have always talked as if we could measure any physical property as accurately as we pleased. To reach any desired degree of accuracy we would have only to design a sufficiently precise instrument. Wave mechanics showed, however, that even in thought experiments with ideal instruments there are limits to the accuracy which can be achieved.

Think how we would go about measuring the positions and velocity of a car moving slowly along a driveway. We could mark the position of the front end of the car at a given instant by making a scratch on the ground. At the same time, we could start a stop-watch. Then we could run to the end of the driveway, where we have previously placed another mark. At the instant when the front of the car reaches this point, we stop the watch. We then measure the distance between the marks, and get the average speed of the car by dividing the distance traveled by the time elapsed. Since we know the direction of the car's motion, we know the average velocity. Thus we know that at the moment the car reached the second mark it was at a certain distance from its starting point and had traveled at a certain average velocity. By going to smaller and smaller intervals we could also get the instantaneous velocity at any point along its path.

How did we get the needed information? We located the car by sunlight bounced off the front end into our eyes. The light permitted us to see when the car reached a mark on the ground. To get the average speed we had to locate the front end twice.

$$\lambda = \frac{c}{f} = \frac{3 \times 10^8 \text{m/sec}}{10^6/\text{sec}} = 300 \text{ m}$$

But suppose that we had decided to use reflected radio waves instead of light of visible wavelength. At 1,000 kilocycles per second, a typical value for radio signals, the wavelength is 300 meters. This wavelength is very much greater than the dimensions of the car. Thus, it would be impossible to locate the position of the car with any accuracy. The wave would reflect from the car ("scatter" is a better term) in all directions. It would also sweep around any man-sized device we may wish to use to detect the wave direction. The wavelength has to be comparable with or smaller than the dimensions of the object before the object can be located well. *Radar* uses wavelengths from about 0.1 cm to about 3 cm, so a radar apparatus could be used instead of sunlight. But even radar would leave uncertainties as large as several centimeters in the two measurements of position. The wavelength of visible light is less than 10^{-6} m. For visible light, then, we could design instruments that would locate the position of the car to an accuracy of a few thousandths of a millimeter.

Let us now turn from car and driveway, and think of an electron moving across an evacuated tube. We will try to measure the position and speed of the electron. But we must change our method of measurement. The electron is so small that we cannot locate its position by using visible light. (The wavelength of visible light, small as it is, is still at least 10^4 times greater than the diameter of an atom.)

We are attempting to locate an electron within a region the size of an

The extreme smallness of the atomic scale is indicated by these pictures made with techniques that are near the very limits of magnification—about 10,000,000 times in these reproductions.

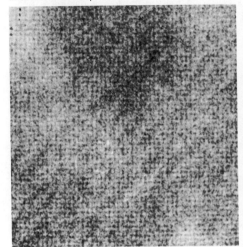

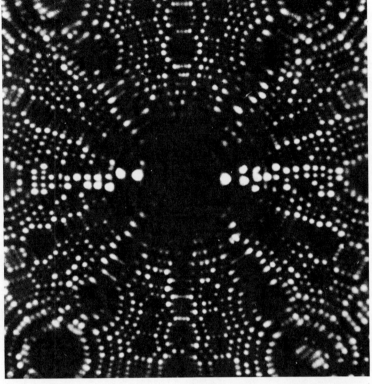

Pattern produced by electron beam scattered from a section of a single gold crystal. The entire section of crystal shown is only 100Å across. This is smaller than the shortest wavelength of ultraviolet light that could be used in a light microscope. The finest detail that can be resolved with this "electron microscope" is just under 2Å. So the layers of gold atoms (spaced slightly more than 2Å) show as a checked pattern; individual atoms are beyond the resolving power.

Pattern produced by charged particles repelled from the tip of a microscopically thin tungsten crystal. The entire section shown is only about 100Å across. The finest detail that can be revealed by this "field-ion microscope" is about 1Å. The bright spots indicate the *locations* of atoms along edges of the crystal, but should not be thought of as pictures of the atoms.

SG 20.15

atom (about 10^{-10} m across). So we need a light beam whose wavelength is about 10^{-10} m or smaller. But a photon of such a short wavelength λ (and high frequency f) has very great momentum (h/λ) and energy (hf). From our study of the Compton effect, we know that such a photon will give the electron a strong kick when it is scattered by the electron. As a result, the velocity of the electron will be greatly changed, into a new and unknown direction. (This is a new problem, one we did not even think about when measuring the position of the car!) Hence, when we receive the scattered photon we can deduce from its direction where the electron *once was;* in this sense we can "locate" the electron. But in the process we have changed the velocity of the electron (in both magnitude and direction). To say this more directly: the more accurately we locate the electron (by using photons of shorter wavelength), the less accurately we can know its velocity. We could try to disturb the electron less by using less energetic photons. But because light exists in quanta of energy *hf,* a *lower*-energy photon will have a *longer* wavelength. And this would create greater uncertainty about the electron's *position!*

To summarize: *we are unable to measure both the position and velocity of an electron to unlimited accuracy.* This conclusion is expressed in the *uncertainty principle,* first stated by Werner Heisenberg. The uncertainty principle can be expressed quantitatively in a simple formula, derived from Schrödinger's wave equation for the motion of particles. Let Δx represent the uncertainty in position, and Δp the uncertainty in momentum. The product of these two uncertainties must be equal to, or greater than, Planck's constant divided by 2π:

$$\Delta x \, \Delta p \geq \frac{h}{2\pi}$$

SG 20.16–20.18

The same reasoning (and equation) holds for the experiment on the car. But the limitation has no practical consequence with such a massive object. (See the worked-out example below.) It is only on the atomic scale that the limitation becomes evident and important.

Q9 If photons used in finding the velocity of an electron disturb the electron too much, why cannot the observation be improved by using less energetic photons?

Q10 If the wavelength of light used to locate a particle is too long, why cannot the location be found more precisely by using light of shorter wavelength?

The Uncertainty Principle: Examples

Applied to a large mass.

Consider a car, with a mass of 1000 kg, moving with a speed of about 1 m/sec. Suppose that in this experiment the inherent uncertainty Δv in the measured speed is 0.1 m/sec (10% of the speed). What is the minimum uncertainty in the position of the car?

$$\Delta x \, \Delta p \geq \frac{h}{2\pi}$$

$$\Delta p = m \, \Delta v = 100 \text{ kg·m/sec}$$

$$h = 6.63 \times 10^{-34} \text{ joule·sec}$$

$$\Delta x \geq \frac{6.63}{6.28} \times \frac{10^{-34} \text{ joule·sec}}{10^2 \text{ kg·m/sec}}$$

$$\Delta x \geq 1 \times 10^{-36} \text{ m.}$$

This uncertainty in position—many orders smaller than the size of atoms—is much too small to be observable. In this case we can determine the position of the body with as high an accuracy as we would ever need.

Applied to a small mass.

Consider an electron, with a mass of 9.1×10^{-31} kg, moving with a speed of about 2×10^6 m/sec. Suppose that the uncertainty Δv in the speed is 0.2×10^6 m/sec (10% of the speed). What is the minimum uncertainty in the position of the electron?

$$\Delta x \, \Delta p \geq \frac{h}{2\pi}$$

$$\Delta p = m \, \Delta v = 1.82 \times 10^{-25} \text{ kg·m/sec}$$

$$h = 6.63 \times 10^{-34} \text{ joule/sec}$$

$$\Delta x \geq \frac{6.63}{6.28} \times \frac{10^{-34} \text{ joule/sec}}{1.82 \times 10^{-25} \text{ kg·m/sec}}$$

$$\Delta x \geq 5 \times 10^{-10} \text{ m.}$$

The uncertainty in position is of the order of atomic dimensions, and is significant in atomic problems. It is impossible to specify exactly where an electron is in an atom.

The reason for the difference between these two results is that Planck's constant h is very small—so small that the uncertainty principle becomes important only on the atomic scale. For ordinary-sized objects, the equations give the same result as if h had the value zero.

The chief use made of the uncertainty principle is in general arguments in atomic theory rather than in particular numerical problems. We do not really need to know exactly where an electron is. But we sometimes want to know if it *could* be in some *region* of space.

20.6 Probability interpretation

To explore dualism further we need to review some ideas of probability. In some situations no single event can be predicted with certainty. But it may still be possible to predict the *statistical probabilities* of certain events. On a holiday weekend during which perhaps 25 million cars are on the road, statisticians predict that about 600 people will be killed in accidents. It is not known which cars in which of the 50 states will be involved in the accidents. But, on the basis of past experience, the *average* behavior is still quite accurately predictable.

It is in this way that physicists think about the behavior of photons and material particles. As we have seen, there are basic limitations on our ability to describe the behavior of an individual particle. But the laws of physics often enable us to describe the behavior of large collections of particles with good accuracy. Schrödinger's equations for the behavior of waves associated with particles give us the *probabilities* for finding the particles at a given place at a given time.

To see how probability works, consider the situation of a star being photographed through a telescope. As you have already seen (for example on the page on Diffraction and Detail in Chapter 13), the image of a point source is not a precise point. Rather, it is *diffraction pattern*—a central spot with a series of progressively fainter circular rings.

The image of a star on the photographic film in the telescope would be a similar pattern. Imagine now that we wished to photograph a very faint star. If the energy in light rays were not quantized, it would spread continuously over ever-expanding wave fronts. Thus, we would expect the image of a very faint star to be exactly the same as that of a much brighter star—except that the intensity of light would be less over the whole pattern. However, the energy of light *is* quantized: it exists in separate quanta, "photons," of definite energy. A photon striking a photographic emulsion produces a chemical change in the film at a single location—not all over the image area. If the star is very remote, only a few photons per second may arrive at the film. The effect on the film after a very short period of exposure would be something like the diffraction pattern in drawing A in the margin. As the exposure continued, the effect on the film would begin to look like B. Each successive photon falls on the photographic plate as if its location were decided by some roulette wheel—a wheel fixed to yield eventually not a completely random pattern but one with the radial symmetry shown in C. Finally, a pattern like C would be produced, just like the image produced by a much brighter star with a much shorter exposure.

For tremendous numbers of quanta, the overall distribution is very well described by the distribution of wave intensity. For small numbers of quanta, the wave intensity is not very useful for predicting where they will go. We expect them to go mostly to the "high-intensity" parts of the image, but we cannot predict exactly where. These facts fit together beautifully if we consider the wave intensity at a location to indicate the *probability* of a photon going there!

A similar connection can be made for de Broglie waves and particles of matter. For this purpose, rather than considering a diffraction pattern

These sketches represent successive stages of a greatly enlarged image of a distant star on a photographic plate.

A

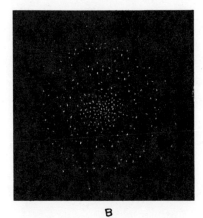

B

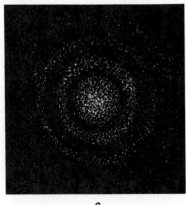

C

formed by an electron beam, let us consider a bound electron wave. Such a wave is confined to a region of space by the electric attraction of a positive nucleus and a negative electron. For example, the de Broglie wave associated with an electron is spread out all over an atom. But we need not think of the *electron* itself as spread out. It is still quite useful to think of the electron as a particle moving around the nucleus. In that case, the wave amplitude at some location represents the *probability* of the electron being there.

According to modern quantum theory, the hydrogen atom does not consist of a localized negative particle moving around a nucleus as in the Bohr model. Indeed, the theory does not provide any picture of the hydrogen atom. A description of the probability distribution is the closest thing to a picture that the theory provides. The probability distribution for the lowest energy state of the hydrogen atom is represented in the drawing at the left below. The probability distribution for a higher energy state, still for a single electron, is represented in the drawing at the right. In each case, whiter shading at a point indicates greater probability.

However, quantum theory is not really concerned with the position of any individual electron in any individual atom. Instead, the theory gives a mathematical representation that can be used to predict interaction with particles, fields, and radiation. For example, it can be used to calculate the probability that hydrogen will emit light of a particular wavelength. The intensity and wavelength of light emitted by a large number of hydrogen atoms can then be compared with these calculations. Comparisons such as these have shown that the theory agrees with experiment.

To understand atomic physics, we deal with the average behavior of many atomic particles. The laws governing this average behavior turn out to be those of wave mechanics. The waves, it seems, are waves whose amplitudes are a measure of probability. The information (concerning the probability with which a particle will reach some position at a given time) travels through space in waves. These waves can interfere with each other in exactly the same way that water waves do. Now, for example, think of a beam of electrons passing through two slits. We can consider the

As we have discussed in connection with kinetic theory and disorder, it is easy to predict the average behavior of very large numbers of particles, even though nothing is known about the behavior of any single one of them.

electrons to be waves and compute their interference patterns. These patterns determine the directions in which there are high wave amplitudes (high probability of electrons going there). If there are no more slits or other interactions of the waves with matter, we can continue our description in terms of particles. We can say that the electrons are likely to (and on the average will) end up going in such and such directions with such and such speeds.

The success of wave mechanics emphasized the importance of the dual wave-particle nature of radiation and matter. But how can a particle be thought of as "really" having wave properties? The answer is that matter, particularly on the atomic scale, need *not* be thought of as being either "really" particles or "really" waves. Our ideas of waves and particles, taken from the world of visible things, just do not apply on the atomic scale.

In describing something that no one has ever seen or ever can see directly, it would be surprising if we could use the concepts of the visible world unchanged. It appeared natural before 1925 to talk about the transfer of energy in either wave terms or particle terms. Indeed, such terms were all physicists needed or knew at the time. Almost no one suspected that *both* wave and particle descriptions could apply to light and to matter. And even today our imagination and language has only these two ideas—waves and particles—to stumble along on. Until new concepts appear, dualism cannot be wished away, but will remain the best way to handle experimental results.

Max Born, one of the founders of quantum mechanics, has written:

> The ultimate origin of the difficulty lies in the fact (or philosophical principle) that we are compelled to use the words of common language when we wish to describe a phenomenon, not by logical or mathematical analysis, but by a picture appealing to the imagination. Common language has grown by everyday experience and can never surpass these limits. Classical physics has restricted itself to the use of concepts of this kind; by analyzing visible motions it has developed two ways of representing them by elementary processes: moving particles and waves. There is no other way of giving a pictorial description of motions—we have to apply it even in the region of atomic processes, where classical physics breaks down.

See "Dirac and Born" in *Reader 5.*

The idea that the wave represents the probability of finding its associated particle in some specific condition of motion has had great success. Yet many scientists found it hard to accept the idea that we cannot know exactly what any one particle is doing. The most prominent of such disbelievers was Einstein. In a letter to Born written in 1926, he remarked:

SG 20.23

The quantum mechanics is very imposing. But an inner voice tells me that it is still not the final truth. The theory yields much, but it hardly brings us nearer to the secret of the Old One. In any case, I am convinced that He does not play dice.

Thus, Einstein agreed with the usefulness and success of wave mechanics. But he refused to accept probability-based laws as the final level of explanation in physics. The remark about not believing that God played dice—an expression he used many times later—expressed his faith that more basic, deterministic laws are yet to be found. Like Einstein, some other scientists refused to accept the probability laws in quantum mechanics. But no one has yet succeeded in replacing Born's probability interpretation of quantum mechanics.

Scientists agree that quantum mechanics works. It gives the right answers to many questions in physics. It unifies ideas and occurrences that were once unconnected. And it has produced many new experiments and new concepts. On the other hand, there is still vigorous argument about its basic significance. It yields probability functions, not precise trajectories. Some scientists see in this aspect of the theory an important indication of the nature of the world. For other scientists, the same fact indicates that quantum theory is incomplete. Some in this second group are trying to develop a more basic, non-statistical theory. For such a theory, the present quantum theory is only a special, extreme case. As in other fields of physics, the greatest discoveries here may be those yet to be made.

"Deterministic" means here that if all the conditions of an isolated system are known and the laws describing interaction are known, then it is possible to predict precisely—according to "strict causality"—what happens next, without any need for probability ideas.

SG 20.19–20.23

Q11 In wave terms, the bright lines of a diffraction pattern are regions where there is a high field intensity produced by constructive interference. What is the probability interpretation of quantum mechanics for the bright lines of a diffraction pattern?

Q12 Quantum mechanics can predict only probabilities for the behavior of any one particle. How, then, can it predict many phenomena—for example, half-lives and diffraction patterns—with great certainty?

"Sea and Sky", by M. C. Escher

EPILOGUE In this unit we have traced the concept of the atom from the early ideas of the Greeks to the quantum mechanics now generally accepted by physicists. The search for the atom started with the qualitative assumptions of Leucippus and Democritus who thought that their atoms offered a rational explanation of the behavior of matter. However, for many centuries most natural philosophers thought that other explanations, not involving atoms, were more reasonable. Atomism was pushed aside and received only occasional consideration until the seventeenth century.

With the growth of the mechanical philosophy of nature in the seventeenth and eighteenth centuries, particles (corpuscles) became important. Atomism was reexamined, mostly in connection with physical properties of matter. Galileo, Boyle, Newton and others speculated on the role of particles for explaining the expansion and contraction of gases. Chemists speculated about atoms in connection with chemical change. Finally, Dalton began the modern development of atomic theory, introducing a quantitative conception that had been lacking—the relative atomic mass.

Chemists, in the nineteenth century, found that they could correlate the results of many chemical experiments in terms of atoms and molecules. They also found that there are relations between the properties of different chemical elements. Quantitative information about atomic masses provided a framework for the system organizing these relations—the periodic table of Mendeleev. During the nineteenth century, physicists developed the kinetic theory of gases. This theory—based on the assumption of very small corpuscles, or particles, or molecules, or whatever else they might be called—helped strengthen the position of the atomists. Other work of nineteenth-century physicists helped pave the way to the study of the structure of atoms—through the study of the spectra of the elements and of the conduction of electricity in gases, the discovery of cathode rays, electrons, and x rays.

Nineteenth-century chemistry and physics converged, at the beginning of the twentieth century, on the problem of atomic structure. It became clear that the uncuttable, infinitely hard atom was too simple a model: that the atom itself is made up of smaller particles. And so the search for a model with structure began. Of the early models, that of Thomson gave way to Rutherford's nuclear atom, with its small, heavy, positively charged nucleus, surrounded somehow by negative charges. Then came the atom of Bohr, with its electrons thought to be moving in orbits like planets in a miniature solar system. The Bohr theory had many successes and linked chemistry and spectra to the physics of atomic structure. But beyond that, it could not advance substantially without giving up an easily grasped picture of the atom. The tool needed is the mathematical model, not pictures. Quantum mechanics enables us to calculate how atoms behave; it helps us understand the physical and chemical properties of the elements. But at the most basic level, nature still has secrets. The next stage in the story of physics is the nucleus at the center of the atom. Is the nucleus made up of smaller components? Does it have laws of physics all its own?

The study of the nucleus has been one of the most exciting branches of physics in the twentieth century. Progress in nuclear physics has advanced not only basic science but also technology, which both supplies tools for research and applies some of the results of research in practical ways. These applications—including the production of electricity from nuclear energy, the many clinical and industrial uses of radiations, and of course the military weapons, have had economic, social and political consequences. The use and control of nuclear technology, therefore, are often front-page news, and citizens find it necessary to inform themselves about these problems in order to participate effectively in decisions that affect their lives.

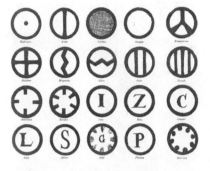

Limitations on the length of this book make it impossible to present here a detailed account of the development of nuclear physics. Such an account is available in a separately published Supplemental Unit of the Project Physics Course materials, entitled *The Nucleus.* But we can at least offer here a preview of some concepts and a very brief outline of the development of nuclear physics.

The first step toward our modern understanding of the atomic nucleus was the discovery of radioactivity by Henri Becquerel in 1896. He found the element uranium to emit previously unknown rays which were highly penetrating and could darken a photographic plate. Subsequent research by Pierre and Marie Curie led to the discovery of more radioactive elements—thorium, polonium and radium. Rutherford and others showed that these radioactive elements emitted three types of "radiation"—α rays (or α particles), which are high-speed ionized helium atoms (nuclei of helium atoms); β rays (or β particles), which are high-speed electrons; and γ rays, which are electromagnetic radiations similar to x rays. The α particles cause intense ionization and have little penetrating power. The particles can travel many meters in air or several centimeters in a solid such as aluminum. Gamma rays are highly penetrating, being able to pass through several centimenters of lead or several feet of concrete.

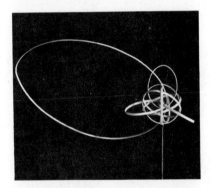

Rutherford and Frederick Soddy explained the nature of radioactive changes by means of their theory of radioactive transformation. They proposed that a radioactive atom which emits an α particle or a β particle, breaks into two parts—the α or β particle that was emitted, and a heavy leftover part which is physically and chemically different from the "parent" atom. This theory made it possible to account for the successive radioactive transformations (or disintegrations) which form a "decay chain" or "series."

Three natural radioactive series were discovered, the uranium, thorium and actinium series. The analysis of these series led Soddy to predict the existence of *isotopes* among the heavy elements. Isotopes are atomic species which have the same atomic number (and so belong chemically to the same element) but differ in atomic mass. Isotopes were indeed found and methods developed for determining their atomic masses. The study of isotopic masses yielded clues to the nature of the forces holding atomic nuclei together.

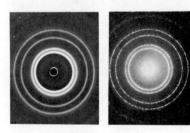

The α particles emitted by radioactive atoms were soon used as projectiles with which to bombard other atoms. The first important result of research of this kind was the discovery by Rutherford that each atom contains a very small nucleus that has practically all the mass of the atom. Another result was the discovery, also by Rutherford, of nuclear reactions—induced transmutations of nuclei. In the first reaction discovered, an alpha particle interacts with a nitrogen nucleus to produce an isotope of oxygen and a hydrogen nucleus (proton). In symbols:

$$N^{14} + He^4 \longrightarrow O^{17} + H^1$$

where the numbers represent the "mass number" of the respective nuclei.

The need for more varied and more energetic projectiles with which to bring about nuclear reactions led to the development of "atom smashers" from the early 1930's on—such as the cyclotron, the Van de Graaff generator, the proton synchrotron and others. The further use and study of nuclear reactions has resulted in the production of many hundreds of previously unknown atomic species, many of which are radioactive. Some of these artificially induced radioactive isotopes are useful in research, in medicine and in technology.

Another important result of the study of nuclear reactions was the discovery in 1932 of the neutron, a neutral particle with a mass close to that of the proton. Atomic nuclei are now thought to be made up of protons and neutrons, and one of the most exciting branches of physics has been the attempt to understand "nuclear forces," the forces between protons and neutrons that hold the atom together.

Still another important result of the study of nuclear reactions was the discovery in late 1938 of *nuclear fission*. Certain heavy nuclei, for example, an isotope of uranium, U^{235}, when bombarded with neutrons, splits into two nuclei of smaller mass with the release of enormous amounts of energy and of more neutrons. This phenomenon has been used to make the "atomic" (more precisely, nuclear) bombs, which put a quick end to World War II, but then confronted the world with different political and military problems. Nuclear fission is also being used for peaceful purposes, for example, for the production of electricity. This application, however, has also set difficult economic, technological and social problems that are far from solved.

Nuclear reactions are of interest to many scientists, including chemists, astrophysicists, and cosmologists. For example, these reactions supply the energy of the stars. In our sun, four hydrogen nuclei (protons) are combined (or fused) into a helium nucleus by means of a series of nuclear reactions. In the process, a large amount of energy is released. Different nuclear reactions provide the energy of other stars, and their study is an important part of astrophysics. The reactions that provide the energy of stars are called "thermonuclear" because they occur at extremely high temperatures—tens of millions of degrees and higher. The release of large amounts of energy by means of fusion reactions on earth have so far been possible only in thermonuclear explosions. Intense research programs are now under way with the purpose of controlling thermonuclear reactions for peaceful applications. For example, the fusion of two isotopes of hydrogen, those with mass two (deuterium) and mass three (tritium) atomic mass units, may eventually be tamed to provide a large, inexpensive, and "clean" source of energy in electric power plants.

We have mentioned only a very few of the fascinating aspects of nuclear physics. (In addition to the Supplemental Unit *The Nucleus,* the Project Physics Course materials also contain two other Supplemental Units, entitled *Elementary Particles* and *Discoveries in Physics,* which has chapters on the discovery of fission and on the discovery of the neutrino.) Research is under way on many other questions which remain to be answered. The search for deeper understanding of the structure and properties of atomic nuclei remains one of the great challenges offered by nature.

Contents   SUPPLEMENTAL UNIT—THE NUCLEUS

20.1 The Project Physics materials particularly appropriate for Chapter 20 include:

Activities
Standing waves on a band-saw blade
Turntable oscillator patterns resembling de Broglie waves
Standing waves in a wire ring

Reader Articles
The Clock Paradox
Ideas and Theories
Mr. Tompkins and Simultaneity
Mathematics and Relativity
Parable of the Surveyors
Outside and Inside the Elevator
Einstein and Some Civilized Discontents
The New Landscape of Science
The Evolution of the Physicist's Picture of Nature
Dirac and Born
I am the Whole World: Erwin Schrödinger
The Fundamental Idea of Wave Mechanics
The Sea-Captain's Box
Space Travel: Problems of Physics and Engineering
Looking for a New Law

20.2 How fast would you have to move to increase your mass by 1%?

20.3 The centripetal force on a mass moving with relativistic speed v around a circular orbit of radius R is $F = mv^2/R$, where m is the relativistic mass. Electrons moving at a speed $0.60\ c$ are to be deflected in a circle of radius 1.0 m: what must be the magnitude of the force applied? ($m_0 = 9.1 \times 10^{-31}$ kg.)

20.4 The formulas ($p = m_0 v$, $KE = \frac{1}{2}m_0 v^2$) used in Newtonian physics are convenient approximations to the more general relativistic formulas. The factor $1/\sqrt{1 - v^2/c^2}$ can be expressed as an infinite series of steadily decreasing terms by using a binomial series expansion. When this is done we find that

$$\frac{1}{\sqrt{1 - \frac{v^2}{c^3}}} = 1 + 1/2\,\frac{v^2}{c^2} + 3/8\,\frac{v^4}{c^4} + 5/16\,\frac{v^6}{c^6} +$$
$$35/128\,\frac{v^8}{c^8} \quad \dots$$

(a) Show, by simple substitution, that when $\frac{v}{c}$ is less than 0.1, the values of the terms drop off so rapidly that only the first few terms need be considered.
(b) We rarely observe familiar objects moving faster than about 3,000 m/sec; the speed of light is 3×10^8 m/sec, so the value of v/c for familiar objects is rarely greater than about 10^{-5}. What error do we suffer by using only the first two terms of the series?
(c) Substitute the first two terms of the series into the relativistic expression

and show that $KE = \frac{1}{2}m_0 v^2$ is a good approximation for familiar objects.

20.5 According to relativity theory, changing the energy of a system by ΔE also changes the mass of the system by $\Delta m = \Delta E/c^2$. Something like 10^5 joules per kilogram of substance are usually released as heat energy in chemical reactions.
(a) Why then aren't mass changes detected in chemical reactions?
(b) Calculate the mass change associated with a change of energy of 10^5 joules.

20.6 The speed of the earth in its orbit is about 18 miles/sec (3×10^4 m/sec). Its "rest" mass is 6.0×10^{24} kg.
(a) What is the kinetic energy of the earth in its orbit?
(b) What is the mass equivalent of that kinetic energy?
(c) By what percentage is the earth's "rest" mass increased at orbital speed?
(d) Refer back to Unit 2 to recall how the mass of the earth is found; was it the rest mass or the mass at orbital speed?

20.7 In relativistic mechanics the formula $\vec{p} = m\vec{v}$ still holds, but the mass m is given by $m = m_0/\sqrt{1 - v^2/c^2}$. The rest mass of an electron is 9.1×10^{-31} kg.
(a) What is its momentum when it is moving down the axis of a linear accelerator at a speed of 0.4 c with respect to the accelerator tube?
(b) What would Newton have calculated for the momentum of the electron?
(c) By how much would the relativistic momentum increase if the speed of the electron were doubled?
(d) What would Newton have calculated its change in momentum to be?

20.8 Calculate the momentum of a photon of wavelength 4000Å. How fast would an electron have to move in order to have the same momentum?

20.9 Construct a diagram showing the change with time that occurs in the frequency of a photon as a result of its collision with an electron.

20.10 What explanation would you offer for the fact that the wave aspect of light was shown to be valid before the particle aspect was demonstrated?

20.11 The electrons which produced the diffraction photograph on page 102 had de Broglie wavelengths of 10^{-10} meter. To what speed must they have been accelerated? (Assume that the speed is small compared to c, so that the electron mass is about 10^{-30} kg.)

20.12   A billiard ball of mass 0.2 kilograms moves with a speed of 1 meter per second. What is its de Broglie wavelength?

20.13   Show that the de Broglie wavelength of a classical particle of mass m and kinetic energy KE is given by

$$\lambda = \frac{h}{\sqrt{2m(KE)}}$$

What happens when the mass is very small and the speed is very great?

20.14   A particle confined in a box cannot have a kinetic energy less than a certain amount; this least amount corresponds to the longest de Broglie wavelength which produces standing waves in the box; that is, the box size is one-half wavelength. For each of the following situations find the longest de Broglie wavelength that would fit in the box: then use $p = h/\lambda$ to find the momentum p, and use $p = mv$ to find the speed v.

(a) a dust particle (about 10^{-9} kg) in a display case (about 1 m across).

(b) an argon atom (6.6×10^{-26} kg) in a light bulb (about 10^{-1} m across).

(c) a protein molecule (about 10^{-22} kg) in a bacterium (about 10^{-6} m across).

(d) an electron (about 10^{-30} kg) in an atom (about 10^{-10} m across).

20.15   Suppose that the only way you could obtain information about the world was by throwing rubber balls at the objects around you and measuring their speeds and directions of rebound. What kind of objects would you be unable to learn about?

20.16   A bullet can be considered as a particle having dimensions approximately 1 centimeter. It has a mass of about 10 grams and a speed of about 3×10^4 centimeters per second. Suppose we can measure its speed to an accuracy of ± 1 cm/sec. What is the corresponding uncertainty in its position according to Heisenberg's principle?

20.17   Show that if Planck's constant were equal to zero, quantum effects would disappear and even atomic particles would behave according to Newtonian physics. What effect would this have on the properties of light?

20.18   Some writers have claimed that the uncertainty principle proves that there is free will. Do you think this extrapolation from atomic phenomena to the world of living beings is valid?

20.19   A physicist has written
It is enough that quantum mechanics predicts the average value of observable quantities correctly. It is not really essential that the mathematical symbols and processes correspond to some intelligible physical picture of the atomic world.
Do you regard such a statement as acceptable? Give reasons.

20.20   In Chapters 19 and 20 we have seen that it is impossible to avoid the wave-particle dualism of light and matter. Bohr has coined the word *complementarity* for the situation in which two opposite views seem valid, and the correct choice depends only on which aspect of a phenomenon one chooses to consider. Can you think of situations in other fields (outside of atomic physics) to which this idea might apply?

20.21   In Units 1 through 4 we discussed the behavior of large-scale "classical particles" (for example, tennis balls) and "classical waves" (for example, sound waves). Such particles and waves in most cases can be described without any use of ideas such as the quantum of energy or the de Broglie matter-wave. Does this mean that there is one sort of physics ("classical physics") for the phenomena of the large-scale world and quite a different physics ("quantum physics") for the phenomena of the atomic world? Or does it mean that quantum physics really applies to all phenomena but is no different from classical physics when applied to large-scale particles and waves? What arguments or examples would you use to defend your answer?

20.22   If there are laws that describe precisely the behavior of atoms, one can reason that the future is completely determined by the present (and the present was determined in the ancient past). This idea of complete *determinism* was uncomfortable to many philosophers during the centuries following the great success of Newtonian mechanics. The great French physicist Pierre Laplace (1748–1827) wrote,
Given for one instant an intelligence which could comprehend all the forces by which nature is animated and the respective situation of the beings who compose it—an intelligence sufficiently vast to submit these data to analysis—it would embrace in the same formula the movements of the greatest bodies of the universe and those of the lightest atom; for it, nothing would be uncertain and the future, as the past, would be present to its eyes. [*A Philosophical Essay on Probabilities.*]

(The later statistical view of kinetic theory may have emphasized the difficulty of actually predicting the future. But is did not weaken the idea of an underlying chain of cause and effect.)

(a) Is LaPlace's statement consistent with modern physical theory?

(b) What implications do you see in relativity theory for the idea of determinism?

(c) What implications do you see for determinism in quantum theory?

20.23 Those ancient Greeks who believed in natural law were also troubled by the idea of determinism. Compare the ideas expressed in the following passage from Lucretius' *On the Nature of Things* (about 80 B.C.) with somewhat analogous ideas of modern physics.

If cause forever follows after cause
In infinite, undeviating sequence
And a new motion always has to come
Out of an old one, by fixed law; if atoms
Do not, by swerving, cause new moves which break
The laws of fate; if cause forever follows,
In infinite sequence, cause – where would we get
This free will that we have, wrested from fate . . .
What keeps the mind from having inside itself
Some such compulsiveness in all its doings,
What keeps it from being matter's absolute slave?
The answer is that our free-will derives
From just that ever-so-slight atomic swerve
At no fixed time, at no fixed place whatever.

20.24 Many scientists like the drawings of M. C. Escher such as that on page 115 because one can read into them some (not-too-farfetched) likeness to notions that are prominent in science. Do you see such a likeness between the drawing on page 115 and the dual nature of light? When does the likeness (analogy) break down?

Opposite: A page from Lucretius' *De Rerum Natura.* (The Pierpont Morgan Library)

¶ T. Lucreti Cari. poetæ philosophici antiquissimi
de rerum natura   liber primus incipit fœliciter.

Eneadū genitrix hominū diuūq; uoluptas
Alma uenus: cæli subter labentia signa
Quae mare nauigerum quae
terras frugiferentis
Concelebras: per te quoniam genus omne animantum
Concipitur. uisitq; exortum lumina solis.
Te dea te fugiunt uenti: te nubila cæli
Aduentumq; tuūm: tibi suauis dædala tellus
Submittit flores: tibi rident equora ponti.
Placatumq; nitet diffuso numine cælum.
Nam simulas speties patefacta est uerna diei
Et reserata uiget genitalis aura fauoni
Aeriæ primum uolucres te diua tuumq;
Significant nutum: perculse corda tua ui
Inde sere pecudes persultans pabula læta
Et rapidos tranant aranis: ita capta lepore.
Te sequitur cupide quocunq; inducere pergis.
Deniq; per maria ac montis flouiosq; rapacis
Frondiferasq; domos auium: camposq; uirentis
Omnibus incutiens blandum per pectora amorem
Efficis: ut cupide generatim sæcla propagent.
Quae quoniam rerum naturam sola gubernas:
Nec sine te quicq̄ dias in luminis oras
Exoritur: neq; fit lætum: neq; amabile quicq̄.
Te sotiam studio scribendis uersibus esse.
Quos ego de rerum natura pangere conor
Meminiadæ nostro. quem tu dea tempore in omni
Omnibus ornatum noluisti excellere rebus.
Quo magis æternum da dictis diua leporem
Effice: ut interea fera monera militiai
Per maria ac terras omnis sopita quiescant.
Nam tu sola potes tranquilla pace iuuare
Mortalis. quoniam bellisera munera mauors
Armipotens regit. ingremium qui sæpe tuum se
Reficit. æterno deuictus uulnere amoris.
Atq; ira suspiciens cereti ceruice reposta
Pascit amore auidos inhians in te dea uisus.
Atq; tuo pendet resupini spiritus ore.

a ij

Periodic Table of the Elements*

Group→ Period↓	I	II												III	IV	V	VI	VII	0
1	1.0080 H 1																		4.0026 He 2
2	6.939 Li 3	9.012 Be 4												10.811 B 5	12.011 C 6	14.007 N 7	15.999 O 8	18.998 F 9	20.183 Ne 10
3	22.990 Na 11	24.312 Mg 12												26.982 Al 13	28.086 Si 14	30.974 P 15	32.04 S 16	35.453 Cl 17	39.984 Ar 18
4	39.10 K 19	40.08 Ca 20	44.96 Sc 21	47.90 Ti 22	50.94 V 23	52.00 Cr 24	54.94 M 25	55.85 Fe 26	58.93 Co 27	58.71 Ni 28	63.54 Cu 29	65.37 Zn 30		69.72 Ga 31	72.59 Ge 32	74.92 As 33	78.96 Se 34	79.91 Br 35	83.80 Kr 36
5	85.47 Rb 37	87.62 Sr 38	88.91 Y 39	91.22 Zr 40	92.91 Nb 41	95.94 Mo 42	(99) Tc 43	101.07 Ru 44	102.91 Rh 45	106.4 Pd 46	107.87 Ag 47	112.40 Cd 48		114.82 In 49	118.69 Sn 50	121.75 Sb 51	127.60 Te 52	126.90 I 53	131.30 Xe 54
6	132.91 Cs 55	137.34 Ba 56	57–71 *	178.49 Hf 72	180.95 Ta 73	183.85 W 74	186.2 Re 75	190.2 Os 76	192.2 Ir 77	195.09 Pt 78	196.97 Au 79	200.59 Hg 80		204.37 Tl 81	207.19 Pb 82	208.98 Bi 83	(210) Po 84	(210) At 85	222 Rn 86
7	(223) Fr 87	226.05 Ra 88	89–103 †	104	105	106													

*Rare-earth metals

138.91 La 57	140.12 Ce 58	140.91 Pr 59	144.27 Nd 60	(147) Pm 61	150.35 Sm 62	151.96 Eu 63	157.25 Gd 64	158.92 Tb 65	162.50 Dy 66	164.93 Ho 67	167.26 Er 68	168.93 Tm 69	173.04 Yb 70	174.97 Lu 71

†Actinide metals

(227) Ac 89	232.04 Th 90	(231) Pa 91	238.03 U 92	(237) Np 93	(242) Pu 94	(243) Am 95	(245) Cm 96	(249) Bk 97	(249) Cf 98	(253) Es 99	(255) Fm 100	(256) Md 101	(253) No 102	(257) Lw 103

*Numbers above the symbols are the average atomic masses (relative to carbon 12). Parentheses enclose the mass number of the longest-lived isotope when there are no stable isotopes.

APPENDIX

APPENDIX

Project Physics

Dear Student,

   While taking this introductory course in physics you have worked
through a great deal of the content and development of the physical
sciences. You now have a good headstart for further study of physics
as well as other fields such as astronomy, chemistry, engineering,
and the history of science. You are now no longer an "outsider," but
are knowledgeable about many of the main currents of scientific
advance over the past centuries.

   Even if you cannot yet solve the detailed problems that a professional physicist may be working on, you do now share with him much of
the cultural heritage of modern physical science. Therefore you can,
if you wish, make an important decision: if you found yourself
intrigued or even just curious about any part of the material in this
course, you should consider going more deeply into these fields as
part of your further schooling--whether or not science will be your
eventual career.

   But in addition to physics, and in addition to the way men and women
make discoveries in science, you have also learned something about the
place of science in society. By now you should have some answers if
anyone should ask "Why physics?" or "What is the relevance of science?"

   It would have been impossible to do justice to these important
questions when you started this course. Now you have first-hand knowledge on which to base your own answers. We, who have worked for years
together with literally hundreds of colleagues and students in our
participating try-out schools, to fashion these books, lab experiments,
film, etc., would like to share with you some of our own answers to
these questions, as a kind of epilogue to the whole Project Physics
Course. We hope you may agree with at least some of our opinions.

   What special reasons are there for thinking that physics, among all
the sciences, is of basic importance? What is the relevance of science
today? We believe there are at least five parts to a complete answer,
and for each part there were examples in the course materials you
have now studied. The fact that the questions about "relevance" have
in the last few years almost become cliches does not change the need
to be clear about the subject. So let us attack it head-on.

Relevance 1: The intellectual excitement of physics

At some points during the year--often, we hope--you yourself have felt the intellectual excitement that accompanies understanding human achievements of the kind that have been chronicled here. This sort of excitement can be derived from the explanation of the motion of planets in our solar system, just as it can from the discovery of the internal structure in Shakespeare's <u>King Lear</u>. You may have felt it, keenly and suddenly, when a theory showed the connection between apparently separate parts of experience, or when a lab experiment succeeded after many tries, or when the computed planetary orbit closed, or when a long derivation that seemed to ramble on and on came suddenly to a resolution like a Bach fugue.

At such a moment, one catches a glimpse that the sort of knowledge which physics leads to can crystallize the confused world of phenomena. Here is a way to see nature's clarity, here is the place to find the necessity which guides all things. Remember how lyrical Kepler became when he found the law that $(\underline{T}^2/\underline{R}^3)$ is a constant? One must not dismiss such a moment of emotion. It does belong in science, too. It is a real and profound experience, an intellectual excitement that every scientist has when he discovers something new, or even when he just reads for the first time of a beautiful piece of work done by someone else. If we did not treasure such experiences, life would grow dull indeed. The joy of intellectual engagement in the deepest phenomena of the material world, and the joy of discovering therein the success of one's own rational and intuitive faculties--these are among the most relevant and ennobling activities one can pursue.

In the <u>Text</u> and in the <u>Reader</u>, you have often encountered remarks by scientists praising the simplicity of physics, the fact that there are only a few really deep laws but that they suffice to deal with the myriad of apparently different observations. From the very beginning, from Chapter 1 where we quickly abandoned the gyrations of a falling leaf as a useful beginning for the study of motion, we learned to look for simple commonalities in all behavior. We have been seeking overall principles that will unify many diverse cases, whether it be a falling leaf in one's backyard or the turning of an unseen solar system at the edge of the universe. Nothing is more astonishing than that it <u>is</u> possible to have such a universal physics! The most distant hydrogen atom is built on exactly the same principle as the one nearest you--as seen by the fact that both emit the same wavelengths of light. All the laws of physics that govern the structure of matter and its behavior in space and time have that universality.

Einstein once expressed these thoughts in a memorable way. Physical theory, he said, has two ardent desires: To gather up as far as possible all pertinent phenomena and their connections; and to help us

> not only to know how nature is and how her transactions are carried through, but also to reach as far as possible the utopian and seemingly arrogant aim of knowing <u>why nature is</u>

<u>thus and not otherwise</u>.....Thereby one experiences, so to
speak, that God Himself could not have arranged those connections in any other way than that which factually exists,
anymore than that it would be in His power to make the number
4 into a prime number. This is the Promethean element of the
scientific experience....Here has always been for me the
particular magic of scientific effort.

Three and a half centuries earlier, Johannes Kepler had used almost
the same words. In the preface of his first book he announced that he
wanted to find out, with respect to the number, positions, and motions
of the planets, "Why they are as they are, and not otherwise." To
a friend he wrote at about the same time that with regard to numbers
and quantity "our knowledge is of the same kind as God's, at least
insofar as we can understand something of it in this mortal life."
  These were by no means sacrilegious thoughts. On the contrary, it
was a pious man who wrote this. As Kepler often stated--and many
scientists since that day have agreed with him--the world that God
made stands before our minds as a kind of puzzle, for us to solve in
order that we may prove we are worthy of the mind given to us for that
very purpose.
  We hope to have shown that physics is neither an isolated, bloodless
body of facts and theories with mere vocational usefulness, nor a
glorious entertainment for an elite of mathematical wizards. (As
a matter of fact, some of the best physicists, including several whose
accomplishments are detailed in this course, were themselves not particularly good at mathematics.) Physics is the study of what makes the
whole world go, and we think it is too beautiful to be kept secret
from anyone, no matter what his or her eventual career plans may be.
To live with more joy and intelligence, one has to know the world in
which one lives, and this surely includes the majestic yet simple
order physicists have found in our universe. Without such a study,
as Galileo said, one may be lost in a labyrinth and not even know it.
To be ignorant of physics may leave one unprepared for living in one's
own time--as an intelligent spectator in the human adventures of our
time no less than as an effective wage-earner and citizen.

Relevance 2: Immediate practical benefits to society

  A second, very different way of seeing the relevance of science is
in terms of the effect science sometimes has in helping to prepare the
base for technological advance. We speak here not of the long-range,
slower effects of which more will be said later, but the quick "spin-
off," the intentional use of basic science "for the relief of man's
estate," in the phrase of the seventeenth-century philosopher
Francis Bacon.
  Many students and critics of science seem to have only this particular aspect in mind when they use the word "relevance." However, useful
though science can be in this sense, it would be quite wrong to settle
merely for the assistance physics can give, say, to the study of such

problems as pollution. We say this for two reasons: First of all
there really is, and need be, relatively little connection between
today's basic physics research and current technological advance. The
gadgets and devices being produced today by industry, even if they are
as sophisticated as those used for space exploration, rely very
little on new research in basic physics or on the discovery of new
laws. They are mostly based on applications of well-known laws and of
techniques developed long ago. On the contrary, people who do basic
research in physics find themselves nowadays much more often in the
position of having to oppose new plans for large-scale technological
"advance" (whether it be a widely deployed ABM system, or excavation by
use of nuclear devices, or supersonic transport planes, all of them
gadgets that in the opinion of the majority of physicists have more
long-range dangers than benefits).

In fact, contrary to folklore, the connection between basic physics
and technical advance is generally indirect or roundabout. Only rarely
is a basic advance made consciously as a prelude to a major technical
improvement. The physicist H.B.G. Casimir illustrated this proposition
by giving examples of progress made as a result of the work of
scientists who did not set out to work for specific well-defined
practical aims:

> One might ask whether basic circuits in computers might
> have been found by people who wanted to build computers. As
> it happens, they were discovered in the 1930's by physicists
> dealing with the counting of nuclear particles because they
> were interested in nuclear physics....
> One might ask whether there would be nuclear power because
> people wanted new power sources, or whether the urge to
> have new power would have led to the discovery of the
> nucleus. Only it didn't happen that way, and there were the
> Curies, and Rutherford, and Fermi, and a few others....
> One might ask whether induction coils in motorcars might
> have been made by enterprises which wanted to make motor
> transport, and whether then they would have stumbled on the
> laws of induction. But the laws of induction had been found
> by Faraday many decades before that....
> Or whether, in an urge to provide better communication,
> one might have found electromagnetic waves. They weren't
> found that way. They were found by Hertz who emphasized the
> beauty of physics and who based his work on the theoretical
> considerations of Maxwell. I think there is hardly any
> example of twentieth-century innovation which is not
> indebted in this way to basic scientific thought.

There is also another reason why it would be quite wrong to seek
relevance for science merely in the rare immediate benefits to
technology. Technological advance all too often brings with it major
social problems that arise as unforeseen by-products, and these
problems cannot be cured or even properly understood through existing

scientific or technological or political means alone. Rather, <u>such cures depend to a large extent on making new, basic scientific advances</u>. To put it differently, at the heart of social problems created by technological advance is the <u>absence</u> of some specific basic scientific knowledge. This fact gives a whole new mandate and a new range of expectations for basic scientific research.

Examples come readily to mind. Thus, it is quite customary to say that the population explosion is in part caused by the advance of medical science (owing to better sanitation, innoculation, antibiotics, etc.). But one can equally well claim that the population explosion is bound to overwhelm us precisely because we do <u>not</u> yet have at hand sufficient knowledge in pure science. That is to say, the complex problem of over-population is due in a large degree to our current ignorance of the basic process of conception--its biophysics, biochemistry, physiology. No wonder that attempts at controlling population are so halting. What is astonishing, rather, is that the first medical school laboratory in the United States specifically designed to study the whole range of scientific problems in the process of reproduction has only been built quite recently.

Similarly, it is sometimes said that progress in physics is "responsible" for the threatening arms race. But it is more accurate to say that arms control treaties were difficult to achieve in good part because of insufficient knowledge of geophysics that made inspection through seismographs of suspected illegal weapons tests difficult and uncertain. A better understanding of geophysics, it turned out, was needed before different nations would consider it safe to enter in arms control treaties that outlaw weapons tests.

The problem of bringing food to hungry people in arid lands that are near the sea, as in Peru or India or Egypt, is to a large extent political, as are most of the problems mentioned above. But it is also a problem of basic science: Before it is possible to design much more economical desalination plants, a more fundamental understanding of the structure of liquids--one of the much-neglected problem areas in current physics and chemistry--and of the phenomena of materials moving through membranes will be needed. And turning to pollution, that is of course also the result of greed, stupidity, apathy, and the consequent lack of law enforcement; but to clean up smog-ridden areas more effectively will require greater basic knowledge than we have today of the physics and chemistry of combustion and of meteorology. And in the meantime, to this day the most effective and insufficiently used device for getting rid of pollution due to solid particles is the electrostatic precipitator, working on the scientific principles we discussed in Unit 4, and known since 1600.

These remarks should serve to oppose two widely current but erroneous notions: one, that basic science is an unnecessary luxury, and should be supported only if it is directed to immediate practical applicability (--as the quotation by Casimir above indicates, things just don't happen that way); and second, that one way of stopping the abuses that come as by-products of technical innovation is to stop science (--whereas in fact curing the abuses depends on scientific advances yet to be made).

Relevance 3: Long-range social benefits

Turning from the immediate to the long-range effects of science that give it relevance, we have seen ample evidence that every person alive today, whether or not he or she has studied science, is intellectually a child of Copernicus and Galileo, Newton and Faraday, Einstein and Bohr. Our imagination and intellectual tools were indeed shaped to a large degree by the advances in the knowledge of physics they and their contemporaries made, long before we were born. Thus the material in the Unit 2 Text and Reader showed how the Copernican and Newtonian world view triumphed in the West, and indeed how the recognition that a uniform law holds sway over all matter everywhere helped to overcome hierarchical thinking, thereby preparing the mind for self-reliant democracy. And again, in Unit 3, we saw that the successes of statistics and of the concepts of energy prepared the ground for the modernization of the Newtonian worldview.

In addition to the long-range influence of science upon the mind--the kind of influence that Newton's work had on the imagination of the poets and theologians from the eighteenth century onward--there are also the more material long-range effects we studied in connection with the advances made by James Watt, Michael Faraday, and Enrico Fermi. From an understanding of how the steam engine works flowed a century-long transformation of society which now is studied under the name of the Industrial Revolution. From Faraday's "toys" came electric motors and generators and, in time, the electric-powered elevators, trains and subways that facilitated the upward and sideways growth of cities. Similarly, the experiments of Fermi's group on neutron-induced artificial radioactivity prepared for the study of nuclear fission, and this in turn led to the design of new sources of energy that may turn out to be the only means for meeting the frantically growing energy needs of our society.

Even more than is true for the immediate practical influences, it usually is impossible to foresee ahead of time the long-range effects of science upon social change. To avoid possible negative effects and to capitalize on positive ones, there is only one policy available: to exert uncompromising watchfulness, as citizens and scientists--calling attention to current flagrant abuses of scientific knowledge or skills, and keeping up-to-date on scientific advance so as to be ready to keep it from being derailed and abused in the future.

Relevance 4: Science as a study that is connected to all other fields

The fourth meaning of the word "relevance" refers to science not as merely a technical study but as one part of the general humanistic development of mankind. We agree fully with the Nobel Prize physicist I.I. Rabi, quoted in the Preface to the Text:

> Science should be taught at whatever level, from the lowest to the highest, in the humanistic way. By which I mean it

should be taught with a certain historical understanding, with a social understanding and a human understanding, in the sense of the biography, the nature of the people who made this construction, the triumphs, the trials, the tribulations.

We can illustrate the need for this sense of humanistic interconnectedness by means of a simple diagram. The physics course as traditionally given in many high schools and colleges is like a string of beads. One subject follows another, from Galileo's kinematics to the most recent advances in nuclear physics--the usual sequence that more or less parallels the historical development of the science, whether this is made explicit or not. But few if any connections are shown with other achievements of human beings who are not physicists, with sciences other than physics, and with studies and activities other than science. And all too often the materials studied in the other courses--in chemistry, in biology, in literature, etc.--also hang there by themselves like so many separate strings of beads.

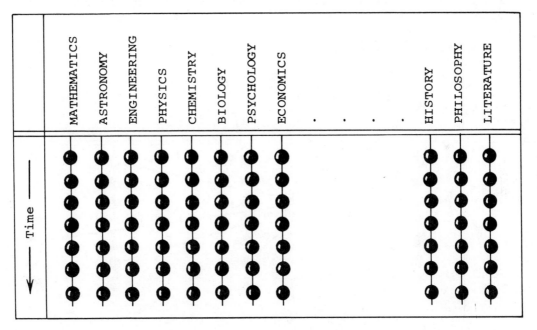

There are some advantages in such a string-of-beads presentation of a course. For example, it is convenient to teach. But ignoring connections that do exist among all these fields does not do justice to the actual state of affairs. A research project in experimental physics, for example, sooner or later draws on material not only from almost every part of a physics course, but also from mathematics, metallurgy, chemical thermodynamics, electronic engineering, computer technology, and many other fields of science--not to speak of group psychology, accounting, and skill in writing a good article about the work. Moreover, nobody who has engaged in actual scientific work can fail to see the influence that advances made in science can have in terms of social and practical consequences. "Pure" physics is an invention that exists only in the most old-fashioned classrooms. If you pick up a real problem in physics (or any other science) there extends from it connections to a number of expected and unexpected problems in fields that at first glance seem to "belong" to other professions.

In this course you have seen many evidences of these connections to subject matter of the kind not usually referred to in physics courses. Think back, for example, to our case study in Unit 2 of Newtonian mechanics as applied to planetary motion, a subject that is one of the "beads" on the physics chain. Newton had studied theology and philosophy and those ideas echoed in the Principia in his sections on the nature of time and space (in the Figure below, link A to philosophy). Within physics itself, Newton brought to a culmination the work of Kepler and Galileo (link B). Much of the established mathematics in Newton's work came from the Greeks (link C). New mathematics, particularly the basic ideas of calculus, were invented by Newton to aid his own progress, thereby advancing the progress of mathematics (link D).

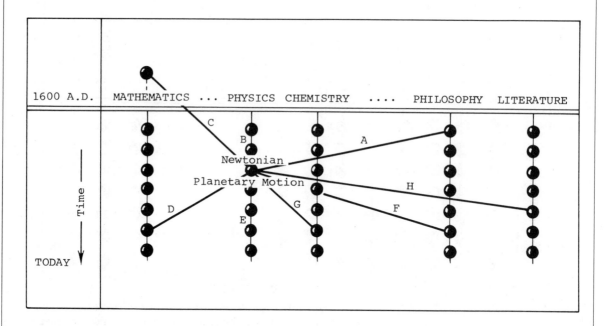

Within physics, all who follow Newton will use his laws and approach (link E). His effects on the philosophy of the deist theologians (link F), on Dalton's atomic models in chemistry (link G), and on the artistic sensibilities of the 18th century in which Newton swayed the muses (link H), were documented in the Text and in the Reader articles.

The same kind of web extends around every one of the chief topics we have discussed in this course. Think of the link from philosophy to the work of Oersted, Ampere, and Faraday in electricity (through their interest in Nature Philosophy). Think of the link reaching from nuclear physics back along the chain to the classical physics of three centuries earlier (as in the discussion of how the mass of the neutron was determined), and the links sideways, to biology, engineering, and politics, through the various applications and by-products of nuclear reactors.

Such links exist between all fields. No doubt you found that some of the topics and persons discussed in our course came up also in other courses you have been taking. If we drew all links between fields on the intellectual map, we would see that instead of the separate strings of beads there really exists a coherent crystal, or, if you will, a tapestry, a fabric of ideas. This view of the relevance of science has deeply penetrated our course: Science is now seen to be in dynamic interaction with the total intellectual activity of an age. In a deep sense, science is part of the study of history and of philosophy, and it may underlie the work of the artist just as it penetrates into the explanation a mother gives to her child of the way things move.

If we therefore tried to think away the whole string with the heading "Physics," the history of Western thought would be almost incomprehensible. We could not understand--and in fact would not have had--much of the work of a John Locke and a Voltaire and an Alexander Pope who, among many others, were frankly inspired by the work of the physicists of their time. Conversely, philosophy, mathematics, and other fields would be far emptier studies without their fulfillment and extension through the work of philosopher-scientists such as Mach, Einstein, and Bohr. Eliminating physics would of course also make nonsense of the history of industrial development following upon Watt's steam engine, Volta's battery, Faraday's motors and generators, etc. A neighboring science such as chemistry could not have developed without models of gases and theories of atomic structure that were largely the work of physicists. In short, if you pull out the thread marked "Physics" from the tapestry, the fabric would unravel like an old sweater; and the same would be true if any of the other threads were pulled out. On this view, therefore, the relevance of any field of knowledge, including science, is that it is an integral part of the total growth of thought.

All too often students have to discover the existence of the fabric of ideas for themselves. For it is a bad habit of some academics to teach their own subject as if it had nothing to do with others. But it is precisely by seeing these connections between fields that one becomes educated rather than only trained. We have made these links explicit in our course in the hope of providing an educational experience that, in a similar manner, you can and should obtain in all your courses.

Relevance 5: Science as a style of life

Modern science is not an elite enterprise for only a self-selected few; nowadays there are literally millions of men and women engaged in it. In the United States alone there are nearly 50,000 people who contribute to physics, and each does so in an individual way. Some prefer to follow their thoughts entirely alone, some are surrounded by students or collaborate with groups of colleagues. Some are in small university laboratories, some in large industrial enterprises. Some accentuate the sober rationality and objectivity which it is possible to achieve in scientific work, others pursue their work with a passion and a daring that makes one dizzy to follow them. Some have no academic degree at all, others are laden with diplomas. But they all share gives a style or way of looking at the world and of life, and this fact science a relevance in addition to the four we have mentioned above. This style has a number of earmarks or components; in concluding this letter, let us list just four:

A. By and large, these people feel at home in the world of nature. It makes sense to them, and they are comfortable with it while knowing full well that the most surprising and important findings in their field are still to be made in the future. To them the world is not a succession of incoherent, unique events. Knowledge about nature gives them a sense of the relations of things--how the world hangs together in an ecological manner. But such knowledge does not "explain away" the phenomena or dull the excitement about them, any more than knowing the rules of baseball makes you less involved in watching the game than you would be if you were ignorant of them. Of course nobody knows all there is to know even about a single one of the sciences. But still, you can feel quite at home in a city even if you have personally walked through only a few percent of all the streets there; if you know the pattern in outline, plus the crucial details of some regions within it, you no longer feel a stranger.

B. Under Relevance 1 above we stressed the intellectual interest in science for society as a whole, but there is also a personal aspect for every scientist or student: Here is a chance to devote one's professional life to something one loves to do. Those who have selected a science for their career, and who are at all good at it, are on a road through a changing landscape along which each can select his own problems to work on. (If only this were possible for people everywhere, so many of whom are trapped in dull routines others have decided for them!) We speak here of science as <u>doing</u>, not just what is contained in books, any more than art is only what is contained in museums and libraries. Being a scientist can be a way of spending one's professional life, day by day, in what one likes to do and does well. It's not like reading a play, or watching it, but like writing it and acting in it. And much of the same satisfaction goes to those who spend most of their lives not as research scientists but as teachers, in high school or college--those who have found that their chief satisfaction is helping young people to realize what role science can play in their lives.

C. Each professional group has its own values, and the values of day-by-day life in science were illustrated in the course also. Nowhere more than in science is intellectual merit and skill honored. No matter who he is, the scientist is taken seriously by his peers for what he can <u>do</u>. Consequently, some minority groups have broken through the unjust social obstacles first by showing their excellence in scientific work. There is in science a great amount of room at the top, as well as an atmosphere of belonging to an international and cosmopolitan community.

One "minority" group that has been of particular concern to scientists is that made up of young people. A whole set of social inventions and devices operates in the life of science in order to recognize and reward talent as early as possible. As you saw again and again (in the <u>Text</u> and in the biographical remarks, in the documentary films <u>People and Particles</u> and <u>The World of Enrico Fermi</u>), the young scientist is welcome and is brought as quickly as possible to participate at the growing edge of new science. As a member of a team he may in some subject be the expert or teacher for others who are his seniors. And unlike the situation in many other fields, it is widely recognized in science that a person is at his best in terms of imaginative contributions while still young.

D. More and more, scientists have recognized that discovery of new knowledge and the teaching of established knowledge do not fulfill all their responsibilities. Rather, scientists are prominent among those who take part in the process of examining the immediate social consequences of scientific and technical advance; their knowledge of science adds to their obligations of citizenship. Most of them, and particularly the young, therefore feel that there is a happy complementarity between taking part in developing the human values of a democratic society and taking part in the growth of science.

* * *

The five meanings of relevance we have now set forth are of course closely related to one another in many ways. They can all be present in the actual lives of actual people. In preparing the materials of this course we have tried to catch our own excitement about physics, its relevance, and its relations to the rest of the world of thought and action--and we hope you have shared some of that excitement with us.

With all good wishes,

Gerald Holton

F. James Rutherford

Fletcher G. Watson

Acknowledgments (continued)

Unit 2

Pp. 21-22 Ptolemy, "The Almagest," Trans. by Taliaferro, R. Catesby, *Great Books of the Western World,* Vol. 16, pp. 5-12 not inclusive, copyright 1952 by Encyclopaedia Britannica, Inc.

P. 29 Rosen, Edward, Trans. "The Commentariolus of Copernicus," *Three Copernican Treatises,* Columbia University Press, pp. 57-58.

Pp. 31-32 Copernicus, "De Revolutionibus," ("On the Revolutions of Heavenly Spheres"), *Great Books of the Western World,* Vol. 16, pp. 514 and 508, copyright 1939 by Encyclopaedia Britannica, Inc.

Pp. 31-33 Rosen, op. cit., pp. 58-59.

P. 38 Knedler, John W., Jr., *Masterworks of Science,* Doubleday and Company, Inc., pp. 67-69.

Pp. 39-40 Copernicus, *Great Books of the Western World,* op. cit., pp. 514, 515, copyright 1939 by Encyclopaedia Britannica, Inc.

Pp. 41, 43 Butterfield, H., *Origins of Modern Science, 1300–1800,* p. 41, copyright © 1957 by The Macmillan Company.

P. 66 Shapley, Harlow, and Howarth, Helen E., *A Source Book in Astronomy,* copyright © 1956 by Harvard University Press.

Pp. 70-71 Drake, Stillman, *Discoveries and Opinions of Galileo,* pp. 29, 31, 51, copyright © 1957 by Doubleday & Company, Inc.

P. 74 Galilei, Galileo, *Dialogue Concerning the Two Chief World Systems,* trans. Stillman Drake, pp. 123-124, copyright © 1967 by University of California Press.

P. 75 Von Gebler, Karl, *Galileo Galilei and the Roman Curia,* trans. Mrs. George Sturge, C. Kegan Paul and Company, p. 26.

Pp. 85-86 Needham, Joseph, and Pagel, Walter, eds., *Background to Modern Science,* The Macmillan Company, pp. 73-74.

P. 86 Stukeley, William, *Memoirs of Sir Isaac Newton's Life,* Taylor and Francis, p. 21, written in 1752.

Pp. 86-87 Anthony, H. D., *Sir Isaac Newton,* p. 96, copyright © 1960 by Abelard-Schuman Ltd.

Pp. 88-89 Newton, Sir Isaac, *The Principia,* Vol. I, Motte's translation revised by Cajori, pp. xvii-xviii, copyright © 1961 by University of California Press.

Pp. 87-89, 98 Ibid., Vol. II, pp. 398-408 and p. 547, copyright © 1962 by University of California Press.

P. 89 Pope, Alexander, *Epitaph Intended for Sir Isaac Newton* (1732).

P. 117 Fontenelle, "Préface sur L'Utilité des Mathématiques et de la Physique" from Oeuvres Complètes (1818), in Randall, John H., Jr., *The Making of the Modern Mind,* p.

254, Revised Edition, copyright 1940 by Houghton Mifflin Company.

P. 119 Wilson, James, *The Works of the Honourable James Wilson,* published under direction of Wilson, Bird, Bronson and Chauncey, pp. 411-412, not inclusive.

P. 120 Burtt, E. A. *The Metaphysical Foundations of Modern Science,* pp. 238-239, Humanities Press, Inc.

P. 121 Laplace, *A Philosophical Essay on Probabilities,* first published in Paris (1814), trans. Truscott, Frederick and Emory, Frederick, Dover Publications, Inc., p. 4.

P. 122 Darwin, Erasmus, quoted by Charles Darwin in his preface to Krause, *Erasmus Darwin,* D. Appleton and Company, p. 44.

Unit 3

P. 1 Desagulier, J. T., *The Newtonian System of the World, The Best Model of Government, an Allegorical Poem.*

P. 2 Descartes, René, *The Philosophical Works of Descartes,* trans. Haldane, Elizabeth S. and Ross, G. R. T., Vol. 1, p. 299, copyright 1931 by Cambridge University Press.

P. 2 "A Free Inquiry into the received Notion of Nature," *The Works of Robert Boyle,* Vol. IV, p. 362.

P. 3 Newton, Sir Isaac, *The Principia,* Motte's translation revised by Florian Cajori, preface to first edition (1687), p. xviii, copyright ©1961 by University of California Press.

P. 5 Lucretius, *On the Nature of Things,* trans. H. Munro, George Bell & Sons, Book II, p. 51.

P. 5 Bacon, Francis, *Complete Essays Including the New Atlantis and Novum Organum,* edit. by Finch, Henry L., Washington Square Press.

P. 6 Lavoisier, Antoine, *Elements of Chemistry,* (1790), a facsimile of an original translation by Robert Kerr with new intro. by Professor Douglas McKie, Dover Publications, Inc.

P. 22 Gerhardt, *Die Philosophische Schriften von Gottfried Wilhelm Leibniz, 1875-90,* Vol. IV, p. 286, Eng. Trans, in Dugas, R., *Mechanics in the Seventeenth Century,* Central Book Co., p. 407.

P. 41 Darwin, Erasmus, *Botanic Garden—The Economy of Vegetation,* J. Moore, p. 49.

P. 43 Savery, Thomas, in Hart, I. B., *James Watt & the History of Steam Power,* copyright ©1961 by Crowell Collier-Macmillan & Co.

P. 50 Joule, James Prescott, *The Scientific Papers of James Prescott Joule,* an illustrated facsimile of the 1884 edition, copyright ©1963 by Dawson of Pall Mall.

P. 56 Ibid.

P. 58 Helmholtz, H. L. F., *Popular Scientific Lectures,* edited by Morris Kline, copyright 1873, 1881, ©1962 by Dover Publications, Inc.

P. 63 Poincaré, Henri, La Science et l'Hypothese, E. Flammarion, excerpt trans. by McClaim, John.

P. 78 Lord Kelvin, "The Size of Atoms," *Nature,* Vol. I, p. 551.

Acknowledgments (continued)

P. 86 Frost, Robert, from "West-Running Brook," *The Poetry of Robert Frost,* ed. by Edward Connery Lathem, p. 259, copyright ©1969 by Holt, Rinehart and Winston, Inc., copyright ©1956 by Robert Frost. Reprinted by permission of Holt, Rinehart and Winston, Inc.
P. 92 Lord Kelvin, "The Kinetic Theory of the Dissipation of Energy," *Proceedings of the Royal Society of Edinburgh,* Vol. 8, p. 325.
P. 93 Nietzsche, Friedrich, "Der Wille zur Macht," *Nietzsche: An Anthology of His Works,* ed. Manthey-Zorn, Otto, Washington Square Press, p. 90.
P. 93 Shelley, Percy Bysshe, *Hellas,* ed. Wise, Thomas J., Reeves & Turner, pp. 51-52 not inclusive.
Pp. 93-94 Poincaré, Henri, *Kinetic Theory,* ed. Stephen Brush, Vol. 2, p. 206, copyright ©1966 by Pergamon Press.
Pp. 120-121 Huygens, Christiaan, *Treatise on Light,* first published in Paris (1690), trans. Thompson, Silvanus P., copyright 1912 by Dover Publications, Inc.
P. 134 Power, Henry, *Experimental Philosophy* (1664), reprinted 1966 by Johnson Reprint Corp., p. 192.
P. 134 Donne, John, "The First Anniversary," *Donne's Poetical Works,* ed. Grierson, Herbert J., Oxford University Press (Clarendon Press imprint), Vol. 1, p. 237.

Unit 4

P. 2 Newton, Sir Isaac, *Newton's Philosophy of Nature,* ed., H. S. Thayer, Haffner Publishing Co., N.Y., 1953, pp. 68-81.
P. 5 Blackmore, Richard, *Creation, A Philosophical Poem,* Robert Johnson, p. 91.
P. 14 Young, Thomas, *Course of Lectures on Natural Philosophy and the Mechanical Arts,* Cox.
Pp. 17-19 Newton, Sir Isaac, *Newton's Philosophy of Nature,* ed., H. S. Thayer, Haffner Publishing Co., N.Y., 1953, pp. 68-81.
P. 19 Thompson, James, *The Poetical Works of James Thompson,* William Tegg and Co., pp. 145-146 and p. 10.
P. 19 Goethe, J. W., *Goethe As A Scientist,* Magnus, Rudolf, translated by Heinz Norden, Henry Schuman, pp. 184-185, copyright 1949 by Heinz Norden.
P. 23 Young, Thomas, *Miscellaneous Works* (London, 1855) Vol. I, p. 415.
P. 25 Galilei, Galileo, *Dialogues Concerning Two New Sciences,* trans. Crew, H. and de Salvio, A., copyright 1952 by Dover Publications, pp. 42-43.
P. 27 Savage, Richard, "The Wanderer," *The Poetical Works of Richard Savage,* ed. Tracy, Clarence, Cambridge University Press, pp. 147-148.
Pp. 30-32 Gilbert, William, *De Magnete,* trans. Mottelay, P. Fleury, copyright 1958 by Dover Publications, pp. 1-14 and p. 121.

P. 48 von Guericke, Otto, Magie, Wm. F., *A Sourcebook in Physics,* McGraw-Hill, 1935, p. 393.
P. 51 Volta, Alessandro, *On the Electricity Excited by the Mere Contact of Conducting Substances of Different Kinds,* Philosophical Transactions of the Royal Society of London, 1800, p. 403.
Pp. 59-60 Ampere, André-Marie, Whittaker, E. T., *A History of the Theories of Aether and Electricity,* Harper & Brothers, N.Y., 1960, p. 84.
P. 74 Faraday, Michael, MacDonald, D. K. C., *Faraday, Maxwell & Kelvin,* Science Studies Series, Doubleday, Garden City, 1964, p. 11.
P. 76 Faraday, Michael, *Faraday's Diary,* G. Bell & Sons, London, 1932, Vol. I, pp. 375-376.
P. 100 Maxwell, James Clerk, *The Scientific Papers of James Clerk Maxwell,* ed., Niven, W. D., Dover Publications, N.Y., 1965, p. 158.
P. 106 Maxwell, James Clerk, *The Scientific Papers of James Clerk Maxwell,* ed., Niven, W. D., Dover Publications, N.Y., 1965, p. 500.
P. 117 Maxwell, James Clerk, *The Scientific Papers of James Clerk Maxwell,* ed., Niven, W. D., Dover Publications, N.Y., 1965, p. 775 of Vol. II.
P. 117 Maxwell, James Clerk, *The Scientific Papers of James Clerk Maxwell,* ed., Niven, W. D., Dover Publications, N.Y., 1965, p.763 of Vol. II.
P. 123 Carroll, Lewis, *The Complete Works of Lewis Carroll,* Random House, N.Y., 1939, pp. 66-67.
Pp. 120-121 Feynman, R. P., *The Feynman Lectures on Physics,* Feynman, R. P., Leighton, R. B., and Sands, M., Vol. 2, Addison-Wesley, 1964, pp. 9-10.

Much of the historical information in Chapter 15, in particular the discussion of the ac-dc controversy, is based on the book by Harold I. Sharlin, *The Making of the Electrical Age* (Abelard-Schuman, New York, 1963). We are grateful to Professor Sharlin for giving his permission to use this material.

Unit 5

P. 3 Excerpts from *The Way Things Are: The De Rerum Natura of Titus Lucretius Caius,* a translation by Rolfe Humphries, copyright ©1969 by Indiana University Press.
P. 5 From "The First Chapter of Aristotle's 'Foundations of Scientific Thought' (Metaphysica, Liber A)," translated by Daniel E. Gershenson and Daniel A. Greenburg, in *The Natural Philosopher,* Vol. II, copyright © 1963 by the Blaisdell Publishing Company, pp. 14-15.
P. 7 From *The Life of the Honorable Henry Cavendish,* by George Wilson, printed for the Cavendish Society, 1851, pp. 186-187.
Pp. 7-8 From "Elements of Chemistry" by Antoine Laurent Lavoisier, translated by Robert Kerr in *Great Books of the Western World,* Vol. 45, copyright 1952 by Encyclopaedia Britannica, Inc., pp. 3-4.

Acknowledgments (continued)

P. 11 From "The Atomic Molecular Theory" by Leonard K. Nash in *Harvard Case Histories in Experimental Science,* Case 4, Vol. 1, copyright 1950 by Harvard University, p. 228.

P. 21 From *The Principles of Chemistry* by Dmitri Mendeleev, translated by George Kamensky, copyright 1905 by Longmans, Green and Company, London, p. 27.

P. 22 Mendeleev, Dmitri, 1872.

P. 31 From "Experimental Researches in Electricity" by Michael Faraday from *Great Books of the Western World,* Vol. 45, copyright 1952 by Encyclopaedia Britannica, Inc., pp. 389-390.

Pp. 45-46 Einstein, Albert, trans. by Professor Irving Kaplan, Massachusetts Institute of Technology.

P. 50 Roentgen, W. K.

P. 59 From "Opticks" by Isaac Newton from *Great Books of the Western World,* Vol. 34, copyright 1952 by Encyclopaedia Britannica, Inc., pp. 525-531.

Pp. 68-69 From *Background to Modern Science,* Needham, Joseph and Pagel, Walter, eds., copyright 1938 by The Macmillan Company, pp. 68-69.

P. 88 Letter from Rutherford to Bohr, March 1913.

P. 91 From "Opticks" by Isaac Newton from *Great Books of the Western World,* Vol. 34, copyright 1952 by Encyclopaedia Britannica, Inc., p. 541.

P. 113 From *Atomic Physics* by Max Born, copyright 1952 by Blackie & Son, Ltd., p. 95.

P. 114 Letter from Albert Einstein to Max Born, 1926.

P. 121 From *A Philosophical Essay on Possibilities* by Pierre Simon Laplace, translated by Frederick W. Truscott and Frederick L. Emory, copyright 1951 by Dover Publications, Inc., p. 4.

Picture Credits (continued)

Unit 2

Cover photograph, p. 116, Albert B. Gregory, Jr.
Facing p. 1, Aztec Calendar Stone in the Museo Nacional, Mexico City. Photo courtesy of the American Museum of Natural History, New York.
P. 1 Collection of Historical Scientific Instruments, Harvard University.
P. 2 Stephen Perrin.
P. 3 Courtesy of the Trustees of the British Museum, London.
P. 4 Frontispiece from *Recueil de plusieurs traitez de Mathématique de l'Academie Royale des Sciences,* 1676.
P. 6, 117 (top margin) Emil Schultess, Black Star Publishing Company, Inc.
P. 9 (top left) John Stofan AMPHOTO; (top right) John Bufkin, Macon, Missouri, Feb. 1964.
P. 11 Mount Wilson and Palomar Observatories
P. 18 DeGolyer Collection, University of Oklahoma Libraries.
P. 28, 117 (margin, second from top) Jagiellonian Library, University of Krakow, Poland.
P. 29 Muzeum Okregowe in Torun. Courtesy of Dr. Owen Gingerich.
P. 42 Jagiellonian Library, University of Krakow, Poland.
P. 46 (top left) from *Atlas Major,* Vol. I, Jan Blaeu, 1664; (bottom left) The Mansell Collection, London; (top center, bottom right) Danish Information Office.

P. 47 Smithsonian Astrophysical Observatory, courtesy of Dr. Owen Gingerich.
P. 48 (top left) from Brahe, Tycho, *Astronomiae Instauratae Mechanica,* Philip von Ohr, Wandsbeck, 1598; (bottom photograph) by John Bryson, reprinted with permission from HOLIDAY, 1966, the Curtis Publishing Company.
P. 50 Mount Wilson and Palomar Observatories.
P. 55 (portrait) The Bettmann Archive.
P. 56 Kepler, Johannes, *Mysterium cosmographicum,* Linz, 1596.
P. 62 Archives, Academy of Sciences, Leningrad, U.S.S.R. Photo courtesy of Dr. Owen Gingerich.
P. 70 Instituto e Museo di Storia della Scienza, Florence, Italy.
P. 71 DeGolyer Collection, University of Oklahoma Libraries.
P. 72 (top) Griffith Observatory, Los Angeles, California (middle photograph) Lowell Observatory Photograph
P. 77 (top) Alinari—Art Reference Bureau; (bottom) Bill Bridges.
P. 82, 117 (bottom margin) Yerkes Observatory.
P. 85 (drawing) from a manuscript by Newton in the University Library, Cambridge; (portrait) engraved by Bt. Reading from a painting by Sir Peter Lely. Trinity College Library, Cambridge.
P. 96 Descartes, René, *Principia Philosophiae,* 1664.
P. 103 Courtesy of National Aeronautics and Space Administration.
P. 106 Cavendish, Henry, *Philosophical Transactions of the Royal Society,* vol. 88, 198.
P. 118 Print Collection of the Federal Institute of Technology, Zurich.

Picture Credits (continued)

Unit 3

Cover photograph, p. 134 "Locomotive Wheels" by Farrell Grehan.

Facing p. 1 Albert B. Gregory, Jr.

P. 2 (watch assembly) Swiss Federation of Watch Manufacturers; (Blake drawing) Whitworth Art Gallery, University of Manchester.

P. 3 Albert B. Gregory, Jr.

P. 4, 135 (top margin) Pictorial Parade, N.Y.C.

P. 5 (thunderhead) Dean Loomis, © Time Inc. (bonfire) Colgate University.

P. 7 (Lavoisier portrait) painted by Jacques Louis David. Courtesy of The Rockefeller University.

P. 12 Boston Patriots Football Club.

P. 14 (hockey players) Pictorial Parade, N.Y.C.; (space vehicle) National Aeronautics & Space Administration; (galaxy) Mount Wilson and Palomar Observatories; (colliding balls) National Film Board of Canada.

P. 17 The Boeing Company.

P. 18 (galaxy) Mount Wilson and Palomar Observatories; (colliding cars) Henry Groskwsky, LIFE MAGAZINE, © Time Inc.

P. 20 (Huygens) Royal Netherlands Academy of Sciences and Letters, Amsterdam.

P. 21 (Descartes) the Franz Hals portrait in the National Art Museum, Copenhagen.

P. 22 (Leibniz) Burndy Library, Norwalk, Conn.

P. 27 "The Little Prince" from THE LITTLE PRINCE by Antoine de Saint Exupéry, copyright 1943 by Harcourt, Brace & World, Inc., reproduced with their permission.

P. 28, 135 (margin, second from top) Russ Kinne—Photo Researchers.

P. 29 A. H. Grossman, LIFE MAGAZINE, © Time Inc.

P. 35 Albert B. Gregory, Jr.

P. 36 Dr. Harold E. Edgerton, M.I.T.

P. 37 Dimitri Kessel, LIFE MAGAZINE, © Time Inc.

P. 39 (camel & waterwheel) C. W. Kirkland, LIFE MAGAZINE, © Time Inc.; (boy on waterwheel) LIFE MAGAZINE, © Time Inc.; (reversible overshot waterwheel) Agricola, Georgius, *De Re Metallica,* 1556, Houghton Library, Harvard University; (windmill) M. G. Walker, LIFE MAGAZINE, © Time Inc.

P. 40 (aeolipile) Science Museum, London.

P. 43 Newcomen Society, London.

P. 44 (Watt in his laboratory) Figuier, Louis, *Les Merveilles de la Science,* Furne, Jouvet et Cie, Paris.

P. 46 (train) Boston & Maine Corporation.

P. 48 (top left, center left, bottom right) Science Museum, London.

P. 49 (top) Franco Tosi—Westinghouse; (bottom) American Institute of Physics.

P. 52 Professor Keith R. Porter, Dept. of Biology, Harvard University.

P. 55 "The Repast of the Lion," by Henri Rousseau, courtesy of The Metropolitan Museum of Art, bequest of Samuel A. Lewisohn, 1951.

P. 57 (Goethe) painting by Angelica Kauffmann, 1787, Harvard College Observatory; (Schelling) pastel by Friedrich Tieck, 1801, collection of Dr. Hermann von Schelling.

P. 58 Koenigsberger, Leo, *Hermann von Helmholtz,* Braunschweig Druck und Verlag, von Friedrich Vieweg und Sohn.

P. 65 (wrecker) Harry Redl, LIFE MAGAZINE, © Time Inc.; (ocean liner) courtesy of Kenyon & Eckhardt, Inc. and Fugazy Travel Bureau, Inc.

P. 70, 135 (margin, third from top) Courtesy AMF-Voit.

P. 71 (balloon) U.S. Air Force.

P. 86 American Institute of Physics.

P. 87 Educational Development Center.

P. 91 (Maxwell) Courtesy of Trinity College Library, Cambridge; (colliding balls) PSSC Physics, D. C. Heath & Co., 1965.

P. 92 (light bulb) Dr. Harold E. Edgerton, M.I.T.; (bonfire) Colgate University; (landscape) "Mount Williamson—Clearing Storm," 1944, Ansel Adams.

P. 93 Thompson, Silvanus P., *Life of William Thomson,* vol. 1, Macmillan and Co., Ltd., London.

P. 94 P. E. Genereux, E. Lynn.

P. 96 Greek National Tourist Office, N.Y.C.

P. 100, 111, 135 (bottom margin) Magnum Photos Inc., N.Y.C. Werner Bischof.

P. 105 Union Pacific Railroad.

P. 117 "Singer with Lyre" from red-figured amphora attributed to the Brygos painter. Courtesy of the Museum of Fine Arts, Boston. John Michael Rodocanachi Fund.

P. 119 National Film Board of Canada.

Pp. 120, 122-123, 125 (ripple tank photos) Courtesy, Film Studio Educational Development Center.

P. 121 Courtesy, College of Engineering, University of California, Berkeley.

P. 125 (radiotelescope) National Radio Astronomy Observatory, Green Bank, W.Va.

P. 128 U.S. Navy.

P. 130 Schaefer and Seawell

P. 133 (anechoic chamber) Bell Telephone Laboratories; (concert hall) Hedrich-Blessing

P. 139 U.S. Navy.

Picture Credits (continued)

Unit 4

Cover photograph, p. 37, p. 120 from the book *A History of Electricity* by Edward Tatnall Canby, © by Eric Nitsche Int'l. Published by Hawthorn Books, Inc., 70 Fifth Avenue, New York, New York.

Facing page 1 (top left) Euler, Leonhard, *Theoria Motuum Planetarum et Cometarum,* Berlin, 1744; (bottom left) Descartes, René, *Principia Philosophiae,* 1664; (top right) Maxwell, James Clerk, *A Treatise on Electricity and Magnetism,* vol. II, Oxford Press, 1892.

P. 3 National Radio Astronomy Observatory, Greenbank, West Virginia.

Pp. 4-5, 121 (top margin) "Grand Tetons & Snake River." Minor White.

P. 7 (Delphi) Greek National Tourist Office; (plane) American Airlines; (light through prism) Bausch & Lomb Optical Co.

P. 8 (camera obscura) Frisius, Reiner Gemma, *De Radio Astronomico et Geometrico Liber,* 1545.

Pp. 11-12 Bausch & Lomb Optical Co.

P. 13 (portrait) Engraved by G. R. Ward, from a picture by Sir Thomas Lawrence. (Young's drawing) from Thomas Young's *A Course of Lectures on Natural Philosophy and the Mechanical Arts,* V. 1, printed for J. Johnson, London, 1807.

P. 14 (portrait) Cabinet des Estampes Bibliothèque Nationale, Paris.

Pp. 15, 16 (diffraction patterns) Cagnet, Francon & Thrierr, *Atlas of Optical Phenomena,* © 1962, Springer-Verlag OHG, Berlin.

P. 16 (radio telescope) National Radio Astronomy Observatory, Greenbank, West Virginia.

P. 24 Collection, The Museum of Modern Art, Lillie P. Bliss Collection.

P. 28, 121 (margin, second from top) Courtesy of the Lawrence Radiation Laboratory, University of California, Berkeley.

P. 34 from a painting by Mason Chamberlain in 1762, engraved by C. Turner. Courtesy of Burndy Library.

P. 35 (portrait) Musée de Versailles; (drawing) from Coulomb's mémoire to the French Academy of Sciences, 1785.

Pp. 46-47 (all photographs) Courtesy of Mr. Harold M. Waage, Palmer Physical Laboratory, Princeton University.

P. 49 (Franklin's drawing) American Academy of Arts and Sciences.

P. 50 The van Marum electrical machine, 1784. Courtesy of the Burndy Library.

P. 51 (portrait) The Science Museum, London.

P. 54 Courtesy of Stanford University.

P. 58 (portrait) Nationalhistoriske Museum, Frederiksborg; (bottom left) from *PSSC Physics,* D. C. Heath and Company, Boston, 1965.

P. 59 (field photo) from *Photographs of Physical Phenomena,* © Kodansha, Tokyo, 1968; (portrait) Bibliothèque de l'Académie des Sciences.

P. 60 (model) Crown copyright. Science Museum, London.

P. 62 (bottom photograph) General Electric Research and Development Center, Schenectady, New York; (field photos) from *Photographs of Physical Phenomena,* © Kodansha, Tokyo, 1968.

P. 63 (left, top to bottom) Magnion, Inc., Burlington, Mass.; Science Museum, London; General Electric Research & Development Center; (right) U.S. Steel Corp., Boston.

P. 65 Dr. V. P. Hessler.

P. 68 Radio Corporation of America.

P. 70, 121 (margin, second from top) Freelance Photographers Guild, New York.

P. 72 Deutsches Museum, Munich.

P. 74 (portrait) The Royal Institution of Great Britain; (drawing) The Royal Institution of Great Britain.

P. 81 Consolidated Edison Company of New York, Inc.

P. 82 Tennessee Valley Authority.

P. 83 (top and bottom) Figuier, Louis, *Les Nouvelles Conquêtes de la Science,* Paris, 1884.

P. 84 (portraits) Thomas Alva Edison Foundation.

P. 85 (patent) U.S. Patent Office Picture Collection.

P. 90 (left) Tennessee Valley Authority; (right) Power Authority of the State of New York.

P. 92 (left top) Westinghouse Electric Corp.; (left bottom) Edison Electric Institute, N.Y.C.

P. 93 (power grid) Edison Electric Institute; (N.Y.C. at night) Con Edison of New York; (N.Y.C. blackout) Bob Gomel, LIFE MAGAZINE, © Time Inc.

P. 95 Power Authority of the State of New York.

P. 98, 121 (bottom margin) Dr. V. P. Hessler.

P. 108 American Institute of Physics.

P. 113 Courtesy of Eastman Kodak Company.

P. 114 (top left) McMath-Hulbert Observatory of University of Michigan; (top right) Harvard College Observatory; (bottom left) Sacramento Peak Observatory, Air Force Cambridge Reasearch Laboratory. Photo courtesy of American Science and Engineering, Inc.; (bottom right) American Science and Engineering, Inc.; (center) Ball Brothers Research Corp., Boulder, Colorado.

P. 115 (top left) U.S. Air Force Photo. Courtesy of News Photo Branch, Defense Information Service; (bottom left) American Science and Engineering, Inc.; (right, top to bottom) M.I.T. Lincoln Laboratory; ibid.; M.I.T. Lincoln Laboratory by D. Downes, A. Maxwell and M. L. Meeks; from *Science Year, The World Book Science Annual.* © 1967 Field Enterprises Educational Corporation, Chicago.

P. 116 (top left) Courtesy of General Electric Company, X-ray Department; (top right) Eastman Kodak Company, Rochester, New York; (bottom left) Brookhaven National Laboratory.

P. 117 (manuscript) Royal Society of Edinburgh, Scotland; (portrait) Trinity College Library, Cambridge, England.

P. 123 John Tenniel drawings.

Partial List of Staff and Consultants

The individuals listed below (and on the following pages) have each contributed in some way to the development of the course materials. Their periods of participation ranged from brief consultations to full-time involvement in the team for several years. The affiliations indicated are those just prior to or during the period of participation.

Advisory Committee

E. G. Begle, Stanford University, Calif.

Paul F. Brandwein, Harcourt, Brace & World, Inc., San Francisco, Calif.

Robert Brode, University of California, Berkeley

Erwin Hiebert, University of Wisconsin, Madison

Harry Kelly, North Carolina State College, Raleigh

William C. Kelly, National Research Council, Washington, D.C.

Philippe LeCorbeiller, New School for Social Research, New York, N.Y.

Thomas Miner, Garden City High School, New York, N.Y.

Philip Morrison, Massachusetts Institute of Technology, Cambridge

Ernest Nagel, Columbia University, New York, N.Y.

Leonard K. Nash, Harvard University

I. I. Rabi, Columbia University, New York, N.Y.

Staff and Consultants

L. K. Akers, Oak Ridge Associated Universities, Tenn.

Roger A. Albrecht, Osage Community Schools, Iowa

David Anderson, Oberlin College, Ohio

Gary Anderson, Harvard University

Donald Armstrong, American Science Film Association, Washington, D.C.

Arnold Arons, University of Washington

Sam Ascher, Henry Ford High School, Detroit, Mich.

Ralph Atherton, Talawanda High School, Oxford, Ohio

Albert V. Baez, UNESCO, Paris

William G. Banick, Fulton High School, Atlanta, Ga.

Arthur Bardige, Nova High School, Fort Lauderdale, Fla.

Rolland B. Bartholomew, Henry M. Gunn High School, Palo Alto, Calif.

O. Theodor Benfey, Earlham College, Richmond, Ind.

Richard Berendzen, Harvard College Observatory

Alfred M. Bork, Reed College, Portland, Ore.

F. David Boulanger, Mercer Island High School, Washington

Alfred Brenner, Harvard University

Robert Bridgham, Harvard University

Richard Brinckerhoff, Phillips Exeter Academy, Exeter, N.H.

Donald Brittain, National Film Board of Canada, Montreal

Joan Bromberg, Harvard University

Vinson Bronson, Newton South High School, Newton Centre, Mass.

Stephen G. Brush, Lawrence Radiation Laboratory, University of California, Livermore

Michael Butler, CIASA Films Mundiales, S. A., Mexico

Leon Callihan, St. Mark's School of Texas, Dallas

Douglas Campbell, Harvard University

J. Arthur Campbell, Harvey Mudd College, Claremont, Calif.

Dean R. Casperson, Harvard University

Bobby Chambers, Oak Ridge Associated Universities, Tenn.

Robert Chesley, Thacher School, Ojai, Calif.

John Christensen, Oak Ridge Associated Universities, Tenn.

Dora Clark, W. G. Enloe High School, Raleigh, N.C.

David Clarke, Browne and Nichols School, Cambridge, Mass.

Robert S. Cohen, Boston University, Mass.

Brother Columban Francis, F.S.C., Mater Christi Diocesan High School, Long Island City, N.Y.

Arthur Compton, Phillips Exeter Academy, Exeter, N.H.

David L. Cove, Los Altos High School, Calif.

William Cooley, University of Pittsburgh, Pa.

Ann Couch, Harvard University

Paul Cowan, Hardin-Simmons University, Abilene, Tex.

Charles Davis, Fairfax County School Board, Fairfax, Va.

Michael Dentamaro, Senn High School, Chicago, Ill.

Raymond Dittman, Newton High School, Mass.

Elsa Dorfman, Educational Services Inc., Watertown, Mass.

Vadim Drozin, Bucknell University, Lewisburg, Pa.

Neil F. Dunn, Burlington High School, Mass.

R. T. Ellickson, University of Oregon, Eugene

Thomas Embry, Nova High School, Fort Lauderdale, Fla.

Walter Eppenstein, Rensselaer Polytechnic Institute, Troy, N.Y.

Herman Epstein, Brandeis University, Waltham, Mass.

Thomas F. B. Ferguson, National Film Board of Canada, Montreal

Thomas von Foerster, Harvard University

Kenneth Ford, University of California, Irvine

Staff and Consultants

Robert Gardner, Harvard University
Fred Geis, Jr., Harvard University
Nicholas J. Georgis, Staples High School, Westport, Conn.
H. Richard Gerfin, Somers Middle School, Somers, N.Y.
Owen Gingerich, Smithsonian Astrophysical Observatory, Cambridge, Mass.
Stanley Goldberg, Antioch College, Yellow Springs, Ohio
Leon Goutevenier, Paul D. Schreiber High School, Port Washington, N.Y.
Albert Gregory, Harvard University
Julie A. Goetze, Weeks Jr. High School, Newton, Mass.
Robert D. Haas, Clairemont High School, San Diego, Calif.
Walter G. Hagenbuch, Plymouth-Whitemarsh Senior High School, Plymouth Meeting, Pa.
John Harris, National Physical Laboratory of Israel, Jerusalem
Jay Hauben, Harvard University
Peter Heller, Brandeis University, Waltham, Mass.
Robert K. Henrich, Kennewick High School, Washington
Ervin H. Hoffart, Raytheon Education Co., Boston
Banesh Hoffmann, Queens College, Flushing, N.Y.
Elisha R. Huggins, Dartmouth College, Hanover, N.H.
Lloyd Ingraham, Grant High School, Portland, Ore.
John Jared, John Rennie High School, Pointe Claire, Quebec
Harald Jensen, Lake Forest College, Ill.
John C. Johnson, Worcester Polytechnic Institute, Mass.
Kenneth J. Jones, Harvard University
LeRoy Kallemeyn, Benson High School, Omaha, Neb.
Irving Kaplan, Massachusetts Institute of Technology, Cambridge
Benjamin Karp, South Philadelphia High School, Pa.
Robert Katz, Kansas State University, Manhattan, Kans.
Harry H. Kemp, Logan High School, Utah
Ashok Khosla, Harvard University
John Kemeny, National Film Board of Canada, Montreal
Merritt E. Kimball, Capuchino High School, San Bruno, Calif.
Walter D. Knight, University of California, Berkeley
Donald Kreuter, Brooklyn Technical High School, N.Y.
Karol A. Kunysz, Laguna Beach High School, Calif.
Douglas M. Lapp, Harvard University
Leo Lavatelli, University of Illinois, Urbana

Joan Laws, American Academy of Arts and Sciences, Boston
Alfred Leitner, Michigan State University, East Lansing
Robert B. Lillich, Solon High School, Ohio
James Lindblad, Lowell High School, Whittier, Calif.
Noel C. Little, Bowdoin College, Brunswick, Me.
Arthur L. Loeb, Ledgemont Laboratory, Lexington, Mass.
Richard T. Mara, Gettysburg College, Pa.
Robert H. Maybury, UNESCO, Paris
John McClain, University of Beirut, Lebanon
E. Wesley McNair, W. Charlotte High School, Charlotte, N.C.
William K. Mehlbach, Wheat Ridge High School, Colo.
Priya N. Mehta, Harvard University
Glen Mervyn, West Vancouver Secondary School, B.C., Canada
Franklin Miller, Jr., Kenyon College, Gambier, Ohio
Jack C. Miller, Pomona College, Claremont, Calif.
Kent D. Miller, Claremont High School, Calif.
James A. Minstrell, Mercer Island High School, Washington
James F. Moore, Canton High School, Mass.
Robert H. Mosteller, Princeton High School, Cincinnati, Ohio
William Naison, Jamaica High School, N.Y.
Henry Nelson, Berkeley High School, Calif.
Joseph D. Novak, Purdue University, Lafayette, Ind.
Thorir Olafsson, Menntaskolinn Ad, Laugarvatni, Iceland
Jay Orear, Cornell University, Ithaca, N.Y.
Paul O'Toole, Dorchester High School, Mass.
Costas Papaliolios, Harvard University
Jacques Parent, National Film Board of Canada, Montreal
Father Thomas Pisors, C.S.U., Griffin High School, Springfield, Ill.
Eugene A. Platten, San Diego High School, Calif.
L. Eugene Poorman, University High School, Bloomington, Ind.
Gloria Poulos, Harvard University
Herbert Priestley, Knox College, Galesburg, Ill.
Edward M. Purcell, Harvard University
Gerald M. Rees, Ann Arbor High School, Mich.
James M. Reid, J. W. Sexton High School, Lansing, Mich.
Robert Resnick, Rensselaer Polytechnic Institute, Troy, N.Y.
Paul I. Richards, Technical Operations, Inc., Burlington, Mass.
John Rigden, Eastern Nazarene College, Quincy, Mass.
Thomas J. Ritzinger, Rice Lake High School, Wisc.
Nickerson Rogers, The Loomis School, Windsor, Conn.

Sidney Rosen, University of Illinois, Urbana

John J. Rosenbaum, Livermore High School, Calif.

William Rosenfeld, Smith College, Northampton, Mass.

Arthur Rothman, State University of New York, Buffalo

Daniel Rufolo, Clairemont High School, San Diego, Calif.

Bernhard A. Sachs, Brooklyn Technical High School, N.Y.

Morton L. Schagrin, Denison University, Granville, Ohio

Rudolph Schiller, Valley High School, Las Vegas, Nev.

Myron O. Schneiderwent, Interlochen Arts Academy, Mich.

Guenter Schwarz, Florida State University, Tallahassee

Sherman D. Sheppard, Oak Ridge High School, Tenn.

William E. Shortall, Lansdowne High School, Baltimore, Md.

Devon Showley, Cypress Junior College, Calif.

William Shurcliff, Cambridge Electron Accelerator, Mass.

Katherine J. Sopka, Harvard University

George I. Squibb, Harvard University

Sister M. Suzanne Kelley, O.S.B., Monte Casino High School, Tulsa, Okla.

Sister Mary Christine Martens, Convent of the Visitation, St. Paul, Minn.

Sister M. Helen St. Paul, O.S.F., The Catholic High School of Baltimore, Md.

M. Daniel Smith, Earlham College, Richmond, Ind.

Sam Standring, Santa Fe High School, Santa Fe Springs, Calif.

Albert B. Stewart, Antioch College, Yellow Springs, Ohio

Robert T. Sullivan, Burnt Hills-Ballston Lake Central School, N.Y.

Loyd S. Swenson, University of Houston, Texas

Thomas E. Thorpe, West High School, Phoenix, Ariz.

June Goodfield Toulmin, Nuffield Foundation, London, England

Stephen E. Toulmin, Nuffield Foundation, London, England

Emily H. Van Zee, Harvard University

Ann Venable, Arthur D. Little, Inc., Cambridge, Mass.

W. O. Viens, Nova High School, Fort Lauderdale, Fla.

Herbert J. Walberg, Harvard University

Eleanor Webster, Wellesley College, Mass.

Wayne W. Welch, University of Wisconsin, Madison

Richard Weller, Harvard University

Arthur Western, Melbourne High School, Fla.

Haven Whiteside, University of Maryland, College Park

R. Brady Williamson, Massachusetts Institute of Technology, Cambridge

Stephen S. Winter, State University of New York, Buffalo

Answers to End-of-Section Questions, Unit 1

Chapter 1

Q1 We have no way of knowing the lengths of time involved in going the observed distances.

Q2 No; the time between stroboscope flashes is constant and the distance intervals shown are not equal.

Q3 An object has a uniform speed if it travels equal distances in equal time intervals; or, if the *distance traveled* divided by time taken = constant, regardless of the particular distances and times chosen.

Q4 Average speed is equal to the distance travelled divided by the elapsed time while going that distance.

Q5

Δt	$\Delta d/\Delta t$	
(5.0)	(1.0)	
(6.0)	(0.8)	(entries in brackets are those
(4.5)	1.1	already given in the text)
(5.5)	0.9	
7.5	0.67	
8.0	0.62	
8.6	0.58	

Q6 Hint: to determine location of left edge of puck relative to readings on the meter stick, line up a straight edge with the edge of puck and *both* marks on meter stick corresponding to a given reading.

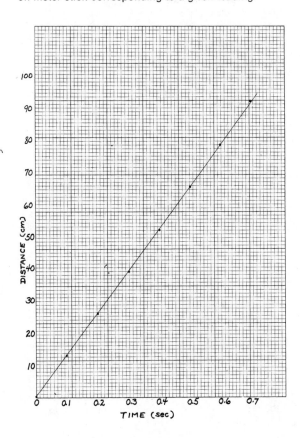

d(cm)	t(sec)
0	0
13	.1
26	.2
39	.3
52	.4
65	.5
78	.6
92	.7

Q7 The one on the left has the larger slope mathematically; it corresponds to 100 miles/hr whereas the one on the right corresponds to 50 miles/hr.

Q8 Most rapidly at the beginning when the slope is steepest; most slowly toward the end where the slope is most shallow.

Q9 $\dfrac{\Delta d}{\Delta t} = \dfrac{2.5 \text{ yds.}}{4 \text{ sec}} = 0.6$ yd/sec from the graph

$\dfrac{\Delta d}{\Delta t} = \dfrac{5 \text{ yds}}{8.5 \text{ sec}} = 0.6$ yd/sec from the table

Q10 Interpolation means estimating values *between* data points; extrapolation means estimating values *beyond* data points.

Q11 An estimate for an additional lap (extrapolation).

Q12 (a) Instantaneous speed means the limit approached by the average speed as the time interval involved gets smaller and smaller.

$v = $ limiting value $\dfrac{\Delta d}{\Delta t}$ as Δt approaches zero.

(b) 6.8×10^{-4} cm/hr

Q13 Instantaneous speed is just a special case of average speed in which the ratio $\Delta d/\Delta t$ does not change as Δt is made smaller and smaller. However, $\Delta d/\Delta t$ always gives average speed no matter how large or how small Δt is.

Q14 $a_{av} = \dfrac{\text{final speed} - \text{initial speed}}{\text{time elapsed}} = \dfrac{60 - 0 \text{ mph}}{5 \text{ sec}}$
$= 12$ mph/sec

Q15 $\dfrac{2 \text{ mph} - 4 \text{ mph}}{1/4 \text{ hr}} = -8$ mph/hr, or -0.13 mph/min.

No, not since *average* is specified.

Chapter 2

Q1 Composition: terrestrial objects are composed of combinations of earth, water, air and fire; celestial objects of nothing but a unique fifth element.
Motion: terrestrial objects seek their natural positions of rest depending on their relative contents of earth (heaviest), water, air and fire (lightest); celestial objects moved endlessly in circles.

Q2 (a), (b), and (c)

Q3 Aristotle: the nail is heavier than the toothpick so it falls faster.
Galileo: air resistance slows down the toothpick more than the nail.

Q4 See Q3 of Chapter 1 p. 15

Q5 An object is uniformly accelerated if its speed increases by equal amounts during equal time intervals. $\Delta v/\Delta t$ = constant

Q6 The definition should (1) be mathematically simple and (2) correspond to actual free fall motion.

Q7 (b)

Q8 Distances are relatively easy to measure as compared with speeds; measuring short time intervals remained a problem, however.

Q9 The expression $d = v\,t$ can only be used if v is constant. The second equation refers to accelerated motion in which v is *not* constant. Therefore the two equations cannot be applied to the same event.

Q10 (c) and (e)

Q11 (d)

Q12 (a), (c) and (d)

Q13 (a)

Chapter 3

Q1 kinematic—(a), (b), (d)
dynamic—(c), (e)

Q2 A continuously applied force

Q3 The air pushed aside by the puck moves around to fill the space left behind the puck as it moves along and so provides the propelling force needed.

Q4 The force of gravity downward and an upward force of equal size exerted by the table.
The sum of the forces must be zero because the vase is not accelerating.

Q5 The first three.

Q6 No, a body moving with constant velocity (and therefore not accelerating) is in equilibrium.

Q7 Vector quantities (1) have magnitude and direction
(2) can be represented graphically by arrows
(3) can be combined to form a single resultant vector by using either the head to tail or the parallelogram method. (Note: only vectors of the same kind are combined in this way; that is, we add force vectors to force vectors, *not* force vectors to velocity vectors, for example.)

Q8 Direction is now taken into account. (We must now consider a change of direction to be as valid a case of acceleration as speeding up or slowing down.)

Q9 W downward, 0,0,0

Q10 Galileo's "straight line forever" motion may have meant at a constant height above the earth whereas Newton's meant moving in a straight line through empty space.

Q11 Meter, kilogram and second

Q12 $m = \dfrac{F}{a} \quad \dfrac{10\text{ N}}{4\text{m/sec}^2} = 2.5$ kg

Q13 False; (frictional forces must be taken into account in determining the actual net force exerted.)

Q14 $Acceleration = \dfrac{0 - 10\text{ m/sec}}{5\text{ sec}} = -2$ m/sec^2

$Force = ma = 2$ kg $\times (-2$ m/sec$^2) = -4$ newtons

(the minus sign arises because the force and the acceleration are opposite in direction to the original motion. Since the question asks only for the magnitude of the force it may be disregarded.)

Q15 10 m/sec^2
150 m/sec^2
60 m/sec^2
0.67 m/sec^2
10 m
0.4 m

Q16 (c) and (f)

Q17 (e) and (f)

Q18 (1) appear in pairs
(2) are equal in magnitude
(3) opposite in direction
(4) act on two different objects

Q19 The horse pushes against the earth, the earth pushes against the horse causing the horse to accelerate forward. (The earth accelerates also but can you measure it?) The swimmer pushes backward against the water; the water, according to the third law, pushes forward against the swimmer; however, there is also a backward frictional force of drag exerted by the water on the swimmer. The two forces acting *on* the swimmer add up to zero, since he is not accelerating.

Q20 No, the force "pulling the string apart" is still only 300 N; the 500 N would have to be exerted at both ends to break the line.

Q21 See text p. 68

Chapter 4

Q1 The same acceleration a_g; its initial horizontal speed has no effect on its vertical accelerated motion.

Q2 (a), (c) and (e)

Q3 They must be moving with a uniform speed relative to each other.

Q4 (a) $T = 1/f = 1/45 = 2.2 \times 10^{-2}$ minutes
(b) 2.2×10^{-2} minutes $\times$ 60 seconds/minute
= 1.32 sec.
(c) $f = 45$ rpm $\times$ 1/60 minutes/sec = 0.75 rps

Q5 $T = 1$ hour = 60 minutes

$v = \dfrac{2\pi R}{T} = \dfrac{2 \times 3.14 \times 3}{60} = .31$ cm/minute

Q6 $f = 80$ vibrations/minute = 1.3 vib/sec
$T = 1/f = 1/1.3 = .75$ sec

Q7 (a) and (b)

Q8 Along a tangent to the wheel at the point where the piece broke loose.

Q9 $\dfrac{mv^2}{R}$

Q10 $4\pi^2 mR$

Q11 The value of the gravitational acceleration and the radius of the moon (to which 70 miles is added to determine R).

Answers to End-of-Section Questions, Unit 2

Chapter 5

Q1 The sun would set 4 minutes later each day.

Q2 Calendars were needed to schedule agricultural activities and religious rites.

Q3 The sun has a westward motion each day, an eastward motion with respect to the fixed stars and a north-south variation.

Q4

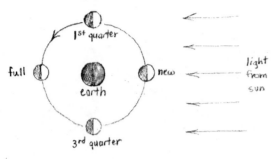

Q5 Eclipses do not occur each month, because the moon and the earth do not have the same planes of orbit.

Q6 Mercury and Venus are always found near the sun, either a little ahead of it or a little behind it.

Q7 When in opposition, a planet is opposite the sun; therefore the planet would rise at sunset and be on the north-south line at midnight.

Q8 After they have been farthest east of the sun and are visible in the evening sky.

Q9 When they are near opposition.

Q10 No, they are always close to the ecliptic.

Q11 How may the irregular motions of the planets be accounted for by combinations of constant speeds along circles?

Q12 Many of their written records have been destroyed by fire, weathering and decay.

Q13 Only perfect circles and uniform speeds were suitable for the perfect and changeless heavenly bodies.

Q14 A geocentric system is an earth-centered system. The yearly motion of the sun is accounted for by assuming that it is attached to a separate sphere which moves contrary to the motion of the stars.

Q15 The first solution, as proposed by Eudoxus, consisted of a system of transparent crystalline spheres which turned at various rates around various axes.

Q16 Aristarchus assumed that the earth rotated daily—which accounted for all the daily motions observed in the sky. He also assumed that the earth revolved around the sun—which accounted for the many annual changes observed in the sky.

Q17 When the earth moved between one of these planets and the sun (with the planet being observed in opposition), the earth would be moving faster than the planet. So the planet would appear to us to be moving westward.

Q18 The direction to the stars should show an annual shift—the annual parallax. (This involves a very small angle and so could not be observed with instruments available to the Greeks. It was first observed in 1836 A.D.)

Q19 Aristarchus was considered to be impious because he suggested that the earth, the abode of human life, might not be at the center of the universe.

His system was neglected for a number of reasons:
(1) "Religious"—it displaced man from the center of the universe.
(2) Scientific—stellar parallax was not observed.
(3) Practical—it predicted celestial events no better than other, less offensive, theories.

Chapter 6

Q1 The lack of uniform velocity associated with equants was (1) not sufficiently absolute, (2) not sufficiently pleasing to the mind.

Q2 (a) P, C
(b) P, C
(c) P
(d) C
(e) P, C
(f) C

Q3 The relative size of the planetary orbits as compared with the distance between the earth and the sun. These were related to the calculated periods of revolution about the sun.

Q4 (b) and (d)

Q5 2° in both cases

Q6 No; precise computations required more small motions than in the system of Ptolemy.

Q7 Both systems were about equally successful in explaining observed phenomena.

Q8 The position of man and his abode, the earth, were important in interpreting the divine plan of the universe.

Q9 They are equally valid; for practical purposes we prefer the Copernican for its simplicity.

Q10 He challenged the earth-centered world outlook of his time and opened the way for later modifications and improvements by Kepler, Galileo, and Newton.

Q11 The appearance in 1572 of a "new star" of varying brightness.

Q12 It included expensive equipment and facilities and involved the coordinated work of a staff of people.

Q13 They showed that comets were distant astronomical objects, not local phenomena as had been believed.

Q14 He made them larger and sturdier and devised scales with which angle measurements could be read more precisely.

Q15 He analyzed the probable errors inherent in each piece of his equipment; also he made corrections for the effects of atmospheric refraction.

Q16 He kept the earth fixed as did Ptolemy and he had the planets going around the sun as did Copernicus.

Chapter 7

Q1 Finding out the correct motion of Mars through the heavens.

Q2 By means of circular motion, Kepler could not make the position of Mars agree with Tycho Brahe's observations. (There was a discrepancy of 8 minutes of arc in latitude.)

Q3 By means of triangulation, based on observations of the directions of Mars and the sun 687 days apart, he was able to plot the orbit of the earth.

Q4 A line drawn from the sun to a planet sweeps out equal areas during equal time intervals.

Q5 Where it is closest to the sun.

Q6 Mars has the largest eccentricity of the planets Kepler could study.

Q7 (a) Law of Elliptical Orbits
(b) Law of Areas
(c) Both (+ date of passage of perihelion, for example)

Q8 The square of the period of any planet is proportional to the cube of its average distance to the sun.

Q9 Kepler based his laws upon observations, and expressed them in a mathematical form.

Q10 Popular language, concise mathematical expression.

Q11 Both the heliocentric and Tychonic theories.

Q12 The sunspots and the mountains on the moon refuted the Ptolemaic assertion that all heavenly bodies were perfect spheres.

Q13 Galileo's observations of the satellites of Jupiter showed that there could be motions around centers other than the earth. This contradicted basic assumptions in the physics of Aristotle and the astronomy of Ptolemy. Galileo was encouraged to continue and sharpen his attacks on those earlier theories.

Q14 No, they only supported a belief which he already held.

Q15 Some believed that distortions in the telescope (which were plentiful) could have caused the peculiar observations. Others believed that established physics, religion, and philosophy far outweighed a few odd observations.

Q16 b, c (d is not an unreasonable answer since it was by writing in Italian that he stirred up many people.)

Chapter 8

Q1 The forces exerted on the planets are always directed toward the single point where the sun is located.

Q2 The formula for centripetal acceleration

Q3 That the orbit was circular

Q4 No, he included the more general case of all conic sections (ellipses, parabolas and hyperbolas as well as circles).

Q5 That one law would be sufficient to account for both.

Q6 He thought it was magnetic and acted tangentially.

Q7 The physics of motion on the earth and in the heavens under one universal law of gravitation.

Q8 No, he thought it was sufficient to simply describe and apply it.

Q9 An all pervasive ether transmitted the force through larger distances. He did not wish to use an hypothesis which could not be tested.

Q10 Phenomenological and thematic

Q11 (a) The forces are equal.
(b) The accelerations are inversely proportional to the masses.

Q12 (a) $2F$
(b) $3F$
(c) $6F$

Q13 (b) $F_{AB} = 4F_{CD}$

Q14 The values of the constant in Kepler's third law $T^2/R^3 = k$ as applied to satellites of each of the two planets to be compared.

Q15 The numerical value of G

Q16 F_{grav}, m_1, m_2, R

Q17 The period of the moon and the distance between the centers of the earth and the moon or the ratio T^2/R^3.

Q18 Similar information about Saturn and at least one of its satellites.

Q19 1/1000; that is, inversely proportional to the masses.

Q20 On the near side the water is pulled away from the solid earth; on the far side the solid earth is pulled away from the water. Since $F \propto 1/R^2$ the larger R is, the smaller the corresponding F.

Q21 All of them

Q22 As the moon orbits its distance to the sun is continually changing, thus affecting the net force on the moon due to the sun and the earth. Also the earth is not a perfect sphere.

Q23 Comets travel on very elongated ellipses.

Q24 No

Answers to End-of-Section Questions, Unit 3

Chapter 9

Q1 False

Q2 No. Don't confuse mass with volume or mass with weight.

Q3 Answer C

Q4 No. Change speed to velocity and perform additions by vector techniques.

Q5 (a), (c) and (d) (Their momenta before collision are equal in magnitude and opposite in direction.)

Q6 Least momentum: a pitched baseball (small mass and fairly small speed)
Greatest momentum: a jet plane in flight (very large mass and high speed)

Q7 (a) about 4 cm/sec. Faster ball delivers more momentum to girl.
(b) about 4 cm/sec. More massive ball delivers more momentum to girl.
(c) about 1 cm/sec. With same gain in momentum more massive girl gains less speed.
(d) about 4 cm/sec. Momentum change of ball is greater if its direction reverses.
(These answers assume the mass of the ball is much less than the mass of the girl.)

Q8 It can be applied to situations where only masses and speeds can be determined.

Q9 Conservation of mass: No substances are added or allowed to escape.
Conservation of momentum: No net force from outside the system acts upon any body considered to be part of the system.

Q10 None of these is an isolated system. In cases (a) and (b) the earth exerts a net force on the system. In case (c) the sun exerts a net force on the system.

Q11 Answer (c) (Perfectly elastic collisions can only occur between atoms or subatomic particles.)

Q12 Answer (d) (This assumes mass is always positive.)

Q13 Answer (c)

Q14 (a) It becomes stored as the object rises.
(b) It becomes "dissipated among the small parts" which form the earth and the object.

Chapter 10

Q1 Answer (b)

Q2 Answer (b)

Q3 Answer (c)

Q4 Answer (c) The increase in potential energy equals the work done on the spring.

Q5 Answer (e) You must do work on the objects to push them closer together.

Q6 Answer (e) Kinetic energy increases as gravitational potential energy decreases. Their sum remains the same (if air resistance is negligible).

Q7 Potential energy is greatest at extreme position where the speed of the string is zero. Kinetic energy is greatest at midpoint where the string is unstretched.

Q8 The less massive treble string will gain more speed although both gain the same amount of kinetic energy (equal to elastic potential energy given by guitarist).

Q9 Multiply the weight of the boulder (estimated from density and volume) by the distance above ground level that it seems to be. (For further discussion see SG 10.15.)

Q10 None. Centripetal force is directed inward along the radius which is always perpendicular to the direction of motion for a circular orbit.

Q11 Same, if initial and final positions are identical.

Q12 Same, if frictional forces are negligible. Less if frictional forces between skis and snow are taken into account.

Q13 Answer (c)

Q14 Answer (c)

Q15 False. It was the other way around.

Q16 Chemical, heat, kinetic or mechanical

Q17 Answer (b)

Q18 Answer (d)

Q19 It is a unit of power, or rate of doing work, equal to 746 watts.

Q20 Answer (d)

Q21 Answer (b)

Q22 Nearly all. A small amount was transformed into kinetic energy of the slowly descending weights and the water container would also have been warmed.

Q23 Answer (a)

Q24 Answer (e)

Q25 The statement means that the energy which the lion obtains from eating comes ultimately from sunlight. He eats animals, which eat plants which grow by absorbed sunlight.

Q26 Answer (c)

Q27 Answer (a)

Q28 Answer (c)

Q29 Answer (c)

Q30 ΔE is the change in the total energy of the system
ΔW is the net work (the work done on the system — the work done by the system)
ΔH is the net heat exchange (heat added to the system — heat lost by the system)

Q31 1. heating (or cooling) it
2. doing work on it (or allowing it to do work)

Chapter 11

Q1 Answer (c)

Q2 True

Q3 False

Q4 Answer (b)

Q5 In gases the molecules are far enough apart that the rather complicated intermolecular forces can safely be neglected.

Q6 Answer (b)

Q7 Answer (b)

Q8 Answer (d)

Q9 Answer (c)

Q10 Both will increase.
Q11 Answer (c)
Q12 Answer (a)
Q13 Answers a, b, c are correct
Q14 (a) unbroken egg
(b) a glass of ice and warm water
Q15 (a) True
(b) False
(c) False
Q16 Answer (b)

Chapter 12

Q1 Transverse, longitudinal and torsional
Q2 Longitudinal. Fluids can be compressed but they are not stiff enough to be bent or twisted.
Q3 Transverse
Q4 No. The movement of the bump in the rug depends on the movement of the mouse; it does not go on by itself.
Q5 Energy (Particles of the medium are *not* transferred along the direction of the wave motion.)
Q6 The stiffness and the density
Q7 (1) Wavelength, amplitude, polarization
(2) Frequency, period
Q8 The distance between any two successive points that have identical positions in the wave pattern.
Q9 (1) 100 cps

(2) $T = \dfrac{1}{f} = \dfrac{1}{100 \text{ cps}} = 0.01$ sec.

(3) $\lambda = \dfrac{v}{f} = \dfrac{10 \text{ m/sec}}{100 \text{ cps}} = 0.1$ meter

Q10 Answer (b)
Q11 $A_1 + A_2$
Q12 Yes. The resulting displacement would be $5 + (-6) = -1$ cm
Q13 Cancellation
Q14 Antinodal lines are formed by a series of antinodal points. Antinodal points are places where waves arrive in phase and maximum reinforcement occurs. (The amplitude there is greatest.)
Q15 Answer (a)
Q16 When the difference in path lengths to the two sources is an odd number of half wavelengths $(\frac{1}{2}\lambda, \frac{3}{2}\lambda, \frac{5}{2}\lambda, \text{etc.})$.

Q17 (1) No motion at the nodes
(2) Oscillates with maximum amplitude
Q18 $\dfrac{\lambda}{2}$
Q19 2L, so that one-half wavelength just fits on the string.
Q20 No, only frequencies which are whole number multiples of the fundamental frequency are possible.

Q21 All points on a wave front have the same phase; that is, they all correspond to crests or troughs (or any other set of similar parts of the wavelength pattern).
Q22 Every point on a wave front may be considered to behave as a point source for waves generated in the direction of the wave's propagation.
Q23 If the opening is less than one-half a wavelength wide the difference in distance to a point P from the two edges of the opening cannot be equal to $\lambda/2$.
Q24 As the wavelength increases, the diffraction pattern becomes more spread out and the number of nodal lines decreases until pattern resembles one half of that produced by a point source oscillator.
Q25 Yes to both (final photograph shows diffraction without interference; interference occurs whenever waves pass each other).
Q26 A ray is a line drawn perpendicular to a wave front and indicates the direction of propagation of the wave.
Q27 The angles are equal.
Q28 Parabolic
Q29 The reflected wave fronts are parallel wave fronts.
Q30 (1) Stays the same
(2) Becomes smaller
(3) Changes so that the wave fronts are more nearly parallel to the boundary. (Or its direction of propagation becomes closer to the perpendicular between the media.)
Q31

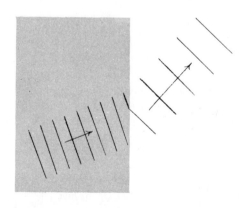

Q32 (1) $f\lambda = v$ relationship
(2) Reflection
(3) Refraction
(4) Diffraction
(5) Interference
Q33 Sound waves are longitudinal.

Answers to End-of-Section Questions, Unit 4

Chapter 13

Q1 No. Eventually diffraction begins to widen the beam.

Q2 Römer based his prediction on the extra time he had calculated it would require light to cross the orbit of the earth.

Q3 Römer showed that light does have a finite speed.

Q4 Experiments carried out by Foucault and Fizeau showed that light has a *lower* speed in water than in air, whereas the particle model required that light have a *higher* speed in water.

Q5 When light enters a more dense medium, its wavelength and speed decrease, but its frequency remains unchanged.

Q6 Young's experiments showed that light could be made to form an interference pattern, and such a pattern could be explained only by assuming a wave model for light.

Q7 It was diffraction that spread out the light beyond the two pinholes so that overlapping occurred and intereference took place between the two beams.

Q8 Poisson applied Fresnel's wave equations to the shadow of a circular obstacle and found that there should be a bright spot in the center of the shadow.

Q9 Newton passed a beam of white light through a prism and found that the white light was somehow replaced by a diverging beam of colored light. Further experiments proved that the colors could be recombined to form white light.

Q10 Newton cut a hole in the screen on which the spectrum was projected and allowed a single color to pass through the hole and through a second prism; he found that the light was again refracted but no further separation took place.

Q11 A shirt appears blue if it reflects mainly blue light and absorbs most of the other colors which make up white light.

Q12 The "nature philosophers" were apt to postulate unifying principles regardless of experimental evidence to the contrary, and were very unhappy with the idea that something they had regarded as unquestionably pure had many components.

Q13 The amount of scattering of light by tiny obstacles is greater for shorter wavelengths than for longer wavelengths.

Q14 The "sky" is sunlight scattered by the atmosphere. Light of short wavelength, the blue end of the spectrum, is scattered most. On the moon the sky looks dark because there is no atmosphere to scatter the light to the observer.

Q15 Hooke and Huygens had proposed that light waves are similar to sound waves: Newton objected to this view because the familiar straight-line propagation of light was so different from the behavior of sound. In addition, Newton realized that polarization phenomena could not be accounted for in terms of spherical pressure waves.

Q16 Reflection, refraction, diffraction, interference, polarization, color, finite speed and straight line propagation (this last would be associated with plane waves).

Q17 No; only that light does exhibit many wave properties and that its speed in substances other than air does not agree with the predictions of a *simple* particle model.

Q18 Light had been shown to have wave properties, and all other known wave motions required a physical medium to transmit them, so it was assumed that an "ether" must exist to transmit light waves.

Q19 Because light is a transverse wave and propagates at such a high speed, the ether must be a very *stiff solid*.

Chapter 14

Q1 He showed that the earth and the lodestone affect a magnetized needle in similar ways.

Q2 Amber attracts many substances; lodestone only a few. Amber needs to be rubbed to attract; lodestone always attracts. Amber attracts towards its center; lodestone attracts towards either of its poles.

Q3 1. *Like charges* repel each other. A body that has a *net positive charge* repels any body that has a *net positive charge*. That is, two glass rods that have both been rubbed will tend to repel each other. A body that has a *net negative charge* repels any other body that has a *net negative charge.*

2. *Unlike charges* attract each other. A body that has a *net positive charge* attracts any body that has a *net negative charge* and vice versa.

Q4 A cork hung inside a charged silver can was not attracted to the sides of the can. (This implied that there was no net electric force on the cork—a result similar to that proved by Newton for gravitational force inside a hollow sphere.)

Q5 $F_{el} \propto 1/R^2$ and $F_{el} \propto q_A q_B$

Q6 F_{el} will be one quarter as large.

Q7 No, the ampere is the unit of current.

Q8 Each point in a scalar field is given by a number only, whereas each point in a vector field is represented by a number and a direction. Examples of scalar fields: sound field near a horn, light intensity near a bulb, temperature near a heater. Examples of vector fields: gravitational field of earth, electric fields near charged bodies, magnetic fields near magnets.

Q9 To find the gravitational field at a point, place a known mass at the point, and measure both the direction and magnitude of the force on it. The direction of the force is the direction of the field; the ratio of the magnitude of force and the mass, is the magnitude of the field.

To find the electric field, place a known positive charge at the point, and measure the direction and magnitude of the force on the charge. The direction of the force is the direction of the electric field. The ratio of the magnitude of the charge, and the charge, is the magnitude of the field.

Note: to determine the force in either case one could observe the acceleration of a known mass or

A31

determine what additional force must be introduced to balance the original force.

Q10 The corresponding forces would *also* be doubled and therefore the *ratios* of force to mass, and force to charge, would be unchanged.

Q11 The negative test body will experience a force *upward.*

Q12 If the droplets or spheres are charged *negatively,* they will experience an electric force in the direction opposite to the field direction.

Q13 Charge comes in basic units: the charge of the electron.

Q14 A negative charge, $(-)$, must also appear somewhere inside the same closed system. (e.g. An $(-)$ electron separates from an atom, leaving it positively charged.)

Q15 It produced a steady current for a long period of time.

Q16 The voltage between two points is the work done in moving a charge from one point to the other, divided by the magnitude of the charge.

Q17 No; the potential difference is independent of both the path taken and the magnitude of the charge moved.

Q18 An electron-volt is a unit of energy.

Q19 If the voltage is doubled the current is also doubled.

Q20 It means that when a voltage is applied to the ends of the resistor and a current flows through it, the ratio of voltage to current will be 5×10^6.

Q21 Apply several voltages to its ends, and measure the current produced in each case. Then find the ratios V/I for each case. If the ratios are the same, Ohm's Law applies.

Q22 The electrical energy is changed into heat energy and possibly light energy. (If the current is *changing,* additional energy transformations occur; this topic will be discussed in Chapter 16.)

Q23 Doubling the current results in four times the heat production (assuming the resistance is constant).

Q24 The charges must be moving relative to the magnet. (They must in fact be moving *across* the field of the magnet.)

Q25 It was found to be a "sideways" force!

Q26 Forces act on a magnetized (but uncharged) compass needle placed near the current. The magnetic field at any point near a straight conductor lies in a plane perpendicular to the wire and is tangent to a circle in that plane and having its center at the wire. The general shape of the magnetic field is circular.

Q27 Ampère suspected that two currents should exert forces on each other.

Q28 (b), (c), (d).

Q29 (b), (c), (e).

Q30 The magnetic force is not in the direction of motion of the particle—it is directed off to the side, at an angle of 90° to the direction of motion. It does NOT do any work on it, since it is always perpendicular to the direction of motion.

Q31 Gravity always acts toward the center of the earth, and is proportional to the mass (it is independent of the velocity).

The Electric Field acts in the direction of the field (or opposite to that direction for negative charges), is proportional to the charge on the object, and is independent of the velocity of the object.

The Magnetic Field acts perpendicularly to both the field direction and the direction of motion, is proportional to both the charge and the velocity, and depends on the direction in which the object is moving.

Chapter 15

Q1 The single magnetic pole is free to move and it follows a circular line of magnetic force around the current carrying wire.

Q2 Faraday is considered the discoverer of electromagnetic induction because he was the first to publish the discovery, and because he did a series of exhaustive experiments on it.

Q3 The production of a current by magnetism.

Q4 The loop is horizontal for maximum current, vertical for minimum. The reason is that the coil is cutting lines of force most rapidly when horizontal, and least rapidly when vertical.

Q5 It reverses the connection of the generator to the outside circuit at every half turn of the loop.

Q6 It comes from the mechanical device which is turning the coil in the magnetic field.

Q7 Use a battery to drive current through the coil.

Q8 Batteries were weak and expensive.

Q9 An unknown workman showed that Gramme's dynamo could run as a motor.

Q10 Too glaring, too expensive, too inconvenient.

Q11 An improved vacuum pump.

Q12 A small current will have a large heating effect if the resistance is high enough.

Q13 Cities became larger, since easy transportation from one part to another was now possible; buildings became taller, since elevators could carry people to upper floors; the hours available for work in factories, stores and offices became much longer.

Q14 There is less heating loss in the transmission wires.

Q15 A current is induced in the secondary coil only when there is a *changing* current in the primary coil.

Chapter 16

Q1 A magnetic field.

Q2 The small displacement of charges that accompanies a changing electric field.

Q3 The four principles are:

(1) An electric current in a conductor produces magnetic lines of force that circle the conductor.

(2) When a conductor moves across externally set up magnetic lines of force, a current is induced in the conductor.

(3) A changing electric field in space produces a magnetic field.

(4) A changing magnetic field in space produces an electric field.

Q4 It was practically the same as the speed of light determined by Fizeau—they differed by only a little more than 1%!

Q5 "Maxwell's Synthesis" is his electromagnetic theory in which he showed the relationship between electricity, magnetism, and light.

Q6 The existence of electromagnetic waves, that they travel at the speed of light, and that they have all the ordinary properties of light, such as reflection, refraction, ability to form standing waves, etc.

Q7 A loop of wire.

Q8 They have very great wavelengths (from tens to thousands of meters).

Q9 The signals travel in nearly straight lines and would otherwise pass into space instead of following the earth's curvature.

Q10 The higher the frequency, the greater is their penetration of matter.

Q11 A RADAR wavelength of 1 meter is about 2×10^6 (2 million) times that of green light which is about 5×10^{-7} meters.

Q12 X rays are produced by the sudden deflection or stopping of electrons; gamma radiation is emitted by unstable nuclei of radioactive materials.

Q13 It was almost unthinkable that there could be waves without a medium to transmit them.

Q14 Albert Einstein's (in his theory of relativity).

Answers to End-of-Section Questions, Unit 5

Chapter 17

Q1 The atoms of any one element are identical and unchanging.

Q2 Conservation of matter; the constant ratio of combining weights of elements. These successes lend strength to the atomic theory of matter and to the hypothesis that chemical elements differ from one another because they are composed of different kinds of atoms.

Q3 No.

Q4 It was the lightest known element—and others were rough multiples.

Q5 Relative mass; and combining number, or "valence."

Q6 2, 4, 5, 1, 2.

Q7 Density, melting point, chemical activity, "valence."

Q8 Because when the elements are arranged as they were in his table, there is a *periodic* recurrence of elements with similar properties; that is, elements with similar properties tend to fall in the same column of the table.

Q9 Increasing atomic mass.

Q10 When he found that the chemical properties of the next heaviest element clearly indicated that it did not belong in the next column but in one further to the right.

Q11 He was able to predict in considerable detail the properties of missing elements, and these predictions proved to be extremely accurate, once the missing elements were discovered and studied.

Q12 Its position in the periodic table, determined by many properties but usually increasing regularly with atomic mass. Some examples are: hydrogen, 1; oxygen, 8; uranium, 92.

Q13 Water, which had always been considered a basic element, and had resisted all efforts at decomposition, was easily decomposed.

Q14 New metals were separated from substances which had never been decomposed before.

Q15 The amount of charge transferred by the current, the valence of the elements, and the atomic mass of the element.

Q16 First, when two elements combine, the ratio of their combining masses is equal to the ratio of their values for A/v. Secondly, A/v is a measure of the amount of the material which will be deposited in electrolysis.

Chapter 18

Q1 They could be deflected by magnetic and electric fields.

Q2 The mass of an electron is about 1800 times smaller than the mass of a hydrogen ion.

Q3 (1) Identical electrons were emitted by a variety of materials; and (2) the mass of an electron was much smaller than that of an atom.

Q4 All other values of charge he found were multiples of that lowest value.

Q5 Fewer electrons are emitted, but with the same average energy as before.

Q6 The average kinetic energy of the emitted electrons decreases until, below some frequency value, none are emitted at all.

Q7

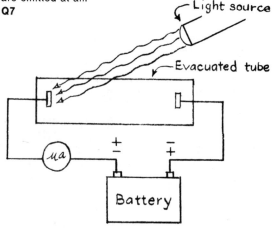

Q8 The energy of the quantum is proportional to the frequency of the wave, $E = hf$.

Q9 The electron loses some kinetic energy in escaping from the surface.

Q10 The maximum kinetic energy of emitted electrons is 2.0 eV.

Q11 When x rays passed through material, say air, they caused electrons to be ejected from molecules, and so produced + ions.

Q12 (1) Not deflected by magnetic field; (2) show diffraction patterns when passing through crystals; (3) produced a pronounced photoelectric effect.

Q13 (1) Diffraction pattern formed by "slits" with atomic spacing (that is, crystals); (2) energy of quantum in photoelectric effect; (3) their great penetrating power.

Q14 For atoms to be electrically neutral, they must contain enough positive charge to balance the negative charge of the electrons they contain; but electrons are thousands of times lighter than atoms.

Q15 There are at least two reasons: First, the facts *never are* all in, so models cannot wait that long. Secondly, it is one of the main functions of a model to suggest what some of the facts (as yet undiscovered) might be.

Chapter 19

Q1 The source emits light of only certain frequencies, and is therefore probably an excited gas.

Q2 The source is probably made up of two parts: an inside part that produces a continuous spectrum; and an outer layer that absorbs only certain frequencies.

Q3 Light from very distant stars produces spectra which are identical with those produced by elements and compounds here on earth.

Q4 None (he predicted that they would exist because the mathematics was so neat).

Q5 Careful measurement and tabulation of data on spectral lines, together with a liking for mathematical games.

Q6 At this point in the development of the book, one cannot say what specifically accounts for the correctness of Balmer's formula (the explanation requires atomic theory which is yet to come). But the success of the formula does indicate that there must be something about the structure of the atom which makes it emit only discrete frequencies of light.

Q7 They have a positive electric charge and are repelled by the positive electric charge in atoms. The angle of scattering is usually small because the nuclei are so tiny that the alpha particle rarely gets near enough to be deflected much. However, once in a while there is a close approach, and then the forces of repulsion are great enough to deflect the alpha particle through a large angle.

Q8 Rutherford's model located the positively charged bulk of the atom in a tiny nucleus—in Thomson's model the positive bulk filled the entire atom.

Q9 It is the number, Z, of positive units of charge found in the nucleus, or the number of electrons around the nucleus.

Q10 3 positive units of charge (when all 3 electrons were removed).

Q11 Atoms of a gas emit light of only certain frequencies, which implies that each atom's energy can change only by certain amounts.

Q12 None. (He *assumed* that electron orbits could have only certain values of angular momentum, which implied only certain energy states.)

Q13 All hydrogen atoms have the same size because in all unexcited atoms the electron is in the innermost allowable orbit.

Q14 The quantization of the orbits prevents them from having other arbitrary sizes.

Q15 Bohr *derived* his prediction from a physical model, from which other predictions could be made. Balmer only followed out a mathematical analogy.

Q16 According to Bohr's model, an absorption line would result from a transition within the atom from a lower to a higher energy state (the energy being absorbed from the radiation passing through the material).

Q17 (a) 4.0 eV (b) 0.1 eV (c) 2.1 eV.

Q18 The electron arrangements in noble gases are very stable. When an additional nuclear charge and an additional electron are added, the added electron is bound very weakly to the atom.

Q19 Period I contains the elements with electrons in the K shell only. Since only two electrons can exist in the K shell, Period I will contain only the two elements with one electron and two electrons respectively. Period II elements have electrons in the K (full) and L shells. The L shell can accommodate 8 electrons, so those elements with only one through eight electrons in the L shell will be in Period II. And so forth.

Q20 It predicted some results that disagreed with experiment; and it predicted others which could not be tested in any known way. It did, however, give a satisfactory explanation of the observed frequency of the hydrogen spectral lines, and it provided a first physical picture of the quantum states of atoms.

Chapter 20

Q1 It increases, without limit.

Q2 It increases, approaching ever nearer to a limiting value, the speed of light.

Q3 Photon momentum is directly proportional to the frequency of the associated wave.

Q4 The Compton effect is the scattering of light (or x-ray) photons from electrons in such a way that the photons transfer a part of their energy and momentum to the electrons, and thus emerge as lower frequency radiation. It demonstrated that photons resemble material particles in possessing momentum as well as energy; both energy and momentum are conserved in collisions involving photons and electrons.

Q5 By analogy with the same relation for photons.

Q6 The regular spacing of atoms in crystals is about the same as the wavelength of low-energy electrons.

Q7 Bohr invented his postulate just for the purpose. Schrödinger's equation was derived from the wave nature of electrons and explained many phenomena other than hydrogen spectra.

Q8 It is almost entirely mathematical—no physical picture or models can be made of it.

Q9 It can. But less energetic photons have longer associated wavelengths, so that the location of the particle becomes less precise.

Q10 It can. But the more energetic photons will disturb the particle more and make measurement of velocity less precise.

Q11 They are regions where there is a high probability of quanta arriving.

Q12 As with all probability laws, the *average* behavior of a large collection of particles can be predicted with great precision.

Brief Answers to Study Guide Questions, Unit 1

Chapter 1
1.1 Information
1.2 (a) discussion (b) 58.3 mph
(c) discussion (d) discussion
(e) discussion
1.3 (a) 6 cm/sec (b) 15 mi. (c) 0.25
min. (d) 3 cm/sec 24 cm (e) 40 mi/hr
(f) 40 mi/hr 120 mi
(g) 5.5 sec (h) 8.8 m
1.4 2.2×10^3 mi
1.5 (a) 9.5×10^{15} m (b) 2.7×10^8 sec
or 8.5 years
1.6 1.988 mph or 2 mph
1.7 (a) 1.7 m/sec (b) 3.0 m/sec
1.8 discussion
1.9 discussion
1.10 discussion
1.11 (a) 0.5, 1.0, 1.5, and 2.0
(b) graph
1.12 Answer
1.13 between 25 and 100 sec; about 900
ft/sec; at about 125 min
1.14 25.6 meters; 4:00 for men, 4:30
for women
1.15 discussion
1.16 discussion
1.17 graph
1.18 graphs
d vs t: $d = 0,9,22,39,5,60.5, 86$ cm
  (approx) at intervals of 0.2 sec
v vs t: $v = 45,65,87.5,105,127$ cm/sec
  (approx) at intervals of 0.2 sec
1.19 (a) Between 1 and 4.5 sec; 1.3
m/sec (b) 0.13 m/sec (c) 0.75 m/sec
(d) 1.0 m/sec (e) 0.4 m (approx)
1.20 (a) 14.1 m/sec (b) 6.3 m/sec²
1.21 315,000 in/sec
1.22 discussion
1.23 discussion

Chapter 2
2.1 Information
2.2 discussion
2.3 discussion
2.4 discussion
2.5 discussion
2.6 discussion
2.7 derivation
2.8 (a), (b), (c)
2.9 discussion
2.10 discussion
2.11 derivation
2.12 17 years $10,000
2.13 discussion
2.14 (a) 57 m/sec² (b) 710 m (c)
−190 m/sec²
2.15 derivation
2.16 discussion
2.17 (a) true (b) true (based on
measurements of 6 lower positions)
(c) true (d) true (e) true

2.18 derivation
2.19 (a) Position

	d	v
A	+	+
B	+	+
C	+	0
D	+	−
E	−	−

(b) derivation (c) discussion
2.20 discussion
2.21 (a) 5.0 m (b) 10 m/sec (c) 15 m
2.22 (a) 10 m/sec (b) 15 m (c) 2 sec
(d) 20 m (e) −20 m/sec
2.23 (a) 20 m/sec (b) −20 m/sec (c)
4 sec (d) 80 m (e) 0 mi/sec
(f) −40 m/sec
2.24 (a) −2 m/sec² (b) 2 m/sec
(c) 2 m/sec (d) 4 m (e) −2 m/sec
(f) 4 sec
2.25 discussion
2.26 (a) 4.3 welfs/surg²
(b) 9.8 m/sec²
2.27 derivation
2.28 derivation
2.29 derivation
2.30 discussion
2.31 discussion
2.32 discussion
2.33 discussion

Chapter 3
3.1 information
3.2 discussion
3.3 (a) construction (b) 2.4 units,
West
3.4 proof
3.5 discussion
3.6 discussion
3.7 discussion
3.8 discussion
3.9 discussion
3.10 discussion
3.11 discussion
3.12 2.8×10^{-4} hr/sec
3.13 6/1
3.14 discussion
3.15 discussion
3.16 discussion
3.17 derivation
3.18 discussion
3.19 (c) 24N (d) 14.8N (e) 0.86N
(f) 9.0 kg (g) 0.30 kg (h) 0.20 kg
(i) 3 m/sec² (j) 2.5 m/sec²
(k) 2.50 m/sec²
3.20 (a) 2.0×10^2 m/sec² 7.8×10^2
m/sec (b) discussion (c) 2.4×10^2
m/sec²
3.21 discussion
3.22 discussion

3.23 2.0 Kg
3.24 discussion
3.25 discussion
3.26 (a) 1 kg, 9.81 N in Paris, 9.80 N
in Washington (b) individual
calculation
3.27 individual calculation
3.28 discussion
3.29 (a) -5×10^{-23} m/sec² (b) 10
m/sec (c) 1×10^{-22} m/sec.
3.30 discussion
3.31 discussion
3.32 (a) diagram (b) 1.7×10^{-24}
m/sec²
(c) $\frac{6 \times 10^{24}}{1}$ (d) diagram

3.33 (a) 862 N, 750N, 638 N (b) The
same as in (a) for scale calibrated in
newtons (c) discussion
3.34 hints for solving motion
problems
3.35 graph
3.36 graph
3.37 − 0.9 yd/sec²

Chapter 4
4.1 Information
4.2 3.8 m/sec²; 5.1 sec; mass
decreases
4.3 discussion
4.4 derivation
4.5 derivation
4.6 1.3 m; at an angle of 67° below
the horizontal; 5.1 m/sec, 78° below
the horizontal
4.7 discussion
4.8 discussion
4.9 discussion
4.10 discussion
4.11 6.0×10^{-2} min, 3.0×10^{-2} min,
1.3×10^{-2} min
4.12 (a) 1.9 sec (b) 32 rpm (c) 50
cm/sec (d) 35 cm/sec (e) 0 (f) 190°/sec,
yes (g) 120 cm/sec² (h) 160
cm/sec² (i) discussion
4.13 discussion
4.14 discussion
4.15 table completion
4.16 (a) 2.2×10^{-10} m/sec²
(b) 4×10^{20} N (c) approximately 1/100
4.17 approximately 10^3 N
4.18 discussion
4.19 (a) Syncom 2 (b) Lunik 3
(c) Luna 4 (d) dosen't change
4.20 5.1×10^3 sec or 85 min
7.9×10^3 m/sec
4.21 discussion
4.22 7.1×10^3 sec or 120 min
4.23 (a) 3.6×10^2 sec (b) 36 Km
(c) discussion
4.24 $t = (m/F)(V_0 - V)$
4.25 discussion
4.26 essay

Brief Answers to Study Guide Questions, Unit 2

Chapter 5
5.1 Information
5.2 Discussion
5.3 (a) 674 seconds
(b) 0.0021%
5.4 Table
5.5 Discussion
5.6 Discussion
5.7 Discussion
5.8 102°, 78°, 78°, 102° starting with the upper right quadrant.
5.9 (a) 15°
(b) Geometric proof and calculation; about 8000 miles.
5.10 a, b, c, d, e, f
5.11 Discussion
5.12 Discussion

Chapter 6
6.1 Information
6.2 Diagram construction
6.3 Discussion
6.4 11 times; derivation
6.5 Discussion
6.6 Discussion
6.7 2.8×10^5 AU
6.8 Discussion
6.9 Discussion
6.10 Discussion
6.11 Discussion
6.12 Discussion

Chapter 7
7.1 Information
7.2 About 1/8 of a degree; about 1/100th of an inch; roughly 1/20th of a degree.
7.3 Discussion
7.4 4%
7.5 Discussion
7.6 $a + c$
7.7 Discussion
7.8 0.209
7.9 .594/1
7.10 Analysis
7.11 (a) 17.9 AU
(b) 35.3 AU
(c) 0.54 AU
(d) 66/1
7.12 $T = 249$ years
7.13 $k = 1.0$ for all three planets
7.14 Discussion
7.15 (a) sketch
(b) R_{av}: 3.4 mm, 5.2 mm, 8.2 mm, 4.6 mm
T: 44^h, 84^h, 168^h, 384^h
(c) k: 485, 495, 501, 470 Hr^2/mm^3
7.16 Discussion
7.17 Discussion
7.18 Discussion

Chapter 8
8.1 Information
8.2 Yes, to about 1% agreement
8.3 Discussion
8.4 Discussion
8.5 Derivation
8.6 Discussion
8.7 $T^2 = \left(\dfrac{4\pi^2}{G}\right)\dfrac{R^3}{m}$
8.8 About 170 times as great
8.9 (a) 1.05×10^3 days^2/AU^3
(b) discussion
(c) discussion
8.10 26,500 mi, or 42,600 km
8.11 5.98×10^{24} kg
8.12 6.04×10^{24} kg
8.13 (a) 5.52×10^3 kg/m^3
(b) discussion
8.14 7.30×10^{22} kg
8.15 Pluto has no known satellite
8.16 (a) 5.99×10^3 sec, or 1.66 hours
(b) 3.55 km/sec
(c) collisions
8.17 Table
8.18 17.7 AU, 0.60 AU, 34.8 AU
8.19 Derivations
8.20 Discussion
8.21 Discussion. No.
8.22 Discussion
8.23 It is useful today.
8.24 Discussion

Brief Answers to Study Guide Questions, Unit 3

Chapter 9

9.1 Information

9.2 Discussion

9.3 (a) Yes
(b) The solar system

9.4 Discussion

9.5 No

9.6 Discussion

9.7 (a) 220.2 g
(b) 20.2 g

9.8 Derivation

9.9 (a) All except v_A' (which $= v_B'$)
(b) $v_A' = \dfrac{m_A v_A}{m_A + m_B}$
(c) 0.8 m/sec

9.10 Dictionary comment

9.11 3.3×10^{-6} kg

9.12 Discussion

9.13 Derivation

9.14 Discussion

9.15 (a) 0.2 sec
(b) About 0.05 m
(c) 5×10^{-14} m/sec
(d) 2.5×10^{-15} m
(e) About 15×10^8 m² or a square of about 40 km on a side

9.16 Yes

9.17 Derivation

9.18 Discussion

9.19 1.2×10^3 kg m/sec; 4×10^2 newtons; 30 meters

9.20 (a) about 100 m/sec
(b) about 4.6 kg m/sec
(c) less than 0.003 sec
(d) at least 1.5×10^3 newtons

9.21 Yes

9.22 Derivation

9.23 (a) $\Delta t = \dfrac{m(v_o - v)}{F}$
(b) $m(v_o - v)$
(c) $\dfrac{m(v_o - v)}{v_e}$

9.24 Derivation

9.25 10 m/sec

9.26 10.5×10^8 kg m/sec

9.27 Discussion

9.28 Discussion

9.29 Discussion

9.30 Discussion

9.31 Discussion

9.32 (a) $0.8 \times$ mass of ball
(b) $-0.8 \times$ mass of ball
(c) $1.6 \times$ mass of ball
(d) Depends on system considered

9.33 Discussion

9.34 Derivation

9.35 Table

9.36 Derivation

9.37 Both speeds $= \dfrac{v}{2}$ but in opposite directions

9.38 Discussion

9.39 Discussion

Chapter 10

10.1 Information

10.2 Discussion

10.3 (a) $v_1 - u$ and $v_2 - u$
(b) No
(c) No
(d) No
(e) Yes
(f) iii
(g) Discussion

10.4 5×10^{-15} joules, 2×10^{14} electrons

10.5 (a) 67.5 joules
(b) 4.5×10^9 joules
(c) 3.75×10^3 joules
(d) 2.7×10^{33} joules

10.6 (a) 2 m/sec², 30 sec, 60 m/sec
(b) 60 m/sec

10.7 (a) -90 joules
(b) 90 joules
(c) 18×10^2 newtons

10.8 2.3×10^2 joules

10.9 (a) 2.2×10^{-3} joules
(b) 5.4×10^{-2} joules

10.10 (a) 0.2 meter
(b) 7×10^9 joules

10.11 Discussion

10.12 Discussion

10.13 (a) 1.1×10^{12} seconds (about 3×10^4 years)
(b) 1.6×10^{-25} meters

10.14 Discussion

10.15 Discussion

10.16 Derivation

10.17 Discussion

10.18 Sketch

10.19 Proof

10.20 (a) 96×10^8 joules
(b) 8.8×10^2 meters
(c) 48×10^5 newtons
(d) Discussion
(e) Discussion

10.21 Discussion

10.22 Discussion

10.23 Discussion

10.24 Discussion

10.25 (b)

10.26 No

10.27 (a) >1000
(b) Discussion

10.28 1/8° C; no

10.29 Rowing 1375 watts or 1.8 H.P.

10.30 1/4 kg

10.31 21.5 days

Brief Answers to Study Guide Questions, Unit 4

Chapter 13

13.1 Information
13.2 7.5 cm
13.3 Discussion
13.4 Discussion
13.5 (a) 4.4×10^9 m
     (b) 3.0×10^8 m/sec
     (c) Positive deviations; conjunction cycle
13.6 (a) 9.5×10^{15} m
     (b) 4,300 years
     (c) 30 times as great
13.7 Derivation
13.8 Discussion
13.9 3 ft; no; no.
13.10 Discussion
13.11 Diagrams
13.12 (a) Diagram
      (b) Discussion
13.13 Proof
13.14 (a) $(m + \frac{1}{2})$ when $m = 0, 1, 2$
      (b) Greater
      (c) Increased separation of fringes
      (d) Increased separation of fringes
      (e) Fainter but more extensive
13.15 Discussion
13.16 Discussion
13.17 Discussion
13.18 6×10^{14} cycles/sec
      10^9 times AM frequencies
      10^7 times FM frequencies
13.19 Discussion
13.20 Discussion
13.21 Vertical
13.22 Discussion

Chapter 14

14.1 Information
14.2 (a) Tripled
     (b) Halved
     (c) No change
14.3 95 km
14.4 Discussion
14.5 Yes; discussion; sketches
14.6 (a) 1.6 N/kg
     (b) 4.2×10^{18} N/kg
     (c) Directly proportional to $\sqrt{}$
14.7 Discussion
14.8 Vector diagrams
14.9 (a) 10^6 coulombs
     (b) 10^{-9} coulombs/m^2
14.10 Sketch (normal to surfaces)
14.11 (a) Discussion (b) help
14.12 6.25×10^{18} electrons
14.13 3.4×10^{42}
14.14 (a) $\frac{1}{2}mv^2 = \frac{1}{2}kq^2/R$
      (b) 1.2×10^{-18} joules
      (c) 1.5×10^6 m/sec
14.15 Metals are conductors
14.16 30 volts
14.17 Same or zero
14.18 Derivation
14.19 3×10^6 volts/meter
14.20 10^7 volts/meter
14.21 (a) 12 volts

(b) zero

(c) 12 volts

14.22 (a) 1.6×10^{-17} joules

(b) 5.7×10^6 m/sec

14.23 (a) 4 amps

(b) 5 ohms

(c) 15 volts

14.24 (a) 10^7 volts

(b) 5×10^8 joules

14.25 Discussion

14.26 20 watts

14.27 (a) 8 watts

(b) 20 watts

(c) 45 watts

14.28 Magnetic field vertical at surface

14.29 (a) north

(b) 1 amp, north

14.30 (a) Derivation

(b) v, B and R

14.31 Derivation

14.32 West

14.33 Discussion

Chapter 15

15.1 Information

15.2 Discussion

15.3 Yes

15.4 All except (d)

15.5 Discussion

15.6 Sketch

15.7 (a) Exercise

(b) Upward

(d) Downward

15.8 Lenz's Law

15.9 Outside magnet

15.10 Opposite

15.11 Discussion

15.12 (a) 1 amp

(b) 10 ohms

(c) burn out

15.13 (a) 1/12 amp

(b) 1440 ohms, the same

15.14 (a) 1 amp

(b) 1/5 watt

(c) 1/2 amp, 1/20 watt

(d) 0.97 amp; 0.19 W; 5.6 W, 0.50 amp, 0.05 W, 6 W

15.15 5 amps

15.16 Derivation

15.17 Low voltage coil

15.18 Discussion

15.19 Discussion

15.20 Report

15.21 Discussion

Chapter 16

16.1 Information

16.2 Symmetry

16.3 No

16.4 Accelerating charge, mutual induction

16.5 (a) Height

(b) Pressure

(c) Field strength

16.6 Deflector orientation

16.7 Light properties

16.8 Discussion

16.9 Discussion

16.10 5×10^6 m; 600 m and 193 m; 11 m

16.11 10 m to 100 m

16.12 Discussion

16.13 Discussion

16.14 Discussion

16.15 Ionospheric reflection of shorter wavelength radiation

16.16 26,500 miles

16.17 Phase difference between direct and reflected waves

16.18 2.6 sec

16.19 Absorption

16.20 Evolution

16.21 Ultraviolet and infrared

16.22 Discussion

16.23 Unnecessary

16.24 Discussion

16.25 Discussion

16.26 Discussion

16.27 Essay

16.28 Essay

Brief Answers to Study Guide Questions, Unit 5

Chapter 17

17.1 Information
17.2 80.3% zinc; 19.7% oxygen
17.3 47.9% zinc
17.4 13.9 times mass of H atom; same
17.5 986 grams nitrogen; 214 grams hydrogen
17.6 9.23 times mass of H atom
17.7 (a) 14.1
  (b) 28.2
  (c) 7.0
17.8 Derivation
17.9 Na; 1   Al; 3   P; 5   Ca; 2   Sn; 4
17.10 (a) Ar—K; Co—Ni; Te—I; Th—Pa; U—Np;
  Es—Fm; Md—No
  (b) Discussion
17.11 Graph
17.12 Graph; discussion
17.13 8.0 grams; 0.895 gram
17.14 (a) 0.05 gram Zn
  (b) 0.30 gram Zn
  (c) 1.2 gram Zn
17.15 (a) 0.88 gram Cl
  (b) 3.14 grams I
  (c) Discussion
  (d) Discussion
17.16 Discussion
17.17 Discussion
17.18 Discussion
17.19 35.45 grams
17.20 Discussion
17.21 Discussion
17.22 1, 3, 5
  2, 4

Chapter 18

18.1 Information
18.2 (a) 2.0×10^7 m/sec
  (b) 1.8×10^{11} coul/kg
18.3 Proof
18.4 Discussion
18.5 Discussion
18.6 2000 Å; ultraviolet
18.7 4×10^{-19} joule; 4×10^{-18} joule
18.8 2.6×10^{-19}; 1.6 eV
18.9 4.9×10^{14}/sec
18.10 (a) 6×10^{14}/sec
  (b) 4×10^{-19} joule
  (c) 2.5×10^{20} photons
  (d) 2.5 photons/sec
  (e) 0.4 sec
  (f) 2.5×10^{-10} photon
  (g) 6.25×10^{17} electrons/sec; 0.1 amp
18.11 1.3×10^{17} photons
18.12 (a) 6.0×10^{23} electrons
  (b) 84×10^{21} copper atoms/cm^3
  (c) 1.2×10^{-23} cm^3
  (d) 2.3×10^{-3}
18.13 (a) $2x = n\lambda$
  (b) $2x =$ any odd number of half wavelengths
  (c) $\cos \theta = 2d/\lambda$ for first order
18.14 1.2×10^{19}/sec
18.15 Discussion
18.16 1.2×10^5 volts; 1.9×10^{-14} joule; 1.2×10^5 eV
18.17 Glossary
18.18 Discussion

Chapter 19

19.1 Information
19.2 Discussion
19.3 Five listed in Text, but theoretically an infinite number.
Four lines in visible region.
19.4 $n = 8$; $\lambda = 3880$ Å
$n = 10$; $\lambda = 3790$ Å
$n = 12$; $\lambda = 3740$ Å
19.5 (a) Yes
(b) $n_i = \infty$
(c) Lyman series 910 Å; Balmer series 3650 Å; Paschen series 8200 Å
(d) 21.8×10^{-19} joule, 13.6 eV
19.6 Discussion
19.7 Discussion
19.8 2.6×10^{-14} m
19.9 (a) Discussion
(b) $10^{-4}/1$
19.10 3.5 m
19.11 Derivation
19.12 Discussion
19.13 List
19.14 Diagram
19.15 Discussion
19.16 Discussion
19.17 Discussion
19.18 Discussion
19.19 Discussion
19.20 Discussion
19.21 Discussion
19.22 Essay
19.23 Discussion

Chapter 20

20.1 Information
20.2 0.14 c or 4.2×10^7 m/sec
20.3 3.7×10^{-14} newtons
20.4 $p = m_o v$ and $KE = m_o v^2/2$
20.5 (a) Changes are too small
(b) 1.1×10^{-12} kg
20.6 (a) 2.7×10^{33} joules
(b) 3.0×10^{16} kg
(c) 5×10^{-7}%
(d) Rest mass
20.7 (a) 1.2×10^{-22} kg·m/sec
(b) 1.1×10^{-22} kg·m/sec
(c) 2.4×10^{-22} kg·m/sec
(d) 1.1×10^{-22} kg·m/sec
20.8 $p = 1.7 \times 10^{-27}$ kg·m/sec; $v = 1.9 \times 10^3$ m/sec
20.9 Discussion
20.10 Diagram
20.11 6.6×10^6 m/sec
20.12 3.3×10^{-33} m
20.13 λ becomes larger
20.14 Discussion
20.15 3×10^{-31} m
20.16 Discussion
20.17 (a) 3.3×10^{-25} m/sec
(b) 5.0×10^{-8} m/sec
(c) 3.3×10^{-6} m/sec
(d) 3.3×10^6 m/sec
20.18 Discussion
20.19 Discussion
20.20 Discussion
20.21 Discussion
20.22 Discussion
20.23 Discussion
20.24 Discussion

INDEX